SAFETY SYMBOLS

SAFETY SYMBOLS	HAZARD	PRECAUTION	REMEDY
Disposal	Special disposal required	Dispose of wastes as directed by your teacher.	Ask your teacher how to dispose of laboratory materials.
Biological	Organisms that can harm humans	Avoid breathing in or skin contact with organisms. Wear dust mask or gloves. Wash hands thoroughly.	Notify your teacher if you suspect contact.
Extreme Temperature	Objects that can burn skin by being too cold or too hot	Use proper protection when handling.	Go to your teacher for first aid.
Sharp Object	Use of tools or glassware that can easily puncture or slice skin	Practice common sense behavior and follow guidelines for use of the tool.	Go to your teacher for first aid.
Fumes	Potential danger from smelling fumes	Must have good ventilation and never smell fumes directly.	Leave foul area and notify your teacher immediately.
Electrical	Possible danger from electrical shock or burn	Double-check setup with instructor. Check condition of wires and apparatus.	Do not attempt to fix electrical problems. Notify your teacher immediately.
Irritant	Substances that can irritate your skin or mucous membranes	Wear dust mask or gloves. Practice extra care when handling these materials.	Go to your teacher for first aid.
Chemical	Substances (acids and bases) that can react with and destroy tissue and other materials	Wear goggles and an apron.	Immediately flush with water and notify your teacher.
Toxic	Poisonous substance	Follow your teacher's instructions. Always wash hands thoroughly after use.	Go to your teacher for first aid.
Fire	Flammable and combustible materials may burn if exposed to an open flame or spark	Avoid flames and heat sources. Be aware of locations of fire safety equipment.	Notify your teacher immediately. Use fire safety equipment if necessary.

Eye Safety
This symbol appears when a danger to eyes exists.

Clothing Protection
This symbol appears when substances could stain or burn clothing.

Animal Safety
This symbol appears whenever live animals are studied and the safety of the animals and students must be ensured.

Florida
Case Studies

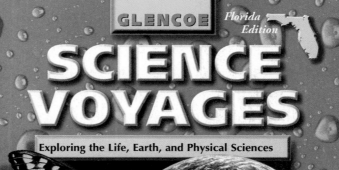

GLENCOE
Florida Edition

SCIENCE VOYAGES

Exploring the Life, Earth, and Physical Sciences

NATIONAL GEOGRAPHIC SOCIETY

Glencoe
McGraw-Hill

Level Red

Case Studies for Level Red

TABLE OF CONTENTS

What are the Florida Case Studies?

Welcome to *Science Voyages* for Florida. Do you like to find out what makes things work—such as the roller coaster at an amusement park? Perhaps you just like to spend time watching the many birds that inhabit Florida. Maybe you have asked yourself why cars can race on Daytona Beach? Whatever your interest, you will come to know that science is an exciting subject that has something for everyone.

The Case Studies on the following pages will help you learn about science in Florida. They also will help you to understand the standards for science that are listed in the Sunshine State Standards for your grade level.

Science—what it is, how it is done, and the effects that scientific developments have on your life—are covered in the articles and illustrations on the following pages. The Case Studies, and the Inquiry Activities that go with them, have been selected to help you understand and remember the Florida Sunshine State Standards. In addition, look for the Florida Science Sites feature that will show some of the many places in your state where you can learn more about science.

How to Use the Florida Case Studies

Science is most useful to you when you recognize scientific concepts in your everyday life. As you read each Case Study, notice that it is about a topic related to Florida. Also notice, at the beginning of each article that it is correlated to a Sunshine State Standard for science. Each Case Study has one or more Inquiry Activities that will give you an opportunity to practice science processes.

These activities also will help you to understand each science standard better and help you remember its importance. At the end of each Case Study, there are references to chapters in your textbook where you will study more about each of the standards.

Florida Science Consultant

Laura Causey
Altoona, Florida

Florida Science Sites

Where to see and do science in Florida

Marianna
⑤

⑭
Pensacola

① Canaveral National Seashore, Titusville
Twenty-four miles of undeveloped beach and wetland environment

② Everglades National Park, Homestead
Over 1.5 million acres of mangroves, rivers, bays, tidal creeks, and hammocks

③ Fairchild Tropical Garden, Miami
Botanical gardens with extensive collections of rare tropical plants

④ Florida Aquarium, Tampa
Florida's aquatic habitats

⑤ Florida Caverns State Park, Marianna
Guided cave tours of stalactities, stalagmites, columns, and draperies

⑥ Florida Museum of Natural History, Gainesville
Unique habitats of Florida and herbarium of recent and fossil plants

⑦ J.N. "Ding" Darling National Wildlife Refuge, Sanibel
Refuge with birds and native vegetation

⑧ Jacksonville Zoological Gardens, Jacksonville
Exotic animals, Reptile House, and Great Apes of the World

⑨ Kennedy Space Center, Merritt Island
Launching site of all U.S. human space flights as well as the space shuttles

⑩ Marie Selby Botanical Gardens, Sarasota
Epiphytes of all kinds, including orchids and a butterfly garden

⑪ Mote Marine Aquarium, Sarasota
Shark pools, manatees, sea turtles, marine fish, native invertebrates and plants

⑫ Mulberry Phosphate Museum, Mulberry
Fossils and bones from prehistoric animals

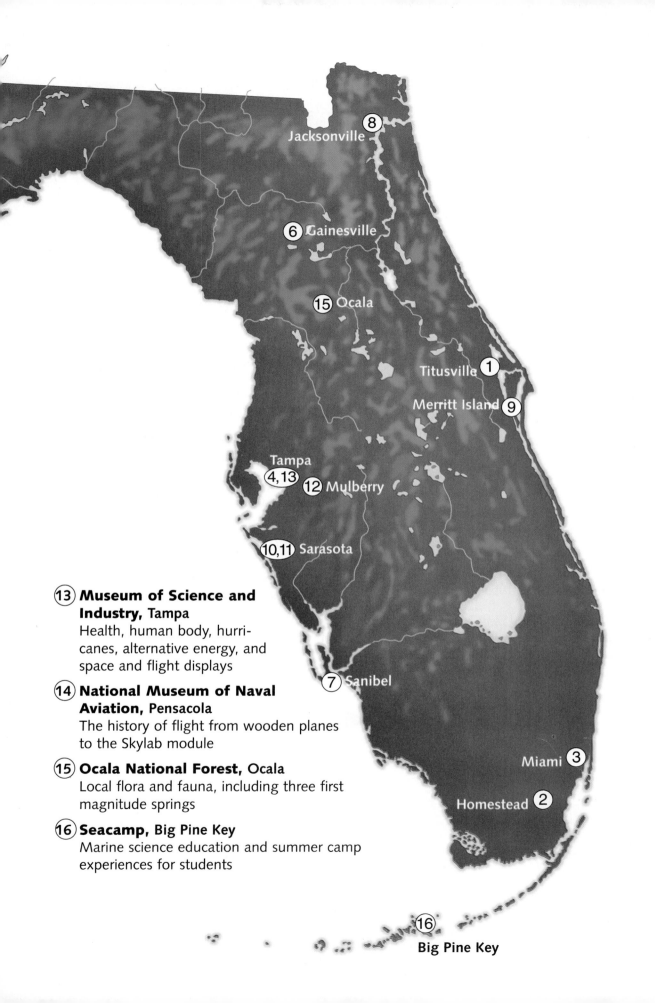

Jacksonville ⑧

⑥ Gainesville

⑮ Ocala

Titusville ①

Merritt Island ⑨

Tampa
④,⑬
⑫ Mulberry

⑩,⑪ Sarasota

⑬ **Museum of Science and Industry,** Tampa
Health, human body, hurricanes, alternative energy, and space and flight displays

⑦ Sanibel

⑭ **National Museum of Naval Aviation,** Pensacola
The history of flight from wooden planes to the Skylab module

Miami ③

⑮ **Ocala National Forest,** Ocala
Local flora and fauna, including three first magnitude springs

Homestead ②

⑯ **Seacamp,** Big Pine Key
Marine science education and summer camp experiences for students

⑯

Big Pine Key

Solar Research in Florida

ENERGY
STANDARD 1: The student recognizes that energy may be changed in form with varying efficiency.

In 1974, the Florida Solar Energy Center was established. Today, it is the largest state solar center in operation where researchers conduct many types of energy research.

The Center is part of Florida's university system. It is located in Cocoa, Florida, on the campus of Brevard Community College and the University of Central Florida, Brevard Campus. Here, students are able to join scientists in research. They research solar energy and ways to use energy more wisely.

Students and scientists work together, conducting many research projects. Projects are in a variety of energy-related fields including solar research, electric research, and fuel cell research. Study of these fields shows that energy can be changed from one form to another with varying efficiency.

Inquiry Activity

Standard SC.B.1.3.2 GLE2
Energy cannot be created or destroyed, but it can be changed from one form to another. Think of as many types of energy as you can and create a list of other forms that these types of energy can be changed into.

The College of Engineering at the University of South Florida also focuses on energy research. Scientists and students in the Electric Vehicle/Solar Energy Program work to build better electric vehicles and to get more people to drive them. In 1991, this program began one of the first electric-vehicle charging centers in the United States. The charging center is solar powered.

Figure FL1-1 This electric car runs on solar energy and produces little or no air pollution.

Solar energy and electric vehicles are at the center of research at the University of South Florida and at the Florida Solar Energy Center. Florida's sunny climate makes solar power an obvious topic for research. It also makes sense that solar power should be used by more and more people in this state.

Solar Energy

Solar energy is energy from the sun. It is considered renewable energy because sunlight is unlimited. Scientists estimate that the sun will shine for at least another five billion years. Solar energy can be absorbed and changed into other forms of energy, including electricity. The conversion of sunlight to electricity requires special devices called solar cells.

Most people use nonrenewable energy in the form of gasoline to fuel their vehicles. When gasoline and other nonrenewable fossil fuels such as coal and natural gas are burned, they release pollutants into the air. Scientists studying solar energy and vehicles that do not burn fossil fuels see the need to reduce pollution and to protect our limited resources.

Inquiry Activity

Standard SC.B.1.3.1 GLE2

The sun produces solar energy. If all of the sun's solar energy were used more carefully the energy it produced each 15 minutes would be enough to supply Earth for an entire year. Calculate how long it would take the sun to produce enough energy to supply Earth for 11 years assuming no increase in consumption.

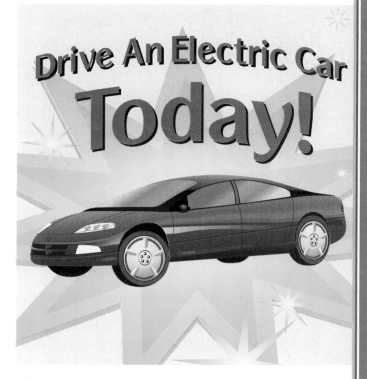

Figure FL1-2 In your Science Journal, describe ways that people could be encouraged to drive electric cars.

Electric Cars

Electricity powers lights, water heaters, air conditioners, televisions, radios, and many other things we use in our daily lives. Electricity can also power vehicles. Electric cars powered by solar-generated electricity offer an environmentally friendly approach to driving.

Using electricity in place of fossil fuels to power vehicles has many benefits. Burning lesser amounts of fossil fuels releases fewer pollutants into the air. Using solar power to generate the electricity needed to recharge electric vehicles lowers the amount of pollutants released into the air. These steps improve air quality.

Electric cars run on electric motors that are powered by rechargeable batteries. The accelerator pedal in an electric car controls the flow of energy from the battery to the motor. An electrical outlet on the car allows the car to be plugged in to recharge its batteries.

Figure FL1-3 This solar cell absorbs sunlight and converts it to electricity.

The research into electric cars needs further development. There are still some problems that researchers at the University of South Florida and the Florida Solar Energy Center are trying to solve. By solving these problems and improving the technology, researchers hope to produce electric cars that can compete with regular fuel-powered cars. Once electric cars become more competitive, consumers will buy more of them.

Imagine stopping for gas every 96 km to 160 km and taking three hours to fill your tank at a gas station. The distance an electric car can go before needing its battery recharged is a problem. Recharging the batteries takes a minimum of three hours, and most cars need to be recharged every 160 km they travel.

Ways to improve the cars' acceleration and ability to climb hills are being researched, as well. Currently, electric cars cannot speed up or climb hills quickly.

Researchers in Florida continue to work on electric-car technology. When electric cars become more competitive in cost and perfomance with gasoline-fueled cars, more people will be willing to drive them. Using electric cars and solar energy will only benefit the environment when more people are driving electric cars and recharging them with the sun's natural energy.

Solar Charging Station

Many Florida charging stations, including the one built at the University of South Florida, depend on sunlight. These stations are like covered parking lots with special roofs covered with solar panels. When their cars need to be charged, drivers park their electric vehicles under the roof and plug them into the stations.

Solar panels contain many solar cells. Solar cells, also called photovoltaic cells, were first developed in 1954. When sunlight falls on them, these cells produce a small electric current. Many solar cells connected together can produce a greater electric current.

Inquiry Activity

Standard SC.B.1.3.1 GLE2
Select three locations in or near your classroom. Predict which location is the best for a photovoltaic (pv) cell. How can you test your predictions using a voltage meter? Record your predictions. Share your predictions with your classmates.

Figure FL1-4 Solar panels collect sunlight and convert it into electrical energy. These panels are located in Lake Worth, Florida.

The concentrated electric current produced by the solar panels recharges the batteries of the electric vehicles. Even when cars are not plugged into the station, the solar panels collect sunlight and generate electric current. Electric current that is created by the charging station but does not go to recharging cars goes to the local electric company to be used by their customers.

Figure FL1-6
Solar panels can be used to power many things, such as this phone booth.

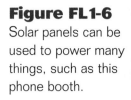

Figure FL1-5 Solar panels produce electricity, but send fewer pollutants into Florida's atmosphere.

Inquiry Activity

Standard SC.B.1.3.1 GLE2

Most electrical energy is produced by burning fossil fuels. Solar panels offer an alternative method for producing electrical energy without burning fossil fuels. Solar energy also produces fewer pollutants. Hypothesize how you could reduce the amount of electrical energy you use each day. Investigate and create a list of ways electrical energy is wasted around you each day.

Going Further

Florida CASE STUDY

Sea Level Rising

PROCESSES THAT SHAPE THE EARTH
STANDARD 2: The student understands the need for protection of the natural systems on Earth.

Salt water surrounds the state of Florida on three sides. The eastern shore and southern tip of the state border the Atlantic Ocean. The western shore borders the Gulf of Mexico. There are over 2000 km of coastline in Florida.

Florida's location shapes its climate and weather. Winds blowing off the water cause milder temperatures on shore. Ocean storms bring strong winds, high waves, and heavy rains to the state.

Any changes in the ocean's tidal or weather patterns affect the coast of Florida. Despite these changes, people still build along the ocean's edge. Beach homes, restaurants, hotels, and other structures line the Florida coastline. Because Florida's average height above sea level is only 30 m, and most coastal areas are only 2 m to 3 m above sea level, these structures could be in danger of washing away or being submerged if the level of the sea were to rise.

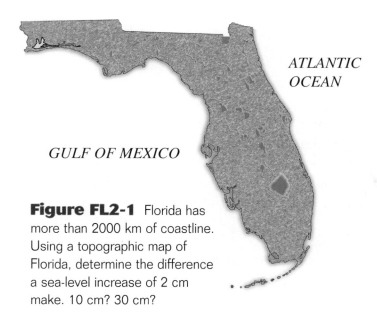

ATLANTIC OCEAN

GULF OF MEXICO

Figure FL2-1 Florida has more than 2000 km of coastline. Using a topographic map of Florida, determine the difference a sea-level increase of 2 cm make. 10 cm? 30 cm?

Figure FL2-2 Florida's low-lying coastal areas would be threatened by a significant sea level rise. This area in St. Petersburg could experience even greater damage during a storm like the one shown, if sea level rose.

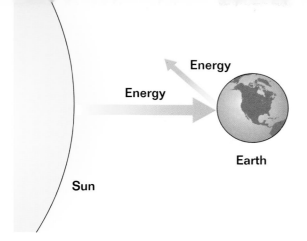

Energy

Energy

Earth

Sun

Figure FL2-3 Some energy from the sun is reflected by Earth back into space.

Global Warming

Global warming occurs when the average temperature of Earth increases. Over the last one hundred years, the average global temperature has risen an estimated 0.6°C. Scientists have constructed climate models to predict how global warming will proceed over the next one hundred years. Many of these models predict even higher temperatures and a more rapid increase in temperatures over the next century.

Increased amounts of certain gases in the atmosphere, called greenhouse gases, can contribute to global warming. Examples of greenhouse gases are carbon dioxide, methane, and ozone. When humans burn fossil fuels, such as coal and natural gas, in cars, power plants, and other industries, some of these gases are released into the atmosphere. As the number of people, cars, and industries increases, the amount of gases released also increases. Some scientists link the cause of global warming to human activities. Keep in mind that some changes and variations in global climate do occur naturally.

Excess greenhouse gases trap heat in Earth's lower atmosphere and at Earth's surface. Trapped excess heat is called the greenhouse effect. The greenhouse effect may lead to global warming. The warmest ten years on Earth all have occurred since 1980.

Inquiry Activity

Standard SC.D.2.3.2 GLE1
The greenhouse effect is caused by the release of greenhouse gases such as carbon dioxide, methane, and ozone into the atmosphere. Using the library or other resources, research sources of these gases. Create a diagram that illustrates the greenhouse effect. Include in your diagram items that illustrate sources of greenhouse gases.

Figure FL2-4 This glacier and the icebergs are found near Antarctica.

Effects of Global Warming

Warmer temperatures may sound good, but the effects are not all positive. Warmer temperatures change weather patterns, including rainfall, wind, and ocean currents. Regional climates can also change. States like Florida that border oceans may be affected the most. Sea levels, coastlines, and animal and plant species will be affected by increased global temperatures.

Increased temperatures could melt the ice caps at the poles. If this happened the melted ice would flow into the oceans, causing an increase in sea level across the globe. Increased sea levels will cause flooding of low-lying coastal areas like those lining Florida's coast.

Scientists predict that increased temperatures could change ocean currents and weather patterns. This could cause more tropical storms and more severe storms to develop. More storms could increase the damage caused to the state.

What can be done?

If patterns of climate change continue, some scientists predict the rate of sea-level rise will increase. Currently, sea levels are rising slowly. Higher tides are visible evidence of this rise in Florida. Increased beach erosion may also be attributed to rising sea levels.

Global warming may cause a great deal of environmental damage. For this reason, many scientists suggest people reduce the amount of greenhouse gases they release into the atmosphere. Using energy more wisely and using renewable energy sources such as solar, wind, and water power are ways people can reduce these gases. Simply driving cars less and turning out lights when they're not needed are two easy things to do that will make a difference.

Inquiry Activity

Standard SC.D.2.3.2 GLE1

Be an energy inspector. Investigate your classroom and other areas of your school to see how energy-efficient they are. Look closely at windows, doors, ceilings, lights, and other electrical devices. Look for insulation on doors and windows. Do the doors and windows shut tightly? What types of lighting are used? Prepare an informative report to discuss what you found.

Figure FL2-5
Flooding similar to the flooding caused by Hurricane Andrew could occur more frequently if global temperatures continue to rise.

Figure FL2-6 Energy-efficient heating and cooling systems, such as these solar panels, can help reduce unnecessary use of fossil fuels.

Figure FL2-7 Car exhaust contains many gases that harm the environment.

Florida researchers are working to find other sources of energy. The Engineering Program at the University of South Florida has programs that focus on ways to reduce greenhouse gases. The Florida Solar Energy Center operates in central Florida. Researchers there are learning how to produce and use energy in more environmentally friendly ways.

Burning fewer fossil fuels could reduce global warming. Habitats and residents of Florida would benefit from this reduction. Protecting the environment from possible damage is easier than repairing it after the damage occurs.

Going Further

To learn more about protecting Earth's natural systems, see:

Protecting Citrus Crops

HOW LIVING THINGS INTERACT WITH THEIR ENVIRONMENT, STANDARD 1: The student understands the competitive, interdependent, cyclic nature of living things in the environment.

Located 1500 km from the nearest commercial citrus-growing region is a unique research center. It is the Citrus Quarantine Facility. Quarantine means to isolate something for reasons such as disease and infection. This center quarantines citrus trees.

The center was established in 1984. Scientists from the United States' main citrus-producing states, Florida and California, work here with scientists from citrus-growing regions around the world. They study many diseases that attack citrus trees.

The location of the facility in Maryland, far away from citrus-producing states, helps to prevent the spread of disease. Scientists can study citrus plant diseases in the facility's greenhouse without threatening

Figure FL3-1 Scientists in Maryland conduct citrus-disease research far from any major citrus crops. This prevents the possible spread of disease to the crops in Florida, Texas, Arizona, and California.

commercial citrus crops. Because citrus crops are Florida's most valuable farm product, it is logical that Florida growers and scientists would seek ways to protect the citrus crops from disease.

Figure FL3-2
Florida's main citrus groves are located in south-central Florida.

Figure FL3-3 Florida growers produce as much as 10 billion kg of oranges each year.

Florida Citrus

Florida growers produce 75 percent of the U. S. orange crop and close to 80 percent of the U. S. grapefruit crop. Florida growers also produce other citrus fruits including limes and tangerines.

The warm summers and cool winters of south-central Florida are ideal for growing citrus trees. This climate is also ideal for the spread and growth of certain types of bacteria and fungi. Because Florida supplies so much citrus to the rest of the country, growers must protect their crops from these and other pests.

There are many diseases caused by bacteria, fungi, and viruses that attack citrus trees. Scientists study these diseases at the Citrus Quarantine Facility, while growers work to prevent the diseases in their fields.

Figure FL3-4 Careful clipping of the citrus fruit from trees prevents bruising as well as infection by certain diseases.

Inquiry Activity

Standard SC.G.1.3.4 GLE2

The United States harvests large quantities of citrus fruit each year. The United States harvests nearly 2 billion kg of grapefruits each year. Calculate how many kg of these grapefruits are produced in Florida.

Fungal Disease on Citrus

The fungus *Phomopsis citri* affects many Florida citrus trees. This fungus is able to grow and feed on branches in the canopy, or top, of citrus trees. When infected trees are sprayed with irrigation waters or by rain, spores produced by the fungus are washed down onto developing fruit. The disease called Phomopsis stem-end rot results.

The main symptom is diseased patches on the skin of the fruit. The diseased area turns brown and this portion of the fruit begins to decay. This disease can weaken the tree, making it easier for the tree to catch another fungal disease, melanose.

Melanose is a common fungal disease. Citrus fruits that are infected with it early in their growth never develop to their full size. Fruit infected later forms small pustules—blisters small filled with a pus-like material. The skin of infected fruit is often very rough. This disease also destroys leaves and stems of citrus trees.

A third fungal disease that Florida growers must be concerned about is greasy spot. This disease attacks the leaves of citrus trees. The main symptom of this fungal infection is spots on the leaves that appear oily. Greasy spot damages leaves and shortens their lives.

Wind, rain, and even dirty tools easily spread fungal diseases. The citrus grower's best defense against these types of infections is fungicides. Fungicides are chemicals designed to kill fungus. Growers regularly spray them on citrus groves to prevent disease and to kill any fungal pests that are present.

Figure FL3-5 These spots are symptoms of aphid transmitted severe citrus tristeza virus.

A tiny insect called the brown citrus aphid carries some forms of this virus and spreads it to healthy citrus trees. When aphids feed on an infected plant, the virus enters their systems. Infected aphids can then spread the virus to healthy plants. They can also pass the virus to their offspring, who can infect even more plants. Planting virus-free trees is the best defense against viral diseases such as this one. Virus-free trees have a natural resistance to viruses that allows them to grow without becoming infected. Replacing infected trees is highly recommended.

Inquiry Activity

Standard SC.G.1.3.4 GLE2

Citrus diseases cause a number of symptoms and require a variety of treatments. Using the library or other resources, research a citrus disease. Prepare an informative poster about the disease. Include illustrations and descriptions of symptoms, treatments, and the cause of the disease.

Viral Disease

The citrus tristeza virus is one of the deadliest viral diseases for citrus trees. Much research is being done on this disease at the Citrus Quarantine Facility. Infected trees suffer from stunted growth, death of limbs, abnormally small fruit, and can even die.

Inquiry Activity

Standard SC.G.1.3.2 GLE1

Viruses depend on other living things. How does an aphid carry a viral disease without becoming infected by the disease? Hypothesize how the aphid can spread the citrus disease without having symptoms of the disease.

Bacterial Disease

Bacteria can attack citrus trees. A common bacterial disease agent is *Xanthomonas campestris*. Rains driven by wind, contaminated tools, and even tornadoes and hurricanes spread this bacteria. This bacteria causes bacterial citrus canker disease. Infected trees develop diseased patches on leaves, stems, and fruit. If the disease spreads, trees lose their leaves and some branches. These trees produce badly misshapen fruit that falls from the tree before it is ripe. The infected trees eventually die.

Figure FL3-6 Small airplanes are often used to spray fungicides on crops. In order to reach the undersides of the leaves, citrus crops must also be sprayed from the ground. Tanks mounted on trucks are commonly used.

Because this disease is spread so easily and causes such destruction, strict rules require that any infected trees be removed from a citrus grove. The Florida Department of Agriculture works together with the U.S. Department of Agriculture to destroy infected plants and quarantine the surrounding areas. Growers must treat and prune all trees within 38 m of the infection. They must quarantine all trees within a 1 mile radius of the infection until all signs of infection are gone. They cannot export any fruit from quarantined areas. It is important to control this disease in Florida. One outbreak could destroy an entire citrus crop, which would have a serious impact on Florida's economy.

Research in Florida

Florida spends millions of dollars each year on citrus research. Most of this money is spent on pest and disease control research at the Maryland facility, at facilities run by the U.S. Department of Agriculture, and at facilities around the state of Florida. The University of Florida has many research stations located around the state, where scientists research citrus problems. Ways to prevent and cure bacterial, viral, and fungal diseases are studied by public and private industries. At the University of Florida's Citrus Research and Education Center in Lake Alfred, researchers use microphones to listen for pests such as weevils. By placing sensitive microphones in the soil, scientists think they may be able to tell dangerous pests from ants and other insects by the way they sound. All researchers seek new technology to improve the quality of fruit produced by Florida growers.

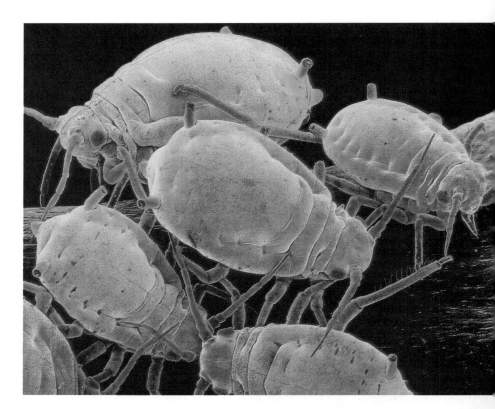

Figure FL3-7 These tiny aphids can infect citrus trees with the deadly tristeza virus.

Magnification: 250×

Going Further

To learn more about the cyclic nature of living things, see:

SC.G.1.3.1 GLE 1	Ch. 15, Sec. 3	**SC.G.1.3.3 GLE 2**
Ch. 14, Sec. 3	Ch. 18, Sec. 1	Ch. 15, Sec. 2
SC.G.1.3.2 GLE 1	Ch. 20, Sec. 1	Ch. 18, Sec. 1
Ch. 12, Sec. 2	Ch. 20, Sec. 2	**SC.G.1.3.4 GLE 1**
Ch. 19, Sec. 2	Ch. 20, Sec. 3	Ch. 19, Sec. 1
Ch. 22, Sec. 1	Ch. 20, Sec. 4	**SC.G.1.3.5 GLE 1**
Ch. 22, Sec. 2	Ch. 21, Sec. 1	Ch. 10, Sec. 3
SC.G.1.3.3 GLE 1	Ch. 21, Sec. 2	Ch. 12, Sec. 1
Ch. 15, Sec. 1	Ch. 21, Sec. 3	
Ch. 15, Sec. 2	Ch. 21, Sec. 4	

Farming Trees

HOW LIVING THINGS INTERACT
WITH THEIR ENVIRONMENT
STANDARD 2: The student understands the conse-
quences of using limited natural resources.

Forests cover half of the state of Florida. These forests and other regions of Florida contain more than 360 species of trees. Of all these types of trees, slash pine trees are the most valuable economically.

Slash pine trees are found in habitats called pine flatwoods. These habitats are common throughout Florida. They are located in the Florida panhandle as well as in northeast, central, and south Florida. They tend to have soil that drains poorly and to be in flat areas.

While pine flatwoods in the southern portion of the state naturally contain only slash pines, other regions contain both slash pines and long-leaf pines. The habitats where both types of pine trees are found support species of low-growing shrubs, trees, and other plants. Many birds and other wildlife find homes in these regions, as well.

Inquiry Activity

Standard SC.G.2.3.3 GLE1

Fires help to maintain pine flatwoods. Lightning strikes start natural fires or wild fires that burn portions of the pine trees as well as plants growing closer to the ground. When park rangers set tracts of land on fire and closely control the boundaries of the fire, this is called a controlled burn. Just like a wildfire, a controlled burn burns portions of the pine trees and the undergrowth. Hypothesize how fire might help to preserve pine flatwoods. Use reference materials to learn about recent wildfires that burned in Florida. Write a report about the causes and consequences of these wildfires.

Figure FL4-1 Pine flatwoods occur often on Florida's landscape. This planted slash pine forest is in the Osceola National Forest.

Figure FL4-2 Today, people fight fires that start in the pine flatwoods, such as this naturally occurring fire in the Ocala National Forest.

Trees as Resources

Forests are important resources. They provide habitats for many forms of wildlife. They produce oxygen, help reduce air and noise pollution, store water, and even help prevent soil erosion. Forests also provide recreational areas for people. Unfortunately, forests are being reduced in size and number across the globe.

As Florida has become more and more developed, people have cut down many of Florida's forests and reduced the size of others. They remove trees to make room for buildings and roads. They also farm and cut trees to make many timber products. Only a small fraction of these cleared lands have been replanted as tree farms to be harvested in later years.

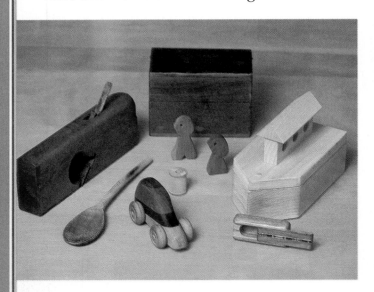

Figure FL4-3 All of these items were made from the wood of trees.

Tree Farms

Tree farms, or tree plantations, are located throughout the state. Some are planted on lands that originally contained pine trees. Others are planted on lands that were once wetlands but have now been drained.

A pine-tree farmer plants only a few types of trees. The main types of trees planted on these plantations are slash pines and loblolly pines. These pines do not support as many insect species and in turn, as many insect-eating species as longleaf pines.

Tree farmers grow the trees on plantations to provide consumers with timber products. Lumber, fuelwood, paper pulp, and medicines are just a few of the products made from trees. Because pine trees are relatively inexpensive to plant and maintain, and they grow relatively quickly, they are a profitable crop to grow.

Figure FL4-4 The trees on this tree farm are all pines and are all the same age. They would be used in even-aged forest management.

Tree Management

Tree farmers can harvest and replant pine trees approximately every 20 years. After planting pine seeds or seedlings in a field, tree farmers apply fertilizers and pesticides to encourage tree growth and kill pests. If properly managed, the trees will be ready to cut in 20 years.

There are different methods used by Florida tree farmers to manage their trees. Each method has advantages and disadvantages.

Even-aged management involves planting trees at approximately the same time. This type of management produces a forest of trees that are similar in age and size. The tree farmer can harvest this type of forest all at once. Even-aged management yields low-quality timber in a short period of time. The tree farmer must replant the stand after harvesting to produce more timber over time.

Uneven-aged management involves planting trees at different times. This type of management produces a forest of trees

Figure FL4-5 Uneven-aged management supports many native species of plants and animals. This forest is in the Osceola National Forest.

Tree Removal

Tree farmers use many methods to harvest their trees. Clearcutting is the most widely used harvesting method. This method removes all trees from a given area at once. Usually trees that are the same size and age are harvested together using clearcutting. Seeds released by harvesting can reforest the field. This method allows the farmer to quickly remove large quantities of timber. However, clearcutting large tracts of land can lead to severe soil erosion.

Seed-tree cutting involves harvesting most trees in an area at the same time. This method leaves a few trees scattered about the site. These trees produce the seeds that start the next crop. Often the tree farmer selects the best trees to be left behind as seed producers. This can lead to better trees in future generations.

Farmers using uneven-aged management use selective cutting to harvest their trees. They select and cut mature trees, leaving the younger trees to continue growing. Removing the mature trees encourages younger trees to grow and gives seedlings enough room and sunlight. Selective cutting prevents soil erosion and

that are many ages and sizes. This forest has more uses than simply to produce timber. This type of forest supports more wildlife. The drawback to farmers is that uneven-aged management yields quality timber, but it takes a long time.

Managing a forest allows the tree farmer to control which wildlife species can survive in the forest. While tree farmers focus on getting as much timber out of their land as possible, scientists encourage them also to be aware of the needs of wildlife for things such as cover, food, and water.

wind damage. It also preserves animal and plant habitats.

Regardless of the harvest method, tree farmers are encouraged to replant trees in their fields. Replanting produces tree crops for the future. Future crops can help to meet growing timber demands of the world's growing population.

Unfortunately, many fields are not replanted. How do you think this could affect the future timber supply?

Figure FL4-6 People are encouraged to replant trees in Florida. Land left without trees can suffer from soil erosion. This pine seedling, when planted, will reduce soil erosion and provide habitat for animals and other plants.

Inquiry Activity

Standard SC.G.2.3.4 GLE1

Tree farmers are not the only people in Florida encouraged to replant trees. Look closely at the land around your school and home. Take notes on areas where trees could be planted to provide shade and wildlife habitats. Check with city or county officials to see what is currently being done to reforest areas near you. Prepare a plan that outlines the steps to take to improve tree coverage in your county.

Going Further

To learn more about the consequences of using limited natural resources, see:

Cleaning Up the Bay

HOW LIVING THINGS INTERACT WITH THEIR ENVIRONMENT, STANDARD 2: The student understands the consequences of using limited natural resources.

Located off the southern tip of the Florida peninsula is a unique coastal ecosystem—the Florida Bay. The bay is located between the Florida Keys and the Gulf of Mexico. At one time, the shallow waters of this bay were clear and filled with marine life.

Freshwater used to flow freely into the bay from the wetland ecosystem of the Everglades. This freshwater kept the concentration of salt in the bay waters lower than the concentration of salt in normal seawater. Many species of fish and other marine organisms used the bay's less-salty water and beds of sea grasses as nurseries for their young.

Today, there are portions of this coastal ecosystem where only a few plants and animals can live. The water quality of this ecosystem has declined over the years. There is much evidence of this reduced water quality. Once-clear water is now a murky green. Sudden uncontrolled algae growth, called an algal bloom, and dying sea grasses are two of the most visible signs of the reduced water quality.

Water Quality

Scientists and other volunteers have routinely monitored the water quality of the bay since the late 1970s. They do this by using chemical tests on water that is collected from different sites. The tests detect levels of many components in the water, including dissolved gases such as oxygen, other chemical compounds, and salt. Routine testing repeatedly reveals several problems with the bay's waters.

Scientists' tests have found that the levels of dissolved oxygen in the water are below normal. Most living organisms require oxygen gas to live. The reduction in the amount of available oxygen has reduced the number of living things that can be supported by the bay waters. Many animals have moved out of the bay. Some plants have died.

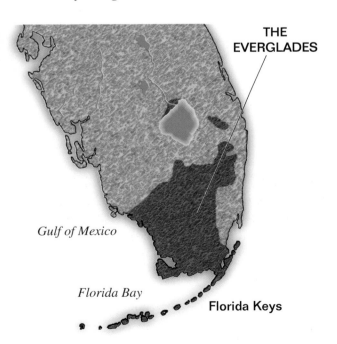

THE EVERGLADES

Gulf of Mexico

Florida Bay

Florida Keys

Figure FL5-1 The Florida Bay is a threatened coastal ecosystem.

Figure FL5-2 Scientists and members of such groups as the Florida Bay Watch volunteer program study the water chemistry of the bay. This program helps keep the bay clean for organisms such as this Great Blue Heron and the mangrove trees.

Inquiry Activity

Standard SC.G.2.3.2 GLE1

There are many abiotic factors that affect life in water ecosystems. Abiotic factors are the nonliving parts of an ecosystem, such as sunlight, salinity, temperature, and oxygen. Hypothesize how changes in these factors can affect organisms living in Florida Bay. Create a list of other abiotic factors that are present in this marine ecosystem.

The tests have shown that the water in Florida Bay is hypersaline. This means salt concentrations are well above normal. The levels of salt in the bay were once lower than seawater, but now they exceed those of normal seawater. Organisms that need lower salt levels can no longer successfully live in the bay.

Another component of these waters that causes problems are some chemicals found in fertilizers. Fertilizers used on land are flowing into the bay. These fertilizers contain chemicals called nutrients that help plants grow.

These excess nutrients are being used by an organism not typically found in abundance in the bay. This organism is algae. The current water conditions in the bay favor rapid growth of algae and cyanobacteria. Many regions are suffering from what are called algal blooms.

Inquiry Activity

Standard SC.G.2.3.3 GLE1

Algae can form thick mats of growth if conditions are favorable and large amounts of nutrients are available. They live close to the surface of the water they are inhabiting, because they are photosynthetic organisms. Photosynthetic organisms convert energy from sunlight into products they need to live. Hypothesize how rapid algae growth in the bay can affect other plants such as sea grasses and animals such as lobster and sponges.

Algal Blooms

Large blooms have occurred and continue to occur in most regions of Florida Bay. As algae grow and reproduce, they form a mat or dense cloud just beneath the surface. This mat of algae causes several problems for the bay.

Sunlight is unable to penetrate the algal bloom. The sea grasses and other marine plants growing beneath the mat of algae cannot get the sunlight they need to conduct photosynthesis. Without the ability to conduct photosynthesis, these plants die.

The large number of algae do produce oxygen from photosynthesis. However, they also use much of the oxygen for their own rapid growth. The lack of other plants producing oxygen reduces the amount of oxygen available to other organisms in the water.

Bloom areas extend for miles across the bay. The damage they cause is evident. Scientists estimate that algal blooms have killed more than 40 000 hectares of sea grasses. Lobster, shrimp, and fish populations have been greatly reduced. Some

Figure FL5-4 Healthy beds of sea grass (*Thallassia sp.*) provide habitats for many marine organisms, such as this cushion sea star.

species of fish no longer live in the bay. Algae have also destroyed sponges. Only ten percent of the bay's sponges still remain.

The damage is spreading. The coral reefs of Florida's Keys are showing signs of distress. At Looe Key and other reefs in the Florida Keys, large numbers of coral are stressed. The fragile coral reef ecosystem is now in danger along with Florida Bay.

Source of the Problem

The current problems in Florida Bay stem from changes made to the Everglades by humans. The U. S. Army Corps of Engineers worked from the early to mid 1900s to redirect water flowing from this wetland environment to Florida Bay. Their plan was to

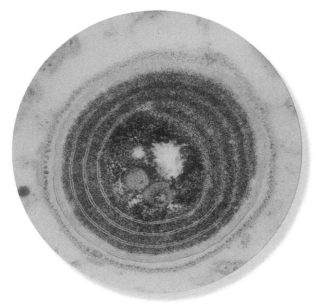

Magnification: 111 020×

Figure FL5-3 Algae and cyanobacteria are organisms that cause complex problems in Florida Bay. This photo shows *cyanobacteraium synechococcus*.

Figure FL5-5 Sponges, gorgonian fans, soft corals (A), and Staghorn corals in the Florida Keys (B) are being destroyed by the algal blooms.

A **B**

build more than 2000 km of water canals to control flooding and to create dry land for farms and cities.

During this period, people drained and filled land and built farms, homes, and businesses. Workers on this project drained approximately half of the Everglades. Only a small portion of freshwater still flowed from this region into the bay.

Figure FL5-6 Thick algal growth smothers the life in Florida Bay.

Inquiry Activity

Standard SC.G.2.3.3 GLE1
Obtain a slide from your teacher containing a sample of algae. Place the slide on the stage of your microscope and observe it. Draw the algae sample. What color is it? What shapes do you see? Do you see any cell structures? Is it dry or is it in water? Record your observations.

Farmers often use fertilizers to help their crops grow. Chemicals in the fertilizers washed into the water supply. As the number of farms increased in southern Florida, the amount of chemicals in the water supply also increased.

The reduced flow of freshwater into the bay caused its salt concentration, or salinity, to increase. The increased amount of chemicals in the water that did flow into the bay overfertilized the bay. Years of reduced freshwater and increased nutrient levels created the current problems in this ecosystem.

Figure FL5-7 Healthy wetlands lead to a healthy Florida Bay. Healthy bay waters provide recreation, resources, and habitat for many organisms.

Currently, steps are being taken to redirect freshwater from the Everglades into Florida Bay. One way is by redirecting canals that carry the water. Some areas that were once drained are now being allowed to return to wetlands.

Many scientists and resource mangers believe the return of freshwater flow to this ecosystem will help repair it. They believe the increased amount of freshwater will reduce the level of salt in the bay. To control the algae in the bay, scientists must also address the levels of pollution in the water. They must find ways to reduce the flow of fertilizers into the bay to further reduce the growth of the algae. The quantity, quality, timing, and distribution of water are all factors that must be addressed to maintain the ecosystems in Florida Bay.

Going Further

To learn more about the consequences of using limited natural resources, see:

Space Exploration

THE NATURE OF SCIENCE
STANDARD 1: The student uses the scientific processes and habits of mind to solve problems.

The John F. Kennedy Space Center (KSC) is located on Florida's east coast near Cocoa Beach. It is one of the National Aeronautics and Space Administration (NASA) centers in our country for space-vehicle launch and space research. Astronauts, engineers, biologists, and other scientists work together at this center. All NASA human space flights are launched from the KSC.

The need to experiment and to explore is a basic part of science. The ideas, energy, curiosity, and determination of many people produce science. The human exploration of space that is carried out from the KSC is perhaps our nation's greatest example of people working together to produce science knowledge.

Science is a process. First, scientists make observations. They then develop explanations for their observations. Research can lead to changes in these explanations. It can also support the original explanation. The study of space is an example of the scientific process. Observations of space made from Earth led to descriptions for the behavior of the planets and the composition of the universe. Actual space exploration by NASA scientists and astronauts from the KSC has allowed scientists to make even better observations.

Figure FL6-1 The Vehicle Assembly Building at Kennedy Space Center is where the shuttle is prepared for space exploration.

Inquiry Activity

Standard SC.H.1.3.1 GLE1

Create your own definition for science. Check your definition with the definition of science from two other sources. Compare the definitions. How are they similar? How are they different? Rewrite your definition so it reflects the two definitions you gathered from other sources.

Figure FL6-2 One of the early space missions was Ranger 7, a lunar probe shown here on an Atlas-Agena rocket in 1964.

Space

Science research does not always answer scientists' questions. But all science research—even if it does not answer questions—helps scientists better understand the problems they are studying. Scientists develop new technologies, or tools, to help them answer their questions.

The technology that produced rockets helped pave the way for space exploration. Rockets allow spacecraft to overcome Earth's gravity. Since rockets were first used to send objects into space, people have improved the technology so that heavier spacecraft can be sent into space.

The first scientific paper to suggest using rockets for space exploration was written in 1903 by a Russian high school teacher. By 1930, rocket research became a major focus of many scientists in the United States, the former Soviet Union, and Germany. Much of the early research on rockets focused on using them as weapons. Eventually, rockets began to be developed to launch spacecraft.

The Russians successfully launched the first artificial satellite into space with a rocket on October 4, 1957. After that, scientists in the United States and other countries soon developed the technology to send satellites into orbit around Earth. The race into space had begun.

For years, scientists have had many questions about space. Do other life forms exist in space? What gases are present in the atmospheres of the other planets? What chemicals are found on the different planets? Rocket technology has opened the door to make observations and to find answers. The Kennedy Space Center is the United States's gateway to these answers.

Inquiry Activity

Standard SC.H.1.3.1 GLE2
Investigate rockets. How do they work? Illustrate a rocket on a piece of drawing paper. Label any major parts of the rocket and describe what the parts do.

Current Activities at KSC

Today, most NASA space missions including all space shuttle missions, are launched on rockets from the KSC. Most space shuttle missions also land on the KSC's 4.5 km long runway.

Launching spacecraft is a complicated business. Everything on a spacecraft, from the most sophisticated computers and rocket engines, to the simplest nuts and bolts, must work for the mission to be a success. First, all the systems must work before the launch. Then, they must work during the almost 20 minutes of violent shaking, extreme temperatures, and massive forces of a rocket launch. The people of the KSC make this possible and successful.

Figure FL6-3 New developments, including carbon-carbon brakes and drag chutes, enable shuttles to land on the Center's runway.

Inquiry Activity

Standard SC.H.1.3.3 GLE1
Researchers have developed the technology to build powerful rocket engines for space shuttles. They burn liquid hydrogen and liquid oxygen to generate the power needed to lift the shuttle into space. Hypothesize how these engines perform a task similar to power plants on Earth. Write a creative paragraph that compares these engines to power plants.

Figure FL6-4 The tiles being attached are used to protect the shuttle from the heat that builds as the shuttle reenters.

Future in Space

Much of what humans know about space and space exploration has come from NASA and the KSC. Yet there is still much to be learned about space. NASA scientists at the KSC have many projects underway that will help them learn more about space.

A major focus of the KSC for the next decade will be preparing and launching most of the pieces of the International Space Station (ISS). This project is scheduled to take over 30 space-shuttle launches to carry the pieces into space and for astronauts to assemble them. When it is complete, the ISS will provide scientists with a permanent place to study in space.

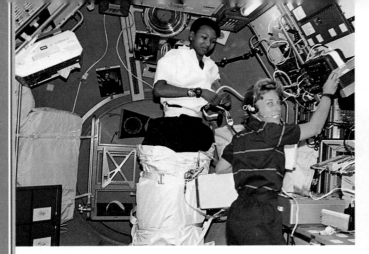

Figure FL6-5 Astronauts Mae Jemison and N. Jan Davis are working in the spacelab-J science module.

Other projects that the KSC is involved in include unmanned missions to explore Mars, the Moon, and the solar system. There are even missions planned to fly by an asteroid and to land a spacecraft on a comet. The KSC will also launch satellites to study aspects of Earth, including the ozone layer, ocean currents and El Niño, and worldwide rainfall. Additionally, NASA scientists are working on developing a new launch vehicle that will launch and return to Earth in one piece. NASA has developed a rocket engine that is powered by energy from the sun.

Doing research, making discoveries, and developing new technology are all part of the scientific process. Florida is fortunate to be part of this process through the KSC.

The process of exploring space will continue as humans try to gain a better understanding of the universe.

Figure FL6-6 Our ability to launch shuttles comes from nearly a century of scientific research. The photo shows the shuttle *Atlantis*.

P/N G90615.11

Going Further

To learn more about using scientific processes, see:

GLENCOE

Florida Edition

SCIENCE VOYAGES

Exploring the Life, Earth, and Physical Sciences

NATIONAL GEOGRAPHIC SOCIETY

Glencoe McGraw-Hill

New York, New York   Columbus, Ohio   Woodland Hills, California   Peoria, Illinois

A Glencoe Program

Glencoe Science Voyages

Florida Student Edition
Florida Teacher Wraparound Edition
Assessment
    Chapter Review
    Sunshine State Science Standards
        Review Book in FCAT Format
    Performance Assessment
    Assessment—Chapter and Unit Tests
    ExamView Test Bank Software
    Performance Assessment in the Science
        Classroom
    Alternate Assessment in the Science Classroom
Study Guide for Content Mastery, SE and TE
Chapter Overview Study Guide, SE and TE
Reinforcement
Enrichment
Critical Thinking/Problem Solving
Multicultural Connections
Activity Worksheets

Laboratory Manual, SE and TE
Science Inquiry Activities, SE and TE
Home Involvement
Teaching Transparencies
Section Focus Transparencies
Science Integration Transparencies
Spanish Resources
Florida Lesson Plans
Lab and Safety Skills in the Science Classroom
Cooperative Learning in the Science Classroom
Exploring Environmental Issues
MindJogger Videoquizzes and Teacher Guide
English/Spanish Audiocassettes
Electronic Teacher Classroom Resources/Interactive
    Lesson Planner CD-ROM
Interactive CD-ROM
Internet Site
Using the Internet in the Science Classroom

The "Test-Taking Tip" and "Test Practice" features in this book were written by The Princeton Review, the nation's leader in test preparation. Through its association with McGraw-Hill, The Princeton Review offers the best way to help students excel on standardized assessments.

The Princeton Review is not affiliated with Princeton University or Educational Testing Service.

Glencoe/McGraw-Hill

A Division of The **McGraw-Hill** Companies

Send all inquiries to:
Glencoe/McGraw-Hill
8787 Orion Place
Columbus, OH 43240

ISBN 0-07-821671-0
Printed in the United States of America.
2 3 4 5 6 7 8 9 10 071/046 06 05 04 03 02 01 00

Series Authors

Patricia Horton
Math and Science Teacher
Summit Intermediate School
Etiwanda, California

Eric Werwa, Ph.D.
Department of Physics and Astronomy
Otterbein College
Westerville, Ohio

Cathy Ezrailson
Science Department Head
Oak Ridge High School
Conroe, Texas

Thomas McCarthy, Ph.D.
Science Department Chair
St. Edwards School
Vero Beach, Florida

Ralph Feather, Jr., Ph.D.
Science Department Chair
Derry Area School District
Derry, Pennsylvania

John Eric Burns
Science Teacher
Ramona Jr. High School
Chino, California

Susan Leach Snyder
Science Department Chair
Jones Middle School
Upper Arlington, Ohio

Lucy Daniel, Ph.D.
Teacher, Consultant
Rutherford County Schools
Rutherfordton, North Carolina

Ed Ortleb
Science Consultant
St. Louis Public Schools
St. Louis, Missouri

Alton Biggs
Biology Instructor
Allen High School
Allen, Texas

National Geographic Society
Educational Division
Washington D.C.

Contributing Authors

Al Janulaw
Science Teacher
Creekside Middle School
Rohnert Park, California

Penny Parsekian
Science Writer
New London, Conneticut

Gerry Madrazo, Ph.D.
Mathematics and Science Education
  Network
University of North Carolina, Chapel Hill
Chapel Hill, North Carolina

Series Consultants

Chemistry

Douglas Martin, Ph.D.
Chemistry Department
Sonoma State University
Rohnert Park, California

Cheryl Wistrom, Ph.D.
Associate Professor of
    Chemistry
Saint Joseph's College
Rensselaer, Indiana

Earth Science

Tomasz K. Baumiller, Ph.D.
Museum of Paleontology
University of Michigan
Ann Arbor, Michigan

Maureen Allen
Science Resource Specialist
Irvine Unified School District
Laguna Hills, California

Connie Sutton, Ph.D.
Department of Geoscience
Indiana University
Indiana, Pennsylvania

Physics

Thomas Barrett, Ph.D.
Department of Physics
The Ohio State University
Columbus, Ohio

David Haase, Ph.D.
Professor of Physics
North Carolina State
    University
North Carolina

Life Science

William Ausich, Ph.D.
Department of Geological
    Sciences
The Ohio State University
Columbus, Ohio

Dennis Stockdale
Asheville High School
Asheville, North Carolina

Daniel Zeigler, Ph.D.
Director
Bacillus Genetic Stock Center
The Ohio State University
Columbus, Ohio

Reading

Nancy Farnan, Ph.D.
School of Teacher Education
San Diego State University
San Diego, California

Gary Kroesch
Mount Carmel High School
San Diego, California

Safety

Mark Vinciguerra
Lab Safety Instructor
Department of Physics
The Ohio State University
Columbus, Ohio

Curriculum

Tom Custer, Ph.D.
Maryland State Department of
    Education
Challenge/Reconstructed
    Schools
Baltimore, Maryland

Series Reviewers

Jhina Alvarado
Potrero Hill Middle School
for the Arts
San Francisco, California

Richard Cheeseman
Bert Lynn Middle School
Torrance, California

Linda Cook
Rider High School
Wichita Falls, Texas

John B. Davis
Niagara-Wheatfield
Central School
Sanborn, New York

Shirley Ann DeFilippo
Timothy Edwards
Middle School
South Windsor, Connecticut

Janet Doughty
H J McDonald Middle School
New Bern, North Carolina

Jason Druten
Jefferson Middle School
Torrance, California

Lin Harp
Magellan Middle School
Raleigh, North Carolina

Doris Holland
West Cary Middle School
Raleigh, North Carolina

Deborah Huffine
Noblesville Intermediate
School
Noblesville, Indiana

Paul Osborne
DeValls Bluff High School
DeValls Bluff, Arkansas

Erik Resnick
Robert E. Peary Middle School
Gardena, California

Robert Sirbu
Lowell Junior High School
Oakland, California

Michael Tally
Wake County
Public Schools
Raleigh, North Carolina

Cindy Williamson
Whiteville City Schools
Whiteville, North Carolina

Maurice Yaggi
Middlebrook School
Wilton, Connecticut

Donna York
Anchorage School District
Anchorage, Alaska

Activity Testers

Clayton Millage
Science Teacher
Lynden Middle School
Lynden, Washington

Science Kit and Boreal Laboratories
Tonawanda, New York

Contents in Brief

Contents

Contents

Contents

Contents

Contents

Contents

Contents

Contents

UNIT 7 Exploring Space 632

Contents

Science Connections

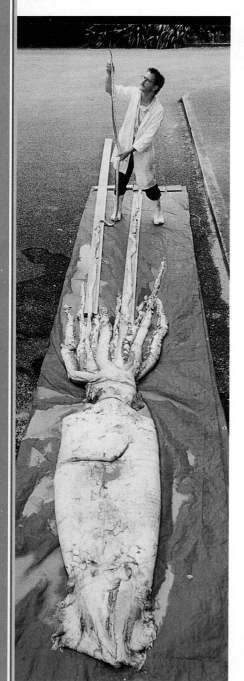

History of Science

How it Works

Reading & Writing in Science

Science & Math

Science & Society

Activities

Activities

Mini Lab

Speed

Friction

Explore Activities

Problem Solving

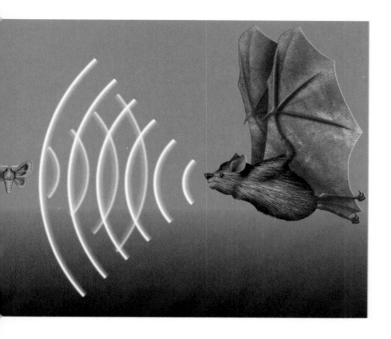

Skill Builders

Skill Activities

The Nature of Science

What's Happening Here?

A girl dangles her fingers in the cool, clear waters of Minnesota's Lake Itasca (below), source of the mighty Mississippi River. Does she realize that the water she touches will pass by great cities of America's heartland and form the borders of ten states? Hundreds of miles south of the lake, the river loses speed as it enters the Gulf of Mexico, drops its sediment, and creates a bird-foot delta (left) as its grand finale. Like the girl on the lake, we don't see what lies beyond our immediate surroundings. Science can help us explore the unknown and discover patterns that organize and guide our curiosity. Today, with the help of scientific tools such as the infrared survey camera that captured this image of the delta, we can see farther and more clearly into the world beyond our senses.

*inter*NET CONNECTION

Explore the Glencoe Science Web Site at **www.glencoe.com/sec/ science/fl** to find out more about topics found in this unit.

The Nature of Science

Chapter Preview

Skills Preview

Skill Builders
- Compare and Contrast
- Separate and Control Variables

Activities
- Model
- Observe and Infer

MiniLabs
- Observe and Infer

Reading Check ✓

As you read about the nature of science, think about the role of fact and opinion in this field. Is there a place for opinion in science? Why or why not?

Explore Activity

The scientist in the photograph is excavating, or digging up, the remains of an ancient, elephant-like mammal called a mastodon in South Dakota. Excavations to unearth bones or other evidence of past life are often slow processes that involve a lot of careful work. Care must be taken so that the remains are not broken or destroyed as they are removed from the soil. Try your hand at excavating an oatmeal cookie without destroying the treasures within.

Model an Excavation

CAUTION: *Never eat or drink in the science lab and never use lab glassware as food or drink containers.*

1. Obtain an oatmeal cookie with raisins and walnuts from your teacher.

2. Place the cookie on a piece of waxed paper.

3. Use a biology probe to carefully remove the raisins and walnuts from the cookie without damaging either.

4. Wash your hands with soap and water when you have finished.

5. Give all pieces of the excavated cookie to your teacher for disposal.

In your Science Journal, write a paragraph that explains how probing the cookie might be similar to removing bones, tools, or other evidence of ancient life from Earth's crust.

1•1 How Science Works

What You'll Learn

- ▶ Archaeology is the study of the cultural remains of ancient people
- ▶ Science is a process of understanding the world
- ▶ Technology is the use of scientific knowledge

Vocabulary
science
technology

Why It's Important

- ▶ Science and technology are important parts of your every-day world.

Groundbreaking News!

It was Friday morning and the students in Ms. Garcia's science lab were anxiously waiting for class to start. Unlike most days in science class at York Middle School, this class would be a field trip to the north end of the school. Students were eager to observe work that would result in the long-awaited gymnasium. The students in group 4—Ben, Emily, Maria, and Juan—peered out the windows. They saw bulldozers and other construction equipment much like the one shown in **Figure 1-1** pull up to the school. With pencils and notebooks in hand, the interested students hiked out to the site. They watched as massive shovels moved hundreds of kilograms of dirt from one spot to another.

Buried Treasure?

All of a sudden, the power-shovel operator stopped the giant scoop in midair. He looked curiously into the hole he was making as he climbed from his seat high above the ground. He called some of the other workers over. They all stared into the pit. One of the workers motioned for Ms. Garcia and her students to come a little closer. Everyone was surprised at what they saw. A piece of broken pottery was sticking out from the loose soil.

Figure 1-1 Construction efforts sometimes unearth prehistoric sites.

Science in Action

One worker suggested that the pottery might be only one of thousands of pieces of trash that were buried long before the school was built. Another worker, however, wasn't so sure. He thought that the pottery could perhaps be an ancient piece of art, such as the one shown in **Figure 1-2A.** Nonetheless, a decision was made to stop the excavation, at least for the moment.

Back in the classroom, the students talked excitedly about the find. This, they all agreed, was real science. **Science,** they knew, is the process of trying to understand the world.

Calling in the Experts

While not wanting to dampen their enthusiasm, Ms. Garcia reminded the students that the piece of pottery might be something that was thrown out only decades ago. To be sure, however, the school's principal called an archaeologist at the local college. An *archaeologist,* such as the two shown in **Figure 1-2B,** is a scientist who studies the cultural remains of ancient peoples. Cultural remains might be tools, weapons, rock drawings, buildings, or pottery, such as that found at the school. Dr. Lum, the students were told, would be at the school on Monday to examine the pottery.

Ms. Garcia suggested that her students go to the library to research more about the history of their area. Ben and the others in his group quickly began their research. Maria thought that it would be a good idea to take notes on their findings. That way, they could compare what they found with what Dr. Lum told them on Monday. The others in the group agreed and put their science notebooks into their backpacks before heading to the library.

Figure 1-2

A Archaeologists study pottery and other items found at sites to learn more about ancient peoples.

B Archaeologists work in the field to gather data.

Researching the Past

Once at the library, Juan used an encyclopedia to begin his research. He found out that archaeology is a branch of science that studies the tools and other cultural remains of humans. There are two major branches of archaeology, as shown in **Figure 1-3.** One branch focuses on groups of people who lived before history was written. The other branch studies civilizations that developed since people began writing things down. To his surprise, Juan also discovered that archaeology covers a time span of more than 3 million years. About 3.5 million years ago, he read, our first ancestors appeared on Earth.

The other students took turns finding out about the history of their area. Ben found out that many scientists hypothesize that the first people came to North America from Asia about 12 000 years ago. Over thousands of years, these people migrated to different parts of the country. Emily and Maria discovered that the area around their city was settled about 2000 years ago. After locating a few more sources, the students took notes on all the information they had gathered. Emily suggested that they also should write down any questions they had about the pottery or the science of archaeology. Juan, Ben, and Maria agreed and each wrote down a few questions. The group left the library anxious to hear how its findings would compare with what Dr. Lum would have to say on Monday.

Reading Check

What is archaeology?

Figure 1-3

A One branch of archaeology studies the cultural remains of people who lived before history was written.

Dr. Lum's Visit

Dr. Lum arrived a few minutes before nine o'clock. The students could hardly contain their excitement. When the bell rang, Emily's hand shot up. She was hoping to be the first to ask the scientist about the pottery. But, before calling on her, Dr. Lum explained that she wanted to give the students a little background information and then she would answer questions.

Dr. Lum began by saying that it is important to preserve prehistoric sites and remains for present and future generations. She also said that many archaeological sites, like the one on the school grounds, are found by accident. More scientific work would have to be done before construction on the site could continue. Several kinds of technology would be used to study the area, such as computers and cameras. **Technology** is the use of knowledge gained through science to make products or tools people can use. **Figure 1-4** shows some common types of technology.

Dr. Lum explained that a radar survey would be conducted to help study the find at the school. This type of technology, Dr. Lum explained, helps scientists "see" what's beneath the ground without disturbing the site. Experts from other fields of science probably would be called upon to help evaluate the site. For instance, geologists, scientists who study Earth processes, might be contacted to help with soil studies.

Figure 1-4
Computers and robots are two examples of technology. **Name at least three other forms of technology.**

B ▸ Archaeologists also study civilizations that have developed since people began recording history. **The two branches of archaeology cover a time span of how many years?**

Working Together

Dr. Lum ended her talk by suggesting that the students go back to the site with her. There, she would examine what had been found. She also would try to answer any questions the students might have about the find.

Maria and Emily led the group of curious students back toward the north end of the school yard. Dr. Lum used her hand lens to examine the piece of pottery carefully. After a few minutes, she announced that she was sure the pottery was old and that an archaeological dig, or excavation of the site, was in order. The students asked if they could participate in the dig. Dr. Lum said she would welcome all the help they could give.

Digging In

Weeks passed before the radar surveys were complete. The students in Ms. Garcia's class spent most of their time learning about how an archaeological excavation is done. Maria reported to the class that the holes and ditches being dug around the site would help determine the size of the site. She also added that it was important that the site be disturbed as little as possible. By keeping the site intact, much of the history of the site could be retold.

Finally, the day came when the students could participate in the dig. Each was given a small hand shovel, a soft paintbrush, and a pair of gardening gloves, such as those shown in **Figure 1-5.** Each student was paired with an amateur archaeologist. All of those involved were instructed to work slowly and carefully in order to excavate this important piece of their city's past.

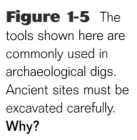

inter NET
CONNECTION

Visit the Glencoe Science Web Site at **www. glencoe.com/sec/ science/fl** for more information about archaeology.

Figure 1-5 The tools shown here are commonly used in archaeological digs. Ancient sites must be excavated carefully. **Why?**

Clues to the Past

Many pieces of pottery, along with some tools, were found at the site. Before the artifacts were removed from the soil, college students working with Dr. Lum took pictures or made drawings of the pieces. These were used to make maps showing the exact location of each artifact before it was excavated. The maps also would be used to show differences in the site both vertically and horizontally.

Lab Work

Each piece was given a number that described its location and its orientation in the soil. After the artifacts were registered and cataloged, they were removed from the site. Dr. Lum told the students that she would take the finds back to her lab. There, they would be cleaned, studied, and stored, as shown in **Figure 1-6.**

Dr. Lum explained that chemical analyses of the pottery and tools would be used to determine the exact age of each piece. Based on her knowledge of the area, Dr. Lum thought that the site was at least several thousand years old.

Figure 1-6 After artifacts are excavated, they're cleaned and tagged for further study.

Section Assessment

1. What is archaeology?
2. Describe some common forms of technology.
3. Why do scientists conduct radar surveys of archaeological sites?
4. **Think Critically:** Why are maps of prehistoric sites often made before removing the artifacts?
5. **Skill Builder**
   Comparing and Contrasting
   Compare and contrast science and technology. If you need help, refer to Comparing and Contrasting in the **Skill Handbook** on page 686.

Using Computers

Word Processing Use some local reference books to find out about the prehistoric history of your state or the area around your town. Write a creative yet factual story based on what you find. If you need help, refer to page 698.

Model an Archaeological Dig

Possible Materials

- Small stones and pebbles
- Craft sticks
- Bits of black tissue paper
- Toothpicks
- Sand
- Small plastic, inter-locking building blocks
- Small paintbrushes
- Plastic shovels
- Large plastic dish-washing tub or clear storage box
- Ruler, pencil, and paper

Have you ever put together a model airplane? If so, your model was a small version of a large object. Scientists often use models to study objects that are too large or too small to observe directly. In this activity, your group will construct a model of a prehistoric site. You'll cover the site with sand and give it to another group to unearth. As amateur archaeologists, each of you will attempt to reconstruct the site based on what you find.

Recognize the Problem

What can be learned from an archaeological excavation?

Form a Hypothesis

Think about some of the things you use every day. Based on your basic needs, make a hypothesis as to what you might find at a pre-historic site once inhabited by humans.

Goals

- **Make a model** of a pre-historic site.
- **Design an experiment** to show how the prehistoric site might be excavated.
- **Make a map** of the site you construct.

Safety Precautions

Test Your Hypothesis

Plan

1. Based on the basic needs generated by your group, **make a model** of an ancient site where people once lived. You might want to include a hearth used for cooking, a trash pit, some sort of shelter, a protective wall, a burial site, a water source, and some tools.

2. **Decide** which of the possible materials listed would be best for each item you include in your site. Remember that others will be trying to determine what is contained at your site.

3. How will you cover your site so that other groups can **excavate** the artifacts?

4. Using the ruler, **determine** a way to make a map of your site.

Do

1. Make sure your teacher approves your plan before you proceed. Make any suggested changes in your plan before you start.

2. **Make the model** in the plastic dish-washing tub or storage box.

3. **Make a map** of your site.

4. **Exchange** your model with another group. Carefully **excavate** the site your group is given using the brushes and shovels.

5. **Make a map** that shows where you found each item in the model you are excavating.

6. While doing the experiment, **record** your observations in your Science Journal.

Analyze Your Data

1. Were any of the items in the site similar to the items you use or see around your community every day? Were any of the items unfamiliar? **Explain.**

2. Why did you make maps of your site and the site you excavated?

3. Did any of the excavating tools damage or disturb the site?

4. **Write** a report explaining what you found and what it might have been used for.

Draw Conclusions

1. How did your map of the site you excavated **compare** with that produced by the group that made the site?

2. Radar surveys that penetrate the ground are often conducted over possible archaeological sites. Why?

1•2 Scientific Problem Solving

What You'll Learn

► Scientific methods include several steps that are taken to try to solve a problem
► Many scientific experiments test variables
► A control can be used to make comparisons during an experiment

Vocabulary
scientific methods
observation
inference
hypothesis
independent variable
dependent variable
constant
control

Why It's Important

► Scientific methods can help you solve problems.

Scientific Methods

Several steps were taken to solve the pottery problem at York Middle School. When the pottery was found, a decision was made to stop construction. One adult guessed that the pottery was fairly old. An expert was called to verify the guess made about the pottery. Based on prior knowledge and further testing, it was concluded that the pottery was from a prehistoric culture.

Step-by-step procedures of scientific problem solving are called **scientific methods.** Any scientific method involves several steps. These steps can vary from situation to situation and aren't necessarily done in a specific order. The basic steps in a commonly used scientific method are shown in **Figure 1-7.** Let's take a look at each step in turn.

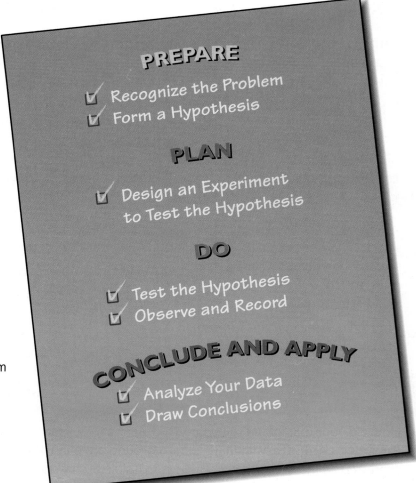

Figure 1-7 This illustration shows one way to solve a problem or find an answer to a question. **What are scientific methods used for?**

PREPARE
☑ Recognize the Problem
☑ Form a Hypothesis

PLAN
☑ Design an Experiment to Test the Hypothesis

DO
☑ Test the Hypothesis
☑ Observe and Record

CONCLUDE AND APPLY
☑ Analyze Your Data
☑ Draw Conclusions

Figure 1-8 Gathering information in the library or on the Internet can make your problem-solving tasks easier. **Besides books and computers, what other resources can you use to help you gather information?**

Recognize the Problem

Ben thought about all the science he had learned over the past few months. He was eager to find out more about the world around him. What can I explore, he thought to himself as he looked around his bedroom. It was then that Ben noticed that the plant on his window sill was droopy. He quickly watered the wilting plant. Later in the day, Ben observed that the droopy plant had perked up. He concluded that he should remember to water the plant on a regular basis. So, every day after school, he watered the plant in his room.

After a few weeks, Ben noticed that the leaves on his plant had turned yellow and brown. He knew from science class that plants need water, so why was this plant not doing well? He talked to his teacher about the plant. She suggested that Ben use what he learned in science class to solve his problem. She pointed out that this problem might make a good project for the upcoming science fair.

Ben has already completed the first step in a scientific approach to solving a problem—he recognizes a problem. A scientific problem is simply a question you don't know the answer to. In order to solve his problem, Ben must do research about his plant. Using reference materials such as those shown in **Figure 1-8,** Ben identified his plant as a fig. In his Science Journal, he drew a picture of a plant and listed some facts about it. ☑

Reading Check ☑

What is the first step in a scientific approach to solving a problem?

Flex Your Brain

If you are faced with a scientific problem like Ben's, you can use the *Flex Your Brain* activity on the next page to help you solve the problem. *Flex Your Brain* is a way to keep your thinking on track when you are investigating a topic or a problem. It helps you explore what you already know and can lead you to new conclusions and awareness about a topic. Lastly, *Flex Your Brain* encourages you to review and talk about the steps you took. Communicating the results of your research is an important part of doing science. Scientists share their results so that other scientists can analyze the results or conduct new tests based on previously learned knowledge. Scientists may communicate by writing papers for science journals, speaking before large groups, or talking with other scientists directly. **Figure 1-9** shows some scientists sharing lab results. To learn more about communicating and other science skills, refer to the **Skill Handbook** at the back of this book.

Figure 1-9 These scientists are sharing the results of an experiment with one another.

Problem Solving

Flex Your Brain

Solving problems requires a plan. This plan may be a simple thing that you do in your head, or it may be something more complicated that you actually write down. Use the *Flex Your Brain* activity on the next page to help you organize a plan for solving a problem. You may want to learn more about plants or about archaeological digs. Record your results in your Science Journal. The photograph on the right shows a Science Journal entry. You can use your Science Journal to record observations, express ideas, and draw sketches. Your Science Journal helps you practice communicating your thoughts and ideas, which you can then share with your classmates.

Think Critically: Why does *Flex Your Brain* ask you to share what you learned?

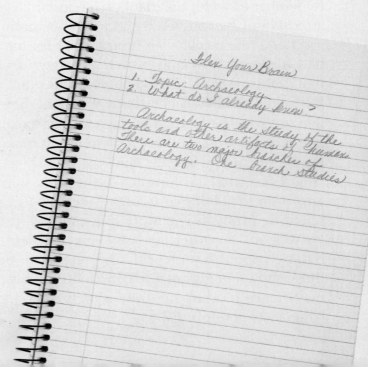

Flex Your Brain

1 Topic: _____

2 ? **What do I already know?**
1. _____
2. _____
3. _____
4. _____
5. _____

3 **Q:** Ask a question
_____

4 **A:** Guess an answer
_____

5 ### How sure am I? (circle one)

Not sure				Very sure
1	2	3	4	5

6 ? **How can I find out?**
1. _____
2. _____
3. _____
4. _____
5. _____

7 EXPLORE

8 **Do I think differently?** → yes / no

9 ? **What do I know now?**
1. _____
2. _____
3. _____
4. _____
5. _____

10 SHARE
1. _____
2. _____
3. _____

1 Fill in the topic.

2 Jot down what you already know about the topic.

3 Using what you already know (step 2), form a question about the topic. Are you unsure about one of the items you listed? Do you want to know more? Do you want to know what, how, or why? Write down your question.

4 Guess an answer to your question. In the next few steps, you will be exploring the reasonableness of your answer. Write down your guess.

5 Circle the number in the box that matches how sure you are of your answer in step 4. This is your chance to rate your confidence in what you've done so far and, later, to see how your level of sureness affects your thinking.

6 How can you find out more about your topic? You might want to read a book, ask an expert, or do an experiment. Write down ways you can find out more.

7 Make a plan to explore your answer. Use the resources you listed in step 6. Then, carry out your plan.

8 Now that you've explored, go back to your answer in step 4. Would you answer differently?

9 Considering what you learned in your exploration, answer your question again, adding new things you've learned. You may completely change your answer.

10 It's important to be able to talk about thinking. Choose three people to tell about how you arrived at your response in every step. For example, don't just read what you wrote down in step 2. Try to share how you thought of those things.

Observe and Infer

Before Ben could communicate his results, he had to plan and carry out his experiment. First, he made and recorded careful observations about his plant. **Observations** can be bits of information you gather with your senses. Most scientific observations are made with your eyes and ears. But, you also can observe with your senses of touch, taste, and smell. Ben observed that many of the leaves had fallen off his plant. The stem, in places, was peeling. Ben also noticed that some white, powdery, smelly stuff was covering the soil in the pot. He stuck his finger into the soil. It was very wet.

Observations like Ben's often lead to inferences. An **inference** is a conclusion about an observation. Ben inferred that he was perhaps watering his plant too often. Can you make any other inferences about why Ben's plant wasn't thriving?

LIFE SCIENCE INTEGRATION

Conserving Water

Deserts are regions of Earth that receive less than 25 cm of precipitation annually. Most of the plants in these natural habitats are cacti. Cacti have thin leaves called spines. Research how the spines and the roots of the cacti help these plants survive in desert areas.

Form a Hypothesis

After a problem has been identified, a scientist may make a hypothesis. A **hypothesis** is a statement that can be tested. Hypotheses are based on observations, research, and prior knowledge of a problem. **Table 1-1** compares and contrasts hypotheses with two other scientific statements—scientific theories and scientific laws. Ben decided to use his inference about watering too often as his hypothesis. His hypothesis was: Fig plants grow best when they are watered only once a week.

Table 1-1

Scientific Statements		
Hypothesis	**Theory**	**Law**
A hypothesis is a statement that can be tested. Hypotheses that are supported by repeated tests are used to form theories.	A theory is an explanation supported by results obtained from repeated experiments. Theories attempt to explain why something happens.	A scientific law describes the behavior of something in nature. Generally, laws predict or describe what will happen in a given situation but don't explain why. **What is the difference between a scientific theory and a scientific law?**

Figure 1-10 The amount of water added to the plants is the variable in this experiment.

A At the beginning of the experiment, similar sized plants received the same amount of sunlight and were planted in the same type of soil. The plant on the right received no water at all. It was the control.

Test Your Hypothesis

In order to test his hypothesis, Ben will carry out an experiment using three plants. An experiment, as you probably already know, is a series of carefully planned steps used to test a hypothesis. In any experiment, it's important to keep everything the same except for the item or variable you are testing so that you'll know which variable caused the results. The one factor that you change in an experiment is called the **independent variable.**

In Ben's proposed experiment, the independent variable will be the number of times he waters each plant in a week. He will then observe how well each plant grows based on the amount of water the plants receive. The growth of the plants is the dependent variable in Ben's experiment. A **dependent variable** is the factor being measured in an experiment. **Figure 1-10** shows an experiment that tests the effects of water on plants.

B Three weeks later, by controlling other factors and changing only one variable—how frequently the plant was watered—the results of the experiment clearly show the effect of water on plants.

Plan the Experiment

In order to truly test only one variable at a time, scientists often use constants. **Constants** are factors in an experiment that stay the same. In his experiment, Ben will use the same size plants, which will be potted with the same kinds and amounts of soil. His teacher pointed out that Ben also must put his plants into identical containers. Other constants in Ben's experiment will be the amount of water he'll use to water each plant and the amount of light each plant will get.

Some experiments also have a control. A **control** is a standard used for comparison. Ben knows that all plants, even cacti, need water. He's just not sure how often a fig plant needs to be watered. His control might be a plant that receives no water during the experiment.

*inter*NET
CONNECTION

Visit the Glencoe Science Web Site at **www. glencoe.com/sec/ science/fl** for more information about doing scientific experiments.

Mini Lab

Observing and Inferring

Procedure

1. Look at the illustration in **Figure 1-11**. It is part of a larger illustration.
2. Record in your Science Journal everything you can observe about the illustration.
3. Use your list of observations to make inferences about what might be happening in the illustration.

Analysis

1. What do you think is happening in the illustration?
2. Compare your inference with the entire illustration on the Reviewing Main Ideas page under Section 1-2. How close was your inference to the illustration?

Figure 1-11 Study this illustration. Then do the MiniLab above to practice observing and inferring—two important science skills.

Do the Experiment

Ben gathered all the materials he would need to test his experiment. Before he starts, Ben knows from Ms. Garcia's labs that he must write down a plan to follow. In his Science Journal, he wrote that he would use three different plants. One (Plant A) would not be watered. This would be his control. A second plant (Plant B) would get watered every day during the week. The third plant (Plant C) would get watered only once a week. His experiment would last one month.

Ben then made a table in which to record his observations. He listed each plant and the number of times it was to get watered. Ben made room in the table for his measurements. He also made a plan to record his observations, which would include the height of each plant, the color of its leaves, and the number of leaves it dropped, if any. To learn more about observing, study **Figure 1-11** and do the MiniLab on this page.

Analyze Your Data

Data are collected during any scientific study. Some data are numeric values such as the length of an object or the temperature of a liquid. Other data include observations that use adjectives and phrases such as *faster than, smaller, not as well as,* and *greener.* An experimenter must record and study the data collected before he or she can draw conclusions about an experiment.

By the end of the month, Ben observed that the few leaves still left on the plant that received no water were brown and shriveled. It had lost most of its leaves. The plant that was watered every day had a few leaves left on its branches, but these leaves didn't look too healthy. Some white, smelly stuff covered the soil. Ben noticed that the plant that was watered once a week had grown the tallest. Many healthy green and white leaves hung from its branches.

Draw Conclusions

After studying his data, Ben was ready to draw some conclusions. A conclusion is a statement based on what has been observed. Ben concluded that not watering a plant caused the leaves to dry out and die. Watering a plant too much also caused the leaves to die. Watering the plant once a week seemed to be the best schedule for a fig plant.

Ben told his teacher about his results. She reminded him that in order to make sure his conclusions were valid, he should repeat his experiment. Ben agreed and did the same experiment again. Based on the results of his second experiment, Ben was able to conclude confidently that watering a plant once a week made it grow well in the temperature and light conditions he used. His hypothesis was supported, and he entered his project in his school's science fair, much like the students shown in **Figure 1-12.**

Figure 1-12

A These students are preparing for their school's science fair.

Plant Observations			
Week	**Plant A**	**Plant B**	**Plant C**
1	10.5 cm	10.3 cm	10.8 cm
2	10.7 cm	11.2 cm	12.6 cm
3	10.9 cm	12.0 cm	14.6 cm
4	11.1 cm	12.4 cm	15.5 cm

B This table shows the results of an experiment similar to Ben's.

Section Assessment

1. Name the steps followed in a commonly used scientific method.

2. How are observations different from inferences?

3. Why should experiments be repeated more than once?

4. **Think Critically:** Why is it important to test only one variable at a time?

5. 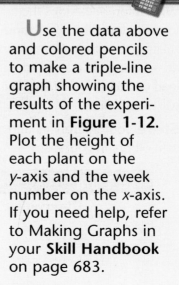 **Skill Builder**
   Separating and Controlling Variables Separating and controlling variables is an important part of conducting an experiment. Do the **Chapter 1 Skill Activity** on page 708 to practice this science skill.

Using Math

Use the data above and colored pencils to make a triple-line graph showing the results of the experiment in **Figure 1-12.** Plot the height of each plant on the y-axis and the week number on the x-axis. If you need help, refer to Making Graphs in your **Skill Handbook** on page 683.

Materials

- Magazine advertisements
- Paper (one sheet)
- Colored pencils or markers

Advertising Inferences

Imagine you're flipping through your favorite magazine and you see an ad showing a skateboard with wings. Would you infer that the skateboard could fly? In this activity, you'll use advertisements to practice the science skills of observing and inferring. Do the products really do what the ads lead you to infer?

What You'll Investigate

What observations and inferences can you make from advertisements?

Goals

- **Make inferences** based on observations.
- **Recognize** the limits of observations.

Procedure

1. **Select** three ads from those supplied by your teacher. In your Science Journal, **make a table** like the one shown below.

2. For each ad, **list** your observations. For example, you may **observe** that there are athletic people pictured in a soda ad.

3. What inferences does the advertiser want you to make from the ad? **Make inferences** that relate your observations to the product that the ad is selling. The soda ad, for example, may lead you to infer that if you drink that soda, you will be athletic.

4. **Share** your inferences and advertisements with others in your class.

Conclude and Apply

1. **Compare** and **contrast** your classmates' inferences with your own. Are there other explanations for the things you observed in the ads?

2. **Create** your own ad to sell a product. Think about what people will observe in the ad and what you want them to infer from it.

3. Have a classmate make inferences about your ad. What did your classmate infer about the ad you created? Is this what you wanted the classmate to infer? **Explain.**

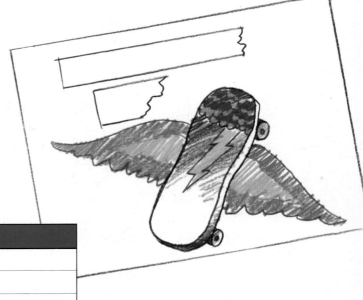

Ad Data		
	Observation	**Inference**
Ad 1		
Ad 2		
Ad 3		

Radar

Radar is an electronic system used to locate and identify distant objects. Police officers (top left) use radar to detect drivers who go over the speed limit. Meteorologists use radar to keep tabs on weather systems (bottom left). Air-traffic controllers rely on radar for tracking airplanes. People who fish use radar to locate schools of fish.

How Radar Works

The term *radar* stands for **RA**dio **D**etecting **A**nd **R**anging system. A radar system is made of several parts. The transmitter generates electromagnetic waves, which are produced by the motion of electrically charged particles. Light, radio waves, and microwaves are all examples of electromagnetic waves. In a radar system, these waves leave the transmitter through one or more antennae. When the waves encounter an object, the radio waves scatter. These scattered waves, often called echoes, are received by other antennae in the radar system. An amplifier increases the signals of these echoes. A computer then processes the signals and displays them on a screen. The distance to the target object, its altitude or depth, and the object's position relative to the radar source also can be displayed on the screen.

Ground Penetrating Radar

A type of radar called ground penetrating radar (GPR) can be used to explore archaeological sites. The system can be used to identify important underground features before a site is excavated. This step helps scientists decide which parts of the site are safe to explore and which should be avoided to prevent damaging the site. Computers process the data gathered by radar and use the information to create three-dimensional maps of the site.

Radar Development in World War II

Even before the United States entered World War II, the first Army radar was patented in May of 1937. By 1941, early warning radars could detect an approaching plane, though not its altitude or size. Radar was one of the most important communication developments of World War II.

For a **preview** of this chapter, study this Reviewing Main Ideas before you read the chapter. After you have studied this chapter, you can use the Reviewing Main Ideas to **review** the chapter.

The Glencoe MindJogger, Audiocassettes, and CD-ROM provide additional opportunities for review.

Section

1-1 HOW SCIENCE WORKS

Science is a process of understanding the world around you. **Technology** is the use of the knowledge gained through scientific thinking and problem solving. Archaeologists, scientists who study the artifacts of ancient people, use both science and technology in their work. Many archaeological sites and the artifacts they contain are found by accident. The excavation of an archaeological find is done slowly and carefully so that the artifacts and the site itself are not damaged or destroyed. Artifacts such as tools and pottery can be dated using chemical analyses. During an archaeological dig, maps are often made to show the location of each artifact with respect to the site. *Describe the two branches of archaeology.*

Reading Check ✓

The suffix *-logy* means "science" or "study of." Identify and define a dozen other branches of science with names that end in *-logy*.

Section 1-2 SCIENTIFIC PROBLEM SOLVING

Scientific methods are step-by-step approaches to solving problems. Steps that can be used in scientific problem solving include identifying the problem, forming and testing a **hypothesis,** analyzing the results of the test, and drawing conclusions. Many scientific experiments involve two variables, or factors, that change. An **independent variable** is a factor that the experimenter changes. The **dependent variable** is the factor that changes as a result of the independent variable. **Constants** are factors in an experiment that don't change. A **control,** when one is included, is a standard used for comparison. *Why should you test only one variable at a time?*

Career CONNECTION

Amanda Shaw, International Science Fair Contestant

Amanda Shaw is an example of how young people can become involved in science. Her science fair project studied the effects of carbon dioxide and plants on global warming. After winning first place in a regional competition, Amanda went on to compete against hundreds of other young scientists at the International Science and Engineering Fair (ISEF). Many scientists first become interested in environmental issues by participating in science fair projects. *What does it take to make a good science fair project?*

Chapter 1 Assessment

Using Vocabulary

a. constant
b. control
c. dependent variable
d. hypothesis
e. independent variable
f. inference
g. observation
h. science
i. scientific methods
j. technology

Each phrase below describes a science term from the list. Write the term that matches the phrase describing it.

1. variable changed by the person doing the experiment
2. a statement that can be tested
3. step-by-step approach to solving problems
4. information you gather with your senses
5. the process of understanding the world around you

Checking Concepts

Choose the word or phrase that best answers the question.

6. A scientist publishes the results of her experiments. Which science skill is she practicing?
   A) observing
   B) inferring
   C) communicating
   D) hypothesizing

7. What technology helps archaeologists to "see" a buried site before they begin excavating it?
   A) mapmaking
   B) digging
   C) radar
   D) experimenting

8. What is the first step in a commonly used scientific method?
   A) forming a hypothesis
   B) recognizing a problem
   C) drawing conclusions
   D) analyzing data

9. Why do scientists make maps of archaeological sites?
   A) to photograph artifacts
   B) to calculate the exact age of artifacts
   C) to record where the artifacts were found
   D) to discover artifacts

10. What is a standard used for comparison in an experiment called?
    A) a constant
    B) an independent variable
    C) a dependent variable
    D) a control

11. What is a conclusion based on an observation?
    A) a control
    B) a hypothesis
    C) an inference
    D) a variable

12. What is a series of carefully planned steps used to test a hypothesis?
    A) a constant
    B) an observation
    C) an experiment
    D) a conclusion

13. Why should an experiment be repeated?
    A) to form a hypothesis
    B) to reduce the chance of error
    C) to change controls
    D) to identify the problem

14. What should an experimenter do after analyzing test results?
    A) identify the problem
    B) draw conclusions
    C) carry out the experiment
    D) form a hypothesis

15. A computer is an example of which of the following?
    A) an experiment
    B) a control
    C) an excavation
    D) technology

Thinking Critically

16. An archaeologist finds a site that contains many different layers of artifacts. What might she conclude about the people who lived at the site?

17. Is every scientific problem solved using the same steps? Explain.

18. Explain why the following statement is false. Scientists do all their work in laboratories.

19. Describe how you might test which laundry soap cleans the best. Be sure to include variables, constants, and a control.

20. Why is it important to accurately record and measure data during an experiment?

Developing Skills

If you need help, refer to the **Skill Handbook.**

21. **Concept Map:** Use the following terms to complete the concept map of a commonly used scientific method shown on this page: *analyze data, form a hypothesis, design an experiment to test the hypothesis,* and *observe and record.*

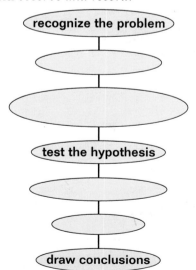

recognize the problem

test the hypothesis

draw conclusions

22. **Separating and Controlling Variables:** Give an example of how Ben controlled variables in his fig plant experiment.

THE PRINCETON REVIEW

Test-Taking Tip

Don't Guess When answering questions about a topic, do not guess. Always return to the original material to reread and get the details from there.

Test Practice

Use these questions to test your Science Proficiency.

1. Min observed that a plant in a shady corner of her bedroom was not growing as well as a plant on the windowsill. She guessed that plants need sunlight to grow and decided to conduct an experiment to test her hypothesis. She put one plant in the cool dark basement of her house and another in the warm bright kitchen. What is wrong with Min's experiment?
   A) She did not form a hypothesis.
   B) She did not control variables.
   C) She did not carry out the experiment.
   D) She did not identify the problem.

2. You see a flock of geese flying south and think that the geese must be migrating to a warmer climate for the winter. Which of the following **BEST** describes how you reached this explanation?
   A) You made an observation, then an inference.
   B) You made an inference, then an observation.
   C) You made an inference, then a conclusion.
   D) You made a conclusion, then a hypothesis.

Chapter Preview

Skills Preview

Skill Builders
- Use Numbers
- Make a Graph

Activities
- Make a Model
- Design an Experiment

MiniLabs
- Measure in SI

Reading Check ✔

Look up words that begin
with the prefixes listed in
Table 2-2. Explain why the
words have these prefixes.

Explore Activity

Carl Lewis goes the distance in both the long jump shown here and in other Olympic events. He won a total of nine gold medals at the Olympic Games in 1984, 1988, 1992, and 1996. Four of his gold medals are in the long jump. His winning jump at the 1996 Olympics was a distance of 8.5 m. Carl Lewis and other athletes depend on accurate and precise measurement in competitions. A fraction of a centimeter can separate the gold and silver medalists in the long jump.

Measuring Length

1. Horses are measured in a unit called *hands.* One hand is about 10 cm. Measure several items using the width of your own hand as *1 hand.*

2. About how many hands long is your arm from shoulder to fingertip? How wide is this book?

3. Now, measure two other objects in the classroom using your hand.

Why switch from hands to meters and centimeters as units of length?

Description and Measurement

What You'll Learn

▶ Different methods of measurement
▶ How exact a measurement is

Vocabulary
measurement
estimation

Why It's Important

▶ Measurement helps you communicate information and ideas.

Measurement

If someone asked you to describe what you are wearing today, what would you say? You'd probably start by describing colors and styles. Then, you might mention sizes: size 7 shoes, size 13 shirt. Every day, you are surrounded by numbers. **Measurement** is a way to describe the world with numbers. It answers questions such as how much, how long, or how far. Measurement can describe the amount of milk in a carton, the cost of a new compact disc, or the distance between your home and your school. It also can describe the volume of water in the oceans, the mass of an atom, or how fast a penguin's heart pumps blood.

Figure 2-1 shows a fossilized *Knightia* fish. This fossil is about 50 million years old. An average *Knightia* was about 10 cm long. About 60 percent of the fish in the Green River shale quarries, from which this fossil comes, are *Knightia*. Scientists use these measurements to describe and understand fossils. Information described with numbers, such as length and age, is a measurement.

CHEMISTRY
INTEGRATION

Descriptions of Matter
A description of matter that does not involve measurement is qualitative. For example, water is composed of hydrogen and oxygen. A quantitative description uses measurement. For example, one water molecule is composed of one oxygen atom and two hydrogen atoms. Give a qualitative and quantitative description of your hand.

Figure 2-1 This *Knightia* fossil fish is from the Green River shale formation in western Wyoming. **Does this photo show the actual size of the fossil? Explain.**

Measurement also can describe events such as the one shown in **Figure 2-2.** In the 1968 summer Olympics, swimmer Debbie Meyer of the United States came in first in the women's 200-m freestyle. She swam the race in 130.5 s. Claudia Poli of Costa Rica won first place in 1996. She swam the 200 meters in 118.16 s. In this example, measurement conveys information about the year of the race, the length, the finishing order, and the time. Information about who competed and in what sport are not measurements but are needed to describe the event completely.

Figure 2-3 This student is about 1.5 m tall. **Estimate the size of the tree in the photo.**

Estimation

You have probably used a ruler, meterstick, or tape measure to find an object's length. What happens when you want to describe a tree's height but you can't measure it with a meterstick? You can use your knowledge about the height of a familiar object to estimate the height of the tree.

Estimation can help you make a rough measurement of an object by guessing. Estimation is based on experience, as shown in **Figure 2-3.** It is useful when you are in a hurry and exact data are not required. Estimation is a valuable skill that improves with experience, practice, and understanding.

Using Estimation

You can compare an object whose length you do not know with familiar objects to estimate its length. When you estimate, you often use the word *about*. One meter is about the height of a doorknob above the floor. One centimeter is about the width of the tip of your smallest finger. One millimeter is about the thickness of a dime. To estimate your height, would you use meters, centimeters, or millimeters? What unit would you use to estimate the size of the point of your pencil?

Estimation also is used to check that an answer is reasonable. Suppose you calculate your friend's running speed as 47 m/s. You are familiar with how long a second is and how long a meter is. Can you picture your friend running a 50-m dash in 1 s? Estimation tells you that 47 m/s is too high a speed, and you should check your work.

Figure 2-4 Precision depends on the tool used.

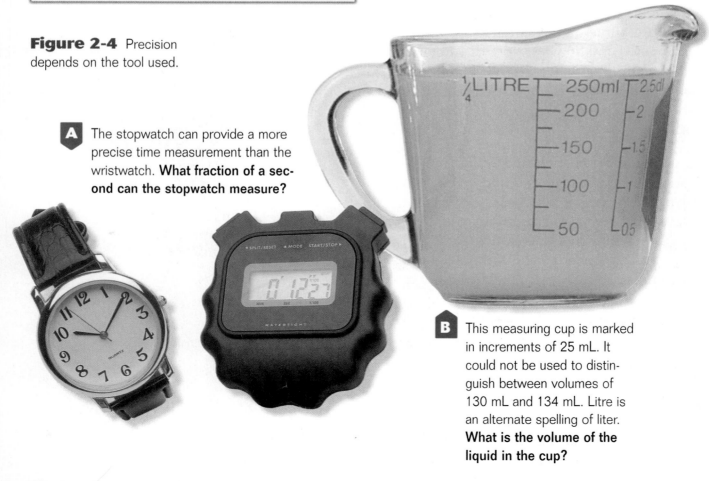

A The stopwatch can provide a more precise time measurement than the wristwatch. **What fraction of a second can the stopwatch measure?**

B This measuring cup is marked in increments of 25 mL. It could not be used to distinguish between volumes of 130 mL and 134 mL. Litre is an alternate spelling of liter. **What is the volume of the liquid in the cup?**

Figure 2-5 Shooting baskets illustrates accuracy and precision.

A When your shots hit all over, they are not accurate or precise.

Precision and Accuracy

Precision describes how carefully you make your measurement. The precision of the tool used determines the precision of the measurement, as shown in **Figure 2-4.** If you measure the width of this book with a ruler marked to millimeters, you can determine the precise width of the book only to the nearest millimeter. A precise measurement can be reproduced. For example, if you measure your desk to be precisely 85 cm high, the person next to you will also measure 85 cm.

Look at an almanac that lists Olympic winners of the past. Winning measurements for some events are given with more precision over time. Times from the 1896 Olympics might be given to the nearest second. Times for later Olympics are given to the nearest tenth of a second, then the nearest hundredth of a second. This is an example of how improved tools make more precise measurements.

Accuracy compares a measurement to the real value. A clock that does not work well could give precise measurements that are inaccurate. **Figure 2-5** illustrates the difference between precision and accuracy. ☑

B When your shots consistently hit a point well to the left of the basket, they are precise but not accurate.

C When your shots are consistently in the basket, they are precise and accurate.

Reading Check ☑
What is accuracy?

Figure 2-6 This laboratory scale can measure to the nearest hundredth of a gram. **What is the mass of the object rounded to the nearest tenth of a gram?**

Rounding a Measure

Sometimes, you have more precision than you need, as shown in **Figure 2-6.** Not all measurements must be made with instruments that measure with great precision. For example, you could measure the length of the sidewalk outside your school to the nearest millimeter. However, you would probably need to know the length only to the nearest meter or tenth of a meter. If your teacher told you the length was 135.841 m, you could round the distance to 135.8 m or 136 m. To round a given value, follow these steps.

1. Look at the digit to the right of the place being rounded.

   - The digit remains the same if the digit to the right is 0, 1, 2, 3, or 4.

   - Round up if the digit to the right is 5, 6, 7, 8, or 9.

2. The remaining digits to the right of the rounding place are eliminated from the rounded answer.

Using Math

Rounding

Example Problem

Refer to the periodic table inside the back cover of this book. The atomic mass of lithium is 6.941 atomic mass units. The atomic mass of neon is 20.180 atomic mass units. You decide that you need to know these values only to the nearest unit to solve a problem. What are the rounded values?

Problem-Solving Steps

1. What number is to the right of the ones place? lithium: 9 neon: 1
2. Do you round the ones place up or down? lithium: up; neon: down
3. **Solution:** lithium: 6.941 rounds to 7 atomic mass units

   neon: 20.180 rounds to 20 atomic mass units

Practice Problem

What are the rounded atomic masses to the nearest tenth of a unit?

Strategy Hint: To round to a certain place, remember to ignore all the numbers more than one place to the right. For example, to round 31 498.89 to the nearest thousand, look at the 4 and round down. Ignore the 8s and 9s that follow the 4.

Precision and Number of Digits

Suppose you want to divide a 2-L bottle of soda equally among seven people. You find $2 \div 7$ on your calculator: 0.285 714 285 7. Will you measure exactly 0.285 714 285 7 L of soda for each person? (Even this number is inexact. Your calculator rounds or cuts off the answer when its display is out of room.) In this case, you need to know that each person gets about 0.3 L. You don't have to copy every digit that appears on your calculator.

A good way to determine the number of digits in the answer when you multiply or divide is to look at the number of digits in each piece of information. In this case, 2 L has one digit and seven people has one digit. The answer should probably have only one or two digits.

Suppose you measure a folder to be 0.008 m thick. You place it on a desk that is 1 m off the ground. Is the top of the folder exactly 1.008 m off the ground? Probably not. The desk might be 1.05 m, or 0.937 m, or any other measure that rounds to 1 m. Because you know the height of the desk only to the ones digit and the height of the folder to the thousandths digit, trying to add them exactly does not make sense. If you round to the ones, the least precise digit in the problem, you get 1 m as the height.

*inter*NET
CONNECTION

Visit the Glencoe Science Web Site at **www.glencoe.com/ sec/science/fl** for more information about measurement.

Section Assessment

1. Estimate the distance between your desk and your teacher's desk. Explain the method you used.

2. Measure the height of your desk to the nearest half-centimeter.

3. Sarah measured her father's garden. It is 11.72 m long. Round the measure to the nearest tenth of a meter.

4. **Think Critically:** You are given two metric rulers, one marked in half-centimeters and one marked in millimeters. Which would be most helpful in measuring small items such as the width of a wire?

5.  **Skill Builder**
   Using Numbers Numbers are used to make measurements. Do the **Chapter 2 Skill Activity** on page 709 to use numbers to describe familiar objects.

Science **Journal** In your Science Journal, describe your backpack. Include one set of qualities that have no measurements, such as color and texture, and one set of measurements, such as width and mass.

Global Positioning System

In the early days of flight, pilots flew relatively close to the ground and navigated by landmarks and natural features such as rivers and mountains. In darkness or bad weather, pilots were out of luck. The invention of radar made it possible to navigate without seeing the ground. Today, pilots can determine their position with even greater precision using the Global Positioning System (GPS). The GPS can determine the position, speed, and direction of movement of a pilot or any other person using the system anywhere on Earth.

How GPS Works

Twenty-four GPS satellites orbit in a circular path 17 500 km above Earth. The satellites, powered by solar cells (see inset), send signals to receivers on Earth. Each receiver measures the distance between itself and every satellite within range. Three satellite readings are enough for people using a GPS receiver to determine their position on Earth's surface. To ensure accuracy, receivers use information from four satellites. The woman at right holds an antenna that is receiving position data from the GPS satellite system.

The GPS measures the time it takes for the receiver to communicate with each satellite. This measurement is used to calculate latitude, longitude, and elevation. If the receiver is moving, its velocity also can be determined. Receivers at ground-based stations with fixed positions are used to check accuracy and to make corrections for errors.

A variety of GPS receiving units are available, with different levels of precision. Small receivers, used by boaters and hikers, are precise to within a few hundred meters. GPS receivers used for making topographic maps and construction layouts measure position to within several centimeters, while those used for measuring difficult terrain such as mountains and rivers can measure accurately to within less than 1 cm.

interNET CONNECTION

To research how scientists use GPS to help them in their studies, visit the Glencoe Science Web Site at **www.glencoe. com/sec/science/fl**.

SI Units

The International System

Can you imagine how confusing it would be if scientists in every country used different measuring systems? Sharing data and ideas would be complicated. To avoid confusion, scientists need a common language. The International System of Units, or **SI,** was established in 1960 as the general system for measurement. It was designed to provide a worldwide standard of physical measurement for science, industry, and commerce. SI uses units such as meter, cubic meter, kilogram, and kelvin, as shown in **Table 2-1.**

The SI units are related by multiples of ten. A unit, such as the meter, can be converted to a smaller or larger unit by multiplying by a power of 10. The new unit is renamed by adding a prefix, shown in **Table 2-2.** For example, one millionth of a meter is one *micro*meter. One thousand grams is one *kilo*gram.

To convert between units, multiply by the appropriate power of ten. For example, to rewrite a kilogram measurement as a gram measurement, multiply by 1000.

Table 2-1

SI Units		
Quantity	**Unit**	**Symbol**
length	meter	m
volume	cubic meter	m^3
mass	kilogram	kg
temperature	kelvin	K
time	second	s

Table 2-2

Prefixes Used with SI Units	
Prefix	**Multiplier**
tera-	1 000 000 000 000
giga-	1 000 000 000
mega-	1 000 000
kilo-	1000
hecto-	100
deca-	10
[unit]	1
deci-	0.1
centi-	0.01
milli-	0.001
micro-	0.000 001
nano-	0.000 000 001

Using Math

Using Unit Analysis

Example Problem

Rafael measured his classroom to be 468 cm long. Find the length in meters.

Problem-Solving Steps

1. Write the number you want to convert. 468 cm
2. Determine what unit you want the answer to be in. meters
3. Write the number of centimeters in a meter as a fraction. In this case, there are 100 cm in 1 m.

   Use $\dfrac{100 \text{ cm}}{1 \text{ m}}$ or $\dfrac{1 \text{ m}}{100 \text{ cm}}$.

4. Write the expression, including the units. Check that the units cancel correctly so the answer will be in meters.
5. **Solution:** $468 \text{ cm} \times \dfrac{1 \text{ m}}{100 \text{ cm}} = 4.68 \text{ m}$

Practice Problem

How many milliseconds are in 23.6 s?

Strategy Hint: Check that the units cancel appropriately before making calculations. For example, if your expression for speed will produce an answer in square meters, you can see that you have made an error before doing any calculations.

Figure 2-7 The actual size of these red blood cells is about 15 micrometers across. **How many meters is this?**

Length

Length is defined as the distance between two points. Length can describe the distance from Earth to Mars or the distance across a cell under a microscope, as shown in **Figure 2-7.** In your science lab, you will usually measure length with a metric ruler or meterstick.

The **meter** (m) is the SI unit of length. One meter is about the length of a baseball bat. The size of a room would be measured in meters.

Smaller objects can be measured in centimeters (cm) or millimeters (mm). The length of your textbook or pencil would be measured in centimeters. Millimeters might be used to measure the width of the letters on this page. To measure the length of small things such as blood cells, bacteria, or viruses, scientists use micrometers (millionths of a meter) and nanometers (billionths of a meter).

Sometimes scientists need to measure long distances, such as the distance a migrating bird travels. To measure such lengths they use kilometers. Kilometers may be most familiar to you as the measure of a race or the distance traveled in a car, as shown in **Figure 2-8.**

Volume

The amount of space an object occupies is its volume. The cubic meter (m^3), shown in **Figure 2-9,** is the SI unit of volume. You can measure smaller volumes with the cubic centimeter (cm^3 or cc). To find the volume of a square or rectangular object, such as a brick or your textbook, measure its length, width, and height, and multiply them. What is the volume of a compact disc case?

You are probably familiar with a 2-liter bottle. A liter is a measurement of liquid volume. A cube 10 cm on a side ($1000\ cm^3$) holds one liter of water. A cube 1 cm on a side ($1\ cm^3$) holds one milliliter of water.

Figure 2-8 Long distances are measured in kilometers. This sign warns drivers in Australia about animals crossing the road. **About how many kilometers is the distance between your home and your school?**

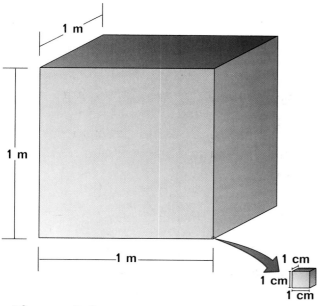

Figure 2-9 A cubic meter equals the volume of a cube 1 meter by 1 meter by 1 meter. **How many cubic centimeters are in a cubic meter?**

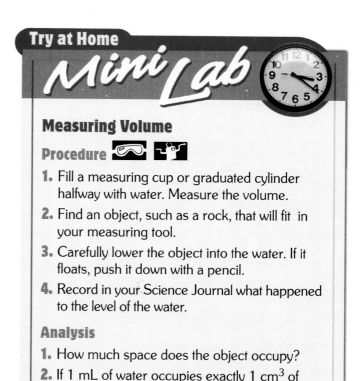

Try at Home

Mini Lab

Measuring Volume

Procedure

1. Fill a measuring cup or graduated cylinder halfway with water. Measure the volume.
2. Find an object, such as a rock, that will fit in your measuring tool.
3. Carefully lower the object into the water. If it floats, push it down with a pencil.
4. Record in your Science Journal what happened to the level of the water.

Analysis

1. How much space does the object occupy?
2. If 1 mL of water occupies exactly $1\ cm^3$ of space, what is the volume of the object?

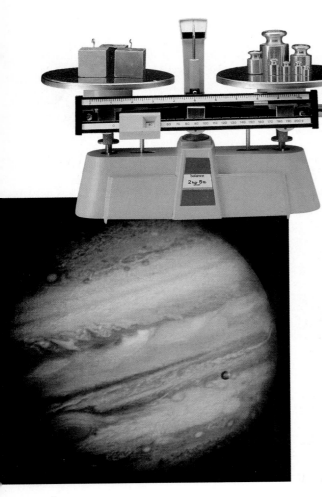

Figure 2-10 Mass is not the same as weight.

A A pan balance compares an unknown mass to known masses.

B Jupiter has a mass of 1.90×10^{27} kg. It does not make sense to talk about the weight of Jupiter because it is not on the surface of Earth or another planet.

Mass

The **mass** of an object measures the amount of matter in the object. The **kilogram** (kg) is the SI unit for mass. One liter of water has a mass of about 1 kg. Smaller masses are measured in grams (g). One gram is about the mass of a large paper clip. You can measure mass with a pan balance, shown in **Figure 2-10A.** The pan balance compares an object to a known mass. It is balanced when the masses on both sides are equal.

Why use the word *mass* instead of weight? Weight and mass are not the same. Mass depends on the amount of matter in an object. Mass never changes, as shown in **Figure 2-10B.** When you ride in an elevator or on the space shuttle, your mass stays the same.

Weight

Weight is a measurement of force. It depends on gravity, which can change depending on where the object is located. A spring scale, shown in **Figure 2-11,** measures weight. The reading on the scale depends on the force pulling the spring. When you start riding up in an elevator, you feel heavier for a moment. When the elevator starts down, you feel lighter for a moment. If you were standing in the elevator on a bathroom scale, which uses a spring, you would see a slight change in your weight. But, if you had a pan balance in the elevator, it would not suddenly tip. The masses in the pans would not change, and it would remain balanced. ✔

Figure 2-11 A spring scale measures an object's weight by how much it stretches a spring. **What is the weight of the rock?**

Reading Check ✔

What does weight measure?

Temperature

The physical property of temperature is used to measure how hot or cold an object is. You may know about the Fahrenheit or Celsius temperature scale on a thermometer. Temperature is measured in SI with the **Kelvin** scale. A 1 K difference in temperature is the same as a 1°C difference in temperature, as shown in **Figure 2-12.** However, the two scales start at different points. Zero degrees Celsius is the freezing point of water at sea level. Water boils at 100°C. Zero kelvin is the coldest temperature possible in nature.

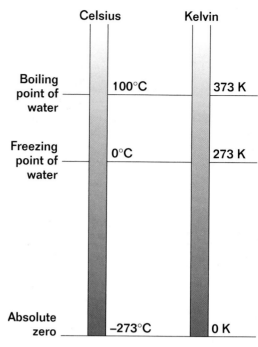

Figure 2-12 The Kelvin scale starts at 0 K.

Time and Rates

Time is the interval between two events. The SI unit of time is the second (s). Time is sometimes measured in hours (h). Though this is not an SI unit, it is easier to use when you discuss long periods.

A **rate** is a ratio of two measurements with different units. One rate you are familiar with is speed, the distance traveled in a given time. Speeds are often measured in kilometers per hour (km/h).

Rates are combinations of SI units. Rates are most often seen with units of time, but any measures with different units can be combined in a rate. Other rates might be

$$\frac{\text{grains}}{\text{liter}}, \frac{\text{insects}}{\text{square meter}}, \text{or } \frac{°C}{\text{hour}}.$$

Section Assessment

1. What property of an object does the cubic meter measure?

2. How would you change a measure in centimeters to kilometers?

3. **Think Critically:** You are given a small metal cube and told to find its mass. What tool(s) will you need, and how will you use the tool(s) to determine its mass?

4.  **Skill Builder**
   Forming Operational Definitions
   Give an operational definition of a spring scale. If you need help, refer to Forming Operational Definitions in the **Skill Handbook** on page 688.

Using Math

A block of wood is 0.2 m by 0.1 m by 0.5 m. Find its dimensions in centimeters. Use these to find its volume in cubic centimeters.

Materials

- Graph paper (1 cm)
- Pencil
- Metric ruler
- Meterstick

Scale Drawing

A scale drawing is used to represent something that is too large or too small to be drawn at its actual size. Blueprints for a house are a good example of a scale drawing.

What You'll Investigate

How can you represent your classroom accurately in a scale drawing?

Goals

- **Measure** using SI.
- **Make** a data table.
- **Calculate** new measurements.
- **Draw** an accurate scale drawing.

Procedure

1. Use your meterstick to **measure** the length and width of your classroom. Note the locations and sizes of doors and windows.

2. **Record** the lengths of each item in a data table.

3. Use a scale of 2 cm = 1 m to calculate the lengths to be used in the drawing. **Record** them in your data table.

4. **Draw** the floor plan. Include the scale.

Conclude and Apply

1. How did you **calculate** the lengths to be used on your drawing?

2. What would your scale drawing look like if you choose a different scale?

3. Sketch your room at home, estimating the distances. **Compare** this to your scale drawing of the classroom. When would you use each type of illustration?

Sample data

Room Dimensions		
Part of room	Distance in room (m)	Distance on drawing (cm)

Communicating Data

Scientific Illustrations

Most science books include some pictures. Photographs and drawings illustrate the ideas in the book. They also can give new information. For example, a drawing of an airplane engine can show how all the parts fit together.

Photographs

A photograph can show an object exactly as it is. A movie can show how an object moves. A movie can be slowed down or speeded up to show interesting features, as shown in **Figure 2-13.** In your schoolwork, you might use photographs in a report. For example, you could show the different types of trees in your neighborhood for a report on ecology.

What You'll Learn

► How to use pictures and tables to give information
► How to identify and use three types of graphs
► How to distinguish the correct use of each type of graph

Vocabulary

table	bar graph
graph	circle graph
line graph	

Why It's Important

► Illustrations, tables, and graphs help communicate data.

Figure 2-13 Photo series are used to create models of motion, such as those models used for designing walking robots or analyzing gymnastic moves.

A This series of photos shows how a bighorn sheep moves when it jumps.

*inter*NET
CONNECTION

Visit the Glencoe Science Web Site at **www.glencoe.com/ sec/science/fl** for more information about scientific illustration.

B This illustrates the arm and leg motion of a runner.

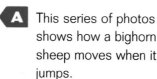

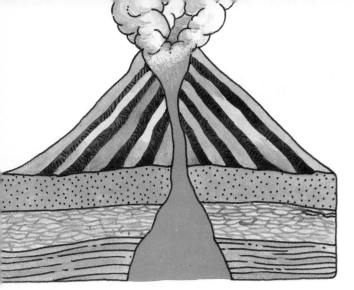

Drawings

Sometimes a photograph is not the best kind of illustration to use. For example, a canyon cut through red rock reveals many rock layers. If the layers are all shades of red, a drawing can show where the line between two layers lies. The drawing can show important things, like the size of each layer, and can leave out unimportant details, like the patterns of dust on the rock.

In your studies, you might use a drawing of the Earth-moon-sun system to explain an eclipse. A drawing also can show things we can't photograph. We do not have photographs of our solar system from far away, but from drawings you know what it looks like. You also will make quick sketches to help model problems. For example, you could sketch the outline of two continents to show how they might have fit together.

A drawing can show hidden things. Geologists can use a drawing to show the inside of a volcano, as in **Figure 2-14.** Architects use drawings to show what the inside of a building will look like. Biologists use drawings to show where the nerves in your arm are found. ☑

Figure 2-14 This drawing shows the layers of rock around a volcano. It also shows the volcano's interior.

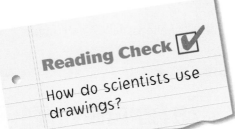

Reading Check ☑

How do scientists use drawings?

Problem Solving

Communicate with Art and Words

Imagine you are an engineer. You have a clever idea for improving a machine. Or, you are a botanist with a new idea about a plant's structure. How do you explain your idea?

To explain your ideas, you must communicate them clearly. One way is with a picture. How hard is it to describe something using only words?

Use a ruler and pencil to sketch a simple design, such as a triangle inside a square. Write a description that would explain how to make the design without actually seeing it. For example, it might start: "Draw a square 15 cm on a side. Mark a point 5 cm to the right of the lower-left corner . . ."

Trade your description with another student and try to draw the design based on the directions. Compare your design with the original.

Think Critically: Explain how this exercise relates to the problem of describing a new invention for people who cannot see it.

Tables and Graphs

Scientists and mathematicians need an organized way to collect and display data. A **table** displays information in rows and columns so that it is easier to read and understand, as seen in **Figure 2-15.** The data in the table could be presented in a paragraph, but it would be harder to pick out the facts or make comparisons.

A graph can show the relationships between the data. A **graph** is used to collect, organize, and summarize data in a visual way. A graph can display one set of data or more. Three common types of graphs are line graphs, bar graphs, and circle graphs.

Line Graph

The table in **Figure 2-15** has two variables, type of animal and speed. A variable is something that can change, or vary. A **line graph** is used to show the relationship between two variables. An example is shown in **Figure 2-16.** Both variables must be numbers. Age and height will work, but age and favorite sport will not. One variable is shown on the bottom line, or axis, of the graph. The other variable is placed along the vertical axis. A line shows the relationship between the two variables.

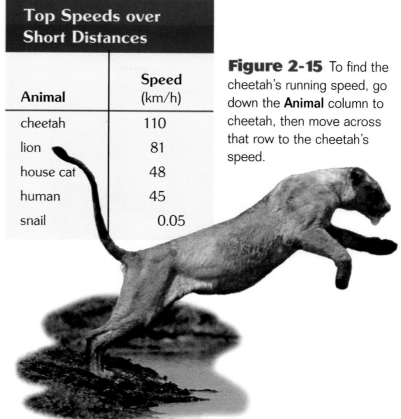

Top Speeds over Short Distances	
Animal	**Speed (km/h)**
cheetah	110
lion	81
house cat	48
human	45
snail	0.05

Figure 2-15 To find the cheetah's running speed, go down the **Animal** column to cheetah, then move across that row to the cheetah's speed.

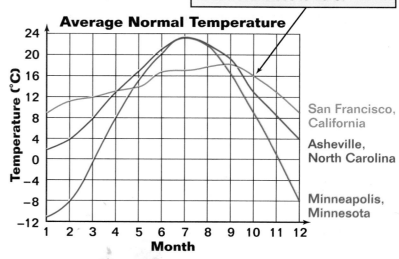

The normal October temperature in San Francisco is 16°C.

Figure 2-16 The line graph has a horizontal axis and a vertical axis. This graph shows that Minneapolis and Asheville reach the same summer temperature, but Minneapolis has a much greater variation in temperature. The normal temperature in San Francisco peaks later than the temperature in the other two cities. It also has less variation.

Average Normal Temperature

San Francisco, California

Asheville, North Carolina

Minneapolis, Minnesota

Figure 2-17

A This bar graph has categories on the horizontal axis and numbers on the vertical axis. You can see that about 53 percent of junior high schools have modems. **What percentage of senior high schools have modems?**

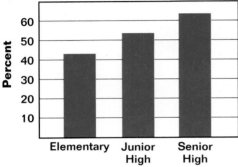

Percentage of Schools with Modems

B The bar graph below has numbers on both axes. Bar graphs can be horizontal or vertical. They can display any numerical data, not just percents. **Based on the bar graph, how did the percentage of homes with computers change between 1991 and 1997?**

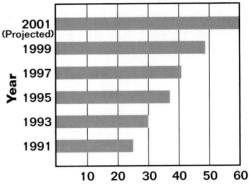

Percentage of Homes with Computers

Figure 2-18 This graph uses a circle divided into sections. All the sections together equal 100 percent. **What category has the greatest number of endangered species?**

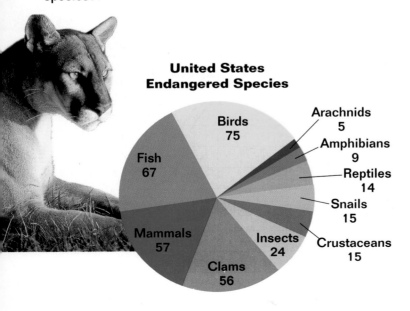

United States Endangered Species

Bar Graph

A **bar graph** uses bars to show the relationships between variables. A bar graph is similar to a line graph. One variable is divided into parts. It can be numbers, such as the time of day, or a category, such as an animal. The second variable must be a number. The bars show the size of the second variable. For example, if you made a graph of the running speed data, the bar for the lion would represent 81 km/h. Examples of bar graphs are shown in **Figure 2-17.**

Circle Graph

Suppose you want to show how many people in your class play soccer. A **circle graph** shows the parts of a whole. The circle represents the whole. The sections of the circle represent the parts of the whole, as shown in **Figure 2-18.**

To make a circle graph, find the percent for each part. Multiply the percent by 360° to find the angle measure of that part. For example, there are 337 endangered species in **Figure 2-18** and 57 are mammals. Mammals account for 17 percent of endangered species. Multiply 360° by 0.17. A 62° section represents the mammals.

Misleading Graphs

When using or making graphs to display data, be careful. The scale of a graph can be misleading. The way you mark the scale on a graph can create the wrong impression, as seen in **Figure 2-19A**.

A broken scale is used for small but significant changes. Examples include a climate warming by 0.01°C a year or the finishing times for the top runners in a marathon, as shown in **Figure 2-19B**.

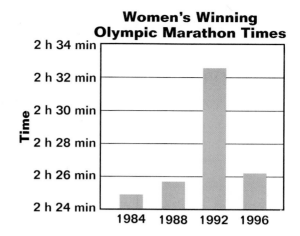

Figure 2-19 An axis that does not start at zero can be misleading. However, it is sometimes necessary.

A The vacation-time graph uses a broken vertical axis (not starting at zero) to make it appear that vacation time has doubled since 1996. The actual increase is about 15 percent.

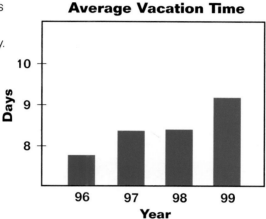

B The difference between the winning times is small. Without the broken axis, all the bars would appear to be the same height because the vertical axis would be divided into hours.

Section Assessment

1. Suppose your class surveys the students in your school about their favorite after-school activities. What type of graph would you use to display your data? Explain your choice.

2. Explain how to use **Figure 2-19B** to find the running time of the 1988 women's Olympic marathon winner.

3. **Think Critically:** How are line, bar, and circle graphs the same? How are they different?

4. **Skill Builder**
   Making and Using Graphs Graph the amount of time you spent reading each day for the past week. What type of graph will you use? If you need help, refer to Making and Using Graphs in the **Skill Handbook** on page 683.

Using Computers

Spreadsheet Use a spreadsheet table to display the total mass of a 500-kg elevator as passengers of 50 kg each are added. If you need help, refer to page 704.

Activity 2 • 2

Pace Yourself

Possible Materials

- Meterstick
- Stopwatch
  watch with a second hand

  Alternate Materials

In a track meet, you run a distance. The distance you are to run has been precisely measured. Officials watch the start to be sure all of the runners begin the race at the same time. The finish line is carefully observed so the timer is stopped at the moment you cross the line. The officials measure your time as precisely as possible. The runner with the shortest time to cover that distance wins. The results are then communicated using tables or other data displays.

Recognize the Problem

Measure running speed for each person in your group and display these data.

Form a Hypothesis

Think about the information you have learned about precision, measurement, and graphing. In your group, make a hypothesis about a technique that will provide you with the most precise measurement of each person's walking and running pace.

Goals

- **Design an experiment** that allows you to accurately measure speed for each member of your group.
- **Display data** in a table and a graph.

Safety Precautions

- Work in an area where it is safe to run.
- Participate only if you are physically able to exercise safely.

Test Your Hypothesis

Plan

1. As a group, decide what materials you will need.

2. How far will you walk? How far will you run? How will you **measure** that distance? How precise can you be?

3. How will you **measure** time? How precise can you be?

4. List the steps and materials you will use to **test your hypothesis.** Be specific. Will you repeat any part of your test?

5. Before you begin, **create a data table.** Your group must decide on its design. Be sure to leave room to record the results for each person's walking and running time. If more than one trial is to be run for each measurement, include room for the additional data.

Do

1. Make sure that your teacher approves your plan and data table before you begin.

2. **Carry out the experiment** as planned and approved.

3. Be sure to **record your data** in the data table as you proceed with the measurements.

Analyze Your Data

1. **Graph** your data. What type of graph would be best?

2. Are your data table and graph easy to understand? Explain.

3. How do you know that your measurements are precise?

Draw Conclusions

1. How is it possible for different members of a group to find different times while **measuring** the same event?

2. What tools would help you collect more precise **data?**

3. What other data displays could you use? What are the advantages and disadvantages of each?

FIELD GUIDE to Laboratory Equipment

FIELD ACTIVITY

Look around your science classroom. Use this field guide to identify the pieces of equipment available in your classroom or in a laboratory. Practice using the equipment provided by your teacher.

Scientists make observations, form hypotheses, plan and do experiments, collect and analyze their data, and draw conclusions. You will do activities in which you also will use scientific methods while you study science. The quality of the information that you gather during the activities will depend upon correct use of laboratory equipment.

Each set of instructions will tell you what materials and equipment you will need to do the activity. Some of the items will be found around your classroom or at home. Others will be the same types of equipment used by scientists in laboratories and out in the field. Safety symbols guide you in how to use them safely. To find out more about safety symbols, refer to the chart inside the front cover of this book.

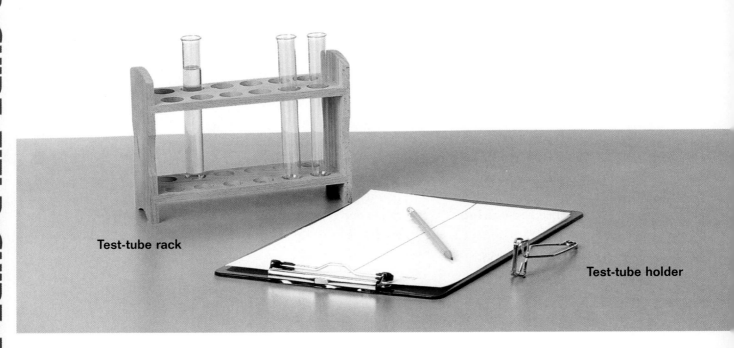

Test-tube rack

Test-tube holder

Laboratory Safety

In the science classroom or laboratory, you are responsible for your own safety and for the safety of your teacher and your classmates. To prevent accidents, be sure to use the following steps.

- Do not perform an activity without your teacher's permission.
- Tie back long hair. Do not wear loose, dangling clothing or jewelry that could catch fire or get caught in something.
- Read through the entire activity before you begin. If you do not understand any part of it, ask your teacher for help.
- Look at the safety symbols. Always wear your goggles, apron, and gloves whenever you are told. Read the safety precautions at the beginning of the procedure.
- Never taste any of the substances you use or make in an activity.
- Immediately report any accident, injury, or damaged equipment to your teacher.

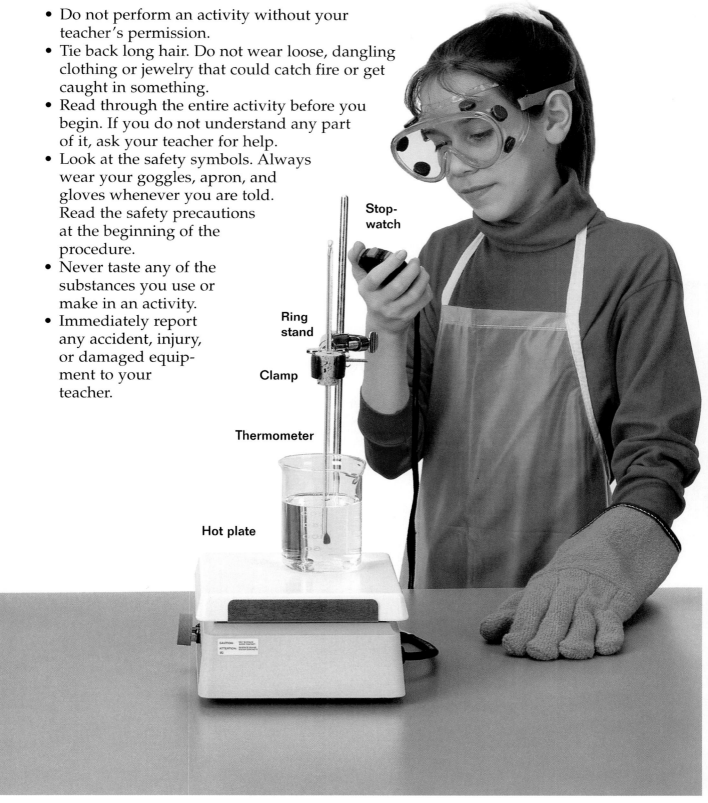

Stop-watch

Ring stand

Clamp

Thermometer

Hot plate

Guide to Labware

Many of your activities will tell you to use the laboratory glassware below. Identify which of the pieces would be most useful for measuring. Explain.

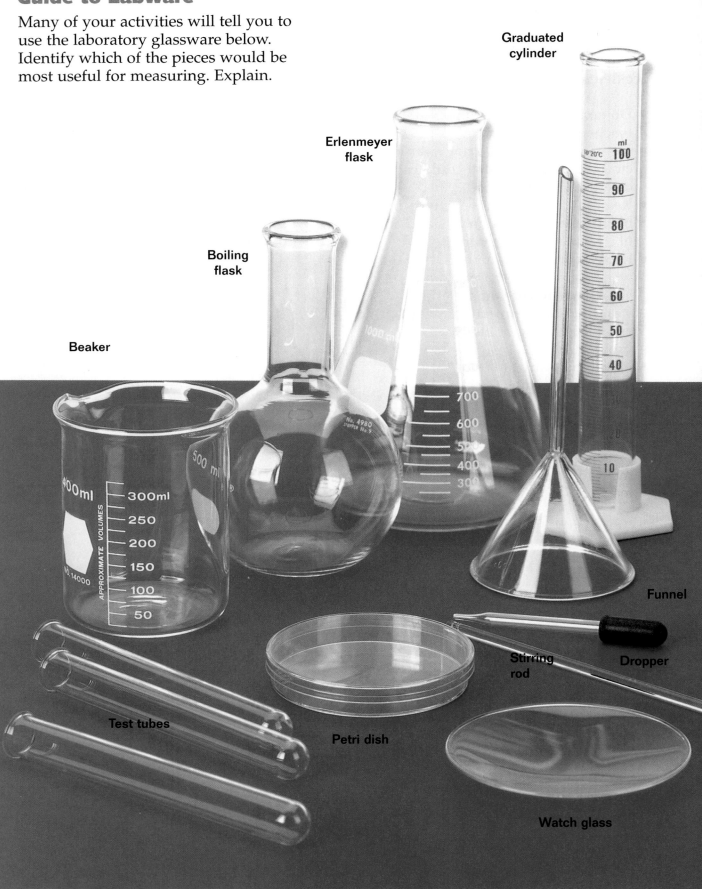

Graduated cylinder

Erlenmeyer flask

Boiling flask

Beaker

Funnel

Stirring rod

Dropper

Test tubes

Petri dish

Watch glass

How to Take Good Measurements

To be sure that your measurements are accurate and precise, laboratory instruments must be used correctly.

Measuring Length

- Never measure from the end of a meterstick (or metric ruler). Place the meterstick next to the object and read the metric scale at each end of the object. Subtract your readings to find the length of the object.
- A meterstick should be read while you are looking straight at the mark. You will have to look directly in front or overhead, not at an angle.

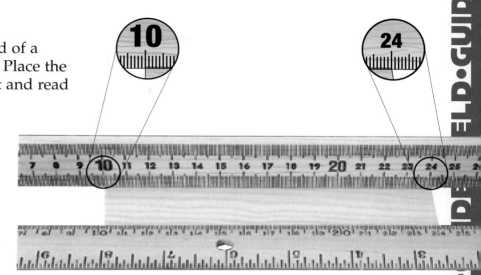

Measuring Liquid Volume and Temperature

- The meniscus is the curve at the top of a liquid. It can curve downward or upward. Look straight at the meniscus when you make your measurement, not above or below.
- A graduated cylinder is used to measure liquid volume. It is often marked in 1-mL segments. To get an accurate measurement, you should read the marking at the bottom of the meniscus.
- Thermometers use liquid volume to measure temperature. The curve of the meniscus will vary due to the type of liquid in the thermometer.

Measuring Mass

- Place the item to be measured in the pan.
- Slide the rider with the largest mass along the balance arm until the pointer drops below zero. Back that rider off one notch.
- Repeat the process with the other two riders. The pointer will swing an equal distance above and below the zero point when the mass of the object is balanced. You do not have to wait for the pointer to stop moving.
- Add the values of the masses on each beam to find the object's mass.

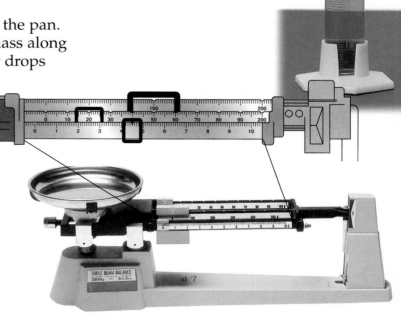

For a **preview** of this chapter, study this Reviewing Main Ideas before you read the chapter. After you have studied this chapter, you can use the Reviewing Main Ideas to **review** the chapter.

The Glencoe MindJogger, Audiocassettes, and CD-ROM provide additional opportunities for review.

Section

2-1 DESCRIPTION AND MEASUREMENT

Measurement is a way to describe the world. Measurements such as length, volume, mass, temperature, and rates are used to describe objects and events. *Name three quantities that could be used to describe your pen.*

ESTIMATION, ACCURACY, AND PRECISION

Estimation is used to make an educated guess at a measurement. It also is used when determining which point on a ruler or other scale is closest to the correct value. Accuracy describes how close a measurement is to the true value. Precision describes the exactness of a measurement. A mass of 55 kg is known to the nearest kilogram. A mass of 55.040 kg is known to the nearest thousandth of a kilogram. *If the digital readout on a scale is 48.049 g, what is the mass to the nearest tenth of a gram?*

Reading Check

Find a graph or other illustration in a newspaper or magazine. Explain its purpose.

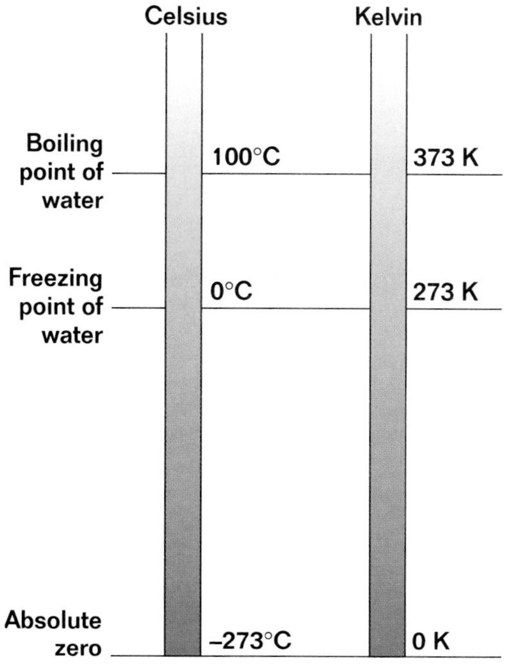

Celsius
Kelvin
Boiling point of water
100°C
373 K
Freezing point of water
0°C
273 K
Absolute zero
–273°C
0 K

Section

2-2 SI UNITS

The international system of measurement is called **SI.** It is used throughout the world for communicating data in trade, commerce, and science. ***Why do scientists need to use the same measurement system?***

The SI unit of length is the **meter.** Volume, the amount of space an object occupies, can be measured in cubic meters. The **mass** of an object is measured in **kilograms.** Temperature can be measured on different scales. The SI unit of temperature is the **Kelvin.** ***What units would you use to describe the speed of a paper airplane?***

Section

2-3 COMMUNICATING DATA

Tables, illustrations, and **graphs** can present data more clearly than explaining everything in words. They help scientists collect, organize, summarize, and display data in a way that is easy to use and understand. ***Why is the graph shown here a better choice for the data than a circle graph?***

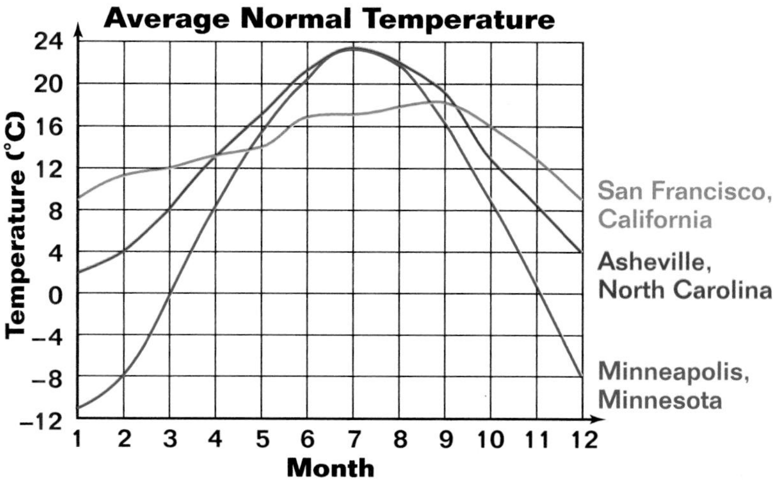

Average Normal Temperature
Temperature (°C)
24
20
16
12
8
4
0
–4
–8
–12
1 2 3 4 5 6 7 8 9 10 11 12
Month
San Francisco, California
Asheville, North Carolina
Minneapolis, Minnesota

Using Vocabulary

a. bar graph
b. circle graph
c. estimation
d. graph
e. Kelvin
f. kilogram
g. line graph
h. mass
i. measurement
j. meter
k. rate
l. SI
m. table

Each phrase below describes a science term from the list. Write the term that matches the phrase describing it.

1. the SI unit for length
2. a description with numbers
3. a method of making a rough measurement
4. the amount of matter in an object
5. a graph that shows parts of a whole

Checking Concepts

Choose the word or phrase that best answers the question.

6. The measurement 25.81 g is precise to the nearest what?
   A) gram
   B) kilogram
   C) tenth of a gram
   D) hundredth of a gram

7. What is the SI unit of mass?
   A) kilometer
   B) meter
   C) liter
   D) kilogram

8. What would you use to measure the length of an object?
   A) graduated cylinder
   B) balance
   C) meterstick
   D) spring scale

9. The cubic meter is the SI unit of what?
   A) volume
   B) weight
   C) mass
   D) distance

10. Which of the following can improve with practice?
    A) length
    B) estimation
    C) precision
    D) mass

11. Thermometers measure temperature with what scale?
    A) volume
    B) mass
    C) Celsius
    D) mercury

12. Which is used to organize data?
    A) table
    B) rate
    C) precision
    D) graduated cylinder

13. To show the number of wins for each football team in your district, use which of the following?
    A) circle graph
    B) line graph
    C) bar graph
    D) SI

14. What organizes data in rows and columns?
    A) bar graph
    B) circle graph
    C) line graph
    D) table

15. To show 25 percent on a circle graph, the section must measure what angle?
    A) 25 degrees
    B) 90 degrees
    C) 180 degrees
    D) 360 degrees

Thinking Critically

16. How would you estimate the volume your backpack could hold?
17. Why do scientists in the United States use SI rather than the English system (feet, pounds, pints, etc.) of measurement?
18. List the following lengths in order from smallest to largest: 1 m, 1 mm, 10 km, 100 mm.
19. When would you use a line graph? Can you use a bar graph for the same purpose?
20. This chapter has treated color as a quality that is not measured. However, computer artists can specify a color by using numbers to describe the amount of each

color of ink to be used at each point in a picture. Why do you think this method of describing color was invented?

Developing Skills

If you need help, refer to the Skill Handbook.

21. **Measuring in SI:** Make a fist. Use a centimeter ruler to measure the height, width, and depth of your fist.

22. **Comparing and Contrasting:** How are volume, length, and mass similar? How are they different? What units are used to measure each?

23. **Making and Using Graphs:** The table gives the area of several bodies of water. Make a bar graph of the data.

Areas of Bodies of Water	
Body of Water	**Area (km²)**
Currituck Sound (North Carolina)	301
Pocomoke Sound (Maryland/Virginia)	286
Chincoteague Bay (Maryland/Virginia)	272
Core Sound (North Carolina)	229

24. **Interpreting Scientific Illustrations:** What does the figure show? How has it been simplified?

25. **Forming Operational Definitions:** Give an operational definition of a pan balance.

Test-Taking Tip

Survey the Surroundings Find out what the conditions will be for taking the test. Will the test be timed? Will you be allowed a break? Know these things in advance so that you can practice taking tests under the same conditions.

Test Practice

Use these questions to test your Science Proficiency.

1. Estimate the percentage of hydrogen in the human body.

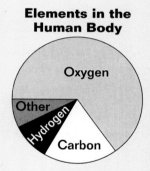

Elements in the Human Body

A) 50 percent
B) 25 percent
C) 10 percent
D) 1 percent

2. What are commonly used units for SI?
   A) meter, cubic meter, kilogram, second
   B) length, volume, mass, time
   C) kilo, deci, centi, milli
   D) inch, mile, foot, pound

Matter

Skills Preview

Skill Builders
- Interpret Data
- Compare and Contrast

Activities
- Make and Use a Table
- Form a Hypothesis

MiniLabs
- Make a Model
- Observe and Infer

Reading Check ✔

Use the headings and sub-headings to make an outline as you read this chapter. Write a few important points under each subheading.

Explore Activity

You've just finished playing basketball. You're hot and thirsty. You reach for your bottle of water and, leaning back, squeeze out a long, thirst-quenching drink. Releasing your grip, you notice that the bottle is nearly empty. But, is the bottle really almost empty? According to the dictionary, empty means containing nothing. When you have finished all the water in the bottle, will it be empty? And, if it's full, what is it full of?

Observe Matter

1. Wad up a small piece of a dry paper towel or tissue paper and tape it to the bottom of the inside of a plastic drinking cup. When you turn the cup upside down, the towel or paper should remain inside the cup.

2. Fill a bowl or sink almost to the top with water. Hold the cup upside down over the water's surface. Slowly push the cup straight into the water as far as you can.

3. Slowly raise the cup straight out of the water. Remove the paper towel and examine it.

Science Journal

In your Science Journal, describe your experiment. Include a description of the paper after you removed it from the cup. Explain what you think happened. Was anything in the cup besides the paper? If so, what was it?

Structure of Matter

What You'll Learn

► What matter is
► What makes up matter
► The parts of an atom
► The models that are used for atoms

Vocabulary
matter
atom
law of conservation
  of matter
electron
nucleus
proton
neutron

Why It's Important

► Matter makes up your body, your environment, and the universe.

What is matter?

Did you decide that the bottle of water and the plastic cup in the Explore Activity were filled with air? Have you wondered what makes up the air around you? It's mostly nitrogen and oxygen. Nitrogen and oxygen are kinds of matter. Scientists define **matter** as anything that has mass and takes up space. So even if you can't see it or catch hold of it, air is matter.

What about the things you *can* see, taste, smell, and touch when you eat lunch in the cafeteria or walk around your neighborhood? These things are also made of matter. What about your own body? Yes, it's matter too. Through science, you will explore the many amazing kinds of matter that make up the universe—things as common as a flower or as spectacular as a supernova, both shown in **Figure 3-1.**

What isn't matter?

You can see the words on this page because of light. Does light have mass or take up space? What about the warmth from the sun or the heater in your classroom? Neither light nor heat take up any space. They don't have any mass either, so they are not forms of matter. Emotions, thoughts, and ideas also are not matter.

Figure 3-1 A flower in your backyard (A) and a supernova (a large exploding star) in a galaxy millions of light-years away (B) seem as different as night and day. But, the flower and supernova are the same in an important way—they're both matter. **How is matter defined?**

What makes up matter?

Suppose you cut a sheet of notebook paper into smaller and smaller pieces, as shown in **Figure 3-2.** Do the pieces seem to be made of the same matter as the large sheet you started with? If you could cut a small enough piece, would it still have the same properties as the large sheet of paper? Or, would it no longer be paper at all? People have asked questions like these—and wondered about what matter is made of—for centuries.

An Early Idea

Democritus, who lived from 460 to 370 B.C., was a Greek philosopher who thought the universe was made of empty space and tiny bits of stuff. He believed that the bits of stuff were so small they could no longer be divided into smaller pieces. He called these tiny pieces of stuff atoms. In fact, the term *atom* comes from a Greek word that means "cannot be divided." In science today, an **atom** is defined as a small particle that makes up most types of matter. Democritus thought that different types of atoms exist for every type of matter. His idea proved to be a small step in understanding the structure of matter that continues today.

Lavoisier's Contribution

Antoine Lavoisier (la VWAH see ay), a French chemist who lived about 2000 years after Democritus, was also curious about matter—especially when it changed from one form to another. Before Lavoisier, people thought matter could appear and disappear during changes such as burning and rusting. You might have thought the same thing—that matter can disappear—if you've ever watched wood burn to embers, then ashes in a fireplace. But, Lavoisier showed that wood and the oxygen it combines with during burning have the same mass as the ash, water, and

Figure 3-2 Paper is made up of carbon, hydrogen, and oxygen. So, if you could cut paper into small enough pieces, it wouldn't be paper at all. **What common type of matter is made up of only hydrogen and oxygen?**

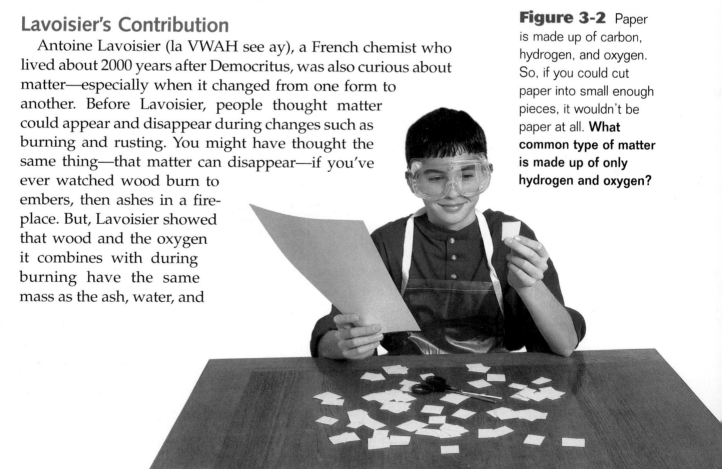

Oxygen

+

Water vapor and carbon dioxide

+

Figure 3-3 When wood burns, matter is not lost. The total mass of the wood and the oxygen it combines with equals the total mass of the water vapor, carbon dioxide, and ashes produced. **When you burn wood in a fireplace, what is the source of the oxygen?**

carbon dioxide (KAR bun di AHK side) produced, as shown in **Figure 3-3.** In the same way, iron and oxygen have the same mass as the rust they form. From Lavoisier's work came the **law of conservation of matter.** This law states that matter is neither created nor destroyed, only changed in form.

Models of the Atom

Scientists often use models for things that are too small to be seen and observed easily, as well as things that are too complicated or too large to be understood easily. Throughout history, scientists have created and used models to help find out what atoms are made of and how they act.

One way to make a model is to make a small version of something larger. For example, if you wanted to design a new kind of sailboat, would you just come up with a design, build a full-sized boat, and hope it would float? It would be smarter—and safer—to first build and test a small model of your design. Then, if it doesn't float, you can change your design and build another model. You can keep trying until the model works. As with the model sailboat, scientists' models are changed as new information is gained.

Dalton's Atomic Model

In the early 1800s, an English schoolteacher and chemist named John Dalton studied the experiments of Lavoisier and many others. Dalton thought that an atomic model could explain the results of these experiments. He named his model *the atomic theory of matter.* Dalton's atomic model, like many scientific models, was a set of ideas—not an object. Dalton believed that matter was made of atoms that were too small to be seen by the human eye. He also thought that each type of matter was made of only one kind of atom. For example, gold atoms make up a gold nugget and give a gold ring its shininess, as well as its other properties.

Sizes of Atoms

Atoms are so small it would take about 1 million of them lined up in a row to equal the thickness of a human hair. To give you a better idea of how small atoms are, look at **Figure 3-4.** Imagine you are holding an orange in your hand. If you wanted to use only your eyes to see the individual atoms on the surface of the orange, the size of the orange would need to increase to the size of Earth. Then, imagine it is covered with billions and billions of marbles. Each marble would represent one of the atoms that make up the skin of the orange.

Figure 3-4 Imagining this orange is the size of Earth can help you visualize the size of an atom.

Figure 3-5 In this experiment, the magnet caused the cathode rays inside the tube to bend. **What do you think would happen to the cathode rays if the magnet were removed?**

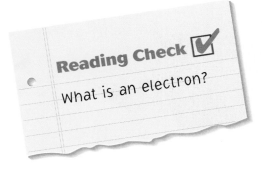

Mini Lab

Making a Model

Procedure 👓

1. Your teacher will give you a sealed shoe box that contains one or more items.

2. Try to find out how many and what kinds of items are inside the box. You cannot look inside the box. The only observations you may make are by handling the box.

Analysis

1. How many items do you infer are in the box? Sketch the apparent shapes of the items and identify them if you can.

2. Compare your procedure with how scientists perform experiments and make models to find out more about the atom.

Reading Check ☑

What is an electron?

Discovering the Electron

One of the many pioneers in the development of today's atomic model was J.J. Thomson, an Englishman. He conducted experiments using a vacuum tube, which is a glass tube that has all the air pumped out of it and then is sealed at both ends. Thomson's tube had metal plates at both ends. The plates were connected to a high-voltage electrical source that gave one of the plates, the *anode,* a positive charge and the other, the *cathode,* a negative charge. During his experiments, Thomson observed rays that traveled from the cathode to the anode. Because the rays came from the cathode, Thomson called them cathode rays. The rays were bent by a magnet, as seen in **Figure 3-5,** showing that the rays were made up of particles that had mass. The rays were bent by charged plates, also. Thomson knew that unlike charges attract each other and like charges repel each other. When he saw that the rays bent toward a positively charged plate, he concluded that the cathode rays were made up of negative particles. These invisible, negatively charged particles, which came from the metal atoms that made up the cathode, are called **electrons.** ☑

Imagine Thomson's excitement at this discovery. He had shown that atoms are not too tiny to divide after all. Rather, they are made up of even smaller subatomic particles. Other scientists soon built on Thomson's results and found that the electron had a small mass—in fact, 1/1837 the mass of the lightest atom, the hydrogen atom. In 1906, Thomson received the Nobel Prize in Physics for his discovery of the electron.

Matter that has equal numbers of positive and negative charges, and therefore has no *net* charge, is said to be neutral. Because most matter is neutral, Thomson knew that atoms had to contain both positive and negative charges. He pictured the atom as being made up of electrons embedded in a ball of positive charge. You might compare his model, shown in **Figure 3-6,** to something like tiny chocolate chips spread around in a ball of cookie dough. But, Thomson's model did not provide all the answers to the questions that puzzled scientists about atoms.

*inter*NET
CONNECTION

Visit the Glencoe Science Web Site at **www. glencoe.com/sec/ science/fl** for more information about electron energy levels in atoms.

Rutherford—The Nucleus

If electrons are the negatively charged particles in atoms, what are the positively charged particles that also must be present? Also, how are the parts of the atom arranged? In 1909, a team of scientists led by Ernest Rutherford in England began to work on the mystery of atomic structure. They bombarded materials with alpha particles. Alpha particles are high-energy, positively charged particles. When the scientists beamed alpha particles at an extremely thin piece of gold foil, they were amazed at the results. Most of the particles passed straight through the foil as if it were not there at all. Other particles changed direction or even bounced back. Rutherford thought the result so remarkable that he later said, "It was almost as incredible as if you had fired a 15-inch shell at a piece of tissue paper, and it came back and hit you."

Rutherford and his team soon concluded that because so many of the alpha particles passed straight through the gold foil, its atoms must be mostly empty space.

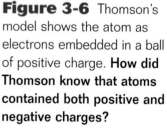

Figure 3-6 Thomson's model shows the atom as electrons embedded in a ball of positive charge. **How did Thomson know that atoms contained both positive and negative charges?**

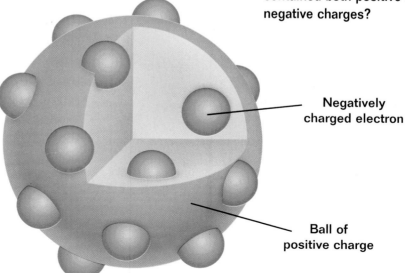

Negatively charged electron

Ball of positive charge

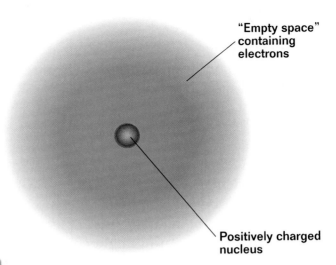

Figure 3-7 Rutherford concluded that the atom must be mostly empty space in which electrons are scattered. He also thought the nucleus of the atom must be small and positively charged. **Where is most of the mass of the atom concentrated?**

"Empty space" containing electrons

Positively charged nucleus

Try at Home

Mini Lab

Inferring Atomic Structure

Procedure

1. Blow up a rubber balloon just enough to inflate it completely. Tie a knot in the balloon's opening to seal in the air.

2. Rub the balloon vigorously against a wool sweater or coat. Hold the balloon against a wall and then let go of it.

3. Take the balloon from the wall and tie a 30-cm length of string to the balloon's neck. Again, rub the balloon vigorously against a wool sweater or coat.

4. Have someone hold the string suspending the balloon. Run a rubber comb through your hair several times. Bring the comb close to the balloon.

Analysis

1. What did the balloon do when you held it against the wall and let go? Electrically charged objects are able to attract things around them that have either an opposite charge or are neutral. What happened to the balloon when it was rubbed against wool?

2. What happened when you brought the comb near the balloon? A rubber comb acquires a negative charge when rubbed through hair. What does that tell you about the charge acquired by the balloon when rubbed against wool?

However, because some of the alpha particles bounced off something that they hit, the gold atoms must contain small, massive, positively charged objects. Rutherford called the positively charged, central part of the atom the **nucleus** (NEW klee us). He named the positively charged particles in the nucleus **protons.** He also suggested that electrons were scattered in the mostly empty space around the nucleus, as shown in **Figure 3-7.**

Discovering the Neutron

Rutherford had been puzzled by one part of his experiments with alpha particles. Alpha particles seemed to be heavier than they should be. What could possibly cause the extra mass? James Chadwick, a student of Rutherford's, answered the question. Chadwick experimented with particles given off by atoms that had been bombarded with alpha particles. He found that, unlike electrons, the paths of these new particles were not affected by an electric field. To explain his observations, he said that these particles came from the nucleus and had no charge. Chadwick called these uncharged particles **neutrons.** His proton-neutron model of the atomic nucleus is still accepted today.

Today's Model of the Atom

Scientists in the early part of the twentieth century uncovered evidence that electrons in atoms were arranged in energy levels. The lowest energy level is closest to the nucleus and can hold only two electrons. Higher energy levels are farther from the nucleus and can contain more electrons. To explain these energy levels, some scientists thought that the electrons might orbit an atom's nucleus—something like how Earth and the other planets of our solar system orbit the sun.

The Electron Cloud Model

As a result of research that continues today, scientists now realize that because electrons are so small and move so fast, their energy levels are not neat, planetlike orbits around the nucleus. Rather, it seems most likely that the electrons move in what is called the atom's *electron cloud,* as shown in **Figure 3-8.** The electron cloud model helps explain what atoms do and what they don't do.

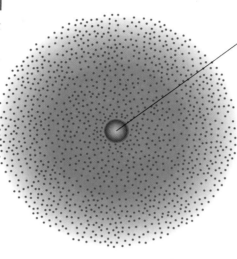

Nucleus

Figure 3-8 One model of the atom pictures the electrons moving around the nucleus in a region called an electron cloud. Dots represent places where electrons might be found. **What does the greater number of dots near the nucleus suggest?**

Section Assessment

1. List five things that are matter and five things that are not matter. Explain your answers.

2. Describe Dalton's contribution to today's understanding of matter.

3. Think of a rule that would help a fourth grader decide which things are matter and which things are not matter.

4. **Think Critically:** What made alpha particles heavier than Rutherford thought they should be?

5. **Skill Builder**
   Observing and Inferring Scientists inferred the structure of the atom based on their observations. Do the **Chapter 3 Skill Activity** on page 710 and practice observing and inferring.

Write a summary of what you learned about atoms. Include all of the vocabulary words listed in the Chapter Assessment in your summary.

3·2 Elements

Organizing the Elements

Have you watched television today? TV sets are common, yet each one is a complex device. The outer case is made mostly of plastic, and the screen is made of glass. Many of the parts that conduct electricity are metals or combinations of metals called alloys. Other parts in the interior of the set contain materials that barely conduct electricity. These different materials have one thing in common. Each is made up of even simpler materials. In fact, if you had the proper equipment, you could separate the plastics, glass, and metals into these simpler materials.

Eventually, though, you would reach a point where you couldn't separate the materials any further. What you would have is a collection of elements. An **element** is a material that cannot be broken down to simpler materials by ordinary means. At this time, 112 elements are known and 90 of them occur naturally on Earth. These elements make up gases in the air, minerals in rocks, and liquids such as water. Examples include oxygen and nitrogen in the air you breathe and the metals gold, silver, aluminum, and iron. The other 22 are known as synthetic elements. Synthetic elements have important uses in medical testing and in smoke detectors and heart pacemaker batteries. These elements, which may be found in stars, have been made in laboratories by machines like the one shown in **Figure 3-9.**

Figure 3-9 This particle accelerator is at Fermilab, which is near Chicago, Illinois. The machine accelerates particles to extremely high speeds. When a particle hits and becomes part of an atom, a different element is formed.

Figure 3-10 When you look for a certain book in the library, a system of organization called the Dewey Decimal System helps you find the book quickly and efficiently. **Describe a system of organization that can help you find a pair of matching, black socks quickly in the morning.**

EARTH SCIENCE
INTEGRATION

Elements in Minerals
The mineral fluorite contains fluoride, a form of the element fluorine. Fluorite is added to water and is used in making toothpastes. It makes tooth enamel harder and helps fight tooth decay.

Suppose that you go to a library to look up information for a school assignment. Or, maybe you want to find a book that a friend told you about. When you go to the library, do you look on shelves at random as you walk up and down the rows? Probably not, unless you have lots of time or are just browsing. More likely, you depend on the library's system of organization to find the book you want quickly and efficiently, as shown in **Figure 3-10.**

The Periodic Table

When scientists need to look up information about an element or select one to use in the laboratory, they want to be quick and efficient, too. Chemists have created a chart called the periodic table of the elements to help them organize and display the elements. When you walk into a laboratory or science classroom, you often see this chart on the wall. Each element is represented by a chemical symbol that contains one to three letters. The symbols are a form of chemical shorthand that chemists use to save time and space—both on the periodic table and in written formulas. The symbols are an important part of an international system that is understood by scientists everywhere.

Using Math

Your body is made up primarily of five elements. By mass, the elements are:

oxygen	65%
carbon	18%
hydrogen	10%
nitrogen	3%
calcium	2%
other	2%

Make a circle graph that represents the elements in your body.

Chlorine
17
Cl
35.453

Atomic Number and Atomic Mass

Look up the element chlorine on the periodic table found inside the back cover of your textbook. Cl is the symbol for chlorine, as shown in **Figure 3-11,** but what are the two numbers? The top number, called the element's atomic number, is always a whole number. The **atomic number** tells you the number of protons in the nucleus of each atom of that element. Every atom of chlorine, for example, has 17 protons in its nucleus.

The number beneath the element's symbol is its atomic mass. An element's **atomic mass** tells you how heavy its atoms are compared with atoms of other elements. The unit scientists use for atomic mass is called the atomic mass unit, which is given the symbol *u*.

Isotopes and Mass Number

All the atoms of an element don't have to have the same mass. Some atoms of an element can have different numbers of neutrons in their nuclei than other atoms. Every chlorine atom contains 17 protons in its nucleus; however, some chlorine nuclei have 18 neutrons and others have 20. These two naturally occurring types of chlorine atoms are called isotopes. **Isotopes** (I suh tohps) are atoms of the same element that have different numbers of neutrons. You can tell someone exactly what type of chlorine atom you are referring to by using its mass number. An atom's **mass number** is the sum of its protons and neutrons [Mass number = number of protons + number of neutrons].

The atoms of chlorine that contain 17 protons and 18 neutrons have a mass number of 35 and are called chlorine-35. Those atoms that contain 17 protons and 20 neutrons are called chlorine-37. These two isotopes of chlorine are shown in **Figure 3-12.**

Figure 3-12 Chlorine is found naturally as two isotopes, chlorine-37 and chlorine-35. Chlorine-37 atoms are heavier than chlorine-35 atoms. The average mass of all chlorine atoms found naturally is 35.453 u. **Which type of chlorine atom is more numerous in nature?**

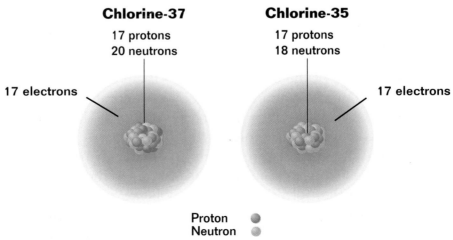

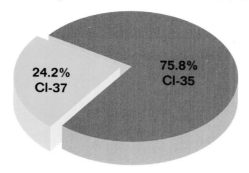

Average Atomic Mass = 35.453 u

24.2%
Cl-37

75.8%
Cl-35

Figure 3-13 Chlorine-35 atoms make up 75.8 percent of chlorine. The remaining 24.2 percent of chlorine atoms are chlorine-37. If you have 1000 atoms of chlorine, 758 of the atoms are chlorine-35. The remaining 242 atoms are chlorine-37. The total mass of the 1000 atoms is 35 453 u, so the average mass of one chlorine atom is 35.453 u. **If an element has only one isotope, how does the mass of the isotope compare with the atomic mass of the element?**

Look at the periodic table block for chlorine, **Figure 3-11.** The element's atomic mass of 35.453 u can be misleading because not one chlorine atom has that mass. About 75 percent of chlorine atoms are chlorine-35 and 25 percent are chlorine-37, as shown in **Figure 3-13.** Therefore, 35.453 u is simply the average mass of chlorine atoms.

Classification of Elements

Elements fall into three general groups: metals, metalloids (MET ul oydz), and nonmetals. You use metals every day because they have many useful physical properties.

Metals generally have a shiny or metallic luster. Metals are good conductors of heat and electricity. For example, copper is often used in electrical circuits and cookware because it conducts heat and electricity well. All metals except mercury are solids at room temperature. Metals are malleable (MAL yuh bul), which means they can be bent and pounded into various shapes. Metals are also ductile, which means they can be drawn into wires without breaking, like the ones shown in **Figure 3-14.** If you look at the periodic table in the back of this textbook, you can see that most of the elements are metals.

Figure 3-14 Metals can be drawn into wires, a property called ductility. A wire's gauge is related to its thickness. A small number means that the wire is thicker.

Figure 3-15 Chlorine, bromine, and iodine are often used as disinfectants. **What nonmetals make up most of the air you breathe?**

Nonmetals are elements that are usually dull. Most are poor conductors of heat and electricity. Many are gases at room temperature, as shown in **Figure 3-15.** The solid nonmetals are generally brittle, meaning they cannot change shape easily without breaking. You can see that, except for hydrogen, the nonmetals are found on the right side of the periodic table.

Metalloids are elements such as silicon and germanium, which have characteristics of both metals and nonmetals. Some are shiny and many are conductors, but they are not as good at conducting heat and electricity as metals. All metalloids are solids at room temperature. Metalloids are found between the metals and nonmetals on the periodic table. ☑

Reading Check ☑

What is a metalloid?

Section Assessment

1. What are isotopes?
2. Explain some of the uses of metals.
3. **Think Critically:** Hector is new to your class today. He missed the lesson on how to use the periodic table to find information about the elements. Describe how you would help Hector find the atomic number for the element oxygen. Explain what this information tells him about oxygen.

4. **Skill Builder**
   Interpreting Data Look up the atomic mass of the element boron in the periodic table inside the back cover of this book. The naturally occurring isotopes of boron are boron-10 and boron-11. Which of the two isotopes is more abundant? Explain your reasoning. If you need help, refer to Interpreting Data in the **Skill Handbook** on page 690.

Using Math

An atom of niobium has a mass number of 91. How many neutrons are in the nucleus of the atom?

An isotope of phosphorus has 15 protons and 15 neutrons in the nucleus of each of its atoms. What is the mass number of the isotope?

Elements and the Periodic Table

The periodic table organizes the elements. But, what do these elements look like, and what are they used for? In this activity, you'll examine some elements and share your findings with your classmates.

What You'll Investigate

What are some of the characteristics of the chemical elements, and what are they used for?

Goals

- **Classify** the chemical elements.
- **Make** your own periodic table that shows the classification of the elements.

Procedure

1. From the list provided by your teacher, select the number of elements you are assigned.
2. **Design** an index card for each of your selected elements. On each element's card, mark its atomic number in the upper left-hand corner and write its symbol and name in the upper right-hand corner.

Materials

- Large index cards
- Merck Index
- Encyclopedia
  * *other reference materials*
- Large bulletin board
- Paper (8½ × 14)
- Thumbtacks
  * *pushpins*

  * *Alternate Materials*

3. Research each of the elements and write several sentences on the card about its appearance, its other properties, and its uses.
4. Based upon its properties, **decide** if each of your elements is likely a metal, a metalloid, or a nonmetal. Use the color of magic marker chosen by your teacher to write the appropriate word—*metal, metalloid,* or *nonmetal*—on each of your cards.
5. Work with your classmates to **make** a large periodic table. Use thumbtacks to attach your cards on a bulletin board in their proper positions on the table.
6. Draw your own periodic table on an 8½ ×14 sheet of paper. Put the elements' symbols and atomic numbers in the proper places on the table.

Conclude and Apply

1. **Interpret** the class data and **classify** the elements into the categories: metals, metalloids, and nonmetals. Highlight each of the three categories in a different color on your periodic table.
2. **Predict** the properties of a yet-undiscovered element located directly under francium on the periodic table.

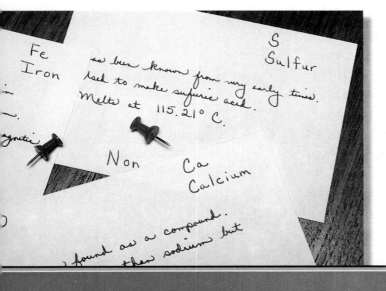

Development of the Periodic Table

Elements such as gold, silver, tin, copper, lead, and mercury have been known since ancient times. As more elements were discovered, people began to recognize patterns in their properties. Later, scientists used the patterns to develop ways of classifying the elements. For example, in 1817, Johann Döbereiner noticed that the atomic mass of strontium was halfway between the masses of calcium and barium, elements with similar chemical properties.

In the Cards

In the mid-nineteenth century, Dmitri Mendeleev published the first periodic table. Mendeleev recognized patterns in the properties and atomic masses of certain elements. In trying to extend the patterns, he created a card for each of the more than 60 elements known at the time. Each card contained the element's symbol, its atomic mass, and its characteristic chemical and physical properties. Mendeleev then arranged the cards on a table in order of increasing atomic mass, grouping elements of similar properties together. The resulting periodic table showed vertical, horizontal, and diagonal relationships. Mendeleev left blank spaces in his table for as-yet-undiscovered elements, and he predicted in detail what the chemical and physical properties of the missing elements would be when they were found.

New Discoveries

With the discovery of the atomic nucleus and isotopes in the early twentieth century, it became apparent that the properties of the elements vary periodically with their atomic numbers. Therefore, modern periodic tables arrange the elements according to atomic number rather than atomic mass. In the mid-1900s, the last major changes to the periodic table resulted from the work of Glenn Seaborg and his coworkers with the discovery of the transuranium elements from atomic number 94 to 102. Locate the element seaborgium on the periodic table. Scientists today continue to discover new elements.

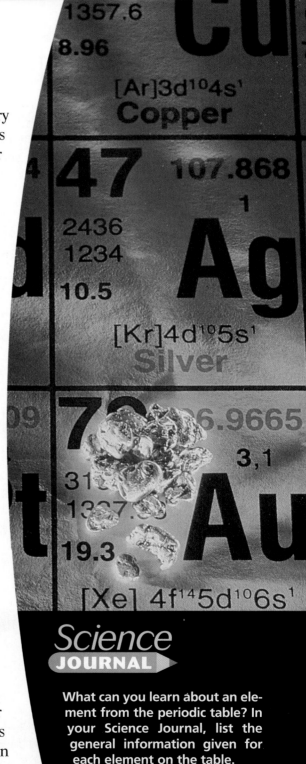

Science JOURNAL

What can you learn about an element from the periodic table? In your Science Journal, list the general information given for each element on the table.

Compounds and Mixtures

Substances

Scientists classify matter in several ways. For example, a sample of matter that has the same composition and properties throughout is called a **substance.** The chemical elements you learned about in Section 3-2 are pure substances. When elements combine with each other, different kinds of matter are formed.

Compounds

What do you call the colorless liquid that flows when you turn on the kitchen faucet? You probably call it water, but maybe you've seen it written H_2O and wondered what that meant. Hydrogen and oxygen both occur naturally as colorless gases, but H_2O tells you that these two elements can combine, as shown in **Figure 3-16,** to form a new, pure substance called a compound. A **compound** is a pure substance whose smallest unit is made up of atoms of more than one element. Millions of compounds can be made from combinations of elements, and the compounds almost always have properties that are different from the elements that make them up. Have you ever used hydrogen peroxide to disinfect a cut? Hydrogen peroxide is another compound made from the elements hydrogen and oxygen.

What You'll Learn

► What a compound is
► The difference between types of mixtures

Vocabulary
substance
compound
law of definite proportions
mixture

Why It's Important

► Compounds and mixtures are part of your everyday life.

Figure 3-16 A space shuttle is powered by the reaction between liquid hydrogen and liquid oxygen. The reaction produces a large amount of energy and a single compound, water. **Why would a car that burns hydrogen rather than gasoline be friendly to the environment?**

Compounds Need Formulas

What's the difference between water and hydrogen peroxide? H_2O is the chemical formula for water, and it tells you more than what elements make up the compound. Look at **Figure 3-17.** Water is made up of two atoms of hydrogen for every one atom of oxygen. H_2O_2 is the formula for hydrogen peroxide. The subscripts, numbers written below and to the right of the elements' symbols, mean that there are two atoms of hydrogen for every two atoms of oxygen in hydrogen peroxide. Carbon dioxide, CO_2, is another common compound. Carbon dioxide is made up of one atom of carbon for every two atoms of oxygen. Carbon and oxygen also can form the compound carbon monoxide, CO, a gas that is poisonous to all warm-blooded animals. As you can see, no subscript is used when one atom is present. The **law of definite proportions** states that a given compound is always made of the same elements in the same proportion by mass. For example, water always has two hydrogen atoms for every oxygen atom. ☑

Reading Check ☑

Propane has three atoms of carbon for every eight atoms of hydrogen. What is propane's chemical formula?

Figure 3-17 The elements hydrogen and oxygen can combine to form two compounds, water and hydrogen peroxide. Although both compounds are made up of the same elements, the ratios of hydrogen and oxygen atoms are different.

A H_2O_2, the formula for hydrogen peroxide, shows that it contains two hydrogen atoms for every two oxygen atoms.

B H_2O, the formula for water, shows that it contains two hydrogen atoms for each oxygen atom. **What is the ratio of hydrogen atoms to carbon atoms in methane, which has the formula CH_4?**

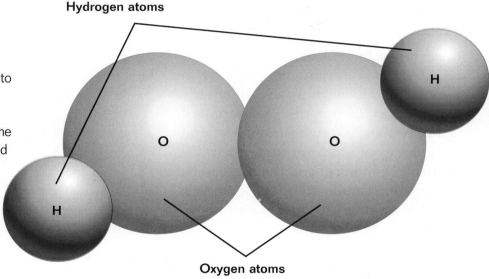

Hydrogen atoms

Oxygen atoms

Mixtures

When two or more substances (elements or compounds) come together but don't combine to make a new, pure substance, a **mixture** results. Unlike compounds, the proportions of the substances in a mixture can be changed. For example, if you put some sand into a bucket of water, you have a mixture of sand and water. If you add more sand or more water, it's still a mixture of sand and water. The makeup of air, a mixture of nitrogen, oxygen, and other gases, can vary somewhat from place to place and time to time. Look around your classroom, home, or neighborhood. What other mixtures do you see? Did you know that your blood is a mixture made up of elements and compounds? It contains white blood cells, red blood cells, water, and a number of dissolved elements. The blood parts can be separated easily and used by different parts of your body.

You can often use a liquid to separate the parts of a mixture of solids. For example, you could add water to a mixture of sugar and sand. Only the sugar would dissolve in the water. The sand could then be separated from the sugar and water by pouring the mixture through a filter. Then, heating would dry off the water, leaving the sugar behind.

*inter*NET
CONNECTION

Visit the Glencoe Science Web Site at **www. glencoe.com/sec/ science/fl** for more information about mixtures.

LIFE SCIENCE
◄ INTEGRATION

Problem Solving

Drinking Water from Salt Water

Suppose you are on a ship or live in a place that is near an ocean but does not have much freshwater for people to drink.

Can you use change in physical state to create a method for removing salt from ocean water? Distillation is the process of heating a mixture to separate its parts. Parts of the mixture boil at different temperatures. A more nearly pure substance results when the vapor from each part is cooled and condensed.

A liquid mixture placed in the flask on the left is heated to boiling. As the vapor passes through the tube in the condenser in the middle, it is surrounded by cold water

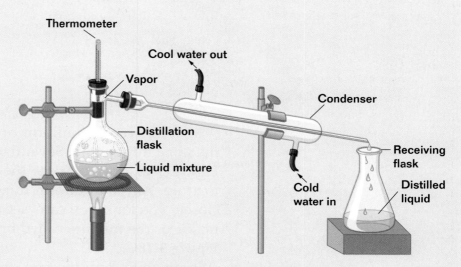

and condenses to a liquid. The liquid drips into the flask on the right.

Think Critically: Examine the distillation system in the photo. How could you use such a system to produce freshwater from ocean water?

Figure 3-18 Many commom materials are uniform mixtures.

A Sterling silver dinnerware is 92.5 percent silver and 7.5 percent copper.

B The tea in this glass is a uniform mixture that is mostly water. **Is the mixture of ice and tea a uniform mixture?**

C The brass trombone is 50 to 80 percent copper and 20 to 50 percent zinc. **A uniform mixture of iron and carbon is used in making cars and many other products. What is this mixture called?**

Mixtures can be uniform or nonuniform. Uniform means the same throughout. Several uniform mixtures are shown in **Figure 3-18.** You can't see the different parts in this type of mixture. Air is a uniform mixture of gases. No matter how closely you look, you can't see the individual parts that make up air or the mixture called brass in the trombone shown in **Figure 3-18C.**

In a nonuniform mixture such as sand and water, you can see the different parts. A pepperoni and mushroom pizza is a tasty kind of nonuniform mixture. Other examples of this kind of mixture include tacos, a stew, a toy box full of toys, or your laundry basket at the end of the week. Several nonuniform mixtures are shown in **Figure 3-19.**

Figure 3-19 Nonuniform mixtures are part of your everyday life.

A You can see pieces of solid orange floating in liquid if you look at a glass of orange juice closely.

B Blood is a nonuniform mixture of many materials, including water, proteins, glucose, and fats. Some of these materials can be separated in the laboratory.

C Areas of different color in a rock show that it is made up of crystals of different materials. **A clear fruit drink is made up of many substances. Why is it a uniform mixture?**

Section Assessment

1. List three examples of compounds and three examples of mixtures.

2. The chemical formula for baking soda is $NaHCO_3$. Use the periodic table to write the names of the elements in baking soda. Which element's atoms are most numerous in baking soda?

3. How can you tell that a substance is a compound by looking at its formula?

4. **Think Critically:** Was your breakfast this morning a compound, a uniform mixture, or a nonuniform mixture? Review the definitions for a compound and a uniform mixture. Explain your answer based on these definitions.

5. **Skill Builder**
   Comparing and Contrasting
   Compare and contrast compounds and mixtures. If you need help, refer to Comparing and Contrasting in the **Skill Handbook** on page 686.

Using Computers

Database Use a computerized card catalog to find out about one element from the periodic table. Include information about the mixtures and/or compounds the element is found in. If you need help, refer to page 699.

Materials

- Test tubes (3)
- Cornstarch
- Sugar
- Baking soda
- Mystery mixture
- Small scoops (3)
- Dropper bottles (2)
- Iodine solution
- White vinegar
- Candle
- Test-tube holder
- Small pie pan
- Matches

Mystery Mixture

Cornstarch, baking powder, and powdered sugar are compounds that look alike. To avoid mistaking one for another, you may need to learn how to identify each one. You can learn chemical tests that identify these different compounds. For example, some compounds react with certain liquids to produce gases. Other combinations produce distinctive colors. Some compounds have high melting points. Others have low melting points.

What You'll Investigate

How can the compounds in an unknown mixture be identified by experimentation?

Goals

- **Test** for the presence of certain compounds.
- **Decide** which of these compounds are present in an unknown mixture.

Safety Precautions

Use caution when handling hot objects. Substances could stain or burn clothing. Be sure to point the test tube away from your face and your classmates while heating.

Procedure

1. **Copy** the data table into your Science Journal. **Record** your results for each of the following steps.

2. Place a small scoopful, or the amount indicated by your teacher, of cornstarch on the pie pan. Do the same for sugar and baking soda. Add a drop of vinegar to each. Wash and dry the pan after you have recorded your observations.

3. Place a small scoopful, or the amount indicated by your teacher, of cornstarch, sugar, and baking soda on the pie pan. Add a drop of iodine solution to each.

4. Place a small scoopful, or the amount indicated by your teacher, of each compound in a separate test tube. Hold the test tube with the test-tube holder. Gently heat the bottom of each test tube with the candle.

5. Now, use steps 2 to 4 to **test** your mystery mixture and find out which of these compounds it contains.

Conclude and Apply

1. Use your observations to form a hypothesis as to which compounds are in your mystery mixture. Describe how you arrived at your conclusion.

2. How would you be able to tell if all three compounds were not in your mystery mixture sample?

3. What would you conclude if you tested baking powder from your kitchen and found that it fizzed with vinegar, turned blue with iodine, and did not melt when heated?

Results of Tests			
To be tested	Vinegar fizzes	Iodine turns blue	Compound melts
Cornstarch			
Sugar			
Baking soda			
Mystery mix			

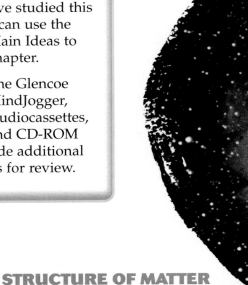

For a **preview** of this chapter, study this Reviewing Main Ideas before you read the chapter. After you have studied this chapter, you can use the Reviewing Main Ideas to **review** the chapter.

The Glencoe MindJogger, Audiocassettes, and CD-ROM provide additional opportunities for review.

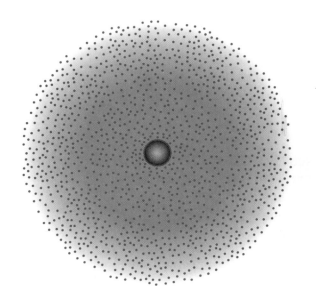

Section

3-1 STRUCTURE OF MATTER

Matter is anything that occupies space and has mass. It includes all the things that you can see, touch, taste, or smell. Matter does not include light, sound, or heat. *Can you think of anything else that is not matter?*

WHAT MAKES UP MATTER?

Matter is made up of atoms. **Atoms** are made of smaller parts called **protons, neutrons,** and **electrons.** Many models of atoms have been created as scientists try to discover and define the atom's internal structure. *What other models do you know about?*

Reading Check ✓

Create a timeline of the important discoveries about atoms. Include the names of the scientists. Check other reference sources for dates when necessary.

^{Section}
3-2 ELEMENTS

Elements are the basic building blocks of matter. Each element has a unique set of properties and is generally classified as a metal, metalloid, or nonmetal. The chemical symbol for each element is understood by scientists everywhere. An element's **atomic number** tells how many protons its atoms contain, and its **atomic mass** tells how heavy its atoms are. **Isotopes** are two or more atoms of the same element that have different numbers of neutrons. *What element has the symbol Co?*

Chlorine
17
Cl
35.453

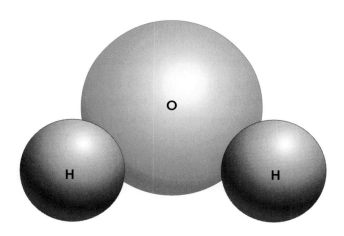

^{Section}
3-3 COMPOUNDS

Compounds are pure substances produced when elements combine. Compounds contain specific proportions of the elements that make them up. A compound's properties are different from those of the elements from which it is formed. *Name five common compounds.*

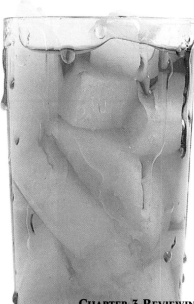

MIXTURES

Mixtures are combinations of compounds and elements that have not formed new, pure substances. Uniform mixtures contain individual parts that cannot be seen. However, you can see the individual parts of nonuniform mixtures. *What are two mixtures of each type that you know about?*

Chapter 3 Assessment

Using Vocabulary

a. atom
b. atomic mass
c. atomic number
d. compound
e. electron
f. element
g. isotopes
h. law of conservation of matter
i. law of definite proportions
j. mass number
k. matter
l. metals
m. metalloids
n. mixtures
o. neutron
p. nonmetals
q. nucleus
r. proton
s. substance

Using the list above, replace the underlined words with the correct Vocabulary word.

1. The particle in the nucleus of the atom that carries a positive charge is the <u>neutron</u>.

2. The new substance formed when elements join is a <u>mixture</u>.

3. Anything that has mass and takes up space is <u>metal</u>.

4. The particles in the atom that account for most of the mass are protons and <u>electrons</u>.

5. Elements that are shiny, malleable, ductile, and good conductors of heat and electricity are <u>nonmetals</u>.

Checking Concepts

Choose the word or phrase that best answers the question.

6. What is a solution an example of?
   A) element
   B) nonuniform mixture
   C) compound
   D) uniform mixture

7. The nucleus of one atom contains 12 protons and 12 neutrons, while the nucleus of another atom contains 12 protons and 16 neutrons. What are the atoms?
   A) chromium atoms
   B) two different elements
   C) isotopes of magnesium
   D) negatively charged

8. What is a compound?
   A) a mixture of compounds and elements
   B) a combination of two or more elements
   C) anything that has mass and occupies space
   D) the building block of matter

9. What does the atom consist of?
   A) electrons, protons, and alpha particles
   B) neutrons and protons
   C) electrons, protons, and neutrons
   D) elements, protons, and electrons

10. In an atom, where is an electron located?
    A) in the nucleus with the proton
    B) on the periodic table of the elements
    C) with the neutron to create a positive charge
    D) in a cloudlike formation surrounding the nucleus

11. How is matter defined?
    A) the negative charge in an atom
    B) anything that has mass and occupies space
    C) the mass of the nucleus
    D) sound, light, and energy

12. What are two atoms that have the same number of protons?
    A) metals
    B) nonmetals
    C) isotopes
    D) metalloids

13. What are the majority of the elements on the periodic table?
    A) metals
    B) metalloids
    C) nonmetals
    D) compounds

14. Which element is a metalloid?
    A) bromine
    B) silicon
    C) potassium
    D) iron

15. What are nonuniform mixtures?
    A) two kinds of mixtures
    B) the same throughout—the parts cannot be seen
    C) made of several different parts that can be seen
    D) like a soft drink

Thinking Critically

16. A chemical formula is written to indicate the makeup of a compound. What is the ratio of sulfur atoms to oxygen atoms in SO_2?
17. An atom contains seven electrons and seven protons. What element is this atom? Explain your answer.
18. What happens to an element when it becomes part of a compound?
19. Cobalt-60 and cobalt-59 are isotopes. How can they be the same element but have different mass numbers?
20. What did Rutherford's gold foil experiment tell scientists about atomic structure?

Developing Skills

If you need help, refer to the **Skill Handbook**.

21. **Interpreting Scientific Illustrations:** Look at the drawings of the two atoms below. Explain whether or not the atoms are isotopes.

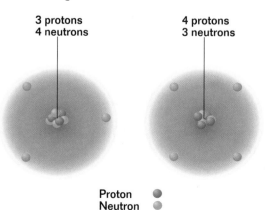

3 protons
4 neutrons

4 protons
3 neutrons

Proton
Neutron
Electron

Test-Taking Tip

What Does the Test Expect of Me? Find out what concepts, objectives, or standards are being tested well before the test. Keep these concepts in mind as you solve the questions.

Test Practice

Use these questions to test your Science Proficiency.

1. Which list of terms **BEST** describes the properties of metals?
   A) dull, brittle, nonconducting
   B) malleable, ductile, shiny, good conductors
   C) shiny, brittle, can conduct electricity
   D) gaseous, high density

2. Mixtures are divided into two categories. Which pair of examples **BEST** represents the two types of mixtures?
   A) a pizza and a tossed salad
   B) a baseball card collection and a CD collection
   C) a soft drink and a taco
   D) an iced soft drink and iced tea

3. What particles are found in the nucleus of a carbon-12 atom?
   A) 12 protons
   B) 12 neutrons and 12 protons
   C) 12 neutrons
   D) 6 protons and 6 neutrons

4. Which of these is **NOT** an element?
   A) water
   B) hydrogen
   C) chlorine
   D) oxygen

Properties and Changes

Chapter Preview

Skills Preview

Skill Builders

- Classify
- Compare and Contrast

Activities

- Design an Experiment
- Observe

MiniLabs

- Measure in SI
- Compare

Reading Check ✔

As you read, complete a chart comparing and contrasting the terms *physical property* and *chemical property*. In another chart, compare the terms *physical change* and *chemical change*.

Explore Activity

Your favorite magazine just arrived in the mail. You open it and see a picture of a place where volcanic ash once thundered down the sides of exploding volcanoes. Sounds as if you're looking at a Hollywood movie set. No, it's Hawaii. Imagine what else you could see there. Cinder cones formed by bubbly lava. Lava tubes once filled with oozing melted rock, or magma. These features and others bear evidence of the changes that happened there. Before you imagine any further, try the activity below to compare some of the kinds of rocks you might find at a volcanic site.

Compare Properties

1. Obtain samples of the volcanic rocks obsidian (ahb SIH dee un) and pumice (PUH mus). The samples should be about the same size.

2. Which sample is heavier?

3. Compare the colors of the two rocks.

4. Look at the surfaces of the two rocks. How are the surfaces different?

5. Place each rock in water and observe whether or not it floats.

Science Journal

In your Science Journal, make a table that compares the observations you made about the rocks.

4•1 Physical and Chemical Properties

What You'll Learn

► Physical properties and chemical properties of matter
► The properties of acids and bases and the difference between them

Vocabulary
physical property
state of matter
density
chemical property

Why It's Important

► You can better describe the world around you.

Physical Properties

Would it surprise you to know that both of the rocks that you examined in the Explore Activity started out as the same kind of lava? Why are they so different? They were produced by two different kinds of volcanic activity. Characteristics that you observe about matter are often related to how that matter was formed.

In the Explore Activity, you used your senses to classify types of matter. This classification helps you better understand what the types of matter are and how they were formed.

Common Physical Properties

Do you have a favorite souvenir—an unusual rock or seashell, a funny hat, or a special cup? Take a minute to describe that souvenir in as much detail as you can. What features did you use in your description—color, shape, and hardness? These features are all properties, or characteristics, of the souvenir. Scientists use the term **physical properties** to describe characteristics you can observe without changing the makeup of the material. You can detect most physical properties with your senses.

Figure 4-1 These seashells can be defined by their properties. **What are some physical properties of one of the seashells?**

All matter, such as the seashell you described in **Figure 4-1,** has physical properties. For most of your life, you have been aware of some physical properties, such as color, shape, smell, and taste. You may not be as familiar with others, such as texture. Texture is how rough or smooth something is. Practice identifying physical properties by listing some physical properties of your science book.

Formation

The physical properties of many materials are related to the way they form. Remember the two rocks you described in the Explore Activity. The two rocks are made of the same materials, but their physical properties are different. One is dark. One is light. One sinks. One floats. One is smooth. The other is rough and jagged. Their physical properties are different because they were formed in different ways. Take a closer look at how they formed.

Pumice is formed from magma (melted or molten rock) that contains a lot of gas (including water vapor). When the molten rock reaches Earth's surface, all the gases expand. Pumice is a frothy mass of glass, with lots of bubbles formed by the escaping gas. The result is a pale-colored rock that is so light it floats on water. Obsidian, on the other hand, is a dark-colored rock that sinks in water. Obsidian came from the same kind of molten rock. However, it contained no trapped gases, so no bubbles formed.

States of Matter

You know that solid pumice is different from liquid magma. Although they're both made of the same material, pumice and magma are examples of different states of matter. The **state of matter** is a physical property that tells you whether a sample of matter is a solid, a liquid, or a gas. Water appears different because it exists in different states, as shown in **Figure 4-2.** If you hold an ice cube in your hand, you have water in its solid state. Water exists in the liquid state in oceans, in rivers, and in your bathtub. It also exists as a gas in the air. In each case, every molecule of water is the same—two hydrogen atoms and one oxygen atom.

Figure 4-2 Water's three physical states—solid, liquid, and gas—are present here. **What is the physical state of water vapor?**

Did you know that there is a fourth state of matter called plasma (PLAS ma)? On Earth, plasma is present in the form of lightning bolts and neon signs. Plasma in the upper atmosphere is responsible for the aurora borealis, the northern lights. Plasma also is found in stars.

Physical Properties of Acids and Bases

What do you think of when you hear the word *acid?* Do you picture a dangerous chemical that can burn your skin, make holes in your clothes, and even destroy metal? Some acids, such as hydrochloric acid, are like that. But, not all acids are harmful. One example is the soft drink shown in **Figure 4-3A.** Every time you eat a citrus fruit such as an orange or a grapefruit, you eat citric and ascorbic (uh SKOR bihk) acids. What properties do these and other acids have in common? Imagine the sharp smell of a freshly sliced lemon. That scent comes from the citric acid in the fruit. Take a big bite out of the fruit shown in **Figure 4-3B** and you would immediately notice a sour taste. If you then rubbed your molars back and forth, your teeth would make a squeak. All of these physical properties are common in acids.

Another type of compound has physical properties that are different from those of acids. These compounds are called bases. A familiar example of a base is ammonia (uh MOHN yuh), often used for household cleaning. If you got a household cleaner that contained ammonia on your fingers and then rubbed your fingers together, they would feel slippery.

*inter*NET
CONNECTION

Visit the Glencoe Science Web Site at **www. glencoe.com/sec/ science/fl** for more information about plasmas.

Figure 4-3 Many foods contain acids.

A A carbonated soft drink contains carbonic and phosphoric (faws FOR ihk) acids.

B Citric and ascorbic acids give citrus fruits their sour taste. **What other sour-tasting foods probably contain acids?**

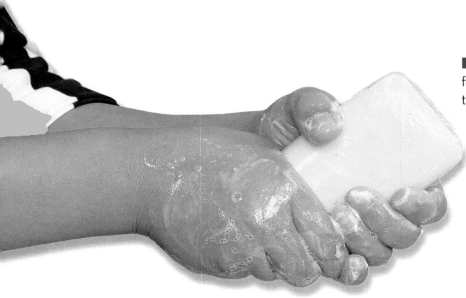

Figure 4-4 Soaps feel slippery because they are bases.

You shouldn't taste soap, which is also a base, but if you accidentally did, you'd notice a bitter taste. A bitter taste and a slippery feel, shown in **Figure 4-4,** are physical properties of bases.

The physical properties of acids and bases are different and can be used to classify them. It is important to note that you should *never* taste, touch, or smell anything in a lab.

Density

Density (DEN sih tee), an important physical property, relates the mass of something to how much space it takes up. In the Explore Activity, you compared the densities of the rock samples when you decided which of two equal-sized rocks was heavier. Which rock was more dense—pumice or obsidian? If someone asked you which of two identical backpacks—one filled with exercise clothes and the other filled with books—is heavier, you'd choose the one with books because books are more dense than exercise clothes. If you found the mass of each full pack and divided each mass by its volume, you could find the density of each backpack and its contents.

Mini Lab

Measuring Volume to Calculate Density

Procedure

1. Fill a 100.0-mL graduated cylinder with water to the 50.0-mL mark.
2. Form a 10.0-g piece of clay into a shape that will fit into the graduated cylinder.
3. Carefully use a string to lower the clay into the graduated cylinder without splashing any water out of the cylinder.
4. Measure the total volume of the water and clay in the cylinder.

Analysis

1. Find the volume of the clay by subtracting the volume of water alone (50.0 mL) from the total volume of the clay and water.
2. Calculate the density of the clay.

Table 4-1

Densities of Some Common Materials	
Material	Density (g/mL)
Air (25°C)	0.00185
Cork	0.22–0.26
Water (4.0°C)	1.000
Aluminum	2.70
Iron	7.87
Nickel	8.9
Silver	10.5
Lead	11.34

Whether or not you realize it, you see examples of density every day. Ice floats in a soft drink because the density of ice is less than that of the soft drink. Why do you shake a bottle of oil-and-vinegar salad dressing before using it? Because oil does not mix with vinegar and is less dense than vinegar, the oil rises to the top.

Density also can be used to identify compounds and elements because each one has its own density, as shown in **Table 4-1.** For example, suppose you have 52 mL (volume) of a liquid. It has a mass of 41 g. You can find the density of the liquid by dividing its mass by its volume.

$$\text{Density} = \frac{\text{mass}}{\text{volume}}$$

$$D = \frac{M}{V} = \frac{41\text{ g}}{52\text{ mL}} = \frac{0.79\text{ g}}{\text{mL}}$$

Using Math

Calculating Density

Example Problem

An astronomer found a small meteorite. The astronomer knew that nickel and iron are often found in meteorites. The meteorite had a mass of 185 g and a volume of 21 mL. What is the density of the meteorite? Is the meteorite mostly nickel or mostly iron?

Problem-Solving Steps

1. $D = \dfrac{M}{V}$

Solution: $\dfrac{185\text{ g}}{21\text{ mL}} = \dfrac{8.8\text{ g}}{\text{mL}}$

The density is 8.8 g/mL.

2. Compare this density to the densities of iron and nickel in **Table 4-1.**
   The density of the meteorite is much closer to the density of nickel than to the density of iron. Therefore, the meteorite is mostly nickel.

Practice Problem

You wonder if a bracelet you bought really is pure silver, which has a density of 10.5 g/mL. The bracelet has a mass of 42 g and a volume of 5.0 mL. What is the density of the metal in the bracelet? Is the metal pure silver? How do you know?

Chemical Properties

You've observed the density and the state of an ice cube. You've described the color and texture of rocks. You've noticed the taste of acid in a lemon and the slippery feel of a base such as soap. However, a description of something using only the physical properties is not complete. What type of property describes how matter behaves?

Common Chemical Properties

If you strike a match on a hard, rough surface, the match will probably start to burn. The element phosphorus (FAWS for us) and wood in the match combine with oxygen in the air to form new materials. Why does that happen? The phosphorus and the wood both have the ability to burn. The ability to burn is a chemical property. A **chemical property** is a characteristic of a substance that allows it to change to a new substance. ✓

You see an example of a chemical property when you leave a half-eaten apple on your desk and it turns brown. The property you observe is the ability to react with oxygen. Two other chemical properties are shown in **Figure 4-5.**

Reading Check ✓ What is a chemical property?

Figure 4-5 The chemical properties of some materials make them dangerous to use.

A Gasoline is flammable. Signs warn customers to keep anything away from gas pumps that could ignite the gasoline. **What chemical property of matches makes them dangerous?**

B Workers who handle poisonous chemicals have to be especially careful.

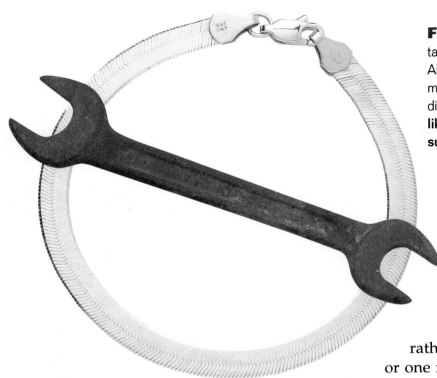

Figure 4-6 The bracelet contains gold. The wrench contains iron. Although both gold and iron are metals, their properties are quite different. **Why would a soft metal like gold be a poor choice for tools such as hammers and wrenches?**

Look at **Figure 4-6.** Would you rather wear a bracelet made of gold or one made of iron? Why? Iron is less attractive and less valuable than gold. Iron and other metals such as aluminum, calcium, and magnesium have an important chemical property that makes them unsuitable for jewelry. For example, think about what happens to iron when it is left out in the air. Iron rusts easily because of its high reactivity (ree ak TIV uh tee) with oxygen in the air. Reactivity is how easily one thing reacts with something else. The low reactivities of silver and gold, in addition to their desirable physical properties, make those metals good choices for jewelry.

Chemical Properties of Acids

Acids and bases have physical properties that make acids taste sour and bases taste bitter and feel slippery. The chemical properties of acids and bases are what make them useful—but sometimes harmful.

Figure 4-7 Aluminum reacts easily with the acids in foods such as tomatoes, which is why you shouldn't cook or store these foods in aluminum. **Why do you think aluminum cans for beverages are coated on the inside?**

Many acids react with, or corrode (kur OHD), certain metals. Have you ever used aluminum foil to cover leftover spaghetti and tomato sauce? The next day, you might find small holes in the foil where it has come into contact with the tomatoes in the sauce, as shown in **Figure 4-7.**

The acids in tomato sauce, oranges, carbonated soft drinks, and other foods won't hurt you. However, many acids can damage plant and animal tissue. Small amounts of nitric (NITE rihk) acid and sulfuric (sulf YER ihk) acid are found in rain in areas that have a lot of pollution in the air.

Figure 4-8 Acid rain has damaged or killed some of the trees in this forest near the Blue Ridge Parkway in North Carolina.

This rain, called acid rain, harms plant and animal life, as shown in **Figure 4-8.** Sulfuric acid that has no water mixed with it is useful in many industries because it removes water from certain materials. However, that same property causes burns on skin that touches sulfuric acid.

Chemical Properties of Bases

A strong base also can damage living tissue. It is not uncommon for someone who smells strong ammonia to get a bloody nose from the fumes. The reason that ammonia feels slippery to the touch is that the base actually reacts with fat that lies under the top layer of skin cells in your fingertips.

Chemists have created a numbering system, called the pH scale, to measure how acidic or basic solutions are. Solutions with pH values below 7 are acidic. pH 7 is neutral. Solutions having pH values above 7 are basic. The most acidic solutions have a pH of 1 or lower, and the most basic solutions have a pH of 14 or higher. You'll use the pH scale when you test for the pH values of some common solutions later in this section.

Acid-Base Indicators

Perhaps you've been to a swimming pool on a hot day and noticed someone testing the water. That's because pool water can harm your skin or encourage the growth of bacteria if it is not within a certain range of pH values. The pH of a solution can be estimated using solutions of dyes called indicators that have different colors at different pH values.

CHEMISTRY
INTEGRATION

The pH Scale
A change of one pH unit represents a tenfold change in acidity or basicity. For example, a solution that has a pH of 5 is ten times more acidic than one with a pH of 6. How much more basic is a solution with a pH of 12 than one with a pH of 10?

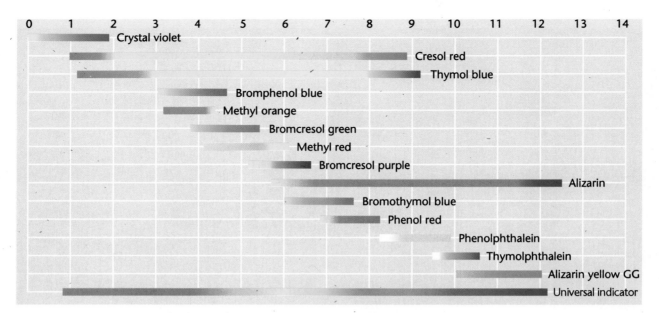

Figure 4-9 Each acid-base indicator changes color over a range of pH values. **What indicator would you choose to show a color change at pH 6?**

To determine the pH of water, you add a certain number of drops of indicator solution to a measured sample of the water and compare the resulting color to a standard chart such as the one shown in **Figure 4-9.**

Acids and Bases React

Acids and bases are often studied together because they react with each other to form water and other useful compounds called salts. Look at **Figure 4-10.** That familiar stuff in your salt shaker—table salt—is the most common salt.

Problem Solving

Predicting Remedies

Bees, wasps, yellow jackets, mosquitoes, fleas, flies, ants, and hornets can ruin a backyard party. When they bite, they inject acidic or basic venom into your skin and tissues. Unless you are allergic to insect stings or bites, the reaction is usually pain, a bump or swelling, itching, and redness.

You're having friends over to enjoy a beautiful spring day in the backyard. Amy, one of your guests, is stung by a bee and is in pain. Bee venom is basic. Assuming that Amy is not allergic to bee stings, how can you use what you know about acids and bases to reduce her pain and discomfort?

The pH of Common Household Items

Item	pH
Carbonated beverage	2.9
Vinegar	2.9
Apple	3.0
Orange juice	3.5
Grapes	4
Tomatoes	4.2
Milk	6.3–6.6
Egg white	7.8
Baking soda	8.4

Think Critically: Think about what you know about acids, bases, and the pH scale. What substance(s) from this household list would best be used to neutralize the venom of a bee sting? Explain why the item(s) you choose might reduce the pain and other symptoms.

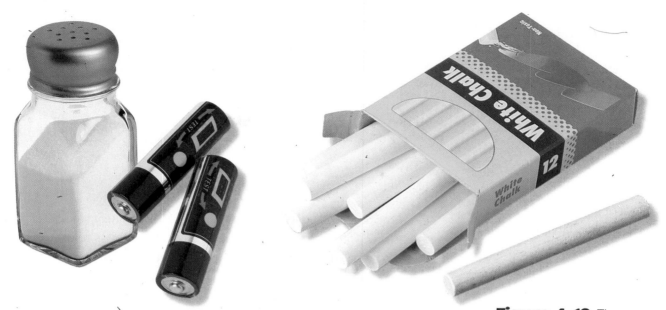

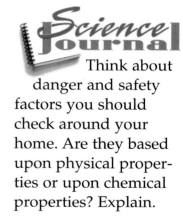

Figure 4-10 These common items contain salts. **What is one way a salt can be formed?**

Table salt, sodium chloride, can be formed by the reaction between the base sodium hydroxide and the acid called hydrochloric acid. Other useful salts are calcium carbonate, which is found in chalk, and ammonium chloride, which is used in certain batteries.

Section Assessment

1. Make a chart and list ten items in your home. On the chart, include the following physical properties for each item: color, state of matter, texture, and hardness.

2. Design three symbols that could be put on containers to warn chemists that a certain chemical could burn easily and be poisonous and corrosive.

3. **Think Critically:** Explain why the temperature at which wax melts is a physical property and not a chemical property.

4. **Skill Builder**
   Classifying Classify each of the following properties as being either physical or chemical. If you need help, refer to Classifying in the **Skill Handbook** on page 679.

   a. Iron will rust when left out in the air.

   b. Silver metal is shiny.

   c. Iodine is poisonous.

   d. Solid sulfur shatters when struck.

Science Journal
Think about danger and safety factors you should check around your home. Are they based upon physical properties or upon chemical properties? Explain.

Homemade pH Scale

Possible Materials

- Vial of pH paper, 1–14
- pH color chart
- Stirring rod
  *spoon
- Wax pencil
  *labels
- Plastic cups
  *beakers
- Distilled water
- Fruit juices
- Vinegar
- Salt
- Sugar
- Soft drinks
- Baking soda
- Soaps and detergents
- Antacids

  *Alternate Materials

The more acidic or basic a solution is, the more likely it is to be harmful. Recall that the pH scale is a way to express how acidic or basic a solution is. In this activity, you will measure the pH of some things you commonly use. You'll use treated paper that turns a color when dipped into a solution. Check the color against the chart to find the pH of the solution.

Recognize the Problem

How acidic or basic are some common household items?

Form a Hypothesis

Think about the properties of acidic and basic solutions. In your group, make a hypothesis about which kinds of solutions you are testing are acidic and which kinds of solutions are basic.

Goals

- **Design an experiment** that allows you to test solutions to find the pH of each.
- **Classify** a solution as acidic or basic according to its pH.

Safety Precautions

Never eat, taste, smell, or touch any chemical or food during a lab.

Test Your Hypothesis

Plan

1. As a group, **decide** what materials you will test. If a material is not a liquid, **dissolve** it in water so you can test the solution.

2. **List** the steps and materials that you need to **test** your hypothesis. Be specific.

3. Before you begin, **copy** a data table like the one shown. Be sure to leave room to **record** results for each solution tested.

4. **Reread** the entire experiment to make sure that all the steps are in logical order.

Do

1. Make sure that your teacher approves your plan and your data table before you proceed. Be sure that you have included any suggested changes.

2. Carry out the experiment as planned and approved. Wash your hands when done.

3. Be sure to **record** your observations in the data table as you **complete** each test.

Analyze Your Data

1. **Compare** your data with the color chart to find the pH of each solution.

2. Were any materials neither acids nor bases? How do you know?

Test Results

Solution to Be Tested	pH	Acid, Base, or Neutral
Distilled water		
Vinegar		
Baking soda		

pH	Color	pH	Color
1		8	
2		9	
3		10	
4		11	
5		12	
6		13	
7		14	

Draw Conclusions

1. Using your data table, **conclude** which types of materials are usually acidic and which are usually basic.

2. Because vinegar is an acidic solution, it can be used to dissolve hard-water deposits. If you run out of vinegar, which of the following—lemon juice, ammonia, or water—could you most likely use instead of vinegar for this purpose?

Road Salt

Salt and Ice

In many climates, winter weather brings snow and ice. These solid forms of water can be dangerous both to vehicles and to people on foot. Faced with icy sidewalks and streets, most people spread rock salt (common salt in rocklike pieces) to clear away ice. Salt changes the freezing point of water. The salt-and-water solution freezes at a temperature lower than the freezing temperature of pure water, which is 0°C. So, applying salt to icy areas melts the ice, unless the ground temperature is colder than 0°C.

Pass (on) the Salt, Please

Putting salt on icy roads can make winter travel safer— but it also causes problems. Cars driven on salted roads can begin to rust after only a few winters. In addition, the added salt can damage the environment. As snow and ice melt, salty water runs off the roads and sidewalks onto nearby land. Too much salt in the soil makes it difficult for many types of plants to grow. Salty water flows into waterways, polluting rivers, lakes, and streams that provide homes for wildlife and water for towns, cities, and farmland.

Salt Substitutes

Sand, cinders, or crushed gravel can be used instead of salt to make snowy roads and walkways less slippery. These materials improve traction but don't harm the environment. However, they don't remove ice because they don't lower the freezing point of water. That's the job of chemical salts called deicers. Deicers also lower the freezing point of water, which keeps snow and ice from attaching to the pavement. CMA (calcium magnesium acetate) is a chemical deicer that causes little or no damage to car bodies or other steel objects. Furthermore, CMA breaks down into harmless compounds that do not hurt plants or pollute water.

Physical and Chemical Changes

Physical Change

It's picnic time. You offer to help carry the food to the picnic table—grilled chicken, potato salad, baked beans, and a big watermelon. On the last trip—with the watermelon—you suddenly lose your hold on the large, slippery fruit. It goes crashing to the ground and splits open. This messy accident is an example of a principle that you will learn in this section—physical change.

What is a physical change?

Most matter can undergo **physical change,** which is any change in size, shape, or form. The makeup of the matter stays the same. Only the physical properties change. Look at **Figure 4-11.** The watermelon underwent a physical change. It went from being one large, round melon to being many smaller pieces splattered all over the floor. It is still watermelon. It just looks different.

Examples of Physical Changes

How can you recognize a physical change? Just look to see whether or not the matter has changed size, shape, or form. If you cut a watermelon into chunks, the watermelon has changed both size and shape. That's definitely a physical change. If you pop one of those chunks into your mouth and bite it, you have changed the watermelon's size and shape again.

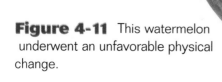

Figure 4-11 This watermelon underwent an unfavorable physical change.

Figure 4-12 Four common changes of state are shown here.

Changes of State

Matter can undergo a physical change in another way, too. It can change from one state to another. After dropping the watermelon, suppose you save the picnic by bringing out frozen fruit bars for dessert. It's a hot day, and the frozen fruit bars start to melt and drip onto the patio as you and your friends eat them. What kind of physical change is happening? A frozen fruit bar is a frozen, solid mixture of water, sugar, food coloring, and flavoring. In the hot sun, the water in the frozen fruit bar changes state and melts, turning into a drippy liquid. As the drops of melted fruit bar on the patio sit in the sun, the water changes state again, evaporating to become a gas. In each case, the fruit bar is composed of the same ingredients. But, the water it contains is in different states as it changes from a solid to a liquid to a gas. Other examples of change of state are shown in **Figure 4-12.**

A The dew on these flowers is liquid water that formed from water vapor in the air.

B When solid ice cream melts, it becomes a liquid.

C Liquid water in perspiration changes to a gas when it evaporates from your skin. **What change of state happens when you make ice cubes?**

D This liquid metal will become solid steel when it cools.

Weathering

Some physical changes, such as the melting frozen fruit bar, happen quickly. Others take place over a long time. Physical weathering is a physical change that is responsible for much of the shape of Earth's surface. Examples are shown in **Figure 4-13.** Examples also can be found in your own backyard. Much of the soil comes from physical weathering. Wind and water erode rocks, breaking them into small bits. Water fills cracks in rocks. When it freezes, the ice splits the rock into smaller pieces of rock. No matter how small the pieces of rock are, they are still made up of the same things that made up the bigger pieces of rock. The rock has simply undergone a physical change. Gravity, plants, animals, and the movement of land during earthquakes also can cause physical changes on Earth.

A

Figure 4-13 You can see the effects of physical weathering caused by water and wind in Yellowstone National Park's Upper Grand Canyon (A) and on this rocky seashore at Point Lobos State Reserve in California (B). **What are some other examples of physical weathering?**

B

Try at Home

Mini Lab

Comparing Chemical Changes

Procedure 🥽 ☠️

1. Separate a piece of fine steel wool into two halves.

2. Dip one half in tap water and the other half in the same amount of salt water.

3. Place both pieces of steel wool on a paper plate and let them sit overnight. Observe any changes.

Analysis

1. What happened to the steel wool that was dipped in the salt water?

2. What might be a common problem with machinery that is operated near an ocean?

Figure 4-14 A chemical change produces the nylon that goes into clothing, carpets, and other common items.

Chemical Change

Your bicycle gets a chip in the paint. Soon, the bike has a spot of rust. A shiny copper penny becomes dull and dark. An apple left out too long begins to rot. What do all these changes have in common? In each of these examples, one or more of the original substances that made up the bike, the penny, and the apple changed into other substances. Such a change is called a **chemical change.**

Examples of Chemical Change

Chemical changes are going on around you—and inside you—every day. When you eat, food undergoes chemical changes so that your body can use it. When plants use water and carbon dioxide to make sugar and oxygen, a chemical change occurs. Many industries make use of chemical changes to manufacture useful products from raw materials, as shown in **Figure 4-14.** Most products—from the salt in your food to the clothes you wear—are produced by chemical change.

Table salt is called sodium chloride. The name tells you that the compound contains the elements sodium and chlorine. Sodium is a silvery-white, soft, metallic solid. It's one of the most reactive common elements and must be stored under oil because it reacts with oxygen and water vapor in the air. If added to water, sodium can even catch fire and sometimes explode. Chlorine is a pale green, poisonous gas that kills living cells and dissolves slightly in water. It's often used to kill germs in drinking water and swimming pools. Sodium chloride, on the other hand, is different from sodium and chlorine. It does not react with the oxygen in air, and its cubelike crystals dissolve readily in water. In nature, salt is found in ocean water and in underground deposits throughout the world where ancient seas have dried up.

Signs of Change

Ice melts, paper is cut, metal is hammered into sheets, and clay is molded into a vase. Seeing signs of these physical changes is easy—something changes shape, size, form, or state. ☑

Sometimes, it's just as easy to tell that a chemical change has occurred. When wood burns, you see it change to ash and other products. One way sodium chloride can be formed is by the reaction between sodium and chlorine in a laboratory. The reaction sounds pretty ho-hum—sodium atoms losing electrons to chlorine atoms. But, watching it happen, as shown in **Figure 4-15,** you see flying sparks and a bright yellow flash, and you hear a bang and a sizzle. In these examples, you know that chemical changes have occurred because you can see that new substances form.

Reading Check ☑

What kind of change is ice melting?

Figure 4-15 Chemical changes can take place rapidly or slowly.

A A spectacular chemical change occurs when sodium, a soft metal, is placed in a flask of chlorine, a yellow-green gas. The reaction produces sodium chloride, which is called table salt, and releases heat and light. **What is another chemical change that releases energy?**

B Iron and oxygen in the air react slowly. This rust is evidence that a chemical change has occurred.

However, it's not always easy to tell when a new substance is formed. What are some other signs of chemical change? One sign is the giving off or taking in of energy. Release of energy is obvious when something burns and heat is given off. Other reactions, like ones in the cold packs that athletic trainers use, actually take in energy. Sometimes, an energy change is so slight or so slow that it's difficult to observe, as when something rusts. You also can tell that a chemical change has occurred if a gas is given off or if water or a solid is formed. For example, when baking soda and vinegar react, carbon dioxide gas and water are produced. Often, a color change is evidence of a chemical change, an example of which is shown in **Figure 4-16.**

Figure 4-16 These leaves change color as a result of chemical changes that happen in the fall.

Section Assessment

1. List five physical changes you can observe in your home. Explain how you decided that each change is physical.

2. When you cook an egg, what kind of change occurs—physical or chemical? Explain.

3. What kind of chemical change occurs in green plants when they manufacture food?

4. **Think Critically:** Which of the following involves a change of state: grinding beef into hamburger, pouring milk into a glass, making ice cream, or allowing soup to cool in a bowl? Explain.

5. **Skill Builder**
   Communicating Do the **Chapter 4 Skill Activity** on page 711 to communicate with other members of your group about how to minimize the weathering of stone by acid rain.

Using Computers

Database Use the information from the Problem Solving activity data table entitled "The pH of Common Household Items" to create a database that lists the pH values of common household products. If you need help, refer to page 699.

Sunset in a Bag

How do you know when a chemical change occurs? You'll see some evidence of chemical change in this activity.

What You'll Investigate

What is evidence of a chemical change?

Goals

- **Observe** a chemical change.
- **Identify** some signs of chemical change.

Safety Precautions

Protect your hands and clothing from chemical spills by wearing gloves and an apron. Dispose of chemicals as directed by your teacher.

Materials

- Baking soda
- Calcium chloride
- Phenol red solution
- Warm water
- Teaspoons (2)
- Resealable plastic bag
- Graduated cylinder (25 mL)

Procedure

1. Add 20 mL of warm water and 5 mL of phenol red solution to the plastic bag. Seal the bag, and gently slosh the solution around to mix it.

2. Open the bag cautiously, and do not point the opening at your face or those of your classmates.

3. Now, add a teaspoon of calcium chloride to the solution in the bag. Again, seal the bag and slosh the contents to mix the solution. Record any changes you observe.

4. Open the bag carefully as before, then quickly add a teaspoon of baking soda. Again, seal the bag and slosh the contents to mix the ingredients together. Record any changes you observe.

CAUTION: *In steps 2 and 4, open the bag cautiously and do not point the opening at your face or those of your classmates.*

Conclude and Apply

1. What evidence of chemical change did you **observe?**

2. How can you tell whether or not energy is released?

3. **Give an example** of a chemical change that does not show an obvious energy change.

For a **preview** of this chapter, study this Reviewing Main Ideas before you read the chapter. After you have studied this chapter, you can use the Reviewing Main Ideas to **review** the chapter.

The Glencoe MindJogger, Audiocassettes, and CD-ROM provide additional opportunities for review.

4-1 PHYSICAL PROPERTY

A **physical property** can be observed without changing the makeup of the material. Physical properties such as color, shape, smell, texture, taste, and density are used to identify and describe materials. A material's **state of matter** is a physical property that tells you whether the material is a solid, a liquid, or a gas. *Metals are flexible and shiny. What kind of properties are these?*

DENSITY

Density tells you the relationship between how heavy a material is and how much space it takes up. Density equals mass divided by volume. A solid floats in a liquid if it is less dense than the liquid. The solid sinks if it is more dense than the liquid. *What material listed in Table 4-1 is least dense?*

CHEMICAL PROPERTY

A **chemical property** indicates whether or not a material can undergo a change that produces one or more new substances. For example, low reactivity is an important chemical property of metals such as silver and gold, which are used in jewelry. Gasoline's ability to burn in an automobile engine and produce energy is a chemical property. *What is a chemical property of oxygen?*

Reading Check ✓

After you read Reviewing Main Ideas, choose a sentence in each section that you feel best represents the main idea of that section.

ACIDS AND BASES

Acids and bases have properties that can be used to identify them. Acids taste sour, corrode metals, and neutralize bases. Bases taste bitter, feel slippery, and neutralize acids. Acids and bases react with each other to produce water and a salt. The pH of a solution tells you how acidic or basic it is. *What is one physical property and one chemical property of an acid?*

Section 4-2 PHYSICAL CHANGE

A **physical change** is a change in the size, shape, form, or state of **matter.** The makeup of the matter stays the same. Water freezing, ice melting, and the physical weathering of rocks are examples of physical change. *What are three common physical changes?*

CHEMICAL CHANGE

In **chemical changes,** one or more new substances are formed. Water decomposing into hydrogen and oxygen, and sodium reacting with chlorine to form sodium chloride are examples of chemical change. *What are some signs that a chemical change has occurred?*

Chapter 4 Assessment

Using Vocabulary

a. chemical change
b. chemical property
c. density
d. physical change
e. physical property
f. state of matter

Using the list above, replace the underlined words with the correct Vocabulary words.

1. <u>Color</u> is mass divided by volume.
2. Color, shape, size, texture, odor, and form are <u>chemical properties</u>.
3. A snowball melting in the sun is undergoing a <u>chemical change</u>.
4. The gaseous state is a <u>chemical change</u>.
5. Iron rusting in air is a <u>physical change</u>.

Checking Concepts

Choose the word or phrase that best answers the question.

6. What are solid, liquid, gas, and plasma?
   A) physical changes
   B) physical properties of soil
   C) chemical changes
   D) states of matter

7. What is the temperature at which something boils?
   A) a chemical change
   B) a chemical property
   C) a physical change
   D) a physical property

8. What kind of change is breaking a window?
   A) chemical   C) neutral
   B) weathering   D) physical

9. What is calculated by dividing mass by volume?
   A) state of matter   C) volume
   B) density   D) mass

10. One or more new substances are formed during what kind of change?
    A) chemical   C) seasonal
    B) physical   D) state

11. What are color, shape, size, texture, odor, and form?
    A) densities
    B) chemical changes
    C) physical properties
    D) chemical properties

12. Release of a gas is often an indication of what?
    A) a base   C) an acid
    B) chemical change   D) density

13. Acid rain damaging a marble statue is an example of what?
    A) chemical property
    B) physical property
    C) state of matter
    D) chemical change

14. What indicates how acidic or basic a solution is?
    A) density   C) color
    B) pH   D) odor

15. What is water condensing on a cold glass an example of?
    A) physical change   C) weathering
    B) state of matter   D) density

Thinking Critically

16. Think about your knowledge of density. Could a bag of feathers be heavier than a bag of rocks? Explain.
17. Sugar dissolves in water. Is this a physical property or a chemical property of sugar?
18. When butane burns, it combines with oxygen in the air to form carbon dioxide and water. What two elements must be present in butane?

19. Identify each of the following as either a physical property or a chemical property.
  A) Glass shatters when hit.
  B) Gasoline burns explosively.
  C) Baking soda is white powder.

20. Identify each of the following as either a physical change or a chemical change.
  A) Metal is drawn out into a wire.
  B) Sulfur in eggs tarnishes silver.
  C) Baking powder bubbles when water is added to it.

Developing Skills

21. Outlining: Make an outline that explains acids, bases, and pH.

22. Recognizing Cause and Effect: Explain what causes a steel structure such as a bridge to rust.

23. Concept Mapping: Copy the concept map below on a separate sheet of paper. Place the terms *matter, physical properties, chemical properties, physical changes,* and *chemical changes* in the proper places in your concept map.

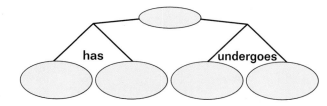

Test-Taking Tip

Don't Be Afraid to Ask for Help Ask for advice on things you don't understand. If you're practicing for a test and you find yourself stuck, unable to understand why you got a question wrong, or unable to do it in the first place, ask for help.

Test Practice

Use these questions to test your Science Proficiency.

1. Which of the following is a chemical property?
  A) A marshmallow is soft.
  B) A marshmallow is white.
  C) A marshmallow can burn if held in a fire too long.
  D) A marshmallow is round.

2. Which of the following is a physical change?
  A) Wood burns in air.
  B) Hydrochloric acid and sodium hydroxide produce sodium chloride.
  C) Iron and oxygen form rust.
  D) An aluminum can is crushed.

3. A solution has a pH of 1. Which response **BEST** describes the solution?
  A) highly acidic
  B) neutral
  C) slightly basic
  D) highly basic

4. Which of these is **NOT** a property of basic solutions?
  A) neutralize acids
  B) have a low pH
  C) taste bitter
  D) feel slippery

2

Interactions in the Physical World

NATIONAL
GEOGRAPHIC

What's Happening Here?

In a warehouse in Salt Lake City, Utah, these table tennis players (left) are "wired for action." They are also equally matched. How so? Because they share a brain! The engineer on the right is directing all the action. Each of the engineer's movements is transferred electronically to the robot named Sarcos. In this unit, you will learn how compound machines, such as robots, are made from simple machines. You will also learn how electrical energy can accomplish such feats. You will explore another way energy moves in the form of electromagnetic waves, including radio, microwaves, and light. Telescopes, such as this one at Kitt Peak, Arizona (below), are used to collect light from distant objects. How do mirrors and lenses help magnify images, and how can scientists study light from the stars? These are a few of the questions you will explore in this unit.

*inter*NET CONNECTION

Explore the Glencoe Science Web Site at **www.glencoe.com/ sec/science/fl** to find out more about topics found in this unit.

Chapter Preview

Skills Preview

Skill Builders
- Map Concepts
- Compare and Contrast

Activities
- Classify
- Measure in SI

MiniLabs
- Compare and Contrast
- Observe

Reading Check ✔

As you read, jot down ways your life would change if there were no waves. What would your life be like? Could you live at all?

Explore Activity

Think about a beautiful autumn day. You are sitting by a lake in a park. You hear music coming from a nearby school band practicing for a big game. A fish jumps out of the water and falls back making a splash. You see a circle of waves that move away from the fish's entry point. The circular waves pass by a floating leaf that fell from a tree nearby. How does the leaf move in response to the waves?

Observe Wave Behavior

1. Set a large, clear, plastic plate (such as the ones carryout meals often come in) on your table.

2. Fill the plate with water to a depth of about 1 cm.

3. Fill a dropper with water.

4. Release a single drop of water onto the water's surface and observe what happens. Repeat as necessary.

5. Float a small cork or 1-cm piece of a soda straw on the surface of the water near the middle of the plate.

6. After the water becomes still again, release single drops at regular intervals from a height of about 10 cm and not directly above the floating object.

7. Repeat the procedure, but release the single drops from a height of about 20 cm.

Science Journal

In your Science Journal, record your observations and describe the movements of the floating object.

5·1 What are waves?

Waves Carry Energy

In the Explore Activity, you saw that falling drops of water can move a floating object. You know that you can make something move by giving it a push or pull. But, the drops didn't hit the floating object. How did the energy from the falling drops travel through the water and move the object? Did you also notice that the ripples that moved in circles from the drop's entry point had peaks and valleys? These peaks and valleys make up water waves.

Waves are regular disturbances that carry energy through matter or space without carrying matter, as shown in **Figure 5-1A.** You also transfer energy when you throw a basketball or baseball to a friend. But, there is an important difference between a moving ball and a moving wave. As shown in **Figure 5-1B,** throwing a ball involves the transport of matter as well as energy.

Mechanical Waves

How does a wave carry energy but not matter? Here is one example you already know about. Sound travels as one type of wave motion. The sounds from a CD player reach your ears when the speakers vibrate back and forth and make sound waves.

What You'll Learn

► Waves carry energy, not matter
► The difference between transverse waves and compressional waves

Vocabulary
wave
mechanical wave
electromagnetic wave
transverse wave
compressional wave

Why It's Important

► You can hear music because of waves.

Figure 5-1 The wave and the ball both carry energy.

 Waves on the water's surface carry energy from place to place, but the water itself moves mostly up and down.

B When you throw a ball to a friend, the ball carries both energy and matter. **What is another example of a moving object carrying both energy and matter?**

The sound waves transfer energy to anything in their path. When the waves reach your ears, they make your eardrums vibrate, as in **Figure 5-2.** If you've ever felt your house shake after a clap of thunder, you know that sound waves can carry large amounts of energy.

Waves that require matter to carry energy are called **mechanical waves.** The matter through which a mechanical wave travels is called a medium. A mechanical wave travels as energy is transferred from particle to particle in the medium. For example, a sound wave travels through the air because energy is transferred from gas molecule to gas molecule. Without a medium, you would not hear sounds. For example, sound waves can't travel in outer space. Imagine that you're standing on the moon. A person standing near you is telling you what she sees. But because there is no air on the moon to carry the sound, you won't hear a word she says—even if she yells at the top of her lungs.

Figure 5-2 When you hear a sound, it's because sound waves traveling through the air make your eardrums vibrate.

Water Waves

Water waves—like the ones you made in the Explore Activity—are also mechanical waves. Each falling water drop touched water molecules when it hit the water's surface. Thus, the droplet's energy was carried from molecule to molecule through the water. Remember that the molecules of water do not move forward along with the wave. Rather, the water's surface moves up and down. In this same way, the wave transfers energy to a boat or other floating object, as shown in **Figure 5-3.** Absorbing some of the energy, the object bobs up and down and moves slowly away from the source of the wave.

Figure 5-3 If you've been on a boat bobbing up and down, you've felt some of the water waves' energy. **How does the boat's motion relate to the direction the water waves travel?**

Electromagnetic Waves

When you listen to the radio, watch TV, or use a microwave oven to cook, you use a different kind of wave—one that doesn't need matter as a medium.

Waves that do not require matter to carry energy are called **electromagnetic waves.** Electromagnetic waves can travel through air. They can even travel through the solid walls of your home. These are the kind of waves that bring you radio and TV programs. Electromagnetic waves also can travel through space to carry information to and from spacecraft. The X rays a doctor uses to see if you broke a bone and the light that carries the sun's energy to Earth are also electromagnetic waves.

Transverse Waves

In a mechanical **transverse wave,** matter moves back and forth at right angles to the direction the wave travels. All electromagnetic waves are transverse waves. You can make a model of a transverse wave. Tie one end of a rope to a doorknob. Hold the other end in your hand. Now, shake the end in your hand up and down. By adjusting the way you shake the rope, you can create a wave that seems to vibrate in place.

Does the rope appear to move toward the doorknob? It doesn't really move toward the door, because if it did, you also would be pulled in that direction. What you see is energy moving along the "rope" wave. You can see that the wave has peaks and valleys at regular intervals. As shown in **Figure 5-4,** the high points of transverse waves are called crests. The low points are called troughs. ☑

inter NET
CONNECTION

Visit the Glencoe Science Web Site at **www. glencoe.com/sec/ science/fl** for more information about electromagnetic waves.

Reading Check ☑

What are the highest points of transverse waves called?

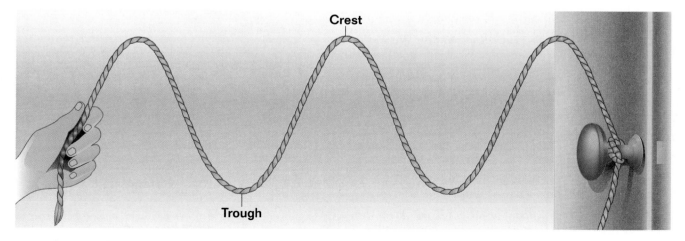

Crest

Trough

Figure 5-4 What does the vibrating rope carry from the hand to the door?

Figure 5-5 Sound waves are compressional waves.

 A This compressional wave carries energy along the spring, while the spring itself vibrates forward and backward.

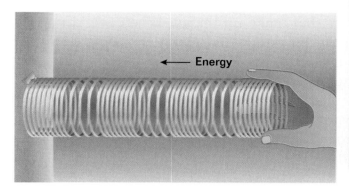

B Vibrating strings make compressional waves that carry the harp's music to your ears. **What do you think vibrates to make compressional waves when a musician plays a trumpet?**

Compressional Waves

Mechanical waves can be either transverse or compressional. In a **compressional wave,** matter in the medium moves forward and backward in the same direction the wave travels. You can make a compressional wave by squeezing together and releasing several coils of a coiled spring toy, as shown in **Figure 5-5A.** When a compressional wave travels along a coiled spring, does the whole spring move along with the wave? If you tied a string around a single coil, you could watch that coil's movement as the wave passes. You would see that the coil moves forward and backward as the wave passes. So, like transverse waves, compressional waves carry only energy forward along the spring. The matter of the spring does not move along with the wave.

Sound Waves

Sound waves are compressional waves. How do you make sound waves when you talk or sing? If you hold your fingers against your throat while you hum, you can feel vibrations. These vibrations are actually the movements of your vocal cords. If you touch a stereo speaker while it's playing, you can feel the vibrations of the speaker, too. The sounds produced by the harp shown in **Figure 5-5B** are made when the strings of the instrument are made to vibrate.

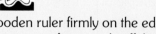

Comparing Sounds

Procedure

1. Hold a wooden ruler firmly on the edge of your desk so that most of it extends off the edge of the desk.
2. Pluck the free end of the ruler so that it vibrates up and down. Pluck it easily at first, then with more energy.
3. Repeat step 2, moving the ruler about 1 cm further onto the desk. Continue until only about 5 cm extend off the edge.

Analysis

1. Compare the loudness of the sounds produced by using little energy with those using more energy.
2. Compare the pitches produced by the longer and shorter lengths of the object.

Making Sound Waves

How do vibrating vocal cords, strings, and other objects make sound waves? To find out, look at the drumhead stretched over the open end of the drum shown in **Figure 5-6.** When the drumhead moves upward, it touches some of the invisible particles that make up the air. When everything is quiet, the air particles are spaced about the same distance apart. But when the drumhead moves up, it pushes the air particles together. These groups of particles that are squeezed together are called a compression. When the drumhead moves downward, the air particles have more room and move away from each other. A place where particles are spaced far apart is called a rarefaction (rar uh FAK shun).

Figure 5-6 A vibrating drumhead makes compressions and rarefactions in the air. **How do your vocal cords make compressions and rarefactions in air?**

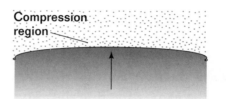

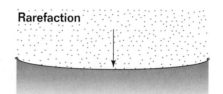

Section Assessment

1. Give one example of a transverse wave and one example of a compressional wave.

2. Why can't a sound wave travel from a satellite to Earth?

3. Is light a mechanical wave or an electromagnetic wave? A transverse wave or a compressional wave?

4. **Think Critically:** How is it possible for a sound wave to transmit energy, but not matter?

5. **Skill Builder**
   Concept Mapping Create a concept map that shows the relationships between the following: *waves, mechanical waves, electromagnetic waves, compressional waves*, and *transverse waves*. If you need help, refer to Concept Mapping in the **Skill Handbook** on page 680.

Using Computers

Word Processing Use word-processing software to write short descriptions of the waves you encounter during a typical day. If you need help, refer to page 698.

Wave Properties

Amplitude

Waves have characteristics that you can see and measure. For example, you can describe a wave in a lake or ocean by how high it rises above, or falls below, the normal water level. This is called the wave's amplitude. The **amplitude** of a transverse wave is one-half the distance between a crest and a trough, as shown in **Figure 5-7A.** In a compressional wave, the amplitude is greater when the particles of the medium are squeezed closer together in each compression and spread farther apart in each rarefaction.

Amplitude and Energy

A wave's amplitude is important. It is a measure of the energy the wave carries. For example, the waves that make up bright light have greater amplitudes than the waves that make up dim light. Waves of bright light carry more energy than the waves that make up dim light. In a similar way, loud sound waves have greater amplitudes than soft sound waves. Loud sounds carry more energy than soft sounds.

If you've seen pictures of a hurricane that strikes a coastal area, you know that the waves caused by the hurricane can damage anything that stands in their path. Waves with large amplitudes carry more energy than waves with smaller amplitudes. The waves caused by the hurricane have much more energy than the small waves or ripples on a pond, as you can see in **Figure 5-7B.**

What You'll Learn

► What wave frequency and wavelength are
► Waves travel at different speeds

Vocabulary
amplitude
wavelength
frequency

Why It's Important

► A wave's energy depends on its amplitude.

Figure 5-7 A wave's amplitude is a measure of how much energy it carries.

A The higher the crests (and the lower the troughs) of a wave, the greater the wave's amplitude is.

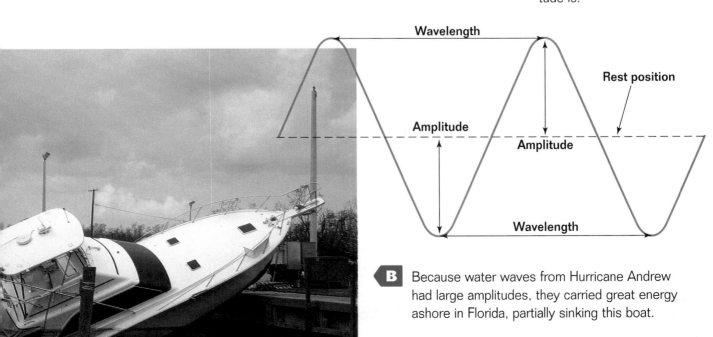

B Because water waves from Hurricane Andrew had large amplitudes, they carried great energy ashore in Florida, partially sinking this boat.

Tsunamis are huge sea waves that are caused by underwater earthquakes or volcanic eruptions. Because of their large amplitudes, tsunamis carry tremendous amounts of energy. They cause great damage when they move ashore.

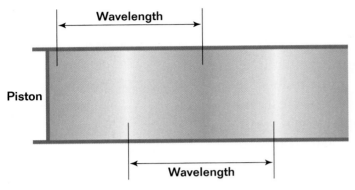

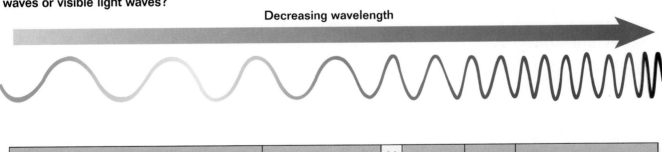

Figure 5-8 The wavelength of a compressional wave is measured from one compression or rarefaction to the next. **When the piston moves to the right, does it make a compression or a rarefaction?**

Figure 5-9 The wavelengths and frequencies of electromagnetic waves vary greatly. **Which waves have longer wavelengths, radio waves or visible light waves?**

Wavelength

Another way to describe a wave is by its wavelength. **Wavelength** is the distance between a point on one wave and an identical point on the next wave—from a crest to a crest or from a trough to a trough, as shown in **Figure 5-7A.** For a compressional wave, the wavelength is the distance between adjacent compressions or rarefactions, as shown in **Figure 5-8.**

Wavelength is an important characteristic of a wave. For example, the difference between red light and green light is that they have different wavelengths. Like all electromagnetic waves, light is a transverse wave. The wavelength of visible light determines its color. In this example, the wavelength of red light is longer than the wavelength of green light. Some electromagnetic waves, like X rays, have short wavelengths. Others, like microwaves in an oven, have longer wavelengths. The range of wavelengths of electromagnetic waves is shown in **Figure 5-9.**

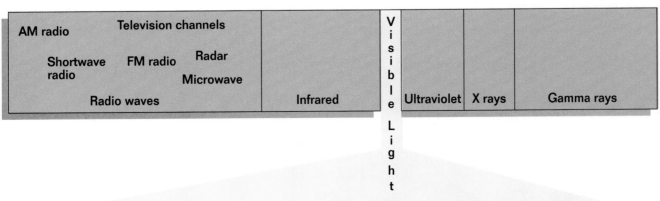

Frequency

The **frequency** of a wave is the number of waves that pass a given point in 1 s. Frequency is measured in waves per second, or hertz (Hz). For a given speed, waves with longer wavelengths have lower frequencies. Fewer long waves pass a given point in 1 s. Waves with shorter wavelengths have higher frequencies because more waves pass a given point in 1 s. Frequency is illustrated in **Figure 5-10A** and **B.**

The wavelength of an electromagnetic light wave determines the color of the light. In a sound wave, the frequency (associated with its wavelength) determines the pitch. Pitch is the highness or lowness of a sound. A flute makes musical notes with a high pitch. A tuba produces notes with a low pitch. When you sing "do re mi fa so la ti do," both the pitch and frequency increase from note to note. In other words, high-pitched sound waves have high frequencies. Low-pitched sound waves have low frequencies. ☑

PHYSICS
INTEGRATION

Global Positioning Systems
Maybe you've used a global positioning system (GPS) receiver to determine your location while driving, boating, or hiking. Earth-orbiting satellites send out electromagnetic radio waves that give the satellites' exact locations and times of transmission. The GPS receiver calculates the distance to each satellite and displays your location to within about 16 m.

Wave Speed

You've probably watched a distant thunderstorm approach on a hot summer day. You see a bolt of lightning flash between a dark cloud and the ground. Do the sound waves, or thunder, produced by the lightning bolt reach your ears at the same instant you see the lightning? If the thunderstorm is many kilometers away, several seconds may pass between the time you see the lightning and you hear the thunder. This happens because light travels much faster in air than sound does. Light is an electromagnetic wave that travels through air at about 300 million m/s. Sound is a mechanical wave that travels through air at about 340 m/s.

Reading Check ☑
What determines the pitch of a sound?

Figure 5-10 Wave A has a longer wavelength and a lower frequency than wave B. **Why does a wave with a long wavelength have a low frequency?**

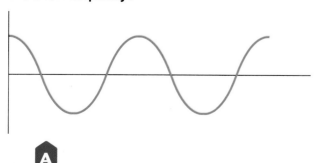

A

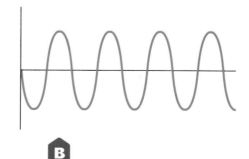

B

Determining Wave Speed

You can calculate the speed of a wave by multiplying its frequency by its wavelength. For example, suppose you know that a sound wave has a frequency of 266 Hz and a wavelength of 1.29 m. (Remember that 266 Hz means that 266 sound waves pass a given point in 1 s.) The wave's speed is given by the following calculation.

$$\text{wave frequency} \times \text{wavelength} = \text{wave speed}$$
$$266 \text{ Hz} \times 1.29 \text{ m} = 343 \text{ m/s}$$

The speed of the wave is 343 m/s.

Light travels through different types of matter at different speeds. For example, the speed of light waves is slightly higher in empty space than in air. And, light waves travel only about 200 million m/s in glass. You can see that this is much slower than the speed light travels in air. The speed of sound waves varies, too. Have you ever heard sounds while swimming underwater? Have you ever put your ear against a wall or on the ground to hear something more clearly? If you have, you may have noticed something interesting. Sound travels faster in liquids and solids than in gases like air.

Using Math

You can calculate the speed of a wave in meters per second (m/s) by multiplying the wave's frequency in hertz (Hz) by its wavelength in meters (m). This calculation is possible because 1 Hz = 1/s. For example, 266 Hz × 1.29 m = 266 1/s × 1.29 m = 343 m/s.

Section Assessment

1. Why is the statement "The speed of light is 300 million m/s" not always correct?

2. How does the frequency of a wave change as its wavelength changes?

3. In what part of a compressional wave are the particles spaced farthest apart?

4. Why is a sound wave with a large amplitude more likely to damage your hearing than one with a small amplitude?

5. **Think Critically:** Explain the differences between the waves that make up bright, green light and dim, red light.

6. **Skill Builder**
   Interpreting Scientific Diagrams
   Scientific diagrams can help you understand wave properties. Do the **Chapter 5 Skill Activity** on page 712 to learn about a compressional wave, its parts, and its wavelength.

Using Math

If a sound wave traveling through water has a speed of 1470 m/s and a frequency of 2340 Hz, what is its wavelength?

Waves on a Spring

Waves are rhythmic disturbances that carry energy through matter or space. Studying waves can help you understand how the sun's energy reaches Earth and sounds travel through the air.

Materials

- Long, coiled spring toy
- Meterstick
- Stopwatch
- Piece of colored yarn (5 cm)

What You'll Investigate

In this activity, you will create transverse and compressional waves on a coiled spring and investigate some of their properties.

Goals

- **Create** transverse and compressional waves on a coiled spring.
- **Investigate** wave properties such as speed and amplitude.

Procedure

1. **Prepare a data table** such as the one shown.

2. Work in pairs or groups and clear a place on an uncarpeted floor about 6 m long and 2 m wide.

3. While one team member grasps one end of the coiled spring toy with one hand, another team member should stretch it to the length suggested by the teacher. **Measure** the length of the coiled spring toy. **CAUTION:** *Coiled springs can be damaged permanently by over-stretching or tangling. Be careful to follow the teacher's instructions.*

4. **Create** a wave by having one team member make a quick sideways snap of the wrist. Time several waves as they travel from one end of the coiled spring toy to the other. Record the average time in your data table.

5. Repeat step 4 using waves that have slightly larger amplitudes.

6. Use one hand to squeeze together about 20 of the coils near you. **Observe** what happens to the unsqueezed coils. Release the coils and **observe** what happens.

7. Quickly push one end of the coiled spring toward your partner, then pull it back to its original position.

8. Tie the piece of colored yarn to a coil near the middle of the coiled spring toy. Repeat step 7, **observing** what happens to the string.

Wave Data	
Length of stretched spring toy	
Average time for a wave to travel from end to end—step 4	
Average time for a wave to travel from end to end—step 5	

Conclude and Apply

1. **Classify** the wave pulses you created in steps 4 and 5 and those you created in steps 6 to 8 as compressional or transverse.

2. **Calculate** and **compare** the speeds of the waves in steps 4 and 5.

3. **Classify** the unsqueezed coils in step 6 as a compression or a rarefaction.

4. **Compare and contrast** the motion of the yarn in step 8 with the motion of the wave. Did the coil that had the yarn attached to it move along the coiled spring toy or did the wave's energy pass through that coil?

Reflection

5·3 Wave Behavior

You've probably yelled to a friend across a gymnasium or down a long hallway. When you did this, you might have heard an echo of your voice. What property of sound caused the echo?

When you look in a mirror, what property of light lets you see your face? Both the echo of your voice and the face you see in the mirror are caused by wave reflection. **Reflection** occurs when a wave strikes an object or surface and bounces off. An echo is reflected sound. Sound reflects from all surfaces. Your echo bounced off the walls, floor, ceiling, furniture, and people. In old western movies, light reflected off a mirror was often used to send a message over long distances. When you see your face in a mirror, as shown in **Figure 5-11A,** reflection occurs. Light that reflects from your face hits the mirror and reflects back to your eyes.

A mirror is smooth and even. However, when light reflects from an uneven or rough surface, you can't see an image because the reflected light scatters in many different directions, as shown in **Figure 5-11B.**

Figure 5-11

A If light didn't reflect from you and the mirror, you wouldn't be able to see yourself in the mirror.

B The building at the far left has a rough surface that scatters light in different directions. Its surface is not smooth and shiny like the building on the right, which is mirrorlike. **Why should a mirror's reflective surface be made as smooth as possible?**

Refraction

You've already seen that a wave changes direction when it reflects from a surface. Can a wave change its direction at other times? Perhaps you've used a magnifying glass to examine your skin, an insect, a coin, or a stamp. An object appears larger when viewed through a magnifying glass. This happens because the light rays from the object change direction when they pass from the air into the glass. They change direction again when they pass from the glass into the air. The bending of a wave as it moves from one medium into another is called **refraction.**

Refraction and Wave Speed

The speed of a wave is different in different substances. For example, light waves move slower in water than in air. Refraction occurs when the speed of a wave changes as it passes from one substance to another. As shown in **Figure 5-12A** and **B,** a line has been drawn perpendicular to the water's surface. This line is called the normal.

Try at Home

Mini Lab

Observing How Light Refracts

Procedure

1. Fill a large, opaque drinking glass or cup nearly to the brim with water.
2. Place a white soda straw in the water at an angle, with approximately one-third of its length extending out of the water.
3. Looking directly down into the cup from above, observe the straw where it meets the water.
4. Placing yourself so that the straw angles to your left or right, slowly back away about 1 m. If necessary, lower your head until you eliminate any unwanted glare from the water's surface. Observe the straw as it appears above, at, and below the surface of the water.

Analysis

1. Describe the straw's appearance as you looked directly down on it.
2. Compare the straw's appearance above and below the water's surface when you looked at it from the side. Draw a diagram and explain the apparent effect.

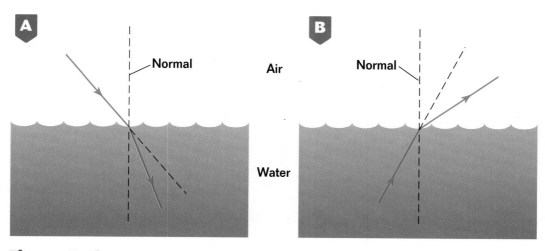

Figure 5-12 As the light ray in A passes from air into water, it refracts toward the normal. As the light ray in B passes from water into air, it refracts away from the normal.

When a light ray passes from air into water, it slows down and bends toward the normal. The more the light ray slows, the more its direction changes. When the ray passes from water into air, it speeds up and bends away from the normal.

You notice refraction when you look at an angle into a lake or pond and spot a fish near the bottom. Refraction makes the fish appear to be closer to the surface and farther away from you than it really is, as shown in **Figure 5-13.** Refraction also gives diamonds and other gems their wonderful sparkle. **Figure 5-14** illustrates how refraction and reflection produce a rainbow when light waves from the sun pass into and out of water droplets in the air. ☑

Reading Check ☑
What produces a rainbow?

Diffraction

It's time for lunch. You're walking down the hallway to the cafeteria. As you near the open door, you can hear people talking and the clink and clank of tableware. But how do the sound waves reach your ears before you get to the door? The sound waves must be able to bend around the corners of the door, as shown in **Figure 5-15A. Diffraction** is the bending of waves around a barrier.

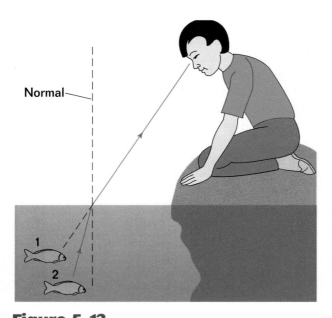

Figure 5-13
Refraction makes the fish at location 2 appear to be at location 1.

Normal

1
2

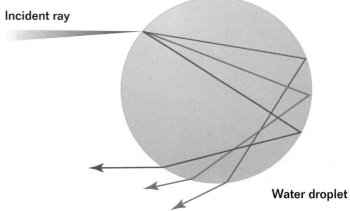

Incident ray

Sunlight

Water droplet

Figure 5-14 Light rays refract when they enter and leave a raindrop, and they reflect from the far side of the drop. Because different colors refract at different angles, they leave the drop separated into the colors of the spectrum. (Ray angles have been shown larger than they actually are for clarity.) **Which color of light shown on the diagram refracts most?**

Figure 5-15 Sound waves and light waves diffract differently through an open door.

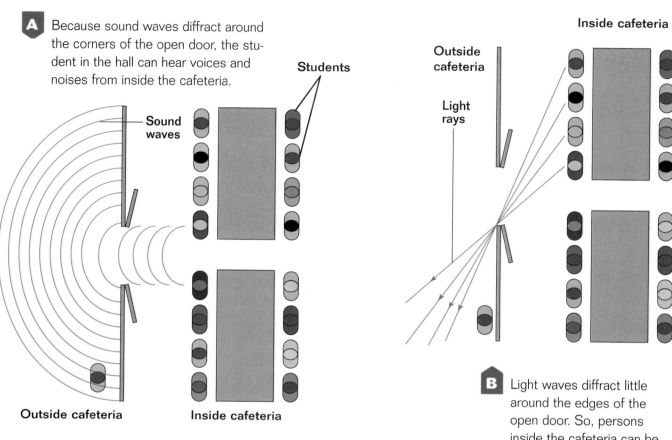

A Because sound waves diffract around the corners of the open door, the student in the hall can hear voices and noises from inside the cafeteria.

Students

Sound waves

Outside cafeteria

Inside cafeteria

Inside cafeteria

Outside cafeteria

Light rays

B Light waves diffract little around the edges of the open door. So, persons inside the cafeteria can be seen only when the student in the hall meets light rays streaming through the door. **How does diffraction explain why a boat inside a harbor rocks slightly from water waves outside the harbor?**

Diffraction of Light

Can light waves diffract, too? You can't see your friends in the cafeteria until you reach the open door, so the light waves must not diffract as much as the sound waves, as shown in **Figure 5-15.**

Are light waves able to diffract at all? As a matter of fact, light waves do bend around the edges of an open door. You can see some effects of light diffraction when you view a bright light through a small slit such as the one between two pencils held close together. However, the amount the light bends is extremely small. As a result, the diffraction of light is far too small to allow you to see around the corner into the cafeteria. The reason that light waves don't diffract much when they pass through an open door is that the wavelengths of visible light are much smaller than the width of the door. Sound waves that you can hear have much longer wavelengths. They bend more readily around the corners of an open door. A wave diffracts best when its wavelength is similar in size to the barrier or opening.

Interference

Imagine a marching band that has only one of each kind of instrument. When this band performs on a football field, will it fill the stadium with sound? Having several of each instrument play the same notes at the same times produces much louder and more spectacular music. For example, the sound waves of many trumpets combine to make sound waves with larger amplitudes. The sound produced by many trumpets is therefore louder than the sound from a single trumpet. The ability of two or more waves to combine and form a new wave when they overlap is called **interference** (ihn tur FEER uns).

Constructive interference occurs when waves meet, for example, crest to crest and trough to trough. The amplitudes of these combining waves add together to make a larger wave, as shown in **Figure 5-16A, B,** and **C.** Destructive interference occurs, for example, when the crest of one wave meets the trough of another wave. In destructive interference, the amplitudes of the combining waves make a smaller wave. Sometimes, they produce no wave at all, as shown in **Figure 5-16D, E,** and **F** on the next page.

Reflected light waves sometimes produce interesting interference patterns. The colorful interference patterns that result from the microscopic pits in compact discs are one example.

interNET CONNECTION

Visit the Glencoe Science Web Site at **www. glencoe.com/sec/ science/fl** for more information about wave interference.

Problem Solving

Scattering Light

Why is the sky blue and the sunset red? Surprisingly, both effects have the same cause. Sunlight contains all colors of the visible spectrum. When sunlight passes through Earth's atmosphere, particles in the air scatter some colors more than others. Shorter-wavelength violet and blue light waves are scattered most, green and yellow waves a little, and longer-wavelength orange and red light waves even less.

The sky appears blue during the day because the scattered blue light waves reflect to your eyes from dust particles and water droplets in the air. However, at sunrise and sunset, the sky appears red because light waves from the sun pass through more of the atmosphere before reaching Earth's surface. With so much of the blue and violet light scattered away, only the orange and red waves reach your eyes.

Think Critically: You've seen the beautiful array of colors in a rainbow on a day that has both sunshine and water droplets in the air. You've viewed the colorful light pattern from a compact disc. What do the blue color of the daytime sky, the red color of a sunset, a multicolored rainbow, and the light pattern from a compact disc have in common? How are they different?

Figure 5-16

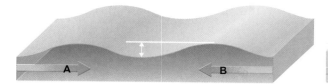

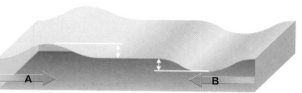

A **Constructive Wave Interference**
Crests of waves A and B approach each other from different directions. The waves have equal amplitudes.

D **Destructive Wave Interference**
A crest of wave A and trough of wave B approach each other from different directions. The amplitude of A equals the amplitude of B.

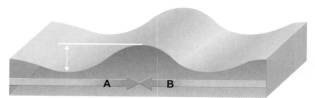

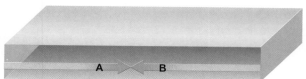

B When crests A and B meet, they briefly form a new wave, A + B, which has an amplitude equal to the sum of the amplitudes of the two waves.

E When the waves meet, they briefly form a new wave, A + B, which has an amplitude of zero for an instant.

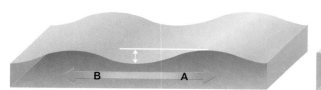

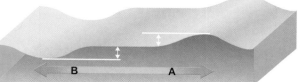

C The waves have passed through each other unchanged.

F The waves have passed through each other unchanged. **Compare and contrast constructive and destructive interference.**

Useful Interference

You may have seen someone cut grass with a power lawn mower or cut wood with a chain saw. In the past, many people who've performed these tasks have damaged their hearing because of the loud noises produced by these machines. Today, ear protectors can reflect and absorb some of the noise from lawn mowers and chain saws. The ear protectors lower the amplitudes of the harmful waves. The smaller-amplitude waves that reach the ears no longer damage eardrums.

Pilots of small planes have had an interesting problem. They couldn't shut out all the noise of the plane's motor. If they did, they wouldn't be able to hear instructions from air-traffic controllers. Engineers invented special earphones that contain electronic circuits. These circuits produce sound frequencies that destructively interfere with engine noise that might be harmful.

However, the sound frequencies produced do not interfere with human voices, allowing the pilot to hear and understand normal conversation. In these examples, destructive interference can be a benefit, as shown in **Figure 5-17**.

Figure 5-17 Some airplane pilots use ear protectors that muffle engine noise but don't block human voices. People who operate chain saws need ear protectors that greatly reduce the engine noise that could be harmful.

Section Assessment

1. White objects reflect light. Why don't you see your reflection when you look at a building made of rough, white stone?

2. If you're standing on one side of a building, how are you able to hear the siren of an ambulance on the other side of the building?

3. What behavior of light enables magnifying glasses and contact lenses to bend light rays and help people see more clearly?

4. **Think Critically:** Why don't light rays that stream through an open window into a darkened room spread evenly through the entire room?

5.  **Skill Builder**
   Comparing and Contrasting When light rays pass from water into a certain type of glass, the rays refract toward the normal. Compare and contrast the speed of light in water and in the glass. If you need help, refer to Comparing and Contrasting in the **Skill Handbook** on page 686.

Science Journal
Look and listen carefully as you travel home from school or walk down the street where you live. What examples of wave reflection and refraction do you notice? Describe each of these in your Science Journal, and explain whether it's an example of reflection or refraction.

NATIONAL GEOGRAPHIC

Graphing Waves

Constructive and Destructive Interference

Waves have special characteristics. The wavelength is the horizontal distance between a point on one wave and an identical point on the next wave. The amplitude is the vertical distance from the crest (or trough) of a wave to a position halfway between crest and trough.

When two waves meet in such a way that a new wave with greater amplitude is formed, it is called constructive interference. If the new wave formed has a smaller amplitude than either original wave or an amplitude of zero, it is called destructive interference.

Problem

Draw a graph for the new wave formed by combining Waves A and B.

Solution

Notice that nine points on each wave are labeled with red dots and numbers. These points will be used to graph the new wave.

To graph the new wave formed by combining Waves A and B, find nine points for the new graph by adding the "height" of Waves A and B at each labeled point.

Point 1 (new): height of Wave A point 1 + height of Wave B point 1 = 0 + 0 = 0.

Point 2 (new): height of Wave A point 2 + height of Wave B point 2 = 2 + 4 = 6.

Point 3 (new): height of Wave A point 3 + height of Wave B point 3 = 4 + 8 = 12.

Continuing the process, you'll find that the remaining points have heights 6, 0, 6, 12, 6, and 0. A graph for the new wave looks like this:

To find a wave's amplitude, count the vertical units between the lowest and highest points on the graph and divide by 2. Because the new wave has greater amplitude (6) than either Wave A (2) or B (4), this problem is an example of constructive interference.

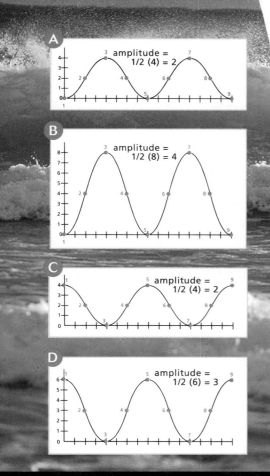

Practice PROBLEMS

In the following problems, draw the graph and determine whether each is a case of constructive or destructive interference.

1. Draw a graph for the new wave formed by combining Waves B and D.

2. Draw a graph representing the combination of Waves C and D.

3. Draw a graph representing the combination of Waves A and C.

4. Draw graphs for two waves of your choice. Show the new wave formed by combining the two.

Activity 5·2

Doing the Wave

Materials

- Coiled spring toy
- Stopwatch
  * *clock with a second hand*
- Meterstick
- Tape

  * *Alternate Materials*

When an earthquake occurs, the waves of energy are recorded at points all over the world by instruments called seismographs. By comparing the data that they collected from their seismographs, scientists discovered that the interior of Earth must be made of layers of different materials. How did the seismographs tell them that Earth is not the same medium all the way through?

Recognize the Problem

Can the speed of a wave be used to identify the medium through which it travels?

Form a Hypothesis

Think about what you know about the relationship between the frequency, wavelength, and speed of a wave in a medium. **Make a hypothesis** about how you can measure the speed of a wave within a medium and use that information to identify an unknown medium.

Goals

- **Measure** the speed of a wave within a coiled spring toy.
- **Predict** whether the speed you measured will be different in other types of coiled spring toys.

Data Sources

Go to the Glencoe Science Web Site at **www.glencoe.com/sec/science/fl** for more information, hints, and data collected by other students.

	Wave Data					
Trial	Length spring was stretched (m)	Number of crests	Wavelength (m)	Number of vibrations timed	Number of seconds vibrations were timed (s)	Wave speed (m/s)
1						
2						
3						

Test Your Hypothesis

Plan 👓

1. **Make a data table** in your Science Journal like the one shown.

2. **Write** a detailed description of the coiled spring toy you are going to use. Be sure to include its mass and diameter, the width of a coil, and what it is made of.

3. Decide as a group how you will **measure** the frequency and length of waves in the spring toy. What are your variables? Which variables must be controlled? What variable do you want to measure?

4. Repeat your experiment three times.

Do

1. Make sure your teacher approves your plan before you begin.

2. Carry out the experiment as you have planned.

3. While you are doing the experiment, **record** your observations and measurements in your data table.

Analyze Your Data

1. **Calculate** the frequency of the waves by dividing the number of vibrations you timed by the number of seconds you timed them. Record your results in your data table.

2. Use the following formula to **calculate** the speed of a wave in each trial.

   wavelength × wave frequency = wave speed

3. **Average** the wave speeds from your trials to determine the speed of a wave in your coiled spring toy.

Draw Conclusions

1. **Post** the description of your coiled spring toy and your results on the Glencoe Science Web Site.

2. **Compare and contrast** your results with the results of other students.

3. How does the type of coiled spring toy and the length it was stretched affect the wave speed? Was your hypothesis supported?

4. Would it make a difference if an earthquake wave were transmitted through Earth's solid mantle or the molten outer core?

For a **preview** of this chapter, study this Reviewing Main Ideas before you read the chapter. After you have studied this chapter, you can use the Reviewing Main Ideas to **review** the chapter.

The Glencoe MindJogger, Audiocassettes, and CD-ROM provide additional opportunities for review.

Section
5-1 WAVES CARRY ENERGY

Waves are rhythmic disturbances that carry energy but not matter. **Mechanical waves** can travel only through matter. Other waves, called **electromagnetic waves,** can travel through space. *What kind of waves carry the sun's energy to Earth? An earthquake's energy through Earth?*

TRANSVERSE AND COMPRESSIONAL WAVES

In a mechanical **transverse wave,** matter in the medium the wave travels through moves back and forth at right angles to the direction the wave travels. In a **compressional wave,** matter in the medium moves forward and backward in the same direction as the wave. *Why doesn't a sound wave travel through space?*

Section
5-2 AMPLITUDE, FREQUENCY, AND WAVELENGTH

Waves can be described by their characteristics. The **amplitude** of a transverse wave is one half the distance between a crest and a trough. **Wavelength** is the distance between a point on one wave and an identical point on the next wave. The **frequency** of a wave is the number of waves that pass a given point in 1 s. *How is the amplitude of a wave related to the amount of energy it carries?*

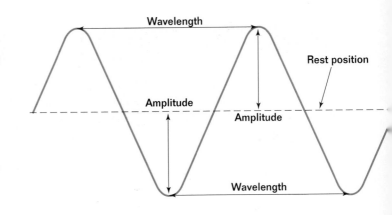

Reading Check ✓

- Construct a chart that compares and contrasts reflection, refraction, diffraction, and interference.

Section 5-3 REFLECTION

Reflection occurs when a wave strikes an object or surface and bounces off. You can see your image in a mirror because of reflection. *How does wave reflection explain echoes in a large canyon?*

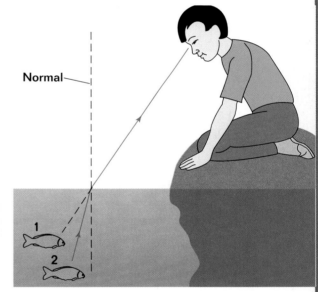

Normal

REFRACTION

The bending of a wave as it moves from one medium into another is called **refraction.** A wave changes direction, or refracts, when its speed changes. *In what situation does a wave not change its direction when it passes from one medium into another?*

DIFFRACTION AND INTERFERENCE

The bending of waves around a barrier is called **diffraction.** The ability of two or more waves to combine and form a new wave when they overlap is called **interference.** *What kind of interference produces waves with the largest amplitudes?*

Chapter 5 Assessment

Using Vocabulary

a. amplitude
b. compressional wave
c. diffraction
d. electromagnetic wave
e. frequency
f. interference
g. mechanical wave
h. reflection
i. refraction
j. transverse wave
k. wave
l. wavelength

Using the list above, replace the underlined words with the correct Vocabulary words.

1. <u>Diffraction</u> is the change in direction of a wave.
2. The type of wave that has rarefactions is a <u>transverse wave</u>.
3. The distance between two adjacent crests of a transverse wave is the <u>frequency</u>.
4. The more energy a wave carries, the greater the <u>wavelength</u> of the wave.
5. A <u>mechanical wave</u> can travel through space.

Checking Concepts

Choose the word or phrase that best answers the question.

6. What is the material through which mechanical waves travel?
   A) charged particles
   B) space
   C) a vacuum
   D) a medium

7. What is carried from particle to particle in a water wave?
   A) speed   C) energy
   B) amplitude   D) matter

8. What are the lowest points on a transverse wave called?
   A) crests   C) compressions
   B) troughs   D) rarefactions

9. What determines the pitch of a sound wave?
   A) amplitude   C) speed
   B) frequency   D) refraction

10. What is the distance between adjacent wave compressions?
    A) one wavelength C) 1 m/s
    B) 1 km   D) 1 Hz

11. What occurs when a wave strikes an object or surface and bounces off?
    A) diffraction   C) a change in speed
    B) refraction   D) reflection

12. What is the name for a change in the direction of a wave when it passes from one medium into another?
    A) refraction   C) reflection
    B) interference   D) diffraction

13. What type of wave is a sound wave?
    A) transverse
    B) electromagnetic
    C) compressional
    D) refracted

14. When two waves overlap and interfere destructively, what does the resulting wave have?
    A) a greater amplitude
    B) more energy
    C) a change in frequency
    D) a lower amplitude

15. What is the difference between blue light and green light?
    A) They have different wavelengths.
    B) One is a transverse wave and the other is not.
    C) They travel at different speeds.
    D) One is mechanical and the other is not.

Thinking Critically

16. Explain what kind of wave, transverse or compressional, is produced when an engine bumps into a string of coupled railroad cars on a track.

17. Is it possible for an electromagnetic wave to travel through a vacuum? Through matter? Explain your answers.
18. Why does the frequency of a wave decrease as the wavelength increases?
19. Why don't you see your reflected image when you look at a white, rough surface?
20. If a cannon fires at a great distance from you, why do you see the flash before you hear the sound?

Developing Skills

If you need help, refer to the Skill Handbook.

21. **Using Numbers:** A microwave travels at the speed of light and has a wavelength of 0.022 m. What is its frequency?
22. **Forming a Hypothesis:** Form a hypothesis that can explain this observation. Waves A and B travel away from Earth through Earth's atmosphere. Wave A continues on into space, but wave B does not.
23. **Recognizing Cause and Effect:** Explain how the object shown below causes compressions and rarefactions as it vibrates in air.

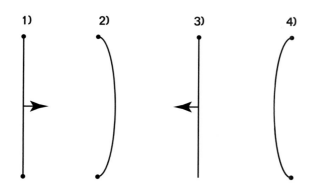

24. **Comparing and Contrasting:** AM radio waves have wavelengths between about 200 m and 600 m, while FM radio waves have wavelengths of about 3 m. Why can AM radio signals often be heard behind buildings and mountains while FM radio signals cannot?

THE PRINCETON REVIEW

Test-Taking Tip

Don't Cram If you don't know the material by the week before the test, you're less likely to do well. Set up a time line for your practice and preparation so that you're not rushed. Then, you will have time to deal with any problem areas.

Test Practice

Use these questions to test your Science Proficiency.

1. Two sounds have the same pitch, but one is louder than the other. What is different about the two sounds?
   A) their amplitudes
   B) their frequencies
   C) their wavelengths
   D) their speeds
2. What produces the colors seen when light reflects from CDs?
   A) wavelength
   B) interference
   C) refraction
   D) compression
3. The speed of a light ray increases as it passes at an angle from one medium into another. What happens to the ray?
   A) Its direction does not change.
   B) It travels along the normal.
   C) It bends toward the normal.
   D) It bends away from the normal.
4. What kind of waves requires a medium?
   A) all transverse waves
   B) only some compressional waves
   C) all electromagnetic waves
   D) all mechanical waves

Motion and Forces

Chapter Preview

Skills Preview

Skill Builders
- Cause and Effect

Activities
- Control Variables

MiniLabs
- Form a Definition

Reading Check ☑

Before you read the chapter, list the vocabulary terms. As you read, write the definitions in your own words.

Explore Activity

Skateboarders who can ride pipes make it look easy. They race down one side and up the other. They rise above the ledge and appear to float as they spin and return. They practice these tricks many times until they get them right. In this chapter, you'll learn how this complicated motion can be explained by forces such as gravity. With an understanding of forces and how they make things move, you will begin to unravel the secrets of these tricks.

The Marble Skateboard Model

1. Using the picture as a guide, use heavy paper to make a model of a half-pipe, the curved surface some skateboarders ride on. Use books to brace the edges. A marble will model the skateboard.

2. Release the marble from a point near the bottom of the curve. Observe the motion. How high does it go? When is its speed greatest?

3. Release the marble from a point near the top of the curve. Observe the motion. Compare this to the marble's motion in step 2.

In your Science Journal, describe your experiment and what you discovered. How did the different starting points affect how high the marble rolled up the side?

6·1 How does speed change?

What You'll Learn

► How to measure speed
► How to measure acceleration

Vocabulary
average speed
rate
acceleration

Why It's Important

► Every movement can be understood using distance, time, speed, and acceleration.

Speed

Think of skateboarding down the side of a half-pipe for the first time. Your heart starts to pound as you move faster and faster. You feel the wind rush against your face. As you reach the bottom, you are going really fast and you feel excitement and fear. You flow through the change in direction as you start up the other side. Your speed decreases as you move higher up the wall. When you reach the top, you are at a near standstill. If you think fast, you can grab hold of the ledge and take a break. Otherwise, back down you go.

How fast were you going?

One way to describe motion is with numbers. To understand how to measure motion, think about the movement of the bicycles as they go down the hill in **Figure 6-1.** To know how fast one of the bicycles is traveling, you must know how far it has gone and how long it has been moving. These are measurements of distance and time.

To calculate any **average speed,** you divide the distance traveled by the time it takes to travel this distance.

$$\text{average speed} = \frac{\text{total distance traveled}}{\text{time}}$$

If the hill is 30 m long and it takes 15 s to travel this distance, then the equation is as follows.

$$\text{average speed} = \frac{30 \text{ m}}{15 \text{ s}} = 2 \text{ m/s}$$

This answer is read as "two meters per second." A **rate** is an expression, like 2 m/s, in which the denominator is time. Speed is the rate at which an object covers a distance. Speed is also called the rate of change of position.

Figure 6-1 To find each bikers's average speed, divide the distance down the hill by the time taken to cover that distance.

Average speed is useful if you don't care about the details of the motion. For example, suppose you went on a long road trip and traveled 640 km in 8 h. You would say you averaged 80 km/h, even though you may have stopped for red lights, got stuck in a traffic jam, or enjoyed a long stretch of high speed on a highway.

When you ride in a car, you can keep track of your speed by reading the speedometer, as shown in **Figure 6-2.** A speedometer allows you to know your speed at any time. How would you determine your speed at the bottom of the skateboard ramp?

Time to Accelerate

Average speed may not tell you everything you want to know. Sometimes, you want to know how motion is changing. **Acceleration** is the rate at which speed or direction changes. Some examples are given in **Figure 6-3.** If you know the change in speed, you can find your acceleration. If you know the acceleration, you can find your speed at any time.

At the top of the skateboard ramp, you are at rest. Your speed is 0 m/s. When you start down, you smoothly speed up, going faster and faster. If the angle of the ramp is made steeper, you will speed up at a greater rate.

Figure 6-2 The odometer in this car measures the distance traveled. The speedometer measures speed. **What units is speed measured in?**

Figure 6-3 Acceleration in the direction of motion speeds you up. If your speed doesn't change, acceleration is 0. Acceleration against the direction of motion slows you down.

Acceleration
→

Acceleration is zero

Acceleration
←

Calculating with Acceleration

Acceleration is found using the following formula.

$$\text{acceleration} = \frac{\text{change in speed}}{\text{time}}$$

$$a = \frac{\text{final speed} - \text{initial speed}}{t}$$

When an object starts from rest, the initial speed is 0. If an object starts at rest and accelerates smoothly to a final speed of 10 m/s in 2 s, the acceleration is found as follows.

$$a = \frac{10 \text{ m/s} - 0 \text{ m/s}}{2 \text{ s}} = 5 \text{ m/s}^2$$

If an object is slowing down, as a skateboard does when the rider brakes, it is accelerating opposite to the direction it is moving. It is losing speed. (Look back at **Figure 6-3.**) You may have heard this called deceleration. This book will use the term *negative acceleration* to describe slowing down because the speed is decreasing. If an object starts at 10 m/s and comes to rest in 2 s, the acceleration is negative.

$$a = \frac{0 \text{ m/s} - 10 \text{ m/s}}{2 \text{ s}} = -5 \text{ m/s}^2$$

Reading Check

What is negative acceleration?

Figure 6-4 As she accelerates at 1 m/s², the skateboarder's speed increases by 1 m/s each second. **What happens to her distance traveled each second?**

Table 6-1

Acceleration 1 m/s²		
Time (s)	Speed (m/s)	Distance (m)
0	0	0.0
1	1	0.5
2	2	2.0
3	3	4.5
4	4	8.0

t = 0 s

t = 1 s

t = 2 s

t = 3 s

You can calculate the skateboard's speed at a given time if you know its acceleration. This would be like having a speedometer attached directly to the board. You can find how fast you are going by using the formula below.

change in speed = acceleration × time

A skateboarder accelerating at 1 m/s² goes 1 m/s faster each second. **Table 6-1** in **Figure 6-4** shows the skateboarder's changing speed. For example, after 3 s the skateboarder is going 3 m/s.

In a car, an odometer measures distance traveled. How could you calculate the distance you travel on a skateboard? For constant acceleration, you can calculate the distance you travel in a given time if you start or end at rest.

$$distance = \frac{1}{2} (acceleration)(time)^2$$

$$d = \frac{1}{2} at^2$$

Using Math

Calculating with Negative Acceleration

Example Problem

You are skating at 4 m/s. You brake with an acceleration of −0.5 m/s². How long does it take you to come to a stop? How far do you travel?

Problem-Solving Steps

1. What is known? acceleration a = −0.5 m/s²; change in speed = 0 m/s − 4 m/s
2. What is unknown? time, t; distance, d
3. Use the equation change in speed = at to find t. Then, use $d = \frac{1}{2} at^2$ to find d.
4. Solution:

change in speed = at

0 m/s − 4 m/s = (−0.5 m/s²)t

−4 m/s = (−0.5 m/s²)t

t = 8 s

$$d = \frac{1}{2} at^2$$

$$d = \frac{1}{2} (0.5 \text{ m/s}^2)(8 \text{ s})^2$$

$$d = 16 \text{ m}$$

You come to a stop in 8 s, after traveling 16 m.

Practice Problem

A ball is thrown straight up with an initial speed of 25 m/s. The acceleration is −10 m/s². How long will it be until the ball comes to a stop? How high will it go?

Strategy Hint: Think about whether values should be positive or negative.

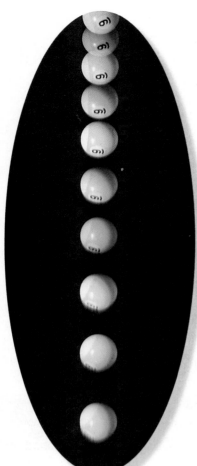

As your speed increases, you cover more and more distance in each second. **Figure 6-5** is a picture of a falling ball taken with a strobe light. The light flashes on and off at a steady rate, so the time between flashes remains the same. The picture lets you see how far the ball falls between flashes. Notice that the distance the ball travels between flashes increases. If the ball were not accelerating, it would move the same distance between each pair of flashes.

We have learned to use numbers to describe and predict motion. This ability has taken humankind to the depths of the oceans and to the moon. The same tools are used to predict the speed of a skateboard and the time for a spacecraft to reach Mars. The science of motion gives you the power to understand how things work and the ability to predict what will happen.

Figure 6-5 The longer an object accelerates, the farther it travels each second. **Falling at 9.8 m/s², how far has the object fallen after 5 s? After 6 s?**

Section Assessment

1. During rush-hour traffic in a big city, it can take 1.5 hours to travel 45 km. What is the average speed, in kilometers per hour, for this trip?

2. Suppose a car traveling 70 m/s brakes and takes 3 s to stop. What is the acceleration in m/s²? How far does the car travel before stopping?

3. A runner accelerates from 0 m/s to 3 m/s in 12 s. What is the acceleration?

4. **Think Critically:** Describe the motion of a skateboard as it accelerates down one side of a half-pipe and then up the other side. What would happen if the up side of the pipe were not as steep as the down side?

5. **Skill Builder**
   Using Numbers Do the **Chapter 6 Skill Activity** on page 713 to learn a problem solving strategy for using numbers in word problems.

Using Math

The space shuttle takes eight minutes to blast off and go into orbit. It accelerates at 30 m/s². How long is this time in seconds? How fast, in kilometers per second, is the shuttle going when it reaches its orbit? How far does it travel during this time?

Time Trials

Before a big car race, all the contestants must pass the time trials. Time trials are races against the clock instead of against other cars.

What You'll Investigate

Can time trials be used to predict the winner of a race?

Goals

- **Conduct** time trials.
- **Test** speed and distance predictions from the results of time trials.

Procedure

1. **Set up** a straightaway using two metersticks, as shown in the picture below. Use the tape to make a starting line at the beginning of the track.

2. **Test** the track with one car. If the car runs into the metersticks, move them further apart or devise some other remedy.

3. Wind up or push the first car, starting with the front of the car on zero of the meterstick. Time its trip to the end of the metersticks.

4. Repeat this at least three times for each car, and **record** your distance and time measurements in a table similar to the one shown.

5. **Calculate** the average time and distance.

Materials

- Metersticks (2)
- Stopwatch or watch that measures in seconds
- Toy cars
- Masking tape

6. **Calculate** the average speed using the averages for the time and distance.

Conclude and Apply

1. **Compare** the average speed of your car with those of your classmates.

2. **Predict** which car should win a 1-m race based on the time trials. Test your prediction.

3. **Predict** which car will travel farthest based on your measurements and observations. Test your prediction.

4. **Explain** whether time trials accurately predict which car will win the race. Were you able to predict which car would travel the furthest? **Explain** why or why not.

Time Trials Data		
Car _____	Time (s)	Distance (m)
Trial 1		
Trial 2		
Trial 3		
Average		

Why do things fall?

What You'll Learn

► How gravity pulls on every-thing
► What forces are and how they act
► The difference between weight and mass

Vocabulary

gravity   balanced
force   forces
weight   inertia
normal force   mass

Why It's Important

► You cannot escape the pull of gravity. It's the force that holds everything in the universe together.

Gravity

When the speed or direction of an object changes, it is accelerating. When you ride down a hill without pedaling your bicycle or jump out of a tree, you are accelerated downward. When you jump off a step, you immediately sense how Earth's gravity changes your speed and direction, although nothing actually grabs you and makes you move. A person who pushes or pulls you must touch you. The touch lets you know your motion is going to change. Earth, however, can pull you without touching you as shown in **Figure 6-6.**

Throughout history, people have tried to explain why things fall. The ancient Greeks were the first to use the word *gravity*, which means "heaviness." If an object fell to the ground, it had gravity. If it didn't fall but rose like smoke, the Greeks said it had *levity*, which means "lightness." The modern explanation of how gravity works was first given by Sir Isaac Newton, who lived in the 1600s. Legend says he developed his ideas about gravity when he observed a falling apple. He reasoned that Earth could pull on the moon in the same way that it pulls on an apple.

Figure 6-6 Gravity accelerates this diver toward Earth. **Does gravity act on the diver while she's standing on the diving board? Explain.**

Gravity is the attraction between all matter. *Newton's law of universal gravitation* states that all matter in the universe pulls on all other matter. A gravitational attraction exists between you and your desk, your book, and Alpha Centari. You don't notice this pull because gravity is weak for small or distant objects. Earth is so large and so close that its pull overwhelms these smaller pulls.

The gravitational pull of Earth gives the same acceleration to all the objects on its surface. Without air resistance, all objects fall with the same acceleration. Usually, air resistance is ignored for simple calculations. On Earth, the acceleration due to gravity is 9.8 m/s^2. If you move far away from Earth or are closer to a large body like the moon, this value changes, as shown in **Figure 6-7**. When a plane goes from 0 km/h to 200 km/h in 6 s, it's acceleration is approximately equal to the acceleration due to gravity on Earth. Fighter pilots who fly planes like the one in **Figure 6-8** can accelerate at more than eight times 9.8 m/s^2 when they make sudden turns. This acceleration is so high that it could make them pass out. To remain conscious, pilots wear pressurized suits.

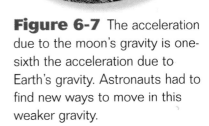

Figure 6-7 The acceleration due to the moon's gravity is one-sixth the acceleration due to Earth's gravity. Astronauts had to find new ways to move in this weaker gravity.

Gravity Is a Force

You have learned that gravity pulls you straight down, and you know that if nothing is there to support you, you will fall. If you do fall, you will accelerate. Acceleration is the sign that a force is acting. A **force** is a push or a pull.

When you stand on the ground, Earth pulls you down and the ground pushes you up. There are many different types of forces. The downward force of gravity on you is called your **weight.**

*inter*NET
CONNECTION

Visit the Glencoe Science Web Site at **www.glencoe.com/ sec/science/fl** for more information about gravity.

Figure 6-8 The test pilot feels an acceleration much greater than the 9.8 m/s^2 of falling. The force

Figure 6-9 The normal force is perpendicular to the surface. On a horizontal surface, the normal force is equal to the weight, but in the opposite direction, so the forces are balanced. **What happens if your weight is greater than the normal force of a stool you stand on?**

Reading Check ☑

What happens to an object acted on by balanced forces?

The upward force of the ground is called the **normal force** because it is normal (perpendicular) to the surface. When the forces acting on an object cancel each other, as in **Figure 6-9,** the forces are **balanced forces.** ☑

Measuring Force

A force is measured by the amount of acceleration it can give a mass. This is described by the following equation, also known as *Newton's second law of motion.*

$$\text{Force} = \text{mass} \times \text{acceleration}$$

$$F = ma$$

If a force can accelerate a 2-kg mass at 4 m/s^2, then the force is found as follows.

$$F = (2 \text{ kg})(4 \text{ m/s}^2)$$
$$= 8 \; \frac{\text{kg} \cdot \text{m}}{\text{s}^2}$$
$$= 8 \text{ N}$$

The force is 8 N. This answer introduces a unit called the newton, abbreviated N. It is named in honor of Sir Isaac Newton.

Forces are measured sometimes using springs. The more you stretch a spring, the harder it is to stretch it further. You may have tried pulling a rubber band. As you pull it back, it gets harder and harder to pull. If you measure how far you stretch it, you can use this to make a force measurement.

LIFE SCIENCE

INTEGRATION

Balanced Forces and Flight
A bird coasting with outspread wings uses balanced forces. The downward force of gravity is balanced by the upward force of air on the wings. What happens if the upward force is greater than the downward force?

Using Force to Calculate Acceleration

Example Problem

A 500-N net force is applied to a 4-kg object. What is the object's acceleration?

Problem-Solving Steps

1. What is known? force, $F = 500$ N; mass, $m = 4$ kg
2. What is unknown? acceleration, a
3. Use the equation $F = ma$.
4. **Solution**

$$F = ma$$
$$500 \text{ N} = (4 \text{ kg})a$$
$$a = 125 \text{ m/s}^2$$

The force provides an acceleration of 125 m/s².

Practice Problem

The same force is applied to a 100-kg object. What is the acceleration?

Strategy Hint: Check that units divide out properly, $\text{N/kg} = \text{m/s}^2$.

This is also how a spring scale, shown in **Figure 6-10,** works. When you measure using a spring scale, it is really the spring force you are reading.

Inertia and Mass

Have you ever noticed how hard it is to move a heavy object, even when it has wheels to help it move? If you try pushing someone much bigger than you who is wearing skates or standing on a skateboard, the person won't budge easily. This quality, **inertia** (ih NUR shah), is a measure of an object's ability to stay at rest or to keep moving. You also may have noticed that it is hard to stop someone who is much bigger than you are once that person is moving. If you think about it, the more matter an object has, the harder it will be to move. **Mass** measures the quantity of matter. Mass therefore describes an object's inertia.

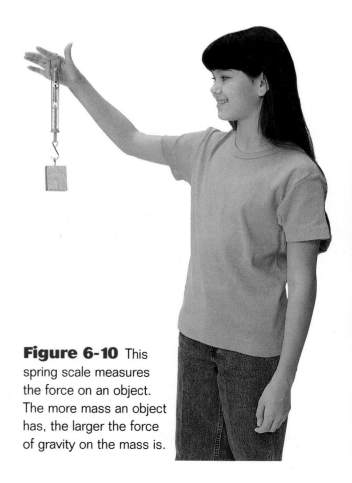

Figure 6-10 This spring scale measures the force on an object. The more mass an object has, the larger the force of gravity on the mass is.

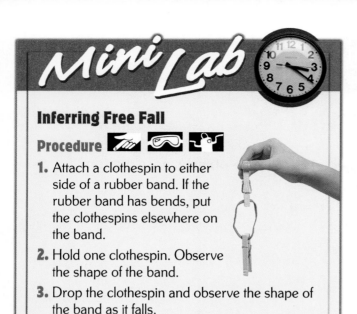

Mini Lab

Inferring Free Fall

Procedure

1. Attach a clothespin to either side of a rubber band. If the rubber band has bends, put the clothespins elsewhere on the band.
2. Hold one clothespin. Observe the shape of the band.
3. Drop the clothespin and observe the shape of the band as it falls.

Analysis

1. What did the rubber band look like as it fell? What does the shape mean?
2. Did the clothespins still have weight when they were falling? Why or why not?

Mass and Weight

Mass and weight are not the same thing, although both measure how much there is of something. Weight is a force due to Earth's gravitational pull. This means your weight changes if you move away from Earth. Mass measures the amount of matter in an object. It does not change. If you take an object to the moon, its weight is one-sixth its Earth weight. The amount of matter in the object, which is measured by its mass, remains the same on Earth or the moon.

You may have heard that the astronauts are weightless as they orbit Earth. This is not true. Earth's gravity holds the space shuttle in an orbit about 400 km above Earth's surface. At this distance, the astronauts weigh about nine-tenths their weight on Earth's surface. They seem to float, as in **Figure 6-11,** because the floor of the shuttle is also falling. There's nothing to stand up on. This is called free fall.

Figure 6-11 Astronauts in free fall are falling toward Earth at the same speed as everything around them. **What would happen if an astronaut dropped a pencil while in free fall?**

Measuring Weight

A familiar tool to measure force is a bathroom scale. It is used to measure weight. It has a small but stiff spring that is attached to a dial. As you step onto the scale, as shown in **Figure 6-12,** you compress the spring. As you compress the spring, you are actually falling. When the spring force and the force of gravity are balanced, the dial on the scale reads your weight.

Just as you have to push harder to move a big mass, Earth must exert more force on a heavy object. If you know an object's mass, you can calculate its weight using the formula $F = ma$.

weight = mass × acceleration due to gravity
$$w = m(9.8 \text{ m/s}^2)$$

For example, if your mass is 50 kg, then your weight is found as follows.

$$w = m(9.8 \text{ m/s}^2)$$
$$= (50 \text{ kg})(9.8 \text{ m/s}^2)$$
$$= 490 \ \frac{\text{kg} \cdot \text{m}}{\text{s}^2}$$
$$= 490 \text{ N}$$

The floor exerts the same force, 490 N, to hold you up.

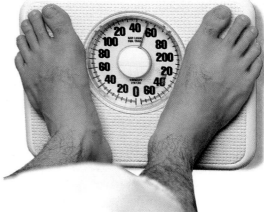

Figure 6-12 A bathroom scale measures the spring force that balances your weight.

Section Assessment

1. Suppose you traveled to a nearby planet and weighed yourself when you landed. If your mass is 50 kg and your portable bathroom scale reads 1240 N, what is the acceleration due to gravity on this planet? How does this compare with your weight on Earth? What planet do you think you are on?

2. Give an example of a force.

3. **Think Critically:** Look back at the Explore Activity at the beginning of the chapter. Now, suppose you roll a marble down the ramp that has twice the mass of the marble used in the Explore Activity. Would you expect the heavier marble to accelerate at a faster, slower, or the same rate as the lighter marble?

4.  **Skill Builder**
   Observing and Inferring When you begin riding up in an elevator, you feel heavier at first. Why? When do you feel lighter? Why? If you need help, refer to Observing and Inferring in the **Skill Handbook** on page 686.

Science Journal When the space shuttle astronauts orbit Earth, they feel like they have no weight, but they know they still have mass. Write about what it must be like to move around and work in free fall.

6·3

How do things move?

What You'll Learn

► How friction affects all motion
► How Newton's laws are used to understand motion

Vocabulary
Newton's laws of motion
friction

Why It's Important

► Newton's laws explain motions as simple as walking and as complicated as a rocket's launch.

Newton's Laws of Motion

In 1665, a deadly plague spread across Europe. People who lived in crowded cities were most affected. Sir Isaac Newton was in college at the time. The school closed down for two years because the disease was spreading rapidly. Newton, who was 23 years old, returned to his house in the country to wait for the plague to end. With no homework assigned, he spent his free time making up his own. He discovered many things about nature, including how gravity works and how light is made up of the colors of the rainbow. He also invented calculus, which is a branch of advanced mathematics. The most important of all his great discoveries was his understanding of how forces cause motion. He realized he could solve any problem of motion using rules now called **Newton's laws of motion,** shown in **Table 6-2.**

Table 6-2

Newton's Laws of Motion	
First Law	An object at rest will remain at rest or an object moving straight at constant speed will continue this motion until an unbalanced force acts on it.
Second Law	An object that has an unbalanced force acting on it will accelerate in the direction of the force.
Third Law	Forces always occur in equal but opposite pairs.

Newton's First Law

Newton's first law states, "An object at rest will remain at rest or an object moving straight at constant speed will continue this motion until an unbalanced force acts on it." For example, you wear a seat belt to hold you firmly in your automobile seat. If the car stops suddenly and you aren't wearing your seat belt, according to Newton's first law, you keep moving at the speed the car was traveling until your body hits something, such as the dashboard or window. Even if the car were moving at slow speed, this could lead to serious injury.

Have you ever been running fast and tried to come to a sudden stop? It's hard not to continue moving forward and fall. Newton's first law means that your body continues moving forward, even though your feet stop.

Figure 6-13 The force of gravity accelerates the sled down the hill. **What gives the sled a negative acceleration, slowing it to a stop at the bottom of the hill?**

Friction

People are sometimes confused about Newton's first law because it seems that familiar objects in motion, like the sled in **Figure 6-13,** always come to rest. Remember that when an object slows down, it has a negative acceleration. Acceleration means an unbalanced force is acting on the object. Friction is one force that slows things down. **Friction** is a force that resists motion between two objects in contact. It always acts opposite to the direction of motion, as shown in **Figure 6-14.**

Speed

Friction

Figure 6-14 Friction between the wheels of the roller blades, the axles, and the ground acts against the direction of motion. This gives the person a negative acceleration, slowing him down.

Reading Check

What type of surface provides little friction?

Have you ever tried to pull a sled or box across rough ground, like a parking lot? This is much harder than pulling it on smooth snow. The size of the friction force depends on the two surfaces involved. In general, the rougher the surface, the greater the friction. For example, if you push a hockey puck on an ice rink, it will go a great distance. If you try to push it with the same force on a smooth floor, it will stop sooner. If you push the puck on a rough carpet, it may barely move. ☑

Newton's Second Law

Remember the normal force from the previous section. When you stand on a flat surface, the downward force of your weight and the upward normal force are balanced. When you stand on a slight hill in skates, gravity pulls straight down on you. The normal force pushes straight out from the hill, as shown in **Figure 6-15.** The forces are not balanced, and you move downhill. The total of all the forces acting is the net force. An object that accelerates must be acted

interNET
C O N N E C T I O N

Visit the Glencoe Science Web Site at **www.glencoe.com/ sec/science/fl** for more information about sports science.

Problem Solving

Illustrating Force

Sports equipment often is designed to increase friction. Good tread on tennis shoes helps you stay upright when running and changing direction. The handles of rackets and bats are designed to be easy to grip. Other sports require less friction. Skiers wax their skis to reduce friction with the trail. Windsurfers ride smooth boards.

Sporting goods companies have teams of scientists who analyze an athlete's movements and design equipment to maximize performance.

Draw an illustration of a rock climber's hand pulling down on a rock. Use arrows to indicate all the forces acting. Label the arrows. What happens when the net force on the climber is upward? Downward? When there is no net force?

Chalk increases friction. How does using chalk affect the net force on the climber?

Think Critically: Give another example of sports equipment that increases friction. How does increasing the friction help you play the sport?

Figure 6-15 On a hill, the normal force is not opposite in direction to the weight. The forces are not balanced, and the net force accelerates you down the hill. **What happens to the net force as the slope becomes more horizontal?**

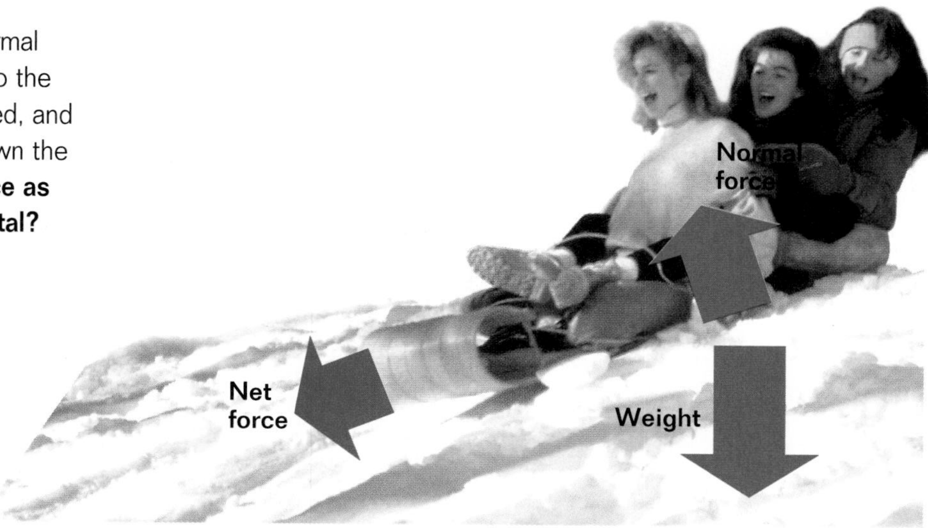

Normal force

Net force

Weight

on by a net force. If the hill were steeper, the net force would be greater, and you would accelerate more quickly. When the forces on an object are balanced, there is no acceleration and the net force is zero. (Look back at **Figure 6-9,** which shows balanced forces.) When the forces on an object are unbalanced, the net force is not zero, and the object accelerates.

As you sit reading this, two forces are acting on you: Earth's gravity downward and the chair's normal force upward. You are not accelerating because they are balanced. The net force is zero. If the leg of your chair suddenly broke, you would accelerate. Why?

Newton's second law describes how forces cause the motion of objects to change. It states, "An object that has an unbalanced force acting on it will accelerate in the direction of the force." Rearrange the $F = ma$ formula you learned.

$$\text{force} = \text{mass} \times \text{acceleration}$$

$$\text{acceleration} = \frac{\text{force}}{\text{mass}}$$

$$a = \frac{F_{net}}{m}$$

You use net force (F_{net}) because only the unbalanced part of a force causes acceleration, as shown in **Figure 6-15.**

According to Newton's second law, when an object feels a net force, its acceleration will depend on its mass. The more mass an object has, the harder it is to accelerate. Imagine using the same force to push an empty grocery cart and one full of heavy groceries. The full cart has much more inertia (mass). The more inertia an object has, the more force you must exert to move it. With the same force acting on the two carts, the full cart will have a much smaller acceleration compared to the empty cart. More mass means less acceleration if the force acting on the objects is the same.

Using Math

A net force of 8 N acts on a 5-kg object. What acceleration does it give the object?

Newton's Third Law

Newton's third law says, "Forces always occur in equal but opposite pairs." If you apply a force to an object, the object will push back on you with an equal force. For example, when you walk, you push back on the sidewalk and the sidewalk pushes forward on you. When you push against the pool wall, as shown in **Figure 6-16,** the wall pushes back on you. How does anything ever move?

The equal but opposite forces in Newton's third law act on *different* objects. When you push on a door to open it, the door pushes back on you. Remember Newton's second law, $a = F_{net}/m$. The friction between your shoes and the floor provides a huge mass, you and the building, for the door's force to act on. You do not move because your acceleration is so small. Your force on the door produces more acceleration than the door's force on you. What would happen if you stood on skates and tried to push a large, heavy door?

Another familiar example is jumping off a boat. If you jump off a small boat, the boat moves back. You are pushing the boat back with your feet with the same force with which it pushes you forward. Because you are a lot heavier than the boat, it will accelerate more and move farther than you do. This situation is reversed when you jump off a big ferry. The force you exert on the boat provides a tiny acceleration to that large mass. You don't notice the ferry moving at all, but the force the boat exerts on you easily propels your smaller mass to the dock.

Figure 6-16 When the swimmer pushes against the pool wall, the wall returns an equal and opposite force. If the swimmer pushes a kickboard away, it pushes back with an equal and opposite force. **What happens if the swimmer and a friend push against each other while floating in the pool?**

A rocket blasting off illustrates Newton's third law, as shown in **Figure 6-17.** The force accelerating the gases downward is equal and opposite to the force accelerating the rocket upward. You can demonstrate this if you throw a heavy ball while standing on skates. You will roll in the direction opposite to your throw.

When you fall, Earth is pulling you down but you also are pulling Earth up. Because Earth has so much more mass than you do, Earth's movement is too small to detect. Astronomers have used Newton's third law to discover planets outside our solar system. A large planet pulls on the star it orbits just enough to cause a tiny motion of the star that astronomers on Earth can measure.

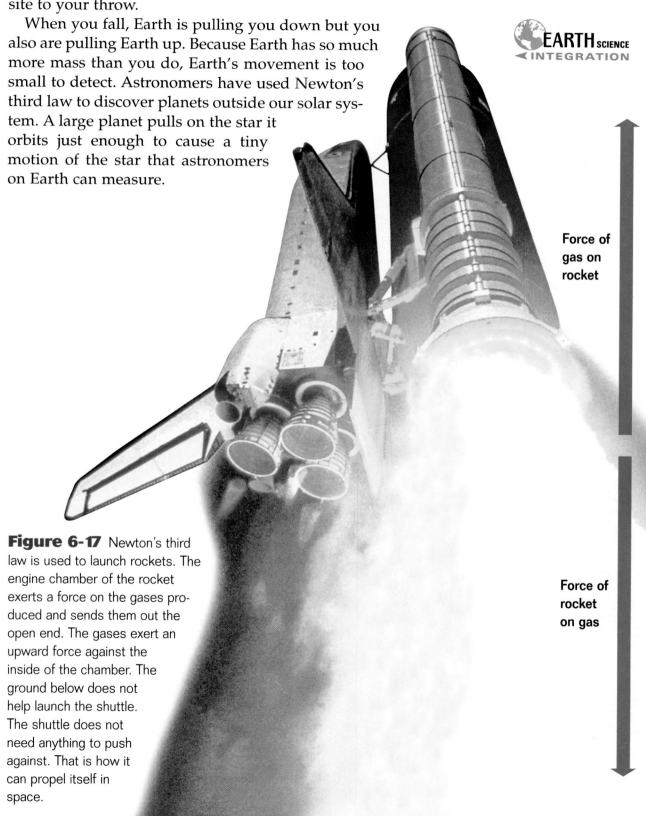

EARTH SCIENCE
◄ INTEGRATION

Force of gas on rocket

Force of rocket on gas

Figure 6-17 Newton's third law is used to launch rockets. The engine chamber of the rocket exerts a force on the gases produced and sends them out the open end. The gases exert an upward force against the inside of the chamber. The ground below does not help launch the shuttle. The shuttle does not need anything to push against. That is how it can propel itself in space.

VISUALIZING Newton's Laws of Motion

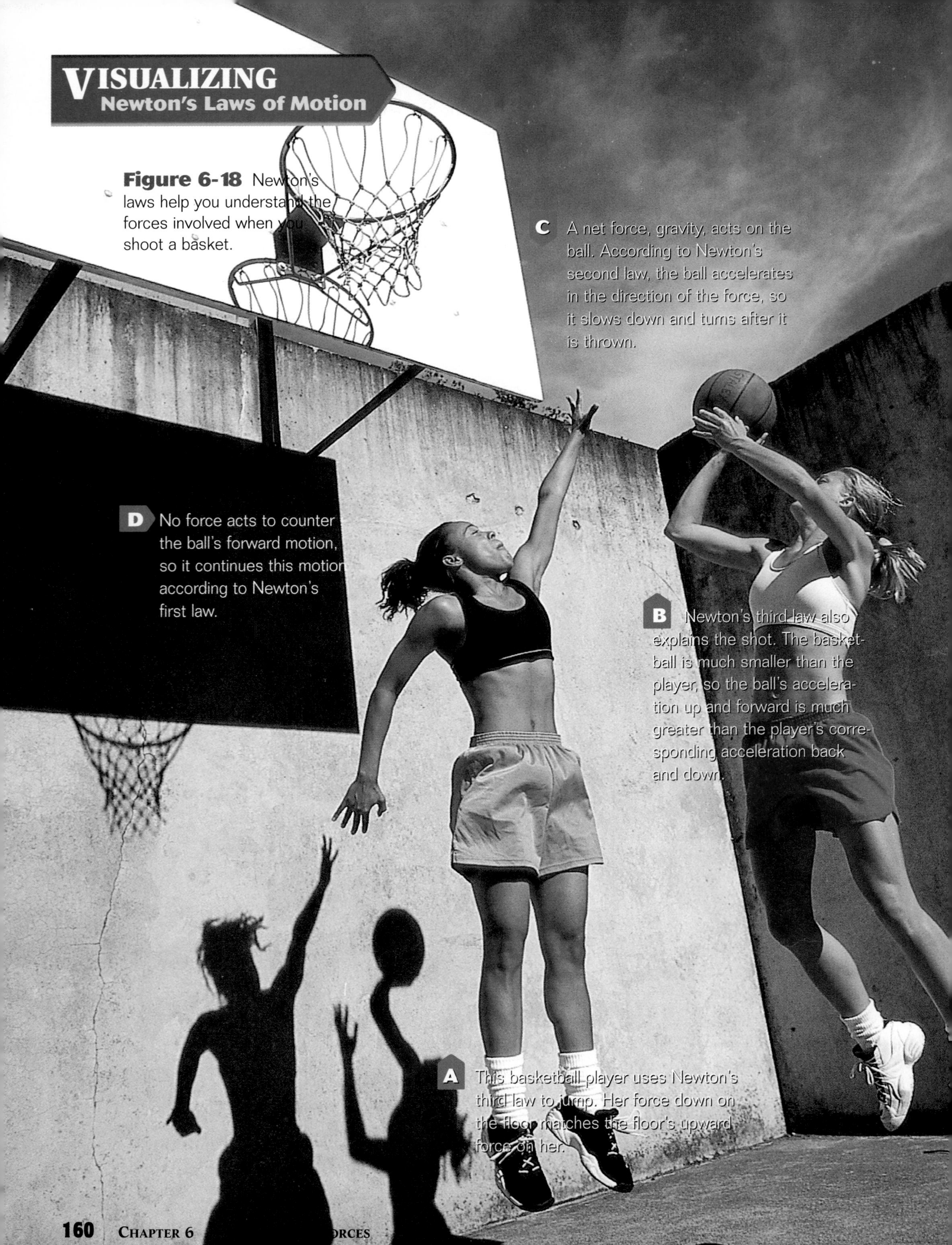

Figure 6-18 Newton's laws help you understand the forces involved when you shoot a basket.

A This basketball player uses Newton's third law to jump. Her force down on the floor matches the floor's upward force on her.

B Newton's third law also explains the shot. The basketball is much smaller than the player, so the ball's acceleration up and forward is much greater than the player's corresponding acceleration back and down.

C A net force, gravity, acts on the ball. According to Newton's second law, the ball accelerates in the direction of the force, so it slows down and turns after it is thrown.

D No force acts to counter the ball's forward motion, so it continues this motion according to Newton's first law.

Examples of Newton's Laws

As you begin to understand Newton's laws, you will see how they explain many motions you observe, as in **Figures 6-18** and **6-19.** When you ride a bicycle, it doesn't move until you start pedaling. An object at rest tends to stay at rest. This is Newton's first law at work. To go faster, you must pedal harder. You apply a force to move the pedal. This transmits a force to the wheels and the bike accelerates. This is Newton's second law. When you pedal at constant speed, the forward force exerted by the wheels and the backward forces of air resistance and friction are balanced. You keep moving at the same speed. This is Newton's first law again. If you are bicycling into a strong wind, you have to exert more force to go at that speed. If you have a tailwind pushing you, you can exert less force. If you coast on a flat surface, then air and friction act against your motion and slow you down. This is an example of Newton's second law—the net force causes negative acceleration and slows you down.

Whenever forces are acting, Newton's third law is also at work. For every force there has to be an equal but opposite force. When you push on the bicycle pedal, the pedal pushes back on you. Think about changing gears on a bike. Different gears make it easier or harder to pedal. When it is hard to pedal, you notice the force of the pedal against your foot.

Figure 6-19 Newton's laws describe what happens when these cyclists speed up, slow down, coast, or stop. **How do Newton's laws explain the motion of a bike coasting down a hill onto a level section of road?**

Figure 6-20 Newton's laws of motion are used to plan the launch, flight, and landing of space-craft. The *Mars Pathfinder* was placed on top of a Delta II launch vehicle to leave Earth. Air bags, parachutes, and rockets allowed *Pathfinder* to land on Mars. Once the rover *Sojourner* was released onto the surface, scientists sent signals from Earth to steer it around rocks and send it to points of interest to take samples.

You easily feel the force of air resistance against your body. Your body, in turn, exerts a force on the air. If you could see the air, you would see it bouncing off you as you plow through it. In every movement you make or see, you can spot Newton's three laws at work. They are used everywhere, as shown in **Figure 6-20.** These laws are the masters of motion.

Section Assessment

1. While you are skating, your friend pushes you from behind with a force of 50 N. If your mass is 45 kg, what is your acceleration?

2. Does friction provide negative acceleration or positive acceleration? Explain.

3. A skydiver falls at a constant speed when the upward force of air resistance balances the downward force of gravity. Is there a net force on the skydiver? Explain.

4. **Think Critically:** Give at least two examples of using inertia to your advantage.

5. **Skill Builder**
   Recognizing Cause and Effect
   Newton's third law is a good example of cause and effect. Explain why, using the example of a ball bouncing off a wall. If you need help, refer to Recognizing Cause and Effect in the **Skill Handbook** on page 687.

Using Computers

Spreadsheets Enter the formula $a = F_{net}/m$ in a spreadsheet. Find the acceleration given to various masses by a force of 100 N. Use masses 10 kg, 20 kg,. . . 100 kg. Also use your own mass, the mass of a car, and other familiar examples. If you need help, refer to page 704.

Building In Safety

The first cars hit the road without today's safety features, such as seat belts, windshields, or brake lights. Of course, there were few cars, and they traveled no faster than a horse and carriage. Today's cars travel at high speeds, and there are millions of cars on the road. As a result, car manufacturers are working to make cars safer, and police and legislatures are concerned with making driving safer.

Newton's laws of motion describe the behavior of an object such as a car or your body inside a car. Understanding Newton's laws is important in designing safe cars and developing safe driving habits.

Seat Belts, Air Bags, and Headrests

Newton's first law states that *an object in motion stays in motion until acted on by an unbalanced force.* When the car you are riding in comes to a sudden stop, your body keeps moving forward. Without a seat belt to hold you in place, you could be thrown against the windshield. An inflated air bag cushions your body, slowing your forward motion more gently than a seat belt alone can. At an auto show, left, a dummy is used to demonstrate the cushioning effect of an inflated air bag.

Newton's first law also indicates that an object at rest remains at rest until acted on by an unbalanced force. If you are sitting in a stopped car that is suddenly struck from behind, the seat presses you forward. A headrest makes sure your head also is pressed forward, preventing your neck from snapping backward painfully.

Braking

Newton's second law, *acceleration equals net force divided by mass,* explains why it takes longer for a heavier car to speed up and to come to a stop. If two vehicles have the same braking force, the heavier vehicle will accelerate more slowly and take longer to stop. A small sports car can brake at 10 m/s², a large sport utility vehicle at 7.5 m/s². At a speed of 100 km/h, the sports car can stop over a distance of about 32 m, while the sport utility vehicle will need roughly 53 m. A driver should allow more distance for braking in a heavier car.

Science
JOURNAL

In a high-speed crash, your body might slow from 25 m/s to 0 m/s in 1 s. This is an acceleration of –25 m/s². Use $F = ma$ to calculate the force on your body during the crash. Compare this to the force of gravity, $F = m(9.8 \text{ m/s}^2)$. In your Science Journal, explain why states require that small children be strapped into a car seat rather than held in someone's lap.

On The Internet

Activity 6•2

Making a Paper Airplane

Materials

* Paper
* Measuring tape (50 m)
* Metric ruler
* Stopwatch
* Balance
* Tape
* Stapler
* Paper clips
* Scissors

When the Wright brothers set out to make the first powered air-plane, they spent time researching flight and studying designs that had failed, as well as gliders that had been successful. They recognized the forces involved in flight, such as gravity, lift, thrust, and drag (a form of friction). If the lift is greater than gravity, then the plane will soar upward in the air. If the thrust is greater than the drag, then the plane will accelerate. Even today, these same forces must be considered when a new airplane is designed.

Recognize the Problem

How can a paper airplane that flies the longest time or the farthest distance be designed?

Form a Hypothesis

The design of the wing plays an important role in maximizing lift while reducing drag. An airfoil is the part of the wing responsible for controlling lift. The size, shape, angle, and cover material of the airfoil determine the lift and the drag that the wing will experience at a certain wind speed. **Form a hypothesis** about how your group can design a paper airplane that will either fly the longest period of time or go the farthest distance.

Goals

* **Research** paper airplane strategies.
* **Design** a paper airplane whose airfoil maximizes lift and minimizes drag.
* **Analyze** and **communicate** experimental results.

Safety Precautions

Data Sources

Visit the Glencoe Science Web Site at **www.glencoe.com/ sec/science/fl** to find more information, hints, and data from other students.

Test Your Hypothesis

Plan

1. You may use a single sheet of any type of paper. You also may cut, fold, tape, glue, or staple the paper to form your airplane.

2. **Design** one or more types of paper airplanes. What type of paper will you use? What will be the shape of the wing?

Do

1. Be sure your teacher approves your plan before you begin.

2. **Build** your design. Record its mass in your data table.

3. **Experiment** with different ways of flying your airplane. Record your observations in your data table.

4. **Modify** your design as you think necessary. Remember to change only one variable at a time.

3. **Sketch** your design. **Organize** the data you expect to collect in a table similar to the one below.

4. The testing area should be flat and open. Where will you test your designs?

5. Tell your teacher when you have finished the airplane that you think will fly as long and as far as possible.

6. Hold a class contest to determine three categories: greatest time in the air, greatest distance flown from starting point, and the greatest overall flight.

Draw Conclusions

1. **Compare and contrast** the designs your class came up with. What features did the winning planes have?

2. How did the planes that flew long distances differ from the planes that flew for a long time?

3. Which design minimized drag? Maximized lift?

4. Post your design at the Glencoe Science Web Site. How do your designs compare with the designs other classes have posted ?

Flight Data

Trial	Mass (g)	Design change	Flight distance (m)	Flight time (s)

Chapter 6 Reviewing Main Ideas

For a **preview** of this chapter, study this Reviewing Main Ideas before you read the chapter. After you have studied this chapter, you can use the Reviewing Main Ideas to **review** the chapter.

The Glencoe MindJogger, Audiocassettes, and CD-ROM provide additional opportunities for review.

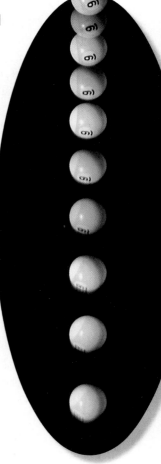

Section

6-1 SPEED AND ACCELERATION

All motion involves time and distance. Taken together, you get **average speed,** distance divided by time. This is used if the details of the motion aren't important. When speed changes, an object **accelerates.** It speeds up or slows down. It can also change direction. For constant accelerations, you can calculate your speed at any time using change in speed = at.

The distance traveled can be determined from the following equation.

$$d = \frac{1}{2}at^2$$

How does a ball move when it is thrown straight up into the air?

Section

6-2 GRAVITY

Gravity is a **force** that pulls on all objects that have mass. The acceleration due to gravity at Earth's surface is 9.8 m/s^2, as long as air resistance is minimal. **Mass** is the amount of matter in an object and is a property of the object. **Weight** is the force of gravity acting on the object's mass. Weight changes when gravity changes. *What is the difference between mass and weight?*

6-3 NEWTON'S FIRST LAW

Inertia and Newton's first law are often confused. **Inertia** is a measurement of how difficult it is to change an object's motion. Newton's first law says an object will remain at rest or moving at constant speed if no net force is acting on it. *Why does your drink slip off the dashboard when the car starts at a green light?*

Reading Check ✓

List examples from your life that illustrate newton's laws of motion. Exchange lists with a partner and check for accuracy.

NEWTON'S SECOND LAW

Newton's second law describes how unbalanced or net forces act on an object. The object will accelerate according to $F_{net} = ma$. Notice, for a certain amount of force, there is less acceleration for objects with more inertia (mass). *Which forces act on the shuttle when it launches? In what direction is the net force?*

NEWTON'S THIRD LAW

Newton's third law states that forces occur in equal but opposite pairs. *What are the forces between your shoes and the ground as you walk?*

Chapter 6 Assessment

Using Vocabulary

a. acceleration
b. average speed
c. balanced forces
d. force
e. friction
f. gravity
g. inertia
h. mass
i. Newton's laws of motion
j. normal force
k. rate
l. weight

For each set of Vocabulary terms below, explain the relationship that exists.

1. inertia, mass
2. average speed, rate
3. force, Newton's laws of motion
4. weight, normal force
5. mass, weight

Checking Concepts

Choose the word or phrase that best answers the question.

6. What is another name for inertia?
   A) weight
   B) gravity
   C) mass
   D) Newton's first law

7. What will an object acted upon by a net force do?
   A) accelerate
   B) remain at rest
   C) gain mass
   D) become balanced

8. Which of the following happens as you move away from Earth?
   A) Mass decreases and weight increases.
   B) Mass decreases and weight decreases.
   C) Mass stays the same and weight decreases.
   D) Mass stays the same and weight stays the same.

9. What does an object's weight depend on?
   A) shape
   B) mass
   C) speed
   D) volume

10. A car is driving at constant speed. Which of the following is **NOT** true?
    A) All the forces acting are balanced.
    B) A net force keeps it moving.
    C) Friction and air resistance are equal to the forward force of the engine.
    D) The car is not accelerating.

11. A large truck bumps a small car. Which of the following is true?
    A) The force of the truck on the car is greater.
    B) The force of the car on the truck is greater.
    C) The forces are the same.
    D) No force is involved.

12. What is the unit for acceleration?
    A) m/s^2
    B) $kg \cdot m/s^2$
    C) m/s
    D) N

13. What decreases friction?
    A) a rougher surface
    B) a smoother surface
    C) more speed
    D) more surface area

14. What would happen to a falling object if the air resistance acting on it became equal to the weight of the object?
    A) It would float.
    B) It would continue to accelerate.
    C) It would move at constant speed.
    D) It would start moving upward.

15. Which of the following is a force?
    A) inertia
    B) acceleration
    C) speed
    D) friction

Thinking Critically

16. You run 100 m in 25 s. If you then run the same distance in less time, does your average speed increase or decrease? Explain.

17. A cliff diver falling at $9.8 \ m/s^2$ takes 1.5 s to hit the water. How high is the cliff?

18. Using the information from the previous problem, at what speed does the diver hit the water?

19. Explain why a fast-moving freight train takes a few kilometers to stop.

20. What is the force of the rocket engines on a 2 million-kg space shuttle if it accelerates at 30 m/s²?

Developing Skills

If you need help, refer to the **Skill Handbook**.

21. Making and Using Graphs: Marion bicycles at an average speed of 10 km/h. Plot a distance-time graph of these data over six hours. How long does it take her to bike 25 km?

22. Measuring in SI: Which of the following speeds is the fastest: 20 m/s, 200 cm/s, or 0.2 km/s? HINT: Express all the speeds in meters per second and compare.

23. Interpreting Data: Use the following data of the acceleration of gravity on various planets and the maximum height a given person can jump.
Which planet has the strongest gravity? Why would it be so hard to jump high on this planet? Where can you jump the highest? What do you think about the size and mass of this place?

Jump Height		
Planet	Gravity (m/s²)	Height (m)
Earth	9.8	0.75
Mars	3.7	2.0
Pluto	0.5	14.7
Jupiter	22.9	0.32

THE PRINCETON REVIEW

Test-Taking Tip

Get to the Root of Things If you don't know a word's meaning, you can still get an idea of its definition if you focus on its roots, suffixes, and prefixes. For example, words that start with *non-*, *un-*, *a-*, *dis-*, and *in-* generally reverse what the rest of the word means.

Test Practice

Use these questions to test your Science Proficiency.

1. Scientific laws cannot be proven true, only supported with the successful results of new experiments. Which of the following does **NOT** support Newton's laws of motion?
A) An object cannot travel faster than the speed of light.
B) The greater the mass of an object, the harder it is to move.
C) An object accelerates in the direction of the net force.
D) When an object feels a force, it returns the force in equal but opposite measure.

2. A man weighs 80 kg. About how much normal force does the floor exert to hold him up?
A) 80 N
B) 400 N
C) 600 N
D) 800 N

Work and Simple Machines

Chapter Preview

Skills Preview

Skill Builders

- Classify
- Compare and Contrast

Activities

- Design an Experiment
- Make a Model

MiniLabs

- Measure in SI
- Compare and Contrast

Reading Check ✔

Before you begin this chapter, write down what you already know about machines such as the lever, ramp, pulley, and wheel and axle.

Explore Activity

Two of the world's greatest buildings, monuments to humanity's progress, were built using very different tools. The Great Pyramid at Giza in Egypt shown at the left was built nearly 5000 years ago using blocks of limestone moved into place by hand with tools such as ramps and levers. In comparison, the Sears Tower in Chicago was built in 1973 using tons of steel that were hoisted into place by gasoline-powered cranes. Both structures were the tallest at the time they were built. But, the work done by each builder was drastically different.

Compare Forces

1. Balance a ruler on an eraser or lump of clay. At one end, place something heavier than the ruler, such as a paperback book. This is the load.

2. Using one finger, push down on the free end of the ruler to lift the load.

3. Repeat the experiment, placing the eraser or clay in various positions. Observe how much force is needed in each instance to lift the load.

Science Journal

In your Science Journal, describe what you discovered. How did the different distances between the load and eraser affect the force needed to lift the load?

7·1 What is work?

Work

What You'll Learn

► How to determine if work is being done
► What work is and how it's calculated
► How power is related to work

Vocabulary

work
power

Why It's Important

► Whenever you lift, push, or pull something, you do work. If you understand work, you can learn to make work easier.

What does *work* mean to you? You may think of household chores; a job at an office, factory, or farm; or the homework you do every night. Scientists also use the word *work*. When a force produces motion parallel to the direction of the force, **work** is done in the scientific sense. The following examples illustrate this definition of work.

When the motion is in the direction of the force, positive work is done. When you throw a ball, you do positive work on the ball, as shown in **Figure 7-1A.** When you pull a sled, you do positive work on the sled.

When the motion is opposite to the direction of the force, negative work is done. When you catch a ball, as shown in **Figure 7-1B,** you exert a force opposite to the ball's motion to bring it to a stop. You do negative work on the ball. When you pull a sled, friction acts against the sled's motion to slow it. Friction does negative work on the sled.

A force at a right angle to the direction of motion cannot perform work. When you carry the ball off the field, you exert an upward force to balance gravity, but the direction of motion is forward, at a right angle to the force. You do no work on the ball. When you pull a sled, the ground exerts a

Figure 7-1

A The player's arm exerts a forward force on the ball during the throw. The ball moves forward. Force and motion are in the same direction, so the player does *positive work* on the ball.

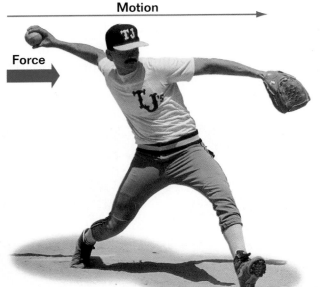

Motion →

Force →

B The player's arm exerts a forward force to stop the ball. The ball and glove are moving backward. Force and motion are in opposite directions, so the player does *negative work.*

Motion →

← Force

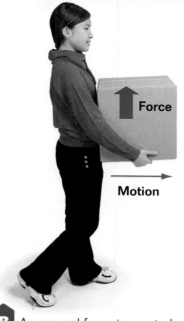

A An upward force is exerted when lifting up the box. The girl does positive work.

B An upward force is exerted while moving the box forward. No work is done.

C An upward force is exerted while lowering the box. The girl does negative work.

normal force upward on the sled, but that force does no work. **Figure 7-2** gives examples of positive work, no work, and negative work.

When you pick up a book bag, you do positive work. The force you exert and the motion of the book bag are in the same direction. When you walk to school at a steady speed carrying your book bag, you do no work on the book bag. Your upward force on the book bag does not act along the direction of motion.

Gravity can do work on an object. After a thrown ball leaves your hand, you no longer exert a force on it. Therefore, you do no work on it. However, gravity does work, pulling the ball toward Earth. However, gravity's work is negative when the ball is going up (motion up, force down) and positive when the ball is going down (motion down, force down).

Another example of a situation where a force does no work is an object in orbit, as in **Figure 7-3.** The sun's gravity is pulling Earth toward the sun with a lot of force. But, Earth does not move toward the sun. Instead, it moves at a right angle to the sun's pull. No movement occurs parallel to the direction of the force, so the force does no work.

Effort Doesn't Always Equal Work

When a person applies force using muscles, work may or may not be done. It takes work to lift a heavy barbell, but not to hold it over your head. In either case, you would say you were working hard. But, for work to be done, the object must move.

Figure 7-2 To hold a box, you exert an upward force equal to gravity's downward force. **What would happen if the girl in C exerted no upward force on the box?**

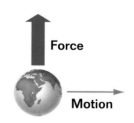

Figure 7-3 When force is at a right angle to the direction of motion, the force does no work.

Figure 7-4 The net force is at an angle to the direction of motion. Only the part of the force parallel to the direction of motion contributes to the work done.

Figure 7-5 Try pushing straight down on a book, pushing straight from one side, and pushing down and to the side. In each case, the downward force does no work. **Does the normal force of the desk on the book do work? Explain.**

CHEMISTRY
INTEGRATION

Work and Energy
Work transfers energy through motion. All forms of energy can do work. For example, chemical energy in your muscles is converted to kinetic energy when you run.

Force in Two Directions

Imagine you have been asked to mow the lawn. As you push the mower, you are exerting a force on it, as shown in **Figure 7-4.** Notice how the force acts through the handle of the mower at an angle to the direction the mower is moving.

By pushing at an angle, you push a little bit downward while also pushing forward. Because the downward push doesn't make the mower move down, no work is done by the downward force. The force in the forward direction moves the mower forward. Only this part of the net force does work. **Figure 7-5** shows another example.

Measuring Work

The formula for work, using W for work, F for force, and d for distance, is as follows.

$$\text{Work} = \text{Force} \times \text{distance}$$
$$W = Fd$$

Work is measured in joules, abbreviated J. This unit is named in honor of James Prescott Joule, who discovered how work and heat are related in engines. One joule is equal to 1 newton times 1 meter ($1\ \text{J} = 1\ \text{N} \cdot \text{m} = 1\ \text{kg} \cdot \text{m}^2/\text{s}^2$).

It takes about 100 N of force to push a lawn mower forward. You also are pushing down with about this same amount of force, but that effort does no work. At the end of mowing a typical lawn, you might have walked 1000 m. The work done is found as follows.

$$\text{Work} = \text{Force} \times \text{distance}$$
$$\begin{aligned} W &= Fd \\ &= (100\ \text{N})(1000\ \text{m}) \\ &= 100\ 000\ \text{J} \end{aligned}$$

The work done is 100 000 N · m, or 100 000 J.

Now, find the work done to lift a 1000-kg car 10 m. Recall that to lift an object takes an upward force of *mg*, the object's mass times the acceleration due to gravity. Use $g = 10$ m/s^2.

$$\text{Work} = \text{Force} \times \text{distance}$$
$$W = Fd$$
$$= mgd$$
$$= (1000 \text{ kg})(10 \text{ m/s}^2)(10 \text{ m})$$
$$= 100\ 000 \text{ kg} \cdot \text{m}^2/\text{s}^2$$
$$= 100\ 000 \text{ J}$$

It seems incredible that mowing the lawn requires the same work as lifting the car. It all depends on how you do the work. Exerting a small force for a long distance can accomplish the same work as exerting a large force for a short distance. The Egyptians used this idea to build the pyramids. Today, tools are designed using the same basic ideas. A wrench makes it easier to remove a nut because you can use less force while pushing over a greater distance. ✔

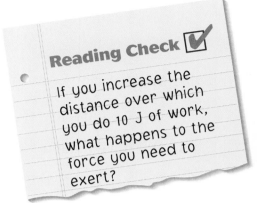

Reading Check ✔

If you increase the distance over which you do 10 J of work, what happens to the force you need to exert?

Power

What does it mean to be powerful? Like work, power is often used in everyday conversation. A person who can motivate people is considered a powerful leader. In science, **power** describes the rate at which work is being done. It measures how much work is being done in a certain period of time, usually a second. It is calculated using the following formula.

$$\text{Power} = \frac{\text{Work done}}{\text{time to do it}}$$

This can be shortened using *P* for power, *W* for work, and *t* for time.

$$P = \frac{W}{t}$$

The unit for power is called the watt, abbreviated W. This unit is named in honor of James Watt, the inventor of an improved and practical version of the steam engine. One watt is equal to 1 joule per second (1 W = 1 J/s).

Power is often used to describe engines. Humanity's ability to harness large amounts of power in huge engines has made it possible to construct buildings like the Sears Tower in Chicago. But, power also can be used to describe the effort put out by animals or people.

Try at Home

Mini Lab

Measuring Work and Power

Procedure

1. Measure the mass of a book.
2. Go to a ramp or stairway. Measure the vertical height of the ramp or stairs.
3. Time yourself walking slowly up with the book.
4. Time yourself walking quickly up with the book.

Analysis

1. Calculate and compare the work done on the book in each case.
2. Calculate and compare the power used to lift the book in each case.
3. Would it always require twice as much power to lift twice as much mass up the stairs? Explain.

Calculating Power

Example Problem
A mountain rises 1300 m from its base. A 50-kg hiker steadily works her way to the top in about two hours. How much power does she supply to make the climb?

Problem-Solving Steps
1. What is known? mass $m = 50$ kg, $g = 10$ m/s^2, distance $d = 1300$ m, time $t = 2$ h $= 7200$ s. The force is equal to her weight, *mg*.

2. What is unknown? power, *P*

3. Use the equation $P = \dfrac{W}{t} = \dfrac{Fd}{t}$.

4. **Solution:** $P = \dfrac{Fd}{t} = \dfrac{mgd}{t} = \dfrac{(50 \text{ kg})(10 \text{ m/s}^2)(1300 \text{ m})}{7200 \text{ s}} = 90$ W

She supplies 90 W to reach the top.

Practice Problem
You push with a force of 25 N for a distance of 12 m. This takes half a minute. What power did you supply?

Strategy Hint: Check that your answer is in the proper units.

Section Assessment

1. How much work would it take to lift a 1000-kg limestone block to the very top of the Great Pyramid, 146 m above the ground?

2. If it takes 50 minutes to cut a lawn, and the work required is 100 000 J, how much power, in watts, is used?

3. **Think Critically:** Explain how you know that work is being done on an object.

4. **Skill Builder**
   Classifying A boy accelerates from a stop to a running speed while holding a ball. He carries the ball as he runs at constant speed. He throws the ball, exerting a force for 65 cm. Then, the ball is thrown back to him, and he stops it by exerting a force for 20 cm. In each case, is positive work, negative work, or no work done on the ball by the boy? If you need help, refer to Classifying in the **Skill Handbook** on page 679.

Using Math

A 7460-W engine is used to lift an I beam weighing 1000-kg up 145 m. How much work must the motor do to lift this mass at constant speed? How long will it take? Is this a reasonable amount of time? Explain.

Activity
7•1

Building the Pyramids

Materials
- Wood block
- Tape
- Spring scale
- Ruler
- 3-ring binder
- Meterstick
- Books

The workers who built the Great Pyramid at Giza needed to move 2.3 million blocks of limestone. Each block weighed more than 1 metric ton. The designers knew how to use ramps to reduce the force needed to lift the blocks into place.

What You'll Investigate

How does the force needed to lift a block a certain height depend on the distance traveled?

Goals

- **Model** the method that was probably used to build the pyramids.
- **Compare** the force needed to lift a block straight up with the force needed to pull it up a ramp.

Procedure

1. Use a pile of books to **model** a half-completed pyramid. **Measure** the height.

2. The wooden block **models** a block of stone. Attach it to the spring scale and **measure** the force needed to lift it straight up the side of the books.

3. Use a binder to **model** a ramp. **Measure** the ramp. **Measure** the force needed to pull the block up the ramp. Be sure to pull parallel to the ramp. Repeat the experiment with at least two other ramp lengths. Fill in the table.

Ramp Data		
Distance (cm)	Force (N)	Work (J)

Conclude and Apply

1. What happens to the force needed as the distance increases?

2. **Compare and contrast** your results for each case.

3. **Calculate** the work in each case.

4. How could you modify your setup to use less force?

Simple Machines

What is a machine?

The modern day is an age of machines. A *machine* is a device that makes work easier by changing the size or direction of the force applied to it. Try opening a can of soup without a can opener. Not only would it take you a long time to get it open, but also the mess made would leave you with little to eat. The can opener, shown in **Figure 7-6,** is a machine that focuses the force of your hand to the area where force is needed. The can opener turns a small force into a large force. Interestingly, the can was invented 130 years before the opener. It stored food so well, it was immediately put to use without a convenient way to get it open. For a long time, a hammer and chisel were used to open cans.

A **simple machine** is a machine with only one movement. Simple machines are the simplest form of tools. They include the inclined plane, lever, wheel and axle, and pulley. A **compound machine** is a combination of simple machines. The can opener is a compound machine that combines several simple machines. Examples of simple and compound machines are shown in the **Field Guide to Machines** at the end of this chapter.

Mechanical Advantage

You can't get something for nothing. The work produced by a machine can never be greater than the work put into it. With the can opener, your hand supplies a force to one end of the handle to dig a blade into the lid of a can. The can opener magnifies your force by increasing the distance over which you can exert that force. **Figure 7-7** illustrates how your arm can be used to magnify the force of your shoulder muscles.

Figure 7-6 The can opener changes the small force of your hand on the handles to a large force on the blade that cuts into the can.

A Hold your arm bent rigidly against your body. Throw a ball using only your shoulder muscles.

B Hold your arm out rigidly from your body. Throw the ball again using only your shoulder muscles.

The force you exert is called the **effort force,** F_e. The force you must overcome is the **resistance force,** F_r. In a can opener, the effort force is provided by your hand and the resistance force is provided by the strength of the can's lid. An ideal can opener would transmit all of your effort force into useful work with no losses. The work done on an ideal machine is the same as the work produced by the machine—work in equals work out. Real machines always spend some of the effort force overcoming friction or other losses. The work done by the effort force is that force multiplied by the distance over which the effort is exerted. The work done by the resistance force is that force multiplied by the distance over which the resistance is exerted. An example is shown in **Figure 7-8.**

Figure 7-7 Your shoulder muscles can generate a certain amount of forward force. Your arm lets you exert that force over a greater distance, magnifying the work done. **Which position would you use to throw a ball?**

$$\text{Work in} = \text{Work out}$$
$$F_e d_e = F_r d_r$$

Figure 7-8 To lift a loaded wheelbarrow (d_r), you must overcome the resistance force (F_r) of the weight. If you lift the handles three times as high as the center of the wheelbarrow is raised (d_e), you can use one-third the effort force (F_e) you would need without the machine.

The principle, work in = work out, is used in every simple machine. As you increase the effort distance, you decrease the effort force needed.

How do you determine the effort force needed to do work with a simple machine? The **mechanical advantage,** *M.A.,* compares the effort force applied to a machine to the resistance force that it must overcome. This is calculated as a ratio.

$$\text{Mechanical Advantage} = \frac{\text{Resistance Force}}{\text{Effort Force}}$$

$$M.A. = \frac{F_r}{F_e}$$

The mechanical advantage tells you the number of times a machine increases the effort force. If a can opener increases an effort force of 20 N to overcome a resistance force of 140 N, *M.A.* = 140 N/20 N = 7. You normally want a large mechanical advantage. Most simple machines discussed in the rest of the section are designed to make work easier by giving you a mechanical advantage.

Inclined Plane

Ramps may have enabled the ancient Egyptians to build their pyramids. In order to move limestone blocks weighing more than 1000 kg apiece, archaeologists hypothesize that the Egyptians built enormous ramps, similar to those used by motorists to enter a highway. An **inclined plane** is a sloped surface, more commonly called a ramp. It allows you to lift a heavy load by using less force over a greater distance. A ramp supports some of the object's weight. ☑

Reading Check

How does an inclined plane help you do work?

Figure 7-9 Using an inclined plane, an effort force of 300 N over 5 m can do the same work as 1500 N over 1 m. **What is the mechanical advantage of the ramp?**

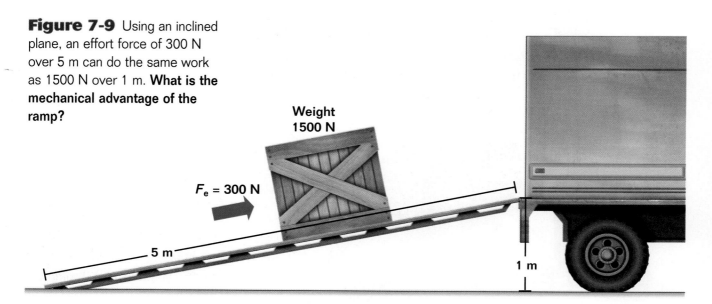

Weight
1500 N

F_e = 300 N

5 m

1 m

Imagine having to lift a 150-kg (1500-N) refrigerator 1 m off the ground onto a truck. This would require (1500 N)(1 m) = 1500 J of work, because you are doing work against gravity. What would help? If you used a 5-m-long ramp, as shown in **Figure 7-9,** the effort distance would be five times farther than the distance straight up. That means the effort force would be now five times less than it was, or 300 N. The inclined plane lets you push a greater distance but with less force. The mechanical advantage of an inclined plane is the length of the inclined plane divided by its height. In this example, the ramp has a mechanical advantage of 5.

Wedge

A **wedge** is a moving inclined plane. It can have one or two sloping sides. A knife, shown in **Figure 7-10,** is an example of a wedge. Your front teeth are wedges. They are designed for cutting. If you examine the teeth of carnivores and herbivores, you will see that carnivores' teeth are more wedge-shaped because they must cut more. Herbivores' teeth are designed for grinding. Scientists can determine what a fossilized animal ate when it was living by examining the teeth.

Screw

A **screw** is an inclined plane wrapped around a shaft, as shown in **Figure 7-11.** It looks like a road that wraps around a mountain. It's a lot easier to make your way up a slope gradually than to go straight up the side. When you screw a fixture into the wall, each turn of the screwdriver pushes the screw a little farther. If the length of the thread wrapped around a screw is four times as long as the screw, the screw has a mechanical advantage of 4. You still have to do the same amount of work, but it is spread out over four times the distance and you can use one-fourth the force.

Figure 7-10 A knife might move downward 10 mm to separate the two sides of the red pepper by 0.5 mm. **What is the mechanical advantage of the knife?**

LIFE SCIENCE
◄ **INTEGRATION**

Figure 7-11 The thread around a screw is an inclined plane. **If the thread is 4 cm long and the screw is 1 cm high, what is the mechanical advantage?**

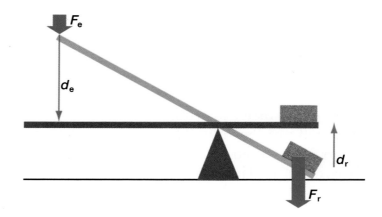

Figure 7-12 A small effort force (F_e), exerted over a large distance (d_e), can move a large resistance force (F_r) a short distance (d_r). **If a lever has a mechanical advantage of 2, what effort force is needed to balance an 80-N resistance force?**

Visit the Glencoe Science Web Site at **www.glencoe.com/ sec/science/fl** for more information about early tools.

Lever

The lever was probably the first simple machine to be invented by prehistoric humans. A **lever** is a rod or plank that pivots about a point. The pivot point is called a **fulcrum.** A digging stick (or modern shovel) is a lever. Baseball bats, brooms, and teeter-totters are also levers.

A heavy load can be lifted a short distance using a small force over a great distance. This is illustrated in **Figure 7-12.** Again, $F_e d_e = F_r d_r$. For the lever to become balanced, the force times the distance from the fulcrum on each side must be equal. Different types of levers are shown in **Figure 7-13.**

Problem Solving

Calculating Work

The first screw was not used to fasten two pieces of wood together, but to raise water. The figure shows one of these devices, called Archimedes' screw. A long tube is wrapped around a cylinder. One end of the tube can go into the water. The other end empties into a container at the top.

As the wheel turns at the top, it dips the tube into the water, so water flows into the tube. As the wheel turns, the water flows along the tube. The water cannot flow out of the bottom of the tube because it would have to go over the top of the screw to get there. Water is moved up along the tube until it reaches the top.

Think Critically: Suppose you have an Archimedes' screw with a cylinder diameter 30 cm. If the tube wraps around the cylinder 40 times, about how long is the tube? If the screw raises water 3 m, what is the mechanical advantage of the machine?

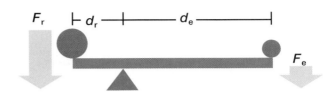

Figure 7-13 In the formula $F_e d_e = F_r d_r$, the distance of each force from the fulcrum can substitute for the distance moved up and down. When $F_e d_e = F_r d_r$, the lever is in balance.

There are three classes of levers, depending on the location of the effort, load, and fulcrum. For each of them, $F_e d_e = F_r d_r$.

A In a first-class lever, such as a pan balance, the fulcrum is between the effort and the load.

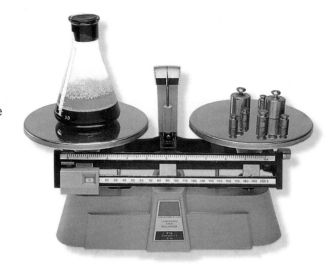

B In a second-class lever, such as a wheelbarrow, the load is between the fulcrum and the effort.

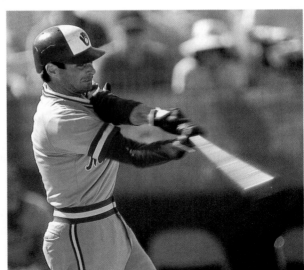

C In a third-class lever, such as a baseball bat, the effort is between the fulcrum and the load. This lever allows you to apply the resistance force over a greater distance.

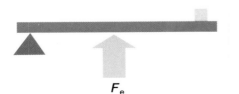

Figure 7-14 A potter's wheel is an example of a wheel and axle. A small force on the outside wheel keeps it spinning.

Wheel and Axle

Have you ever tried to turn a doorknob by holding onto the narrow base of the knob? It is hard to move. The doorknob magnifies the force of your hand. It is an example of a **wheel and axle,** two rigidly attached wheels that rotate together. It was invented around 3500 B.C. to turn a potter's table, as shown in **Figure 7-14.** With a small force at the edge of the wheel, the potter could easily keep the table turning as the pottery was shaped.

A wheel and axle is like a circular lever, as shown in **Figure 7-15.** The center is the fulcrum, and the wheel and axle turn around it.

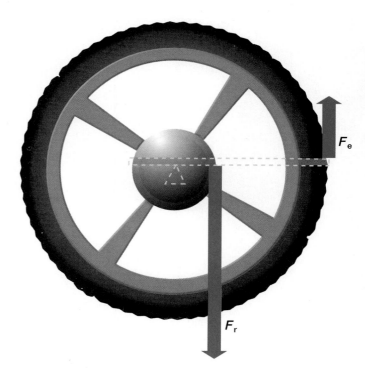

Figure 7-15 The mechanical advantage of a wheel and axle is $\dfrac{\text{radius of wheel}}{\text{radius of axle}}$. A small force on the wheel is transformed into a large force on the axle.

Observing Mechanical Advantage—Pulleys

Procedure 🥽

1. Give broomsticks or dowels to two students to hold. Tie a 3-m long rope to the middle of one stick. Wrap the rope around both sticks four times, leaving about 0.5 m gap between the sticks. The broomsticks are now pulleys.
2. Give the end of the rope to a third student.
3. While the two students pull the broomsticks apart, have the third student pull on the rope.
4. Observe what happens. Repeat using only two wraps of the rope and then using eight wraps.

Analysis

1. Describe what you observed. Could the students hold the sticks apart?
2. Compare and contrast the results with two, four, and eight turns of the rope around the pulleys.
3. With four turns of rope, what length of rope must be pulled to move the pulleys 10 cm closer together? What is the mechanical advantage of this pulley system?

Pulley

To raise a window blind, you pull down on a cord. The blind uses a pulley to change the direction of the force needed. A **pulley** is a surface, such as a wheel, that redirects force using a rope. It allows you to pull down to lift a weight rather than having to lift directly upward, as shown in **Figure 7-16.** You can use your body's weight to help supply effort. A rope thrown over a railing or tree branch can be used as a crude pulley system. This arrangement has a mechanical advantage of one, which means the effort and resistance forces are the same. The only advantage of using a simple pulley is that it is easier on your back. A large mechanical advantage can be created if more than one pulley is used. A double-pulley system is shown in **Figure 7-17,** with one pulley attached to a solid support and the other pulley attached to the load.

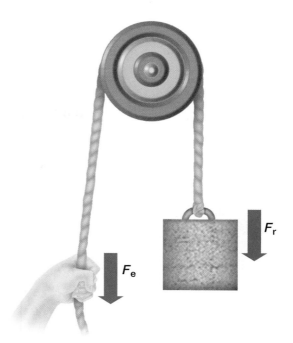

Figure 7-16 A simple pulley changes the direction of the effort force needed to move the load. **What is its mechanical advantage?**

Figure 7-17 In this double-pulley system, the ceiling supports some of the load.

A The person must provide an effort force equal to half the resistance force. The forces along the ropes on either side of a pulley must be equal.

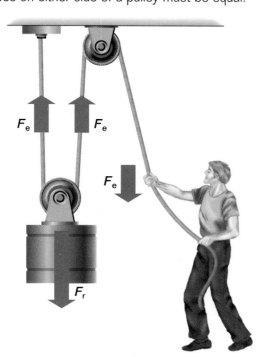

B After pulling 1 m of rope, the load is 0.5 m higher.

Each support rope is 0.5 m shorter.

This rope is 1 m longer.

0.5 m

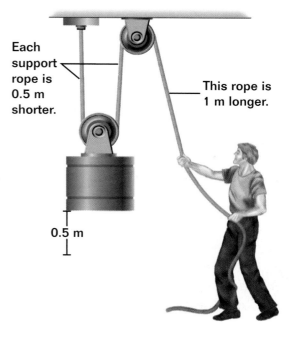

Efficiency

This chapter has calculated the forces and mechanical advantages of ideal machines, which lose nothing to friction or other problems. Real machines always have some loss. The **efficiency** of a machine is its ability to convert the work input, W_{in}, into the work the machine is designed to do, called work output, W_{out}. Efficiency is a percentage and is given by the following formula.

$$\text{efficiency} = \frac{W_{out}}{W_{in}} \times 100$$

An ideal machine has an efficiency of 100 percent. No real machine is perfectly efficient because some friction always steals away part of the work input and converts it to heat. The lever is nearly 100 percent efficient. Even the human body is fairly efficient in converting its chemical energy to useful work. A car is only about 20 percent efficient in converting the chemical potential energy released from the gasoline exploding in the engine into the kinetic energy of movement. Most of the energy is lost as the heat escapes from the hot engine and from friction in the car's many moving parts.

interNET CONNECTION

Visit the Glencoe Science Web Site at **www.glencoe.com/ sec/science/fl** for more information about designing machines.

Section Assessment

1. The Great Pyramid is 146 m high. How long would a ramp need to be to run from the top of the pyramid to the ground and have a mechanical advantage of 4?

2. A lever is used to lift a load with a resistance force of 500 N. The load is 1 m from the fulcrum. How far from the fulcrum must an effort force of 250 N be applied to lift the load?

3. If you put 8000 J of work into a machine with efficiency 60 percent, how much work will you get out?

4. **Think Critically:** Your arm and hand are a compound machine. Identify the simple machines that make it compound. Be creative. Use this machine to explain why it is easier to hold a heavy object close to your body rather than at arm's length.

5.  **Skill Builder**
Compare and Contrast How are a lever and a wheel and axle similar? Do the **Chapter 7 Skill Activity** on page 714 to compare and contrast a lever and a wheel and axle.

Science Journal In your Science Journal, explain how the lever, inclined plane, and wheel and axle are used in a can opener.

Using Electronic Calculators

A pocket calculator is a specialized computer programmed to solve arithmetic problems. The parts of a typical calculator include a power supply, a keypad for entering numbers and calculation commands, and a screen for displaying input numbers and calculation results. The brain of the calculator is a tiny silicon chip. This chip, the calculator's processing unit, performs arithmetic operations.

PARTS OF A CALCULATOR

1 Batteries or solar cells provide electricity.

2 Pressing a number on the keypad closes a contact between the key and the circuit board beneath it. The closed contact allows an electrical signal specific to that key to flow from the circuit board to a storage area in the calculator's processing unit.

3 The processing unit's storage area, or memory, holds all input information until the entire problem has been entered and is ready for processing.

4 With each key stroke, an electrical signal also flows from the processing unit to the screen, which displays the number or symbol.

5 When one of the function keys such as addition or multiplication is pressed, its unique signal is also sent to the processing unit for storage. In simple calculators, this information is not displayed on the screen.

6 Pressing the equal sign sends a signal to the processing unit, instructing it to perform the calculation stored in its memory. The result is sent to the screen for display.

Thinking Critically

1. What are some similarities and differences between pocket calculators and computers?

2. A calculator does exactly what you tell it to do. How can this be limiting? How can it help?

Design Your Own Experiment

Activity 7•2

Pulley Power

Possible Materials

- Single- and multiple-pulley systems
- Nylon rope
- Steel bar to support the pulley system
- Meterstick
  *metric tape measure
- Variety of weights to test pulleys
- Force spring scale
- A brick
  *heavy book
- Balance or scale

*Alternate Materials

It would have taken decades to build the Sears Tower without the aid of a pulley system attached to a crane. Hoisting the 1-ton I beams to a maximum height of 110 stories required tremendous lifting forces and precise control of the beam's movement.

Recognize the Problem

How can you use a pulley system to reduce the force needed to lift a load?

Form a Hypothesis

Write a hypothesis about how pulleys can be combined to make a system of pulleys to lift a heavy load, such as a brick. Consider the efficiency of your system.

Goals

- **Design** a pulley system.
- **Measure** the mechanical advantage and efficiency of the pulley system.

Safety Precautions

The brick could be dangerous if it falls. Don't stand under it.

Test Your Hypothesis

Plan

1. **Decide** how you are going to support your pulley system.

2. How will you measure the effort force and the resistance force? How will you determine the mechanical advantage? How will you measure efficiency?

Do

1. Make sure your teacher has approved your plan before you proceed.

2. **Assemble** the pulley system you designed. You may want to **test**

3. **Experiment** by lifting small weights with a single pulley, double pulley, and so on. How efficient are the pulleys?

4. Use the results of step 3 to **design** a pulley system to lift the brick.

it with a smaller weight before attaching the brick.

3. **Measure** the force needed to lift the brick. How much rope must you pull to raise the brick 10 cm?

Analyze Your Data

1. **Calculate** the theoretical mechanical advantage of your pulley system. (You can refer to the **Field Guide to Machines** at the end of this chapter.)

2. **Calculate** the actual mechanical advantage of your pulley system.

3. **Calculate** the efficiency of your pulley system.

Draw Conclusions

1. **Explain** how increasing the number of pulleys increases the mechanical advantage.

2. How could you modify the pulley system to lift a weight twice as

heavy with the same effort force used here?

3. **Compare** this real machine with an ideal machine.

FIELD GUIDE

to Machines

FIELD *ACTIVITY*

For a week, use this field guide to identify machines that people use in everyday life. Many of the machines you will see are combinations of two or more simple machines. Try to identify all of the simple machines that make up the compound machine. Use the examples on the next pages to estimate the mechanical advantages of each machine.

Whenever and wherever work needs to be done, you can be sure that some type of a machine is involved. The joints in your body are simple machines that allow you to run, jump, bend, and lift. But, the amount of force your body can exert is limited. Machines have been developed that increase or change the direction of the force you can produce. Machines do not change the amount of work done. They only make doing work easier.

How Machines Are Classified

The more you look, the more you will discover machines being used in daily living. Machines can be divided into two categories, simple or compound. Simple machines are all variations of two basic machines—the lever and the inclined plane.

A compound machine is a combination of two or more simple machines. Most machines that you observe people using will be compound machines.

It takes the same amount of work to climb any route to the top of the mountain. It takes much less force when you use the switchback trail.

Simple Machines

Mechanical advantage is a measure of how much help a machine is going to be when you do work. You can estimate mechanical advantage (*M.A.*) for a simple machine by using the formulas below. The formulas give only estimates of *M.A.* because some of the force you apply to a machine must be used to overcome friction. The greater the *M.A.*, the more the machine increases your force.

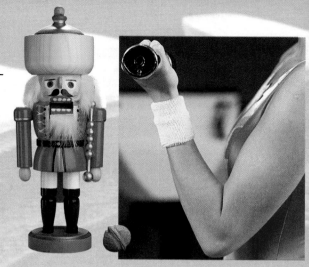

The Lever

$$M.A. = \frac{\text{length of the effort arm}}{\text{length of the resistance arm}}$$

F_r F_e

Resistance arm   Effort arm

The Pulley

$$M.A. = \text{number of ropes supporting the object}$$

F_r F_e

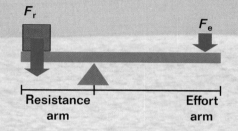

The Wheel and Axle

$$M.A. = \frac{\text{radius}_e}{\text{radius}_r}$$

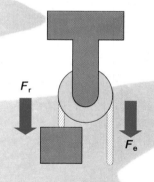

radius$_r$

radius$_e$

F_e

F_r

The Inclined Plane

$$M.A. = \frac{\text{length of slope}}{\text{height of slope}}$$

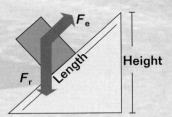

The Wedge

$$M.A. = \frac{(\text{height})}{\text{width}}$$

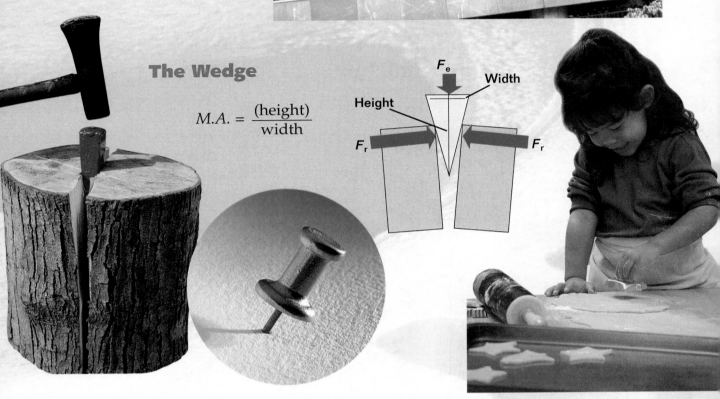

The Screw

$$M.A. = \frac{2\pi \, (\text{radius of circular path})}{\text{gap between ridges}}$$

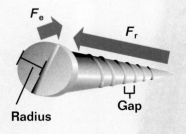

Recognizing Compound Machines

Scissors may look simple, but a pair of scissors is actually a compound machine. Two levers and two wedges combine to make an excellent cutting tool.

A compound machine is made up of two or more simple machines linked together. To estimate the mechanical advantage of a compound machine, multiply the mechanical advantages of each simple machine in the compound machine.

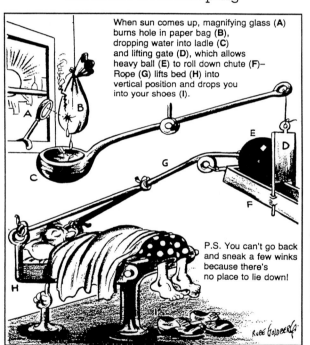

No More Oversleeping

When sun comes up, magnifying glass (**A**) burns hole in paper bag (**B**), dropping water into ladle (**C**) and lifting gate (**D**), which allows heavy ball (**E**) to roll down chute (**F**)– Rope (**G**) lifts bed (**H**) into vertical position and drops you into your shoes (**I**).

P.S. You can't go back and sneak a few winks because there's no place to lie down!

RUBE GOLDBERG

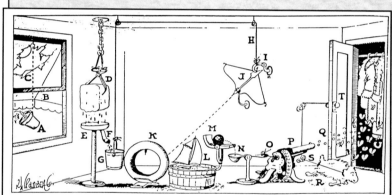

THE PROFESSOR EMERGES FROM THE GOOFY BOOTH WITH A DEVICE FOR THE EXTERMINATION OF MOTHS.

START SINGING. LADY UPSTAIRS, WHEN SUFFICIENTLY ANNOYED, THROWS FLOWER POT (**A**) THROUGH AWNING (**B**). HOLE (**C**) ALLOWS SUN TO COME THROUGH AND MELT CAKE OF ICE (**D**). WATER DRIPS INTO PAN (**E**) RUNNING THROUGH PIPE (**F**) INTO PAIL (**G**). WEIGHT OF PAIL CAUSES CORD (**H**) TO RELEASE HOOK (**I**) AND ALLOW ARROW (**J**) TO SHOOT INTO TIRE (**K**). ESCAPING AIR BLOWS AGAINST TOY SAILBOAT (**L**) DRIVING IT AGAINST LEVER (**M**) AND CAUSING BALL TO ROLL INTO SPOON (**N**) AND PULL STRING (**O**) WHICH SETS OFF MACHINE GUN (**P**) DISCHARGING CAMPHOR BALLS (**Q**). REPORT OF GUN FRIGHTENS LAMB (**R**) WHICH RUNS AND PULLS CORD (**S**), OPENING CLOSET DOOR (**T**). AS MOTHS (**U**) FLY OUT TO EAT WOOL FROM LAMB'S BACK THEY ARE KILLED BY THE BARRAGE OF MOTH BALLS.

IF ANY OF THE MOTHS ESCAPE AND THERE IS DANGER OF THEIR RETURNING, YOU CAN FOOL THEM BY MOVING.

Look at the drawings of these two compound machines. Rube Goldberg used simple machines to invent complicated ways to do simple things. Name the simple machines used in the drawings.

For a **preview** of this chapter, study this Reviewing Main Ideas before you read the chapter. After you have studied this chapter, you can use the Reviewing Main Ideas to **review** the chapter.

The Glencoe MindJogger, Audiocassettes, and CD-ROM provide additional opportunities for review.

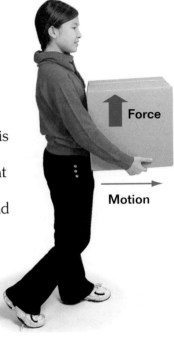

Force

Motion

Section

7-1 WORK

A force does **work** when an object is moved parallel to the direction in which a force is applied. If the force and movement are in the same direction, as when you push a door closed, the work is positive. If the force and movement are in opposite directions, as when you push on a door to prevent it from closing too fast, the work is negative. Only the part of the force along the direction of motion does work.

No work is done when an object is carried forward at constant speed (there is distance but no force in that direction), when an object is held (there is a force but no distance), and when an object is swung in a circle (motion is at a right angle to the direction of force). *Is work done when you climb up the stairs? Explain.*

Forward force

Downward force

Net force

Motion

CALCULATING WORK AND POWER

Work is calculated using the equation $W = Fd$. The unit of work is the joule, $1\ J = 1\ N \cdot m$. Only the force exerted parallel to the direction of motion is included in the calculation. **Power** measures the rate at which work is done. It is defined as follows.

$$P = \frac{W}{t}$$

The unit of power is the watt, $1\ W = 1\ J/s$. *If you do 48 J of work for a distance of 6 m, how much force do you apply? In what direction? If it takes 12 s, what is the power?*

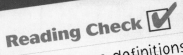

Write science definitions for *work, power, force,* and *efficiency.* Compare them to the common usage definitions of these words.

Section

7-2 SIMPLE MACHINES

A machine reduces the **effort force** needed to counter a **resistance force.** The work is the same, $F_e d_e = F_r d_r$. The **inclined plane, wedge, screw, lever, wheel and axle,** and **pulley** are **simple machines,** which have only one motion.

Mechanical advantage measures the decrease in effort force needed as follows.

$$M.A. = \frac{F_r}{F_e}$$

The larger the mechanical advantage, the more resistance force you can overcome with a given effort force. Because all machines have some loss to friction or heat, **efficiency,** is always less than 100 percent.

$$\text{Efficiency} = \frac{W_{out}}{W_{in}} \times 100$$

If a pulley system has a mechanical advantage of 4, how much rope will you have to pull to lift an 80-kg object 4 m?

 *Career* **CONNECTION**

Yvonne Ho Cardinale, Hydroelectric Engineer

As a hydroelectric engineer, Yvonne Ho Cardinale designs and maintains hydroelectric power plants, which use water stored behind a dam to make electricity. Her tasks include predicting how much electricity a plant can generate based on weather factors. She monitors weather stations and measures snow depth. Then, she uses computer models to help her decide how much water to save behind the dam so that power is produced when it is needed. *If the power plant produces less power, would a motor do work more quickly or slowly?*

Using Vocabulary

a. compound machine
b. efficiency
c. effort force
d. fulcrum
e. inclined plane
f. lever
g. mechanical advantage
h. power
i. pulley
j. resistance force
k. screw
l. simple machine
m. wedge
n. wheel and axle
o. work

Each phrase below describes a science term from the list. Write the term that matches the phrase describing it.

1. comparison of work in to work out
2. force put into a machine
3. a point about which a lever pivots
4. two rigidly attached wheels
5. a comparison of the effort force and resistance force for a machine

Checking Concepts

Choose the word or phrase that answers the question.

6. What is an example of a simple machine?
   A) baseball bat
   B) pair of scissors
   C) can opener
   D) car

7. When friction slows an object, what type of work does the force of friction do?
   A) positive work
   B) negative work
   C) no work
   D) both positive and negative work

8. An ax is a compound machine that includes what?
   A) a lever and wedge
   B) two levers
   C) a wedge and a pulley
   D) a lever and a screw

9. How can the unit for work be written?
   A) W · s
   B) $kg \cdot m^2/s^2$
   C) N · m
   D) all of the above

10. A force of 8 N is exerted over 2 m to stop an object. What is the work done?
    A) 4 J
    B) −4 J
    C) 16 J
    D) −16 J

11. If a machine takes in 50 J and puts out 45 J, what is its efficiency?
    A) 0.9 percent
    B) 1.1 percent
    C) 90 percent
    D) 111 percent

12. A ramp decreases which of the following?
    A) height
    B) effort force
    C) resistance force
    D) effort distance

13. In which example is gravity doing work?
    A) an apple falling
    B) a planet in orbit
    C) a box on a table
    D) a bike rolling on a flat road

14. A force of 30 N exerted over a distance of 3 m does how much work?
    A) 3 J
    B) 10 J
    C) 30 J
    D) 90 J

15. A wheel with a radius of 20 cm is attached to an axle with a radius of 1 cm. An effort force of 100 N on the wheel counters a resistance force of what on the axle?
    A) 5 N
    B) 200 N
    C) 500 N
    D) 2000 N

Thinking Critically

16. Does gravity do positive or negative work on a falling object? Explain.

17. A doorknob is an example of a wheel and axle. Explain why turning the knob is easier than turning the axle.

18. The ground does 1600 J of work to stop a falling ball in 0.05 m. What force was needed?

19. How much effort force is required to lift an 11 000-N I beam using a pulley system with a mechanical advantage of 20?

20. A lever has a 9-N load 1.5 m from the fulcrum. Where should a 0.5-N effort force be applied to balance the load?

Developing Skills

If you need help, refer to the Skill Handbook.

21. Observing and Inferring: Suppose a lever is in balance. Would this arrangement be in balance on the moon, where the force of gravity is less? Explain.

22. Measuring in SI: At the 1976 Olympics, Vasili Aleseev shattered the world record for weight lifting when he lifted 2500 N from the floor to over his head, a point 2 m above the ground. It took him about 5 s to complete the lift. How much work did he do? What was his power?

23. Making and Using Graphs: A pulley system has a mechanical advantage of 5. Make a graph of the possible combinations of effort force and resistance force.

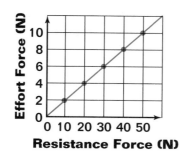

24. Designing an Experiment: Design an experiment to measure the efficiency of the ground in rebounding a basketball.

THE PRINCETON REVIEW

Test-Taking Tip

Study Sterile It's best to study in an environment similar to the one in which you'll be tested. Blaring stereos, video game machines, chatty friends, and beepers are not allowed in the classroom during test time. So why get used to them?

Test Practice

Use these questions to test your Science Proficiency.

1. A student exerts 150 W of power for 30 s. How much work is done?
A) 50 J
B) 75 J
C) 300 J
D) 4500 J

2. A block is pulled across the table with a rope, as shown. Which force does work?
A) the normal force
B) the force of gravity
C) the upward force on the rope
D) the sideways force on the rope

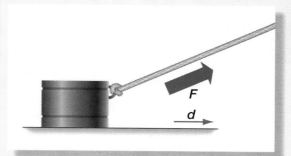

Earth
Materials &
Resources

NATIONAL GEOGRAPHIC

What's Happening Here?

Buried in Earth's crust are great riches. To obtain them, people launch massive operations, such as this gravel quarry on the island of Oahu, Hawaii (left). What makes these resources worth such a tremendous effort? In this unit, you will learn about some of the 4000 minerals found on Earth and why they are valuable. Though we call only certain minerals precious—such as diamonds and gold—all minerals are precious because their supply is limited. In the case of some minerals, rather than mining them until they run out, we can use them again and again. For example, we mine the mineral ore bauxite for its aluminum content and make soda cans from the aluminum. Now, instead of burying the used cans in a landfill, we can recycle them. Crushed and packed soda cans in Kailua-Kona, Hawaii (below), are ready to be shipped to a processing plant where they will be made into new cans.

inter**NET**
CONNECTION

Explore the Glencoe Science Web Site at **www.glencoe. com/sec/science/fl** to find out more about topics found in this unit.

Chapter Preview

Skills Preview

Skill Builders
- Map Concepts
- Measure in SI

Activities
- Compare and Contrast
- Interpret Data

MiniLabs
- Interpret Scientific Illustrations
- Make a Model

Reading Check ✔

Locate a legend, myth, or folktale from another culture that explains the creation of mountains, plains, or other landforms. Share it with the class.

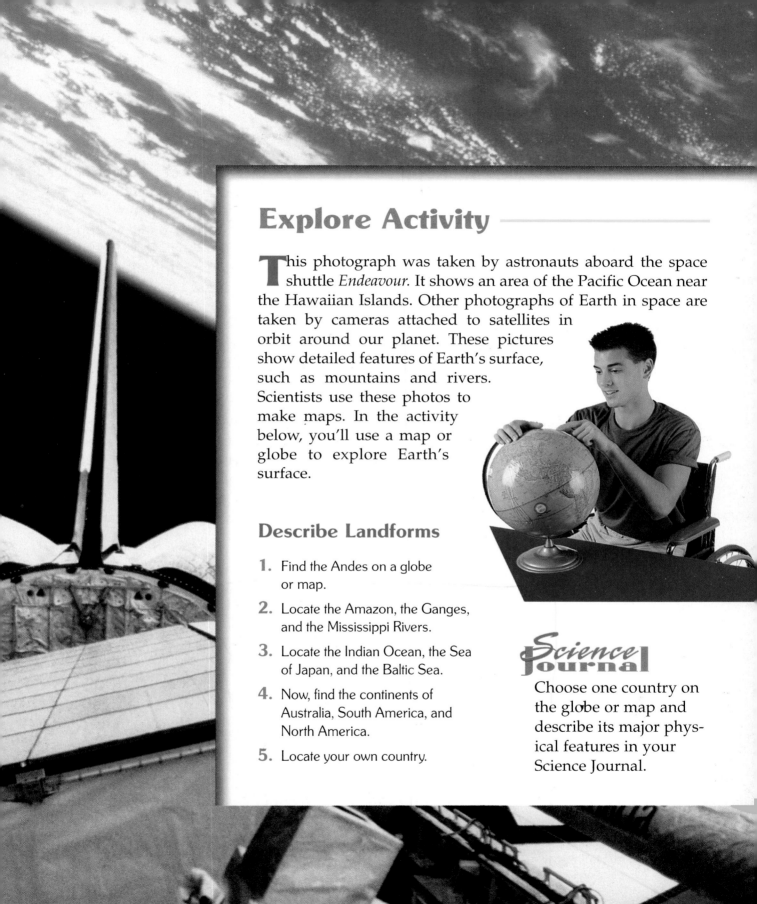

Explore Activity

This photograph was taken by astronauts aboard the space shuttle *Endeavour*. It shows an area of the Pacific Ocean near the Hawaiian Islands. Other photographs of Earth in space are taken by cameras attached to satellites in orbit around our planet. These pictures show detailed features of Earth's surface, such as mountains and rivers. Scientists use these photos to make maps. In the activity below, you'll use a map or globe to explore Earth's surface.

Describe Landforms

1. Find the Andes on a globe or map.

2. Locate the Amazon, the Ganges, and the Mississippi Rivers.

3. Locate the Indian Ocean, the Sea of Japan, and the Baltic Sea.

4. Now, find the continents of Australia, South America, and North America.

5. Locate your own country.

Science **Journal**

Choose one country on the globe or map and describe its major physical features in your Science Journal.

8•1

Plains

What **You'll Learn**

► Differences between plains and plateaus
► Describe folded, upwarped, fault-block, and volcanic mountains

Vocabulary
plain
plateau
folded mountain
upwarped mountain
fault-block mountain
volcanic mountain

Why **It's Important**

► You'll learn how the land around you formed.

A lot of interesting landforms can be seen around the world. A landform is a feature that makes up the shape of the land on Earth's surface. **Figure 8-1** shows the three basic types of landforms: plains, plateaus, and mountains.

We all know what mountains are. In our minds, we can see tall peaks reaching toward the sky. But what do you think of when you hear the word *plains?* You might think of endless flat fields of wheat or grass. That would be correct, because many plains are used to grow crops. **Plains** are large, flat areas. Most plains are found in the interior regions of continents. Those found near the ocean are called coastal plains. Together, interior plains and coastal plains make up one-half of all the land in the United States.

Coastal Plains

Coastal plains are broad areas along the ocean's shore. They are often called lowlands because of their low elevations. Elevation refers to distance above or below sea level. As you might guess, sea level has zero elevation. The Atlantic Coastal Plain is a good example of this type of landform.

Mountains
Plateau
Interior plains
Coastal plains

Figure 8-1 Three basic types of landforms are plains, plateaus, and mountains.

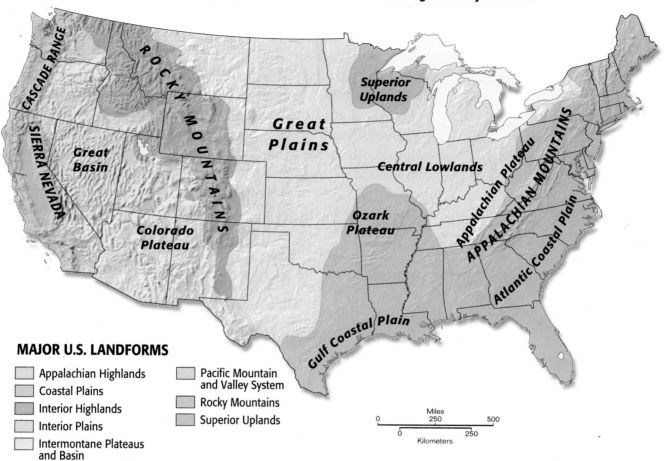

Figure 8-2 The plains, plateaus, and mountains of the United States are divided into eight major regions. **Based upon the information in this map, describe the region that you live in.**

MAJOR U.S. LANDFORMS

- Appalachian Highlands
- Coastal Plains
- Interior Highlands
- Interior Plains
- Intermontane Plateaus and Basin
- Pacific Mountain and Valley System
- Rocky Mountains
- Superior Uplands

Miles
0   250   500
0   250
Kilometers

It stretches along the east coast of the United States. This area has low rolling hills, swamps, and marshes. A marsh is grassy wetland, usually flooded with water.

If you hiked along the Atlantic Coastal Plain, you would know it isn't perfectly flat. Many low hills and valleys have been carved by rivers. What do you suppose caused the Atlantic Coastal Plain to form? It actually began forming under water about 70 million years ago from sediments made of marine organisms that fell to the ancient ocean floor. When sea level dropped, the plain was exposed.

Another example of this landform is the Gulf Coastal Plain shown in **Figure 8-2.** It includes the lowlands in the southern United States that surround the Gulf of Mexico. Much of this plain was formed from sediments deposited by the Mississippi River as it entered the Gulf of Mexico.

Using Math

The elevation of Denver, Colorado, is about 1624.5 m above sea level. The elevation of New Orleans, Louisiana, is 1626 m lower than Denver's. Find the elevation of New Orleans.

Interior Plains

A large part of the center of the United States is called the interior plains. The interior plains of the United States are also shown in **Figure 8-2.** They stretch from the Appalachian Mountains in the east, to the Rocky Mountains in the west, to the Gulf Coastal Plain in the south. They include the rolling hills of the Great Lakes area and the Central Lowlands around the Missouri and Mississippi Rivers.

A large part of the interior plains is known as the Great Plains. They lie between the Mississippi lowlands and the Rocky Mountains. The Great Plains are flat, grassy, dry areas with few trees. They are called high plains because of their elevation. They range from 350 m above sea level at their eastern border to 1500 m above sea level at their western boundary. The Great Plains are covered with nearly horizontal layers of loose materials eroded from the Rocky Mountains. Streams deposited these sediments over the last 28 million years.

Try at Home

Mini Lab

Profiling the United States

Procedure

1. Place the bottom edge of a piece of paper across the middle of **Figure 8-2,** extending from the west coast to the east coast.

2. Mark where different landforms are located along this edge.

3. Use a map of the United States and the descriptions of the landforms in Section 8-1 to help you draw a profile, or side view, of the United States. Use steep, jagged lines to represent mountains. Low, flat lines can represent plains.

Analysis

1. Describe how your profile changed shape as you moved from west to east.

2. Describe how the shape of your profile would be different if you moved from north to south.

Plateaus

If you would like to explore some higher regions, you might be interested in going to the second basic type of landform—a plateau. **Plateaus** (pla TOHZ) are flat,

raised areas of land. They are areas made up of nearly horizontal rocks that have been uplifted by forces within Earth. Plateaus are different from plains in that they rise steeply from the land around them. An example of a plateau in the United States is the Colorado Plateau, which lies just west of the Rocky Mountains. The Colorado River, as shown in **Figure 8-3,** has cut deeply into the rock layers of the plateau, forming the Grand Canyon. Because the Colorado Plateau is located in what is now a dry region, only a few rivers have developed on its surface. If you hiked around on this plateau, you would see a desert landscape.

Mountains

Plains and plateaus are mostly flat. If you want to see a steep rock face, you must go to the third basic type of landform—a mountain. Mountains rise high above the surrounding land, often showing a spectacular view from the top. The world's highest mountain peak is Mount Everest in the Himalayas. It is more than 8800 m above sea level. By contrast, mountain peaks in the United States reach just over 6000 m. Mountains vary greatly in size and in how they are formed. The four main types of mountains are folded, upwarped, fault-block, and volcanic. ✔

Reading Check

What are the four main types of mountains?

Figure 8-3 Rivers cut deep into the Colorado Plateau, as shown by the Colorado River near Moab, Utah. **How are plateaus different from plains?**

Figure 8-4 Folded mountains form when rock layers are squeezed from opposite sides. **When did the Appalachian Mountains form?**

Folded Mountains

The first mountains we will investigate are folded mountains. If you travel through a road cut in the Appalachian Mountains, you'll see rock layers that are folded like the ones in **Figure 8-4.** Folded rock layers look like a rug that has been pushed up against a wall. What do you think caused this to happen?

PHYSICS
INTEGRATION ➤

Tremendous forces inside Earth force horizontal rock layers together. When rock layers are squeezed from opposite sides, they buckle and fold into **folded mountains.** The Appalachian Mountains are folded mountains that formed 250 to 350 million years ago. They are some of the oldest and longest mountain ranges in North America, stretching from Newfoundland, Canada, all the way south to Alabama. At one time, the Appalachians were higher than the Rocky Mountains. Weathering and erosion have worn them down to less than 2000 m above sea level.

Figure 8-5
The southern Rocky Mountains are upwarped mountains that formed when crust was pushed up by forces inside Earth.

Upwarped Mountains

The southern Rocky Mountains in Colorado and New Mexico, the Black Hills in South Dakota, and the Adirondack Mountains in New York are upwarped mountains. **Figure 8-5** shows a mountain range in Colorado. What do you notice about the shape of the mountains? The sharp peaks and ridges are characteristic of upwarped mountains. **Upwarped mountains** are formed when crust is pushed up by forces inside Earth. Over time, the soil and other materials on top of Earth's crust erode, leaving the rock underneath exposed. These rocks then erode to form peaks and ridges.

Figure 8-6 Fault-block mountains such as the Grand Tetons are formed when faults occur. Some rock blocks move up, while others move down. **What types of peaks are characteristic of these mountains?**

Fault-Block Mountains

The Grand Teton Mountains of Wyoming, shown in **Figure 8-6,** and the Sierra Nevada in California formed in yet another way. **Fault-block mountains** are made of huge, tilted blocks of rocks that are separated from surrounding rock by faults. A fault is a large crack in rocks along which there is movement. As **Figure 8-6** shows, when these mountains formed, one block was tilted and pushed up. The other block was pushed down. If you ever go to the Tetons or to the Sierra Nevada, you'll see the sharp, jagged peaks that are characteristic of fault-block mountains.

Volcanic Mountains

Mount St. Helens in Washington and Mauna Loa in Hawaii are two of many volcanic mountains in the United States. **Volcanic mountains** like the one shown in **Figure 8-7** begin to form when molten material reaches the surface through a

Figure 8-7
The volcanic mountains of Hawaii are made of molten material that oozed from Earth's crust and formed cone-shaped structures.

weak area of the crust. The materials pile up, one layer on top of another, until a cone-shaped structure forms. The Hawaiian Islands are huge volcanoes that sit on the ocean floor. Only their peaks stick out above the water.

Plains, plateaus, and mountains offer different kinds of landforms to explore. They range from low coastal plains and high desert plateaus to mountain ranges thousands of meters high.

Section Assessment

1. Describe the eight major landform regions in the United States.

2. What causes some mountains to be folded and others to be upwarped?

3. **Think Critically:** If you wanted to know whether a particular mountain was formed by a fault, what would you look for?

4. **Skill Builder**
   Concept Mapping Make an events-chain concept map to explain how upwarped mountains form. If you need help, refer to Concept Mapping in the **Skill Handbook** on page 680.

Using Computers

Spreadsheet Design a spreadsheet that compares the origin and features of folded, upwarped, fault-block, and volcanic mountains. Label the columns and rows. Explain an advantage of using a spreadsheet to compare different types of mountains. If you need help, refer to page 704.

8·2 Viewpoints

Latitude and Longitude

To explore landforms, you'll want to learn how to find locations on Earth. If you wanted to go to the Hawaiian Islands, how would you describe their location? You might say that they are located in the Pacific Ocean. That's correct, but there is a more exact way to locate places on Earth—lines of latitude and longitude. These lines form an imaginary grid system that shows exactly where places on Earth are located.

Latitude

Look at **Figure 8-8.** The **equator** is an imaginary line that circles Earth exactly halfway between the north and south poles. The equator separates Earth into two equal halves, called the northern hemisphere and the southern hemisphere. The lines running parallel to the equator are called lines of latitude, or parallels. **Latitude** is the distance in degrees either north or south of the equator. Because parallel lines do not intersect, lines of latitude do not intersect.

What You'll Learn

► The difference between latitude and longitude
► How latitude and longitude are used to identify locations
► How to calculate the time and date in different time zones

Vocabulary
equator
latitude
prime meridian
longitude
International Date Line

Why It's Important

► You'll learn how to locate places on Earth.

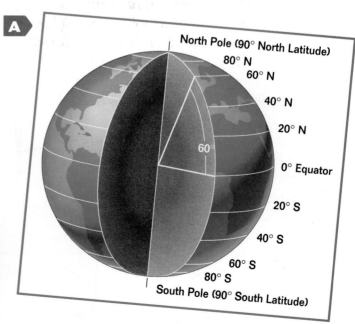

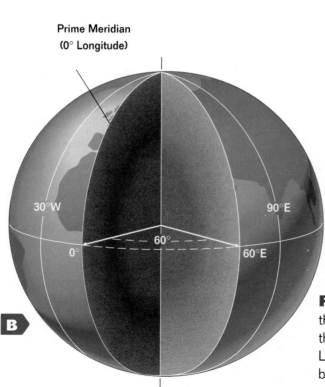

Figure 8-8 Latitude is the measurement of the imaginary angle created between the equator, the center of Earth, and a location on Earth (A). Longitude is the measurement of the angle created between the prime meridian, the center of Earth, and a location on Earth (B).

The equator is numbered 0° latitude. The poles are each numbered 90°. Therefore, latitude is measured from 0° at the equator to 90° at the poles. Locations north of the equator are referred to by degrees north latitude. Locations south of the equator are referred to by degrees south latitude.

Longitude

Latitude lines are used for locations north and south of the equator, but what about locations in east and west directions? These vertical lines, seen in **Figure 8-8B,** have two names—meridians and lines of longitude. Just as the equator is used as a reference point for north/south grid lines, there's a reference point for east/west grid lines—the **prime meridian.** This imaginary line represents 0° longitude. In 1884, astronomers decided the prime meridian should go through the Greenwich (GREN itch) Observatory near London, England.

Longitude refers to distances in degrees east or west of the prime meridian. Points west of the prime meridian have west longitude measured from 0° to 180°, while points east of the prime meridian have east longitude, also measured from 0° to 180°.

The prime meridian does not circle Earth as the equator does. Rather, it runs from the north pole through Greenwich, England, to the south pole. The line of longitude on the opposite side of Earth from the prime meridian is the 180° meridian. East lines of longitude meet west lines of longitude at the 180° meridian.

Using latitude and longitude, you can locate Hawaii more accurately, as shown in **Figure 8-9.** Hawaii is located at 20° north latitude and about 155° west longitude, or 20°N, 155°W. Note that latitude comes first when the latitude and longitude of a particular location are given.

Interpreting Latitude and Longitude

Procedure

1. Find the equator and prime meridian on a world map.
2. Move your finger to latitudes north of the equator, then south of the equator. Move your finger to longitudes west of the prime meridian, then east of the prime meridian.

Analysis

1. Identify the cities that have the following coordinates:
   a. 56°N, 38°E
   b. 34°S, 18°E
   c. 23°N, 82°W
2. Determine the latitude and longitude of the following cities:
   a. London, England
   b. Melbourne, Australia
   c. Buenos Aires, Argentina

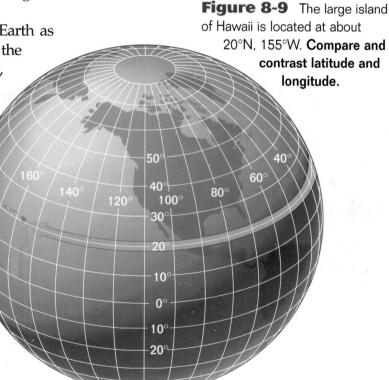

Figure 8-9 The large island of Hawaii is located at about 20°N, 155°W. **Compare and contrast latitude and longitude.**

Earth Time

What time is it right now? That depends on where you are on Earth. Time is measured by tracking Earth's movement in relation to the sun. Earth rotates once every 24 hours. When one half of Earth is facing the sun, the other half is facing away from it. For the half facing the sunlight, it is day. For the half in darkness, it is night.

Time Zones

How can you know what time it is at different places on Earth? Earth is divided into time zones. Because Earth takes 24 hours to rotate, it is divided into 24 time zones, each one hour different. Each time zone is 15 degrees wide on a globe or map. The United States has six different time zones. Look at **Figure 8-10.** Because Earth is rotating, the eastern United States starts a new day while the western part of the country is still in darkness. ☑

As you can see in **Figure 8-11,** time zones do not strictly follow lines of longitude. Time zone boundaries have been adjusted in local areas. For example, if a city were split by a time zone boundary, the results could be confusing. In such a situation, the time zone boundary is moved outside of the city.

Calendar Dates

One day ends and the next day begins at midnight. If it is 11:59 P.M. Tuesday, two minutes later it is 12:01 A.M. Wednesday. The calendar moves forward to the next day in each time zone at midnight.

You gain or lose time each time you travel through a time zone. If you travel far enough, you gain or lose a whole day. The **International Date Line** is the transition line for calendar days. If you were traveling west across the International Date Line, located at the 180° meridian, you would move your calendar forward one day. If you were traveling east, you would move your calendar back one day.

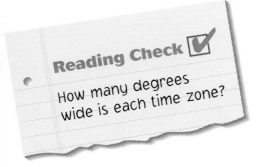
Figure 8-10 There are six time zones in the United States.

A Atlanta, Georgia, lies in the eastern time zone. Students there would be on their way to school at 7:00 A.M.

B But, a student in Los Angeles, California, which lies in the Pacific time zone three hours earlier, would still be fast asleep. **What time would it be in Los Angeles when the students in Atlanta returned home at 3:00 P.M.?**

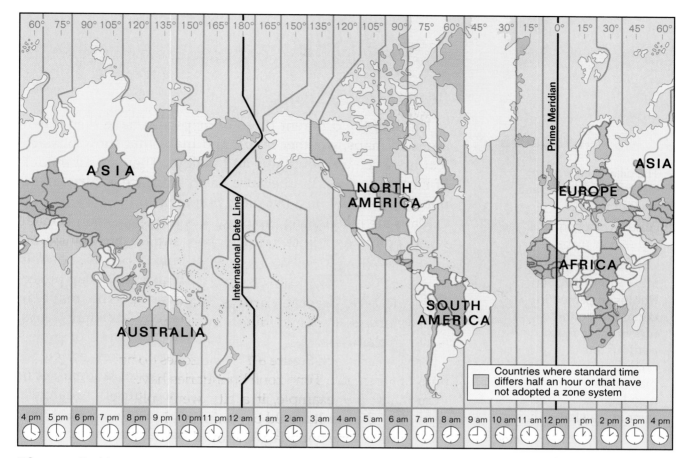

Figure 8-11 Lines of longitude roughly determine the locations of time zone boundaries. These boundaries are adjusted locally to avoid splitting cities and other political subdivisions (such as counties) into different time zones.

Section Assessment

1. How do lines of latitude and longitude help us find locations on Earth?

2. What are the latitude and longitude of New Orleans?

3. **Think Critically:** How could you leave home on Monday to go sailing, sail for an hour on Sunday, and return home on Monday?

4. **Skill Builder**
   Interpreting Scientific Illustrations
   Use a world map to find the approximate latitude and longitude of the following locations: Sri Lanka; Tokyo, Japan; and the Falkland Islands. If you need help, refer to Interpreting Scientific Illustrations in the **Skill Handbook** on page 692.

Using Math

If you left London on the Concorde jet airplane at 8 A.M. London time, you would arrive in New York at 6 A.M. New York time. You would have crossed five time zones during your flight. How long would your trip have taken?

8•3 Maps

Map Projections

What You'll Learn

► The difference among Mercator, Robinson, and conic projections
► Features of topographic maps and satellite maps

Vocabulary

Mercator projection
Robinson projection
conic projection
topographic map
contour line
contour interval
map scale
map legend
remote sensing

Why It's Important

► Different kinds of maps work better for different purposes.

Think of the different types of maps you have seen. There are road maps, weather maps, and maps that show physical features such as mountains and valleys. They are all models of Earth's surface. But because Earth's surface is curved, it is not easy to show on a flat piece of paper.

Maps are made using projections. A map projection is made when points and lines on a globe's surface are transferred onto paper, as shown in **Figure 8-12.** Map projections can be made in several different ways. But, all types of projections distort either the shapes of landmasses or their areas. Antarctica, for instance, might look smaller or larger than it really is.

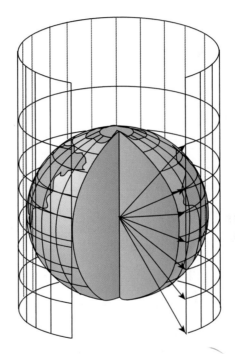

Figure 8-12 Because Earth's surface is curved, all types of map projections distort either the shapes of landmasses or their areas.

A In a Mercator projection, lines of longitude are drawn parallel to each other. **What does this do to areas near the poles?**

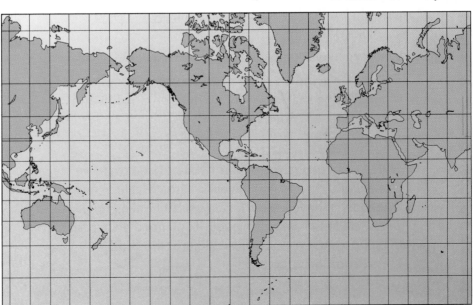

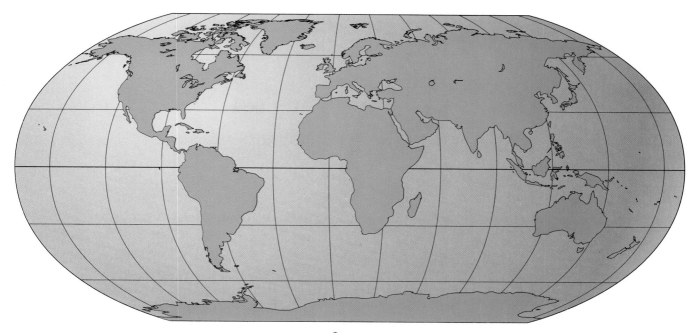

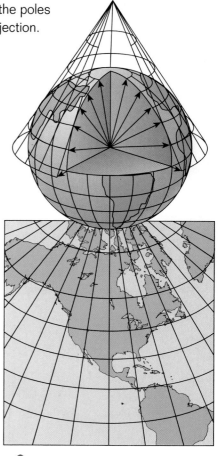

B A Robinson projection shows less distortion near the poles than a Mercator projection.

Mercator Projection

A **Mercator projection** has correct shapes of continents, but their areas are distorted. Lines of longitude are projected onto the map parallel to each other. As you learned earlier, only latitude lines are parallel. Longitude lines meet at the poles. When longitude lines are projected as parallel, areas near the poles appear bigger than they should. Look at Greenland in the Mercator projection in **Figure 8-12A.** It appears to be larger than South America. Greenland is actually much smaller than South America. Mercator projections are mainly used on ships.

Robinson Projection

A **Robinson projection** has accurate continent shapes and shows accurate land areas. As shown in **Figure 8-12B,** lines of latitude remain parallel, and lines of longitude are curved as they would be on a globe. This results in more correct continent shapes.

Conic Projection

A third type of projection is a conic projection. You use this type of projection, shown in **Figure 8-12C,** whenever you look at a road map or a weather map. **Conic projections** are used to produce maps of small areas. They are made by projecting points and lines from a globe onto a cone.

C A conic projection is accurate for small areas of Earth. **What could you use this type of map for?**

Figure 8-13 A topographic map shows changes in the elevation of Earth's surface.

A Wizard Island is a volcanic cinder-cone that forms an island in Crater Lake, Oregon.

B Different points of elevation are projected onto paper.

C The points of elevation are connected to form a topographic map of the island. **What do contour intervals tell us about elevation?**

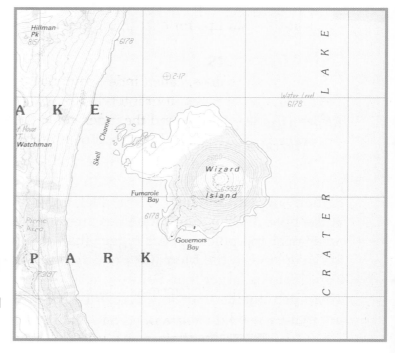

Topographic Maps

If you wanted to go hiking, a conic map projection would get you to the mountain. Next, you would need a detailed map showing the hills and valleys of that specific area. A **topographic map** shows the changes in elevation of Earth's surface. With a topographic map, you could tell how steep the mountain trail is. It would also show natural features such as mountains, hills, plains, lakes, and rivers, and cultural features such as roads, cities, dams, and other structures built by people.

Contour Lines

Before starting your hike up the mountain, you would look at the contour lines on your topographic map to see the trail's changes in elevation. A **contour line** is a line on a map that connects points of equal elevation. Elevation refers to the distance of a location above or below sea level. The difference in elevation between two side-by-side contour lines is called the **contour interval.** If the contour interval were 10 m, then when you walked between those two lines on the trail, you would have climbed or walked down 10 m.

As **Figure 8-13C** shows, the elevation of the contour interval can vary. For mountains, the contour lines might be close and the contour interval might be as great as 100 m. This would tell you that the land is steep because there is a large change in elevation between lines. However, if there isn't a great change in elevation and the contour lines are far apart, your map might have a contour interval of 5 m. **Table 8-1** gives additional tips for examining contour lines.

Index Contours

Some contour lines, called index contours, are marked with their elevation. If the contour interval is 5 m, you can tell the elevation of other lines around the index contour. You would add or subtract 5 m from the elevation shown on the index contour.

*inter***NET**

CONNECTION

Visit the Glencoe Science Web Site at **www. glencoe.com/sec/ science/fl** for more information about maps.

Table 8-1

Contour Rules

Here are some rules to remember when examining contour lines.

1. **Contour lines close around hills and basins or depressions.** To decide whether you're looking at a hill or basin, you can read the elevation numbers or look for hachures. Hachures are short lines at right angles to the contour line that are used to show depressions. These lines point toward lower elevations. See **Figure 8-14.**

2. **Contour lines never cross.** If they did, it would mean that the spot where they cross would have two different elevations.

3. **Contour lines form Vs that point upstream whenever they cross streams.** This is because streams flow in depressions that are beneath the elevation of the surrounding land surface. When the contour lines follow the depression, they appear as Vs pointing upstream on the map.

Map Scale

Another thing you would want to know before you set out on your hike is, "How far is it to the top of the mountain?" Because maps are small models of Earth's surface, distances and sizes of things on a map are proportional to the real thing on Earth. This is done by using scale distances.

The **map scale** is the relationship between the distances on the map and actual distances on Earth's surface. Scale is often represented as a ratio. For example, a topographic map of the Grand Canyon may have a scale that reads "1:80 000." This means that one unit on the map represents 80 000 units on land. If the unit you wanted to use was a centimeter, then 1 cm on the map would equal 80 000 cm on land. The unit of distance may be in feet or millimeters or any other measure of distance. However, the units of measure on each side of the ratio must always be the same. A map scale may also be in the form of a small bar that is divided into units. The units are scaled down to match real distances on Earth.

Map Legend

Topographic maps and most other maps have a legend. A **map legend** explains what the symbols used on the map mean. Some frequently used symbols for topographic maps are shown in **Figure 8-14.**

Three-Dimensional Maps

Topographic maps are two-dimensional models used to study features on Earth's surface. To unravel Earth's complex structure, however, scientists need to know what Earth looks like inside. With computers, topographic maps are digitized to get a three-dimensional or 3-D view of features such as rock beds or river systems. Digitizing is a process by which points are located on a coordinate grid.

Map Uses

As you have learned, there are many different ways to view Earth. The map you choose to use will depend upon your need. For instance, if you wanted to determine New Zealand's location relative to Canada, you would probably examine a Mercator projection. In your search, you would use lines of latitude and longitude, and a map scale. If you

Reading Check ✓

What is a map scale?

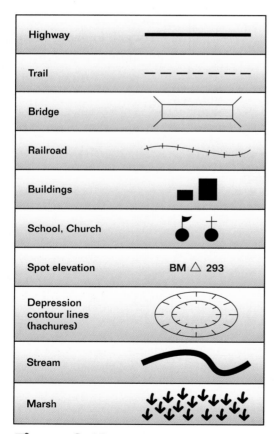

Highway	
Trail	
Bridge	
Railroad	
Buildings	
School, Church	
Spot elevation	BM △ 293
Depression contour lines (hachures)	
Stream	
Marsh	

Figure 8-14 Here are some typical symbols used on topographic maps.

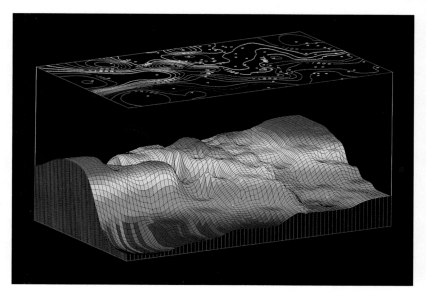

Figure 8-15 This computer-generated map shows a river system in Montana. **How does this map differ from a topographic map?**

wanted to travel across the country, you would rely on a conic projection. You would also use a map legend to help you locate features along your trip. And, if you wanted to scale the highest peak in your county, you would take along a topographic map.

As **Figure 8-15** shows, mapmaking, also called cartography, has experienced a technological revolution in the past few decades. Remote sensing and computers have changed the way maps are made. Read on to learn more about remote sensing.

Problem Solving

Interpreting a Topographic Map

The map at right is a topographic map of an area in California. One sunny day, two hikers started from the point marked with the + on the map. One hiker climbed the peak of Cedar Mountain, while the other climbed the peak of Orr Mountain.

Both traveled at the same rate on flat or gentle slopes. Their climbs slowed as the ground grew steeper. Study the map, then answer the questions below.

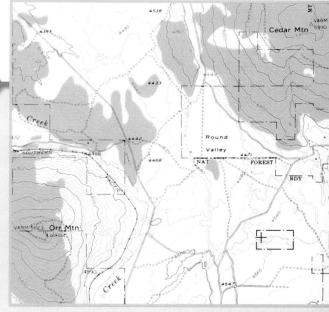

1 cm = 1.3 km

Solve the Problem

1. Which peak is higher?

2. Which hiker had the steeper climb? Explain using contour lines.

3. Name three items found in a map legend that the hiker heading for Orr Mountain crossed before reaching his or her goal.

Think Critically

1. If each hiker could choose any route to his or her destination, which one do you think reached his or her goal first? Explain.

2. Once at the top, could the hiker on Cedar Mountain see the hiker on Orr Mountain? Why or why not?

Remote Sensing

Scientists use remote-sensing techniques to collect much of the data used for making maps. **Remote sensing** is a way of collecting information about Earth from a distance. Satellites and sonar are two remote-sensing devices.

Topex-Poseidon Satellite

The Topex-Poseidon Satellite (*Topex* stands for "topographic experiment") uses radar to compute the distance to the ocean's surface. Radar waves are high-frequency radio signals that are beamed from the satellite to the ocean. As **Figure 8-16** illustrates, a receiving device then picks up the returning echo as it bounces off the water. The distance to the water's surface is calculated using the radar speed and the time it takes for the signal to be reflected. Using satellite-to-sea measurements, computers can draw maps of ocean features.

Global Positioning System

The Global Positioning System, or GPS, is a satellite-based, radio-navigation system that allows users to determine their exact position anywhere on Earth. Twenty-four satellites orbit 20 200 km above the planet. Each satellite sends an accurate position and time signal. The satellites are arranged in their orbits so that signals from at least six can be picked up at any given moment by someone using a GPS receiver. By processing the signals coming from multiple satellites, the receiver calculates the user's exact location. GPS technology is a valuable navigational tool. It is also used to create detailed maps and to track wildlife.

Sea Beam

Sonar refers to the use of sound waves to detect ocean-bottom features. First, a sound wave is sent from a ship toward the ocean floor. A receiving device then picks up the returning echo when it bounces off the bottom. Shipboard computers measure the distance to the bottom using the speed of sound in water and the time it takes for the sound to be reflected.

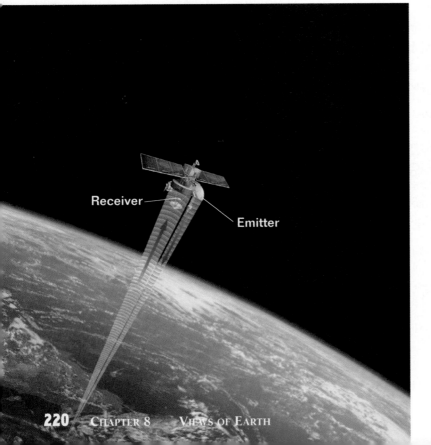

Figure 8-16 Using high-frequency radio waves, the Topex-Poseidon Satellite can map ocean floor features.

Receiver

Emitter

Using a technology called Sea Beam, scientists make accurate maps of the ocean floor. A ship equipped with Sea Beam, shown in **Figure 8-17,** has more than a dozen sonar devices, each aimed at different parts of the sea. Computers assemble these sonar data into detailed, continuous maps of the ocean floor.

Figure 8-17 This underwater formation was mapped using data from Sea Beam.

Section Assessment

1. Why does Greenland appear to be larger on a Mercator projection than it does on a Robinson projection?

2. Why can't contour lines ever cross?

3. Name two remote-sensing devices.

4. **Think Critically:** Suppose you have a topographic map with a contour interval of 50 m. According to the map scale, 1 cm on the map equals 1 km. The distance between points A and B on the map is 8 cm. Four contour lines lie between them. How far apart are the points, and what is the change in elevation?

5. **Skill Builder**
   Making Models Architects use detailed maps called scale drawings to help them plan their work. Do the **Chapter 8 Skill Activity** on page 715 to make a scale drawing of your classroom.

Science **Journal** Draw a map in your Science Journal that your friends could use to get from school to your home. Include symbols and a map scale.

Design Your Own Experiment

Activity 8·1

Modeling Earth

Have you ever built a model plane, train, or car? Modeling is more than just fun. Models are used to help engineers and designers build actual planes, trains, and cars. A topographic map is a two-dimensional model—on flat paper. How can you build a three-dimensional model of a landform?

Possible Materials

- Fine-point, transparency marker
- Blank transparency
- Overhead projector
- Sheet of white paper
- Pencil
- Tape
- Corrugated cardboard sheets
  * foam board sheets
- Scissors
- Glue
- Metric ruler

  Alternate Materials

Recognize the Problem

How can a 3-D model be made of an area shown on a topographic map?

Form a Hypothesis

Based on the drawing below, state a hypothesis about how you can make a large model of Blackberry Hill, such that its base is the length of a piece of notebook paper.

Goals

- **Design and make a 3-D model** that shows the relationship between topographic maps and landforms.
- **Interpret** data from your model.

Safety Precautions

Be careful while working near the overhead projector light. It can get hot. While using scissors, be careful not to cut yourself.

Test Your Hypothesis

Plan

1. With your partner, **design** a way that you can make an enlarged **copy** of the topographical features of Blackberry Hill using a transparency marker, overhead projector, pencil, sheet of white paper, and tape. **Write down** the steps you will take.

2. **Explain** how you can use the contour lines on your white paper as patterns for making the different layers of your model.

3. **Describe** a way to make your 3-D model using stacked sheets of cardboard or foam board.

Do

1. Make sure your teacher approves your plan before you proceed.

2. Read over your entire plan to make sure that all steps are in a logical order.

3. **Build** your model as planned.

4. While the activity is going on, **record** observations in your Science Journal.

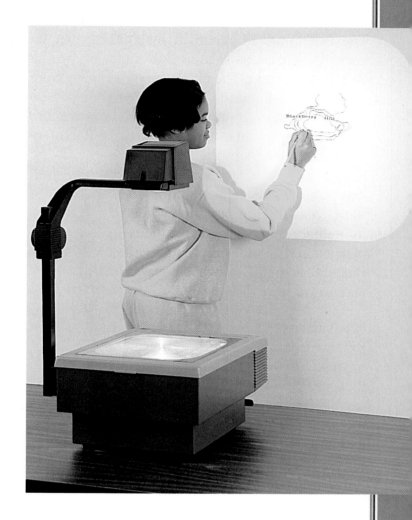

Analyze Your Data

1. **Compare** your model with other students' models. How are they similar? How are they different?

2. **Determine** the horizontal scale of your model.

Draw Conclusions

1. **Infer** what the height of each sheet in your model represents.

2. **Describe** the most difficult part of making your model.

Mapmaking

Ancient Maps

The beginnings of recorded mapmaking can be traced to ancient civilizations such as Babylonia, Egypt, India, China, and Mesopotamia. The oldest surviving maps were made on clay tablets and mosaic tile. Those early maps were used to mark property boundaries and to keep records for taxation. Other early cultures used maps for different purposes. Marshall Islanders in the Pacific made navigation charts. In Mexico, people mapped roads. In the sixth century B.C., the Greeks used information gathered by military and sailing expeditions to map bodies of water and landmasses. But, Greek maps drawn on paper or parchment have disappeared.

Map Improvements

By the thirteenth century, advances in mathematics led to more accurate measurements. Mapmakers, called cartographers, used these measurements and their observations of physical features to create more detailed maps. The development of the printing press and engraving techniques made maps more widely available. From the sixteenth to nineteenth centuries, explorers provided increasingly accurate maps of coastlines and interior areas.

View from Above

Aerial photography (inset) revolutionized mapmaking through photogrammetry—making measurements from photographs. Today, photographs from space satellites give cartographers even greater details of Earth. In addition, modern cartographers use computers to make and update maps. When they enter data on a computer, the computer draws the map. Digital map data can be used in many ways. For instance, computer programs in cars can inform drivers where they are and how to reach their destinations.

Science JOURNAL

Pretend you have hidden a treasure. In your Science Journal, draw a map that would lead a friend to the treasure.

Making a Topographic Map

Materials

- Plastic model landform
- Water tinted with food coloring
- Transparency
- Clear, plastic storage box with lid
- Beaker
- Metric ruler
- Tape
- Transparency marker

Have you ever wondered how topographic maps are made? Today, radar and remote-sensing devices aboard satellites collect data, and computers and graphic systems make the maps. In the past, surveyors and aerial photographers collected data. Then, maps were hand drawn by cartographers, or map-makers. In this activity, you can try your hand at cartography.

What You'll Investigate

How is a topographic map made?

Goals

- **Make** a topographic map.
- **Compare and contrast** contour intervals.

Procedure

1. Using the ruler and the transparency marker, make marks up the side of the storage box 2 cm apart.

2. **Secure** the transparency to the outside of the box lid with tape.

3. Place the plastic model in the box. The bottom of the box will be zero elevation.

4. Using the beaker, **pour** water into the box to a height of 2 cm. Place the lid on the box.

5. Use the transparency marker to **trace** the top of the water line on the transparency.

6. Using the scale 2 cm = 10 m, **mark** the elevation on the line.

7. Remove the lid and **add** water until a depth of 4 cm is reached.

8. **Map** this level on the storage box lid and **record** the elevation.

9. Repeat the process of **adding** water and **tracing** until you have the hill **mapped.**

10. **Transfer** the tracing of the hill onto a sheet of white paper.

Conclude and Apply

1. What is the contour interval of this topographic map?

2. How does the distance between contour lines on the map show the steepness of the slope on the landform model?

3. **Determine** the total elevation of the hill.

4. How was elevation represented on your map?

5. How are elevations shown on topographic maps?

6. Must all topographic maps have a 0-m elevation contour line? **Explain.**

7. **Compare** the contour interval of an area of high relief with one of low relief on a topographic map.

For a **preview** of this chapter, study this Reviewing Main Ideas before you read the chapter. After you have studied this chapter, you can use the Reviewing Main Ideas to **review** the chapter.

The Glencoe MindJogger, Audiocassettes, and CD-ROM provide additional opportunities for review.

Section 8-1 LANDFORMS

The three main types of landforms are plains, plateaus, and mountains. **Plains** are large, flat areas. **Plateaus** are relatively flat, raised areas of land made up of nearly horizontal rocks that have been uplifted by forces within Earth. **Mountains** rise high above the surrounding land. They vary greatly in size and how they are formed. *Which type of mountain is shown here?*

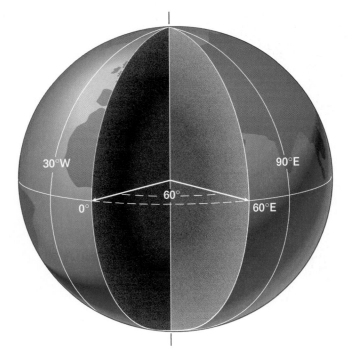

Section 8-2 VIEWPOINTS

Latitude and **longitude** form an imaginary grid system that enables points on Earth to be located exactly. **Latitude** is the distance in degrees north or south of the equator. Lines of latitude are parallel to the equator. **Longitude** is the distance in degrees east or west of the prime meridian. The prime meridian runs through Greenwich, England. *What line of longitude is located on the side of Earth opposite to the prime meridian?*

Reading Check ✓

● Locate three or four words that are not on the vocabulary list but were unfamiliar to you before you read this chapter. Define these words.

Section

8-3 MAPS

Topographic maps show the changes in elevation of Earth's surface. **Mercator, Robinson,** and **conic projections** are made by transferring points and lines on a globe's surface onto paper. *Why are all map projections distorted in either the shapes of landmasses or the areas of landmasses?*

REMOTE SENSING

Remote Sensing is a way of collecting information about Earth from a distance. Satellites and sonar are two remote-sensing devices. Using sonar, for instance, scientists can make detailed maps of the ocean floor. Other remote-sensing devices are used to navigate or track wildlife. *What is the Global Positioning System?*

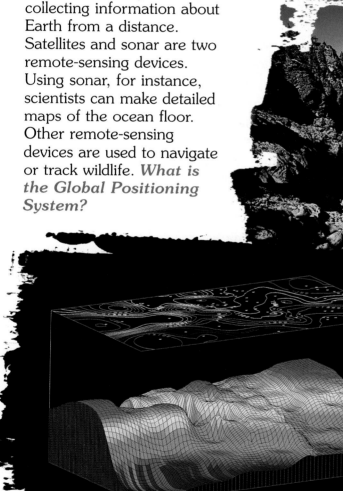

Chapter 8 Assessment

Using Vocabulary

a. conic projection
b. contour interval
c. contour line
d. equator
e. fault-block mountain
f. folded mountain
g. International Date Line
h. latitude
i. longitude
j. map legend
k. map scale
l. Mercator projection
m. plain
n. plateau
o. prime meridian
p. remote sensing
q. Robinson projection
r. topographic map
s. upwarped mountain
t. volcanic mountain

For each set of terms below, choose the one term that does not belong and explain why it does not belong.

1. contour interval, contour line, conic projection
2. map scale, latitude, longitude
3. upwarped mountain, equator, volcanic mountain
4. plain, plateau, prime meridian
5. Mercator projection, Robinson projection, remote sensing

Checking Concepts

Choose the word or phrase that best answers the question.

6. What makes up about 50 percent of all land areas in the United States?
   A) plateaus   C) mountains
   B) plains   D) volcanoes

7. Where is the north pole located?
   A) 0°N   C) 50°N
   B) 180°N   D) 90°N

8. What kind of mountains are the Hawaiian Islands?
   A) fault-block   C) upwarped
   B) volcanic   D) folded

9. What do we call lines parallel to the equator?
   A) lines of latitude   C) lines of longitude
   B) prime meridians   D) contour lines

10. How many degrees apart are the 24 time zones?
    A) 10   C) 15
    B) 34   D) 25

11. Which type of map is distorted at the poles?
    A) conic   C) Robinson
    B) topographic   D) Mercator

12. Which type of map shows changes in elevation at Earth's surface?
    A) conic   C) Robinson
    B) topographic   D) Mercator

13. What is measured with respect to sea level?
    A) contour interval   C) conic projection
    B) elevation   D) sonar

14. What marks are used to show depressions on topographic maps?
    A) degrees   C) hachures
    B) scales   D) legends

15. Which major U.S. landform includes the Grand Canyon?
    A) Great Plains
    B) Colorado Plateau
    C) Gulf Coastal Plain
    D) Appalachian Mountains

Thinking Critically

16. How would a topographic map of the Atlantic Coastal Plain differ from a topographic map of the Rocky Mountains?

17. If you left Korea early Wednesday morning and flew to Hawaii, on what day of the week would you arrive?

18. If you were flying directly south from the north pole and reached 70° north latitude, how many more degrees of latitude would be left to pass over before reaching the south pole?

19. Using a map, arrange these cities in order from the city with the earliest time to that with the latest time on a given day: Anchorage, Alaska; San Francisco, California; Bangor, Maine; Columbus, Ohio; Houston, Texas.

20. What does a map scale of 1:50 000 mean?

Developing Skills

If you need help, refer to the Skill Handbook.

21. Measuring in SI: What is the area in square kilometers of the topographic map in the Problem Solving feature in Section 8-3?

22. Comparing and Contrasting: Compare and contrast Mercator, Robinson, and conic map projections.

23. Concept Mapping: Make a network tree concept map that explains how topographic maps are used. Use the following terms: *topographic maps, mountains, rivers, natural features, contour lines, changes in elevation, equal elevation, hills,* and *plains.*

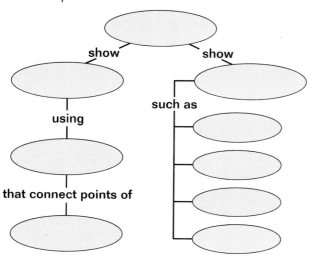

Test-Taking Tip

Stock Up on Supplies Be sure to supply yourself with the test-taking essentials: number two pencils, pens, erasers, a ruler, and a pencil sharpener. If the room doesn't have a pencil sharpener, a broken pencil can be a problem.

Test Practice

Use these questions to test your Science Proficiency.

1. The Adirondack Mountains are upwarped mountains. Today, the rock material that was once present on the tops of these mountains is gone. Why?
   A) The rock material was pushed inside Earth.
   B) Sharp peaks and ridges formed over the rock material.
   C) The rock material became magma.
   D) The rock material was eroded.

2. Ships use sonar to detect and map ocean-bottom features. Which of the following events occurs first in the map-making process?
   A) Computers transform sonar data into detailed maps.
   B) A sound wave is sent from the ship to the ocean floor.
   C) Computers calculate the distance from the ship to the ocean floor.
   D) A receiving device picks up the echo of sonar bouncing off the ocean floor.

9

Resources

Chapter Preview

Skills Preview

Skill Builders
- Make and Use a Graph

Activities
- Design an Experiment
- Interpret Data

MiniLabs
- Model

Reading Check ✓

List the chapter vocabulary in a column. Next to each word, write what you think the word means. As you read, change your definitions whenever needed.

Explore Activity

Do you know that you use resources 24 hours a day? Even when you are asleep, resources are used to light streetlights and heat your home. Resources also were used to make your pajamas, your sheets, and the bed you sleep in. Where do these resources come from? Look no farther than the nearest farm or forest for the resources that provide you with countless products. Where do we get the resources to meet our energy needs? Coal, oil, and natural gas provide much of our energy, but we also harness energy from wind, water, and the sun. In fact, the greatest source of energy on Earth is the sun.

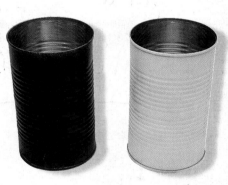

Observe Sun Energy

1. Get two empty tin cans from your teacher. Paint the outside of one can black or wrap it in black construction paper. Paint the outside of the other can white or wrap it in white construction paper.

2. Fill both cans with cool tap water. Record the temperature of the water in each can.

3. Tape a piece of black construction paper over the top of the black can. Tape a piece of white construction paper over the top of the white can. Place both cans in direct sunlight.

4. After an hour, record the temperature of the water in both cans.

Science Journal

Which had the greater increase in temperature—the water in the black can or the water in the white can? How does the color of an object affect its ability to absorb energy from the sun? Which color of clothing would be best for summer?

9•1 Energy Resources

Generating Energy

Does your day start like this? You wake up to the BEEP-BEEP of the alarm clock. You switch on the light and stumble toward the bathroom. You take a hot shower, then head back to your bedroom to dress. You flip on the radio to hear the weather report so you know what to wear. Your day has hardly begun and already you've used electricity at least four times. Have you ever wondered where your electricity comes from?

Fossil Fuels

In the United States, electrical power plants are the main sources of energy for homes and factories. Energy is the ability to change things, such as the temperature, speed, or direction of an object. When energy is used to change things, energy itself often changes from one form to another. Wood, for instance, contains chemical energy. As wood is burned, its chemical energy is changed into heat and light energy. Most power plants produce electricity by burning fossil fuels. **Fossil fuels** are energy resources formed from the decaying remains of ancient plants and animals. Coal, oil, and natural gas are examples of fossil fuels. Let's take a closer look at how these important energy resources are formed.

What You'll Learn

▶ Advantages and disadvantages of using fossil fuels
▶ Nonrenewable resources

Vocabulary
fossil fuel
pollution
acid rain
nonrenewable

Why It's Important

▶ Energy resources provide the electricity you use.

VISUALIZING Coal Formation

Figure 9-1 Coal is formed from the remains of ancient swamp vegetation.

 As the plants died and fell into the swamp, they were covered by layers of sediment. Over time, heat and pressure caused the decayed plants to form into a solid layer of lignite.

Coal

The coal we use today began to form millions of years ago in swampy regions where huge, fernlike plants grew in abundance. When the plants died and fell into the swamp, they were covered by sediments such as mud, sand, and other dead plants. Layer upon layer of sediments piled up. The weight of these sediments pressed down on the decayed matter. The intense pressure generated heat. The combination of heat and pressure changed the decayed material into a soft, brown coal called lignite. Over time, more and more layers of sediments piled on top of the lignite, and further changes occurred in the coal, as shown in **Figure 9-1.**

Oil and Natural Gas

Most geologists agree that oil and natural gas form over millions of years from the decay of algae and tiny ocean animals that are called plankton. The process begins when these organisms die, fall to the seafloor, and pile up. Over the course of centuries, these decaying organisms pile up on the ocean floor. Over time, thick layers of sand and mud are deposited over the decayed organisms, in the same way that coal is buried by sediments. As with coal, the combination of pressure and heat causes chemical reactions to occur.

LIFE SCIENCE
INTEGRATION

Fossilized Shells
Through experience, geologists have found that when they drill into Earth's crust and find certain types of fossil shells, oil is probably nearby. These fossil shells are often the remains of tiny ocean organisms called foraminifera (fuh ram uh NIHF ra). Find out more about foraminifera. In your Science Journal, write a brief paragraph explaining why foraminifera are commonly found near oil deposits.

B More layers of sediment piled on top of the lignite and compressed it even further. With the deeper layers, temperatures also increased and lignite became bituminous coal.

C When layers of bituminous coal were severely compressed and heated by forces within Earth, the layers changed into anthracite coal, the hardest of all coals.

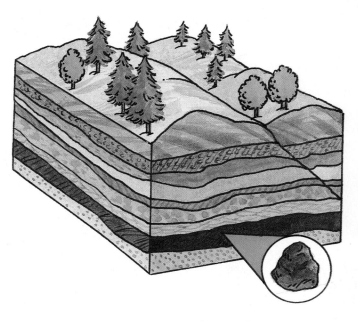

Figure 9-2 Engineers drill through layers of rock to reach underground deposits of oil and natural gas.

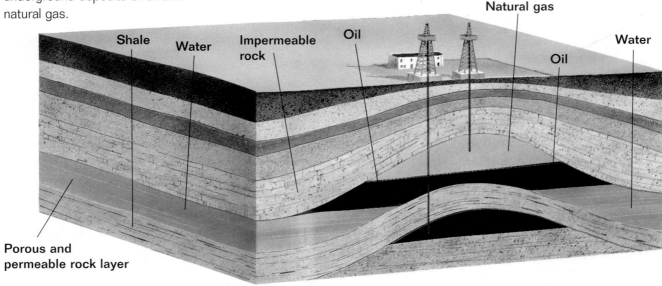

Shale   Water   Impermeable rock   Oil   Natural gas   Oil   Water

Porous and permeable rock layer

The decayed material eventually forms the liquid we call oil and the gases we call natural gas. **Figure 9-2** shows how engineers reach the oil and natural gas stored in Earth.

Pollution and Fossil Fuels

Think again of all the ways you use electricity each morning. Your life would be very different if we didn't have fossil fuels to generate energy. Fossil fuels are important resources. However, when they are burned to produce energy, environmental problems can occur. When fossil fuels are burned in cars, power plants, homes, and factories, gases such as nitrogen oxide and sulfur oxide and tiny bits of soot and dust are released into the air. These substances cause pollution. **Pollution** is the introduction of harmful waste products, chemicals, and substances into the environment. ☑

Air pollution can make your throat feel dry or your eyes sting. Many people have trouble breathing when air pollution levels are high. For the elderly and people with lung or heart problems, air pollution can be deadly. In the United States, about 60 000 deaths each year are linked to air pollution.

People aren't the only living things that are harmed by air pollution. Acid rain causes a lot of damage to other organisms. **Acid rain** is produced when gases released by burning oil and coal mix with water in the air to form acidic rain or snow. Some scientists hypothesize that when acid rain falls on the ground, plants and trees die. When acid rain falls into rivers and lakes, it can kill fish.

Reading Check ☑

What is pollution?

Spare the Air

The best solution for air pollution is prevention. Reducing the number of pollutants released into the air is easier to do than cleaning up the pollutants already in the air. As shown in **Figure 9-3,** new cars are made today that release fewer harmful gases and use less fuel than older models. Governments around the world also are working together to find ways to reduce the amount of air pollutants that are released into the atmosphere by factories.

Nonrenewable Resources

Problems with fossil fuels aren't limited to pollution alone. We may find ourselves running out of these energy resources if we use up our supply of fossil fuels. Can this happen? Many people think so. Remember that the process of fossil fuel formation can take millions of years. Plants and animals that die today won't become fossil fuels for many centuries. What impact does this factor have on our use of fossil fuels? Are we using them faster than they are being replaced?

Figure 9-3 Modern cars use catalytic converters and unleaded gasoline. Both features help reduce the amount of pollutants released into the air. The streamlined shape and tires of modern cars help increase gas mileage, which in turn helps reduce use of fossil fuels.

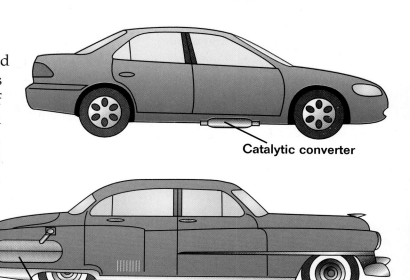

Catalytic converter

Gas tank

1950s-type car

Problem Solving

Estimate Car Pooling Benefits

Sally, Fred, Jose, and Tania live in the same neighborhood and work in the same city. Each drives 60 km round-trip to work, five days a week, 50 weeks a year. Each pays 4 dollars per workday to park his or her car. It costs each 20 cents per kilometer for gasoline and car maintenance. Tania has suggested that they start a car pool to save money.

Think Critically: How much money could each driver save if they participate equally in the car pool? Assume that the four drivers take their two-week vacations at the same time and that their four cars get similar gas mileage. In your Science Journal, show the steps you took to calculate your answer.

> mileage = 60 km for 5 days a week
> 50 weeks/year
>
> parking costs = $4/day
> gasoline and maintenance = 20 cents/km

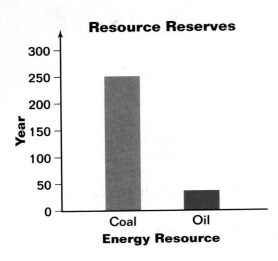

Resource Reserves

Figure 9-4 This graph shows available reserves of coal and oil. **What might you do at home to help lower use of fossil fuels?**

If you answered yes, you're right. Some energy resources are being used faster than natural processes can replace them. Resources that cannot be replaced by natural processes in less than 100 years are **nonrenewable.** Fossil fuels are nonrenewable. This means that we may run out of these important sources of energy someday. The question is, when?

How much is left?

At current rates of use, coal provides about 29 percent of the world's energy needs, and oil and natural gas provide almost 61 percent. As **Figure 9-4** shows, scientists estimate that we have enough coal reserves to last 200 to 300 years at present rates of usage. But, our available reserves of oil may be used up within 30 to 40 years.

How can we solve this problem? Conserving electricity helps reduce pollution. It also helps lower the use of fossil fuels. Can you think of other ways to help? How about this—we can use other energy resources in addition to fossil fuels to meet our energy needs. In the next section, you'll learn about alternative sources of energy that can be used again and again.

Section Assessment

1. Why is coal considered a nonrenewable resource?
2. Describe two problems with the use of fossil fuels.
3. Explain how acid rain forms.
4. Why are coal, oil, and natural gas called fossil fuels?
5. **Think Critically:** Why are you likely to find natural gas and oil deposits together, but less likely to find coal deposits at the same location?
6. **Skill Builder**
   Recognizing Cause and Effect
   Explain how keeping a television on overnight has an impact on the environment. Relate your answer to use of fossil fuels. If you need help, refer to Recognizing Cause and Effect in the **Skill Handbook** on page 687.

Using Math

In the United States, there are 5630 cars for every 10 000 people. In Cambodia, a country in Southeast Asia, there is only one car for every 10 000 people. The population of the United States is about 263 million; the population of Cambodia is nearly 10 million. How many cars are in each country?

Solar Cells

Solar cells are devices that use sunlight to produce electricity. They can be used to warm and light houses and other buildings as well as to run appliances, pump water, and power a car. Some watches, calculators, and toys run on solar energy, and solar cells also provide power for objects in space, such as the *Hubble Space Telescope* shown at left.

HOW A SOLAR CELL WORKS

1 The central part of a solar cell is made of two thin layers of substances called semiconductors. A semiconductor is an element that conducts an electric current better than a nonmetal but not as well as a metal.

2 These layers are sandwiched between metal contacts that connect the solar cell with an electric circuit.

3 The entire solar cell is enclosed in glass or some other transparent material.

4 When sunlight strikes the cell, some electrons gain enough energy to break free from the atoms in the semiconductors.

5 This electron flow creates an electric current through the electric circuit.

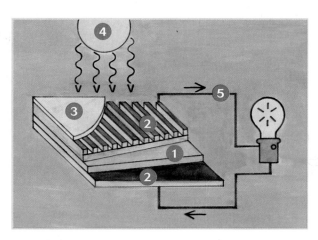

Career
CONNECTION

Currently, more than 200 000 homes around the world use solar cell systems to provide all their electricity. Such systems, however, are still expensive to produce. Solar engineers are working to improve the efficiency of these systems. A solar engineer must have a degree in electrical engineering and a good knowledge of math, physics, and graphic design. Find out more about the jobs done by these engineers. Then, make a list of the kinds of companies and agencies that might employ solar engineers.

Think Critically

1. What do you think is the purpose of the outer-glass shell of a solar cell?

2. Solar cells can be linked to form solar panels. Solar panels can be used to heat houses. Do you think such a heating system would be more efficient in Nome, Alaska, or Houston, Texas? Explain.

9•2 Alternative Energy Resources

What You'll Learn

► Different kinds of renewable resources
► Advantages and disadvantages of using alternative energy resources

Vocabulary
renewable
solar energy
hydroelectric power
geothermal energy
nuclear energy

Why It's Important

► Many alternative sources of energy are renewable.

Other Sources of Energy

When you sit in the sun, walk in the wind, or swim against an ocean current, you are feeling the power of resources that can be used to meet our energy needs. But unlike fossil fuels, sun, wind, and water are energy resources that can be used again and again. They are constant—the sun has shone for millions of years and will shine for millions more. Energy resources that can be recycled or replaced by natural processes in less than 100 years are considered **renewable.** Some renewable energy resources include the sun, wind, water, and geothermal energy.

Solar Energy

Suppose you're a scientist trying to find a single source of energy to meet all the world's needs. You might look to the sun for a solution. Energy from the sun is renewable and it doesn't cause pollution. Plus, enough energy from the sun reaches Earth in an hour to supply all the energy the world

Figure 9-5 The mirrors on this tower in France collect energy from the sun. **Describe one advantage of solar-energy use.**

uses in one year. Currently, we do not have the technology to harness all of the sun's energy. But we do use energy from the sun, called **solar energy**, for many things. One example is shown in **Figure 9-5**. This towering structure of flat mirrors is located outside the town of Odeillo, France. The mirrors are positioned to focus energy from the sun on one part of the tower. The heat is used to run a laboratory inside the tower, where temperatures can reach as high as 3300°C.

Figure 9-6 The model train and the calculator shown here receive their power from the sun.
What are solar cells?

Solar Cells

Other types of solar-energy technology are much simpler than the example shown in **Figure 9-5**. For instance, you may have used a solar calculator to complete your homework assignments. Solar calculators, such as the one shown in **Figure 9-6,** are powered by solar cells, which collect light and change it into electricity. In a solar cell, thin layers of silicon—a hard, dark-colored element—are sandwiched together and attached to tiny wires. As light strikes the different layers, it produces an electrical current.

Is solar energy the answer?

Nonpolluting, renewable, and abundant—solar energy sounds like a wonderful way to generate energy, doesn't it? So why don't we rely on solar energy to meet all of our energy needs?

Solar energy has some serious drawbacks. It's available only when the sun is shining, so solar cells can't work at night. In addition, different parts of Earth receive different amounts of solar energy. If you live in an area that is cloudy much of the time, it's doubtful that solar energy can meet all of your energy needs because solar cells work less efficiently during cloudy days. At this point, we don't have the technology to harness and store effectively all the sun's vast energy. Until we do, some scientists think that the best solution to energy problems may be to use fossil fuels and solar energy, in combination with other energy sources. You'll read about these next. ☑

Reading Check ☑
Describe one problem with solar energy use.

Energy from Wind

Imagine this. Outside, the sky is a clear shade of blue and the wind scatters fallen leaves across the street. Inside, a kite hangs in your closet. Can you think of a good way to spend the day?

A windy day is perfect for flying a kite. A strong wind can lift a kite high in the sky and whip it all around. When you fly a kite, you use energy from the wind. Energy from wind was and still is used to send sailboats skimming across the ocean. In the past, windmills, such as the one shown in **Figure 9-7,** used wind energy to grind corn and pump water. Today, windmills also are used to generate electricity. When a large number of windmills are placed in one area for the purpose of generating electricity, the area is called a wind farm.

Like all forms of energy, energy from the wind has advantages and disadvantages. Wind is nonpolluting; it produces no environmental harm or waste. However, only a few regions of the world have winds strong enough to generate electricity on a large scale. Also, wind isn't steady. Sometimes it blows too hard; sometimes it stops altogether.

Figure 9-7 This windmill in California uses energy from the wind to pump water.

Figure 9-8 Water in the reservoir is released through gateways into pipes near the base of the dam.

A The pipes lead to the turbines. Because of the weight of the water in the reservoir above, the water in the pipes is under great pressure as it falls to the turbines.

Hydroelectric Power

If you've ever watched a river flow, you've seen a form of energy in action. Energy from moving water can also generate electricity. The production of electricity by water is called **hydroelectric power.** People in southern Canada and the eastern United States use the power of the water in the Niagara Falls to generate hydroelectric power for a number of large cities. In other places where there are no natural waterfalls, people have built concrete dams to produce hydroelectricity. The Shasta Dam, on northern California's Sacramento River, is the tallest structure of its type in the world. What happens to the water of the Sacramento River behind the dam?

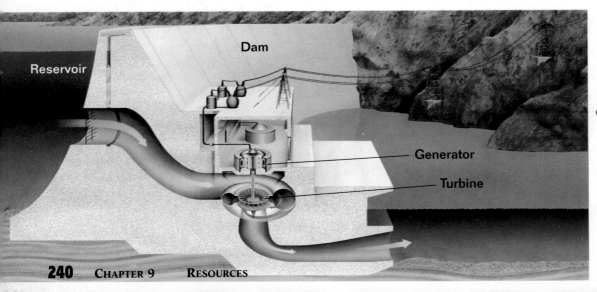

B The pressure of the water turns the turbines that drive the electrical generators in the plant.

The river water that backs up behind a dam creates a reservoir or large reserve of water. Many reservoirs are big enough to be considered lakes. Lake Shasta, the reservoir created by the dam on the Sacramento River, is 56 km wide. Look at **Figure 9-8** to see how a dam and a hydroelectric power plant work to generate electricity.

Hydroelectric Power Problems

Like solar power and energy from the wind, hydroelectric power doesn't cause pollution and it's renewable. But this energy resource has its problems. When dams are built, the reservoir located behind the dam can fill with sediment, and increased erosion can occur downstream. Land above the dam is flooded and wildlife habitats are disturbed. In addition, dams and power plants have already been built near most rivers suitable for generating hydroelectricity. Other places can't use hydroelectric power because they're not located near fast-flowing water.

Energy from Earth

Another renewable energy resource can be found under Earth's surface near beds of hot molten rock called magma. The heated rocks that surround the magma produce **geothermal energy,** or heat energy from Earth, which can be used to generate electricity. **Figure 9-9** shows a geyser in New Zealand that produces geothermal energy. A geyser forms when water reaches the heated rocks and turns to steam. Heat and pressure from surrounding layers of rock produce steam and force it up in powerful spurts through openings in Earth's crust. This is an example of geothermal energy that occurs when magma is located close to Earth's surface. People in Iceland and California use the hot water and steam from the geysers to heat their homes.

Sometimes magma is not found close to Earth's surface, so engineers have to drill wells to reach the heated rock that surrounds the magma.

Mini Lab

Modeling the Effects of Heat

Procedure

1. Fill a glass beaker with cold water.
2. Fill a small, clear plastic bottle nearly full of cold water. Add several drops of food coloring to the bottle.
3. Carefully lower the small bottle into the beaker so that the bottle is upright underwater. Hold the bottle in place, if necessary. Observe what happens to the colored liquid inside the bottle.
4. Repeat the experiment, but this time fill the bottle with hot water. Observe what happens to the colored liquid inside the bottle.

Analysis

1. How did heat affect the movement of the colored liquid inside the bottle?
2. Changes in heat and pressure force hot water under Earth's surface to rise. How is the movement of the colored liquid in the bottle similar to the movement of hot water under Earth?

Figure 9-9 Geothermal energy is generated by geysers such as this one in New Zealand.

Heat and pressure then force the steam to rise to Earth's surface. There, it can be used to turn mechanical energy into electrical energy, much like the energy of moving water can be used to produce electricity.

Geothermal Energy Problems

As you've been learning, the use of each type of energy resource has advantages and disadvantages. Geothermal energy is no exception. Like fossil fuels, geothermal energy can release gases into the atmosphere that pollute the air. In addition, only a few places have magma near Earth's surface. To generate geothermal power elsewhere, deep wells must be drilled. This process is expensive and can disrupt natural habitats near the well.

inter NET
C O N N E C T I O N

Visit the Glencoe Science Web Site at **www. glencoe.com/sec/ science/fl** for more information about nuclear energy.

Nuclear Energy

Atoms are the basic units of matter, and each atom contains a nucleus. All nuclei (singular *nucleus*) store energy. Scientists have found a way to generate energy from atoms. This is called nuclear energy. **Nuclear energy** is produced by splitting the nuclei of certain elements. In this process, known as fission, neutrons inside the nuclei are released. This produces heat energy that is used to change water into steam. The steam is then used to change mechanical energy into electrical energy, as shown in **Figure 9-10.**

The most commonly used fuel in nuclear power plants is the ore uranium. Uranium has a nucleus that can be split easily. Once the ore is mined, it's refined and placed in long, metal pipes called fuel rods. The fuel rods sit in a pool of cooling water within a nuclear reactor, shown in **Figure 9-11.** Energy is released when neutrons given off by the uranium split the nuclei of other uranium atoms, which in turn release more neutrons and more energy. This process, known as a chain reaction, happens very fast.

Figure 9-10 Heat energy is generated by fission within the nuclear reactor. This heat is used to change water into steam. The steam moves the turbine, which is connected to a generator that produces electrical energy.

Nuclear Energy Problems

Nuclear energy produces more than electricity; it also produces nuclear waste. This waste material is highly radioactive. This means that the waste contains materials that can cause cancer or have other

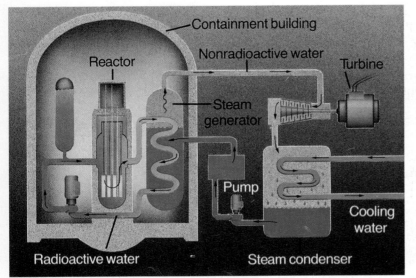

harmful effects on living things. Some of the waste will remain radioactive for more than 10 000 years. Nuclear waste must be handled and stored carefully to keep it from harming living things or from entering the environment. As you may have guessed, this is a major drawback in using nuclear power.

Nuclear Energy Use

Because of potential problems in storing nuclear waste, nuclear energy has seen limited use in the United States. Electricity generated from nuclear power makes up only eight percent of the total energy used in the United States. Worldwide, about 25 countries use nuclear energy to generate electricity. France leads the world in production of nuclear energy—more than 80 percent of France's energy needs are met by nuclear power.

Currently, the use of nuclear energy and renewable energy resources is limited. But improvements in technology may enable these resources, particularly the sun, to be major sources of energy in the future.

Figure 9-11 Fuel rods are placed in a nuclear reactor. Most of the high-level radioactive waste in the United States comes from used fuel rods.

Section Assessment

1. What is a renewable resource?
2. What are some advantages and disadvantages of solar energy, wind energy, and hydroelectric energy?
3. Compare and contrast nuclear energy use in the United States and France.
4. **Think Critically:** A well is drilled near a body of magma to produce electricity. Explain how energy changes form during this process.
5.  **Skill Builder**
   Using Numbers Wind farms and solar power plants take up a good deal of land. Do the **Chapter 9 Skill Activity** on page 716 to interpret how much land is required for these alternative energy sources.

Science Journal In your Science Journal, develop a plan to meet your town's energy needs using at least three different energy resources. Describe the energy sources that will provide electricity to buildings and homes. Explain why you chose each resource.

9·3 Water

What You'll Learn

- How important water is to living things
- Different sources of water
- How the location of water affects where humans live

Vocabulary
groundwater
point source
nonpoint source

Why It's Important

- You'll learn how water becomes polluted and what you can do to help keep it clean.

Figure 9-12
All living things need clean water to survive.

Water—A Vital Resource

Have you ever seen a picture of Earth from space, such as the one shown in **Figure 9-12A?** What strikes you most about the photograph? Earth has lots of water, doesn't it? In fact, about 70 percent of Earth is covered by water. This water continually moves through the water cycle, which is shown in **Figure 9-12B.** Water helps shape Earth's surface through the processes of erosion and deposition. Most importantly, water keeps all living things alive. Without water, living things could not carry out important life processes, such as growth and waste removal. Do you know that the bodies of most organisms are made up mostly of water? Scientists estimate that two-thirds of the weight of the human body is water. Water may be our most valuable resource. That's why it's important to know as much as we can about water, including how much is available and where it comes from.

Usable Water

Of the vast amount of water on Earth, only a small portion is available for use by humans. Approximately 97 percent of the world's total water supply is salt water in the oceans. That leaves only three percent as freshwater, and more than three-fourths of that is frozen in glaciers and ice caps. Thus, less than one percent of Earth's total

A About 70 percent of Earth is covered by water. **How much is available for use by humans?**

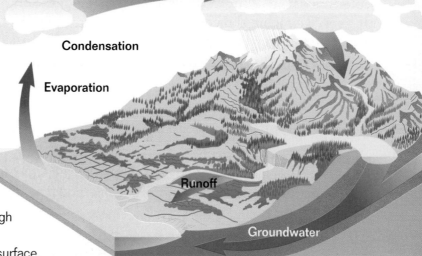

Precipitation

Condensation

Evaporation

Runoff

Groundwater

B The water cycle shows how water moves through the atmosphere, on the surface, and under the surface.

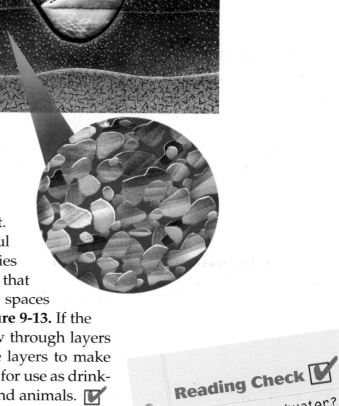

Figure 9-13 Groundwater is found under Earth's surface in small spaces between bits of soil and rock. **How do people reach groundwater?**

water supply is available for us to use for drinking, cooking, and other purposes. This one percent is found either underground or in lakes, streams, and rivers.

Groundwater

When you turn on a faucet, water flows out. Where does this water come from? One plentiful source of fresh water is groundwater that lies under Earth's surface. **Groundwater** is water that soaks into the ground and collects in small spaces between bits of soil and rock, as shown in **Figure 9-13.** If the small spaces are connected, the water can flow through layers of rock and soil. People drill down into these layers to make wells. They then pump the water to the surface for use as drinking water, for factories, or for watering crops and animals.

In the United States, groundwater provides 40 percent of public water supplies. Industries and farms also use groundwater. In many agricultural areas, groundwater is the only source of water available. Is this important resource renewable or nonrenewable? Some people consider groundwater renewable because it is part of the water cycle, which recycles water constantly. But, it takes a long time for groundwater to move through rock layers. Therefore, it can take a long time to clean up groundwater if it becomes polluted. Because of this, clean, usable groundwater should be considered a nonrenewable resource.

Reading Check ✔

What is groundwater?

Surface Water

Not all places get their water from underground. If you live in a city or town, you may be using surface water. Surface water comes from streams, rivers, ponds, lakes, and reservoirs—it's the water we can see easily on Earth's surface. Do you use surface water or groundwater to meet your water needs? If you don't know, find out. Ask your teacher or parents, or check with your city water department.

Water Use

Nothing is as refreshing as a glass of cold water on a hot summer day—except maybe a cool dip in a city pool. Our bodies need water to survive, but we also depend on water for recreational uses such as swimming, boating, and fishing. We need water to bathe, wash clothes, cook food, and water plants, and these are just a few of the ways we use water.

Water is also used by industries to manufacture products and to transport some of those products on boats to stores and factories. Boats also are used to transport people across oceans or along rivers. Farmers use water to irrigate crops and water animals. Can you think of any other uses for water? Many plants and animals live in oceans, lakes, or rivers. They spend their entire lives in water. Water is their home. What do you think might happen to these living things if the water they live in were polluted?

Figure 9-14 shows the impact polluted water can have on fish. Not a pretty sight, is it? Keep in mind that the same pollutants that can kill fish in rivers also can make their way into a city's water supply. That's why it's important to clean water before we use it and to clean it again after we use it. Before we examine some methods used to make sure that water supplies are clean and safe, let's take a look at how water can become polluted.

Try at Home
Mini Lab

Observing How Water Is Cleaned

Procedure

1. Fill a clean, empty mayonnaise jar two-thirds full of water.
2. Add a cup of potting soil to the jar.
3. Put the lid on the jar, close it tightly, then shake the jar until the water becomes muddy.
4. Put the jar aside and let it stand for two days.

Analysis

1. What happened to the soil in the jar? What happened to the water?
2. Look at **Figure 9-16.** Which part of the water-purification process did you model? Explain.
3. Which types of impurities would not be removed by the processes modeled in this activity?

Figure 9-14 This fish kill occurred on the lower Neuse River in North Carolina in 1995.

Figure 9-15 Water pollution can cause serious problems.

A This stream in Spain was polluted by industrial wastes.

B This oil spill, the dark color leaking from the tanker, may threaten marine organisms and nearby beaches.

Water Pollution

Have you ever seen a stream such as the one shown in **Figure 9-15A?** The chemicals found in the stream are an example of water pollution. Water pollution occurs when debris, chemicals, or biological materials are added to water. These pollutants lower its quality. Some pollution comes from a single, identifiable source called a **point source.** If an oil tanker such as the one shown in **Figure 9-15B** begins leaking, a skim of oil is released into the sea and directly pollutes the water. You can see the pollution occurring. Have you ever seen examples of this type of pollution near your home or school?

Most types of pollution are hard to trace to a single source. The pollution comes from many different sources, called **nonpoint sources,** such as industries, homes, and farms. How can a farm pollute water? Chemical fertilizers are used to increase crop yields. These fertilizers can be carried away by runoff and deposited in streams, lakes, and wetlands. Some of these chemicals seep into the ground and can pollute groundwater supplies. Can you think of any way that you might cause water pollution? If you spill gasoline in your driveway, the gasoline will be carried away by runoff. It can enter the city sewage system or a stream and eventually make its way into a drinking water supply.

Using Math

If all the world's water were represented by 100 mL in a graduated cylinder, how much of the water in the cylinder would be available to use as freshwater?

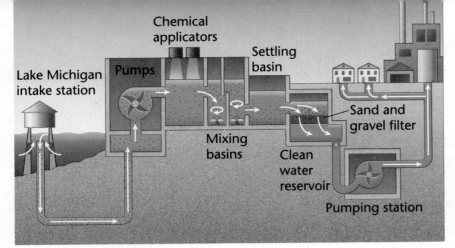

Figure 9-16 In this water-purification plant, water is pumped into a tank, where chemicals are added to kill microorganisms. The water is then mixed and run through a settling basin. Large particles of matter settle out. Smaller particles are filtered by sand and gravel. Clean water is then pumped to consumers.

Diagram labels: Lake Michigan intake station; Pumps; Chemical applicators; Settling basin; Mixing basins; Sand and gravel filter; Clean water reservoir; Pumping station

interNET
CONNECTION

Visit the Glencoe Science Web Site at **www. glencoe.com/sec/ science/fl** for more information about ways to reduce water pollution.

Cleaning Up Water

Many countries are working together to reduce the amount of water pollution. For example, the United States and Canada have agreed to clean up the pollution in Lake Erie, which borders both countries. The U.S. government also has passed several laws to keep water supplies clean. The Safe Drinking Water Act is a set of government standards designed to ensure safe drinking water. The Clean Water Act gives money to states to build water-treatment plants, such as the one shown in **Figure 9-16.** Water is cleaned at such plants before being used for drinking and other purposes.

Is there anything you can do to help reduce water pollution? Sure, there is. Keep pet wastes, leaves, oil, and other debris from entering storm drains, which often lead directly to streams or lakes. Properly dispose of hazardous substances, such as used oil, antifreeze, and paint; *do not* pour them down a storm drain.

Water Distribution

As you have learned, water is vital to the survival of all living things. Take a look at the map shown in **Figure 9-17.** Do you see a relationship between the location of major centers of population and major bodies of water? People usually build cities near shorelines and along large rivers. As you can see from the map, desert areas don't have many cities or towns.

Living near large bodies of water has its problems. Sometimes there are floods. Sometimes the water is too polluted to use. That's why so many countries have passed laws to reduce water pollution and to monitor the quality of the water supply. Water is a valuable resource—every bit as valuable as the energy resources you studied earlier. As you continue with the discovery of the many resources around you, you will gain an understanding of other natural resources.

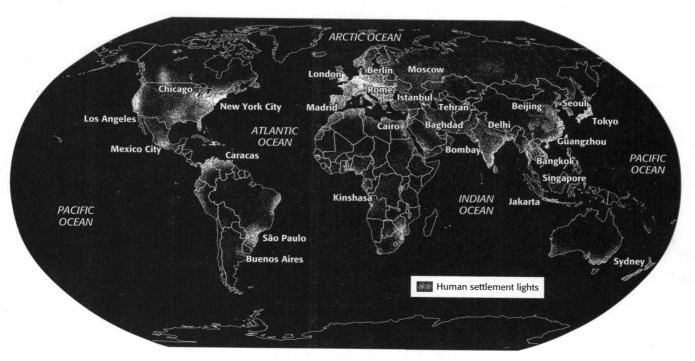

Figure 9-17 This map shows that most of the world's population is centered around large bodies of water. The lighter, white areas indicate human settlement. The lighter the area, the more dense the population.

Section Assessment

1. Why is water considered one of our most valuable resources?

2. List three ways that humans use water. Describe where the water comes from for each of these uses.

3. **Think Critically:** Some cities are located near desert areas. How do you think they might meet their demands for water?

4. **Skill Builder**
   Concept Mapping Make an events chain concept map that shows how soap chemicals in a bucket of water might end up as pollution in a local stream. If you need help, refer to Concept Mapping in the **Skill Handbook** on page 680.

*inter***NET**
CONNECTION

Visit the Glencoe Science Web Site at **www.glencoe.com/ sec/science/fl** for more information about the Clean Water Act. Then write a brief summary of how this legislation encourages water-quality standards in the United States.

Using Water

Materials

- Calculator

Water is an important resource that we use every day. You wash dishes and clothes and you wash yourself and brush your teeth. All of these activities require water. The average person in the United States uses about 397 L of water each day. Do this activity to see how much water you use.

What You'll Investigate

How much water does your family use in three days?

Goals

- **Calculate** how much water the people in your household use in three days.
- **Make a plan** to reduce the amount of water used by your family.
- **Describe** how people use water.

Procedure

1. Use the table on this page to **calculate** how much water your family uses.

2. For three days, have the people who live in your house **keep a record** of when they do the activities listed in the table. If your family members forget to mark down their water usage, complete the activity using your own water-usage record.

3. The numbers in the table describe approximately how many liters an average person uses in a single day for the activity listed. **Multiply** these numbers by the number of people in your household who did these activities.

4. **Add up** the totals for each day. The final sum will be the total amount of water used for these activities in three days.

Conclude and Apply

1. How much water did your family use in three days?

2. **Study** the activities listed in the table. Do you see any ways to reduce the amount of water used?

3. **Develop** a detailed plan to reduce the amount of water your family used.

4. **Study** the table again. It lists only a few ways in which your family uses water. **Describe** at least three other activities not listed in the table.

Activity	Conditions	Amount of Water Used
Washing dishes by hand	Water is running all the time	113 L/person/day
Washing dishes by hand	Sink is filled with water	19 L/person/day
Washing clothes in machine	Small load with high water setting	68 L/person/day
Washing clothes in machine	Full load with high water setting	45 L/person/day
Taking a shower	10 minutes long	150 L/person/day
Taking a bath	Bathtub is full of water	113 L/person/day
Flushing the toilet	Water-saving toilet	23 L/person/day
Brushing teeth	Water is running all the time	17 L/person/day

Land

Land as a Resource

Has your neighborhood changed lately? How about the outskirts of your town? Perhaps a grassy field has been turned into a parking lot, or some nearby farmland has become a place where new homes were built. These changes, shown in **Figure 9-18,** are examples of the different ways we use land as a resource. How else do we use land?

Land Use

Think about where your food comes from. We need land to raise the crops and animals we use for food. A simple peanut butter-and-jelly sandwich requires land to grow the wheat needed to make bread, land to grow peanuts for the peanut butter, and land to grow the sugarcane and fruit for the jelly. A hamburger? Land is needed to raise cattle and to grow the grain the cattle eat.

Think about your home, your school, and other places you go, like a park or a shopping mall. The things that you buy in the shopping mall come from factories. All these buildings take up space. This means that every time we build a house, a mall, or a factory, we use more land. Land is a renewable resource because in most cases, it can be used over and over again. But one look at a globe will show you that the amount of land is limited. Therefore, we have to make wise choices when it comes to land use.

What **You'll Learn**

► Land is a renewable resource
► Why trees are renewable resources, but forests are not
► How we use mineral resources

Vocabulary
conservation
ore

Why **It's Important**

► You'll know what resources are used to make some of the things you use every day.

Figure 9-18 This farmland will soon be a new housing development. **What are some other ways that we use land?**

Using Land Wisely

People need food, clothing, jobs, and a place to live, and each of these things takes space. But, preserving natural habitats, such as the one shown in **Figure 9-19,** is also important. Remember, a habitat is the place where organisms live. Ponds, wetlands, and forests are examples of natural habitats. If we fill in a wetland to construct an apartment building, an important natural habitat is lost.

Laws help to protect against habitat loss and help us use land wisely. Before major construction can take place in a new area, the land must be studied to determine the impact construction will have on the living things, the soil, and the water in the area. If endangered plants or animals live in the area, construction may not be allowed.

Problems can also arise when we use land for farming or grazing animals. If these activities are not done properly, soil can become eroded from overuse. **Figure 9-20** shows how farmers and ranchers work to reduce soil erosion problems.

Figure 9-19 People are working to protect natural habitats in many areas, such as this tropical rain forest in Costa Rica.

Resources from Land

We use land to grow crops, raise animals, and to live on. In addition to meeting our needs for food and shelter, land provides us with two other important resources: forests and minerals.

Figure 9-20

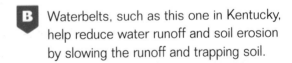

A Improper use of rangeland can cause soil erosion, as seen in this photo from Brazil.

B Waterbelts, such as this one in Kentucky, help reduce water runoff and soil erosion by slowing the runoff and trapping soil.

Figure 9-21

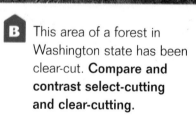

A Certain trees in this forest were cut down and new trees planted in their place. This is an example of select-cutting.

Forests

Look around your classroom. Do you see books, paper, desks, and pencils? All these products are made of wood. They come from trees in a forest that were cut down and taken to a lumberyard to be processed into boards and other wooden products.

In addition to providing us with much-needed wood, forests play an important role in keeping Earth's atmosphere in balance. How? Remember what you learned about photosynthesis. In this process, trees and other plants use carbon dioxide, water, and sunlight to make oxygen and carbohydrates. As forests grow, they take in carbon dioxide. If an entire forest is cut down, it doesn't take in carbon dioxide, and more of this gas is left in the atmosphere. Increases in atmospheric carbon dioxide may cause global warming, which is a rise in temperatures around the world. Global warming may lead to changes in climate that could impact natural habitats all over Earth.

B This area of a forest in Washington state has been clear-cut. **Compare and contrast select-cutting and clear-cutting.**

Forest Conservation

Because forests are such a valuable resource, they must be used with care. That's why many states now have forest conservation laws. **Conservation** is the careful use of resources with the goal of reducing damage to the environment. In **Figure 9-21,** some methods of forest conservation are shown.

In select-cutting, shown in **Figure 9-21A,** a limited number of trees are cut, and new trees are planted in their place. The young saplings grow among the older trees. By the time all of the original trees are cut, a new forest has gradually grown.

LIFE SCIENCE
◄ **INTEGRATION**

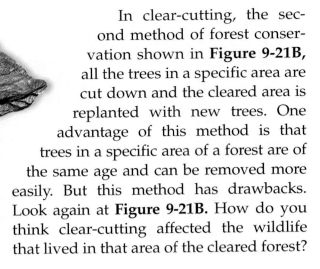

Figure 9-22 Motorcycle parts and saw blades are two of many products made from the iron ore hematite.

In clear-cutting, the second method of forest conservation shown in **Figure 9-21B**, all the trees in a specific area are cut down and the cleared area is replanted with new trees. One advantage of this method is that trees in a specific area of a forest are of the same age and can be removed more easily. But this method has drawbacks. Look again at **Figure 9-21B**. How do you think clear-cutting affected the wildlife that lived in that area of the cleared forest?

Renewable or Nonrenewable?

If you've ever planted a tree, you know that it takes time for a tree to grow. Some trees take many years to mature. Still, trees can be viewed as a renewable resource because as one tree is cut, another can be planted in its place.

Forests, on the other hand, are nonrenewable. Why? Individual trees can be replanted. But, forests are complex ecosystems that support countless living things. A forest ecosystem takes more than 100 years to develop. If many or all of the trees are removed from one forest, it could take centuries for the forest ecosystem to develop again.

Mineral Resources

Take a moment to look around the classroom again. List three or four items that you use every day. Now, try to decide what resources they were made from. It's easy if the item is made of wood. But what about the metal in your desk, in the door handle, or surrounding the windows? Metal objects come from mineral resources, which are found in rocks. So minerals are another type of resource that we get from land.

No matter which type of rock you pick up, it's likely made up of a number of valuable minerals. Generally, it costs more to get those minerals out of the rock than the minerals are worth. But, sometimes we find large deposits of minerals in one place. These minerals can be classified as ores. An **ore** is a mineral resource that can be mined at a profit. **Figure 9-22** shows common uses for iron ore.

Reading Check

What is an ore?

Problems with Using Ores

Ores, like fossil fuels, are resources found under Earth's surface. To get to ores, large quantities of soil and rock often must be moved. This process is called mining. Mines can look unsightly and the waste rock produced by mines can pollute surface water. Air pollution also is produced when large industrial plants such as the one shown in **Figure 9-23** process the ores, generating dust and soot particles. Thus, the use of ores, like fossil fuels, affects the environment. Care must be taken to mine and use the ores in ways that do not harm water resources, living things, and natural habitats.

Resource Use

As you have learned, using each type of resource has advantages and disadvantages. In addition, the way we use one resource often impacts another. For instance, burning too many fossil fuels causes air and water pollution. We can replant trees to conserve a forest, but the trees may die if they're exposed to acid rain caused by burning fossil fuels. We can manage a farm carefully to lessen soil erosion, but if our water is polluted from chemical runoff caused by mines, the crops will suffer regardless. Successful resource management is possible only if we use all of Earth's resources wisely.

Figure 9-23
Industrial plants, such as the one shown here in Ohio, can create air pollution when they burn fossil fuels to generate electricity or to manufacture products.

Section Assessment

1. We have only a limited amount of land, yet land is a renewable resource. Why?

2. Trees are renewable resources, but forests are not. Why?

3. Compare and contrast minerals and ores.

4. **Think Critically:** About 117 000 km^2 of tropical rain forests are cut down each year. Why should people everywhere be concerned about the loss of forests located in the tropics?

5. **Skill Builder**
   Using a Word Processor Using a word processor, compile a list of do's and don'ts for forest conservation. If you need help, refer to Using a Word Processor in the **Technology Skill Handbook** on page 698.

Science Journal

Research one of the resources discussed in this section. Describe an environmental problem associated with its use. In your Science Journal, write a report that explains possible solutions to this problem.

Design Your Own Experiment

Activity 9•2

Using Land

Imagine planning a small town. Your job in this activity is to draw up a master plan to decide how 100 square units of land can be turned into a town.

Recognize the Problem

How should land resources be used?

Form a Hypothesis

People need homes in which to live, places to work, and stores from which to buy things. Children need to attend schools and have parks in which to play. How can all of these needs be met when planning a small town?

Goals

• **Design** a plan in which 100 square units of land can be turned into a town.

Parts of Your Town	Number of Blocks Needed
Office buildings	6 blocks in one group
Industrial plant	6 blocks in one group
School	1 block
Landfill for garbage	4 blocks in one group
Houses and apartments	44 blocks—can be broken up
Stores and businesses	19 blocks—can be broken up
Park	20 blocks—can be broken up

Test Your Hypothesis

Plan

1. **Make** a square graph 10 blocks across and 10 blocks down. The graph represents a 100-square-unit piece of land.

2. The table on the previous page shows the different parts of a town that need to be included in your plan. The office buildings and industrial plant are places where the people of the town will work. They are each 6 blocks in size. These blocks must be treated as one group—they cannot be divided. The landfill is 4 blocks in size. It, too, cannot be broken up.

Do

1. Make sure your teacher approves your plan before you proceed.

3. All other town parts can be broken up as needed. Stores and businesses are areas in which shops are located, as well as medical offices, restaurants, churches, and cemeteries.

4. As a group, **discuss** how the different parts of the town might be put together. Should the park be in the center of town or near the edge of town? Should the school be near the offices or near the houses? Where should the landfill go?

5. How will you show the different town parts on your grid paper?

2. As a group, **plan** your town. Check over your plan to make sure that all town parts are accounted for.

Analyze Your Data

1. Where did you place the office buildings and the industrial plant? Why were they placed there? Where did you place the houses, school, and businesses?

Explain why you placed each one as you did.

2. Did you make one park or many parks? What are the advantages of your park(s) plan?

Draw Conclusions

1. Where did you place the landfill? Will any of the townspeople be upset by its location? To answer this question, it may help to know what direction the wind usually blows from in your town.

2. Where would you put an airport in this town? Keep in mind safety issues, noise levels, and transportation needs.

For a **preview** of this chapter, study this Reviewing Main Ideas before you read the chapter. After you have studied this chapter, you can use the Reviewing Main Ideas to **review** the chapter.

GLENCOE TECHNOLOGY

The Glencoe MindJogger, Audiocassettes, and CD-ROM provide additional opportunities for review.

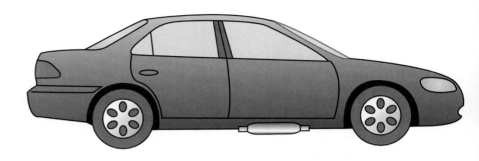

Section 9-1 ENERGY RESOURCES

Fossil fuels such as coal, oil, and gas are **nonrenewable** energy resources. They are being used faster than Earth can replace them. Fossil fuels provide us with much-needed energy, but certain problems are associated with their use. *What is acid rain?*

Section 9-2 ALTERNATIVE ENERGY RESOURCES

Alternative energy resources, such as **solar energy**, energy from the wind, **hydroelectric power**, and **geothermal energy** are constant and will not run out. For this reason, they are considered **renewable**. Though some of these resources do not cause pollution, certain drawbacks are associated with their use. *Why can't wind energy be used to meet all of the world's energy needs?*

Reading Check ✔

What words beginning with the prefix *non-* could you use to describe solar energy? To describe fossil fuels?

Section 9-3 WATER

Less than one percent of Earth's total water supply is in a form that people can readily use. We use water to meet our basic needs, and we use it for industry, agriculture, and recreation. Clean water can become a nonrenewable resource if water supplies are overused or polluted. *Why is most water on Earth unusable as drinking water or for agriculture and industry?*

Section 9-4 LAND

Land is a valuable resource used for food, shelter, and other needs. Land also provides us with two other important resources: wood and minerals. All of Earth's resources must be managed wisely. If one resource is polluted or overused, other resources can be affected as well. *Give an example of a way to harvest trees that conserves forests.*

Chapter 9 Assessment

Using Vocabulary

a. acid rain
b. conservation
c. fossil fuel
d. geothermal energy
e. groundwater
f. hydroelectric power
g. nonpoint source
h. nonrenewable
i. nuclear energy
j. ore
k. point source
l. pollution
m. renewable
n. solar energy

Each of the following sentences is false. Make the sentence true by replacing the italicized word with a word from the list above.

1. Solar energy is an example of a *nonrenewable* resource.
2. Careful use of resources with the goal of reducing damage to the environment is called *pollution.*
3. *Nuclear energy* forms from the remains of dead plants and animals.
4. Water that soaks into the ground and collects in the small spaces between bits of rock and soil is called *acid rain.*
5. The introduction of harmful waste products, chemicals, and substances into the environment is called *conservation.*

Checking Concepts

Choose the word or phrase that best answers the question.

6. What does nuclear energy produce?
   A) solar energy
   B) radioactive waste
   C) conservation
   D) nonrenewable resources
7. What is water in rivers, streams, lakes, and reservoirs called?
   A) peat
   B) surface water
   C) groundwater
   D) natural gas

8. Which of the following is an example of a fossil fuel?
   A) wind
   B) water
   C) natural gas
   D) uranium
9. Approximately what percent of the energy used in the United States comes from coal?
   A) 12
   B) 22
   C) 32
   D) 52
10. What kind of resource can be mined for a profit?
    A) solar cell
    B) wind
    C) dam
    D) ore
11. What kind of energy is generated by large dams built on rivers?
    A) wind
    B) nuclear
    C) hydroelectric
    D) solar
12. When many windmills are located in one place in order to generate electricity, what do they form?
    A) wind farm
    B) dam
    C) oil well
    D) nuclear reactor
13. Where does the heat energy from geothermal energy come from?
    A) water
    B) atoms
    C) heated rocks
    D) wind
14. When gases released by burning coal or oil mix with water in the air, what can they form?
    A) acid rain
    B) fission
    C) conservation
    D) groundwater
15. A nonrenewable resource can't be replaced in less than how many years?
    A) 5
    B) 10
    C) 50
    D) 100

Thinking Critically

16. With all of the paper products that we use every day, why don't we run out of trees?
17. Some heavily populated countries cause less environmental damage than countries with far fewer people. Why?

18. A shark that lives at sea is found dead. It has traces of chemicals in its body that, in turn, can be traced to pesticides used on farms. How can this happen?

19. Why shouldn't nuclear wastes be stored near an area prone to earthquakes?

20. Once a mineral resource is classified as an ore, will it always remain an ore? Explain your answer.

Developing Skills

If you need help, refer to the Skill Handbook.

21. **Sequencing:** If a well were drilled into a rock layer that contains oil, natural gas, and water, which substance would be encountered first? Explain.

22. **Comparing and Contrasting:** Compare and contrast solar energy and wind energy.

23. **Interpreting Scientific Illustrations:** The figure below shows a water-purification plant. In your own words, describe the path water takes from a stream to your faucet.

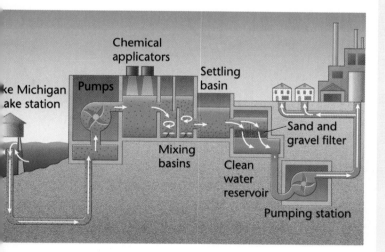

24. **Making and Using Tables:** Make a table that shows the advantages and disadvantages of each energy resource discussed in this chapter.

THE PRINCETON REVIEW

Test-Taking Tip

Use Roots to Learn The roots of words can help you group words together as you learn them. If you learn that *trans-* means "across," as in *transfer*, you might then remember the meaning of words like *transplant, transform,* and *transverse.*

Test Practice

Use these questions to test your Science Proficiency.

1. Trees are considered renewable resources, but forests are not. Which of the following statements **BEST** explains why?
   A) Forests are complex ecosystems that take longer than 100 years to develop.
   B) Forest conservation methods haven't been developed yet.
   C) Forests are not classified as resources.
   D) Forests can never grow back.

2. The use of nuclear energy is limited in the United States. Which of the following statements **BEST** explains why?
   A) There are no nuclear power plants in the United States.
   B) The use of nuclear energy releases too much carbon dioxide into Earth's atmosphere.
   C) Used fuel rods contain radioactive waste that must be handled carefully and stored in a place where they can't harm the environment.
   D) Nuclear power plants are inefficient in generating electricity.

Earth's Air and Water

What's Happening Here?

In September 1996, the wrath of Hurricane Fran was unleashed on the East Coast. In this computer-enhanced satellite image (left), the hurricane spirals westward toward Florida. How do the winds whip themselves into such a frenzy? A hurricane begins with a cascade of cool, heavy air at its center. Its fury is fueled by energy from a warm ocean below. Far inland, stormy weather bombards ranchers in northern Colorado as they deliver hay from a feed sleigh to hungry cattle (below). In this unit, you will learn how weather is created by the interaction of Earth's atmosphere and water. You will learn not only about the storms but also about the winds flowing in the atmosphere and the currents flowing in the oceans. These everyday weather occurrences, in the long run, affect our lives even more than violent weather.

interNET CONNECTION

Explore the Glencoe Science Web Site at **www.glencoe.com/sec/ science/fl** to find out more about topics found in this unit.

10 Atmosphere

Chapter Preview

Skills Preview

Skill Builders
- Predict
- Map Concepts

Activities
- Analyze Data
- Compare and Contrast

MiniLabs
- Observe and Infer
- Measure in SI

Reading Check ✔

Before reading this chapter, list the vocabulary terms for each section. As you read, write a definition next to each term.

Explore Activity

Do you know how windsurfing works? A surfer uses the power of the wind to skim a surfboard across water. You've probably used the power of wind to fly a kite or to sail a boat. Do you know where wind comes from? Temperature differences in the air play a large role in creating wind. The Explore Activity that follows will help you observe the effects of temperature.

Observe Temperature Effects

1. Your teacher will pour a small quantity of water into a soda can.

2. The can will be heated until the water boils.

3. Then the heat will be turned off, and the can will be submerged upside down in cold water.

Science Journal

What happens as the can cools? In your Science Journal, hypothesize why this happens. How is this related to windsurfing?

10·1 Earth's Atmosphere

Makeup of the Atmosphere

It's early morning in the future. You're getting dressed for work. As you eat breakfast, the weather report comes over the computer screen: "Smog levels higher than normal. Temperatures near 38°C. The ozone layer in the stratosphere thinner than yesterday." You'll need your filter mask to protect your lungs from the smog. Pollution in the atmosphere has raised the temperature. You'll have to wear cool clothing. The thinner ozone layer requires you to use a strong sunblock lotion to protect yourself from skin cancer.

This scenario may not sound pleasant, but it's a future you may face. Because your life depends on the air you breathe, you need to know about the atmosphere, its composition, its structure, how it affects you, and how you affect it.

Atmospheric Gases

The atmosphere surrounding Earth extends from Earth's surface to outer space. The atmosphere is a mixture of gases with some suspended solids and liquids. **Figure 10-1** is a graph of the gases in Earth's atmosphere. Nitrogen is the most common gas. Oxygen makes up 21 percent of our atmosphere. We need oxygen to breathe. Water vapor makes up from zero to four percent of the atmosphere. When the percentage of water vapor is higher, the percentages of other gases are slightly lower.

Figure 10-1 This graph shows the percentages of the gases that make up our atmosphere.

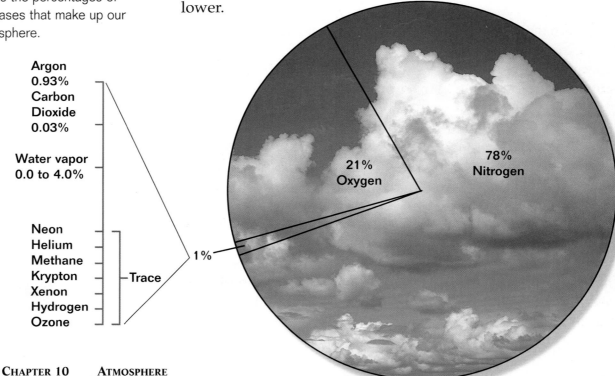

Argon 0.93%
Carbon Dioxide 0.03%
Water vapor 0.0 to 4.0%
Neon
Helium
Methane
Krypton
Xenon
Hydrogen
Ozone
Trace
1%
21% Oxygen
78% Nitrogen

Figure 10-2 Smog lies over Mexico City. **How does brown smog form?**

The atmosphere also contains smog, a type of pollution. The kind of smog affecting an area depends on the pollutants. Car exhaust expels dust and gases into the air. These pollutants mix with oxygen and other chemicals in the presence of sunlight, causing a brown smog, as shown in **Figure 10-2.** Other gases caused by burning coal or oil cause a gray smog.

Another component of smog is ozone. Ozone is a gas made up of three oxygen molecules bonded together. Ozone occurs naturally in the upper atmosphere, but it is not normally found in the lower part of the atmosphere. When it is formed in the air above cities, ozone is considered a pollutant. In the lower atmosphere, ozone can harm plants and damage our lungs.

Atmospheric Solids and Liquids

Gases aren't the only thing making up Earth's atmosphere. Dust, salt, and ice are three common solids found in the atmospheric mixture. Dust gets into the atmosphere when wind picks it up off the ground and carries it along. Ice is common in the form of hailstones and snowflakes. Salt is picked up from ocean spray.

The atmosphere also contains liquids. The most common liquid in the atmosphere is water droplets found in clouds. Water is the only substance that exists as a solid, liquid, and gas in Earth's atmosphere.

Figure 10-3 Earth's atmosphere extends hundreds of kilometers upward. The first 15 km on this diagram are not to scale.

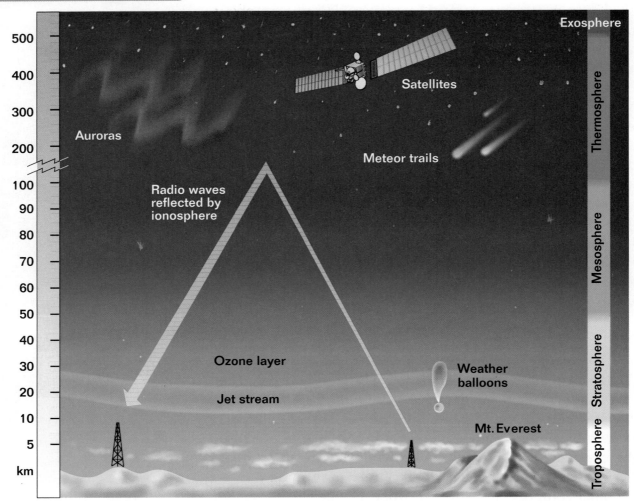

Structure of the Atmosphere

In the beginning of this chapter, you read about an imaginary weather forecast from the future. The forecast predicted a high smog level and a thin ozone layer in the stratosphere. Both conditions affect your health but in different ways. Where in the atmosphere does smog occur? Where can you find not just ozone but the ozone layer?

Figure 10-3 illustrates Earth's five main atmospheric layers: the troposphere, stratosphere, mesosphere, thermosphere, and exosphere. Each layer has unique characteristics.

Lower Layers of the Atmosphere

We live in the **troposphere,** the layer closest to the ground. The troposphere contains 75 percent of the atmospheric gases, as well as dust, ice, and liquid water. Weather, clouds, and smog occur in the troposphere.

Above the troposphere lies the stratosphere. As **Figure 10-3** shows, a layer of ozone exists within the stratosphere. This ozone layer was mentioned in the future forecast because the ozone layer directly affects your health. You'll learn more about this layer in Section 10-2.

Upper Layers of the Atmosphere

Beyond the stratosphere are the mesosphere, thermosphere, and exosphere. One important layer of the thermosphere is the **ionosphere,** a layer of electrically charged particles. When solar energy hits these particles, the particles can interfere with certain kinds of radio waves sent from Earth. During the daytime, energy from the sun interacts with the particles in the ionosphere, which causes the particles to absorb AM radio waves. At night, without solar energy, AM radio transmissions bounce off the ionosphere. This bouncing allows radio transmissions from one side of the globe to be received on the other side of the globe. **Figure 10-4** illustrates this.

The exosphere is the uppermost part of Earth's atmosphere. Beyond it lies space. If you were an astronaut traveling upward through the exosphere, you would encounter fewer and fewer molecules. Eventually, you would find so few molecules that, for all practical purposes, you would be out of Earth's atmosphere and in space. But, there's no clear boundary between the atmosphere and space.

Figure 10-4 Radio waves can be received by antennas around the globe (A). At night, AM radio waves that strike the ionosphere at sharp angles pass through to space, but other waves strike at lower angles and are reflected back toward Earth (B).

Radio waves

Ionosphere

Transmitter

Antenna

The space shuttle orbits Earth in the exosphere, 280 km above Earth's surface. So few molecules exist here that the wings of the shuttle, used in the lower atmosphere, are useless. The spacecraft must rely on bursts from small rocket thrusters to maneuver.

Reading Check ✓

How does the space shuttle maneuver?

Atmospheric Pressure

Gases in the atmosphere have mass and a gravitational attraction to other matter. The gravitational attraction between Earth and molecules of gas causes atmospheric gases to be pulled toward Earth. Yet, atmospheric gases extend upward hundreds of kilometers. The weight of the gases at the top of the atmosphere presses down on the air below, compressing the molecules and increasing the density of the air. The air at the bottom of the atmosphere, close to Earth, is more dense. This dense air exerts more force than the less-dense air at the top of the atmosphere. Force exerted on an area is known as pressure.

Where do you think air pressure is greater—in the exosphere at the top of the atmosphere or in the troposphere near Earth's surface? Air pressure is greater nearer Earth. At sea level on Earth's surface, more molecules are pushing down from above.

Problem Solving

Interpreting Atmospheric Pressure

Atmospheric gases extend hundreds of kilometers above Earth's surface, but the molecules that make up these gases are fewer and fewer in number the higher you go. This means that air pressure decreases with altitude. The graph on this page shows these changes in air pressure. Note that altitude on the graph only goes up to 36 km. The troposphere and the stratosphere are represented on the graph, but other layers of the atmosphere are not. Study the graph, then answer the questions below.

Think Critically: Does air pressure increase more rapidly at high or low altitudes? Why doesn't air pressure drop to zero on the graph? At what altitude would it drop to zero?

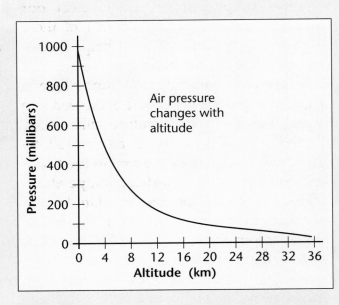

Air pressure changes with altitude

Figure 10-5 Air pressure decreases with elevation. **How might this affect a mountain climber?**

Going Up

In general, atmospheric pressure is greatest near Earth's surface and decreases as you move upward away from sea level. That means air pressure decreases as you go up in the mountains. **Figure 10-5** shows a mountain climber. Some people find it harder to breathe in high mountains. Fewer molecules exist at high elevations, so air pressure is less.

Atmospheric Temperatures

You don't have to climb a mountain to find lower air pressure. Anywhere on Earth where the atmosphere is heated, air molecules move with greater energy. In heated air, fewer molecules occupy a cubic centimeter of space. As a result, there is less air pressure. Colder air has more molecules occupying a cubic centimeter of space. This causes high air pressure. These areas of high and low pressure are often marked on weather maps because they affect our weather. Tracking the movement of these high- and low-pressure areas helps meteorologists forecast the weather.

Temperatures affect Earth's atmosphere in another way. The atmosphere is divided into layers based on temperature differences. Earth's atmospheric gases are heated by absorbing energy from the sun. In the troposphere near Earth's surface, temperatures decrease with an increase in altitude. Just above it in the stratosphere, molecules of ozone absorb the sun's ultraviolet radiation, heating that layer. While some layers contain gases that easily absorb the sun's energy, other layers do not. Because of this, the various layers have different temperatures.

Measuring the Mass of Air

Procedure

1. On a pan balance, find the mass of an inflatable ball that is completely deflated.
2. Hypothesize about the change in the mass of the ball when it goes from being deflated to inflated.
3. Inflate the ball to its maximum recommended inflation pressure.
4. Determine the mass of the fully inflated ball.

Analysis

1. What change occurs in the mass of the ball from deflation to inflation?
2. Infer from your data whether air has mass.

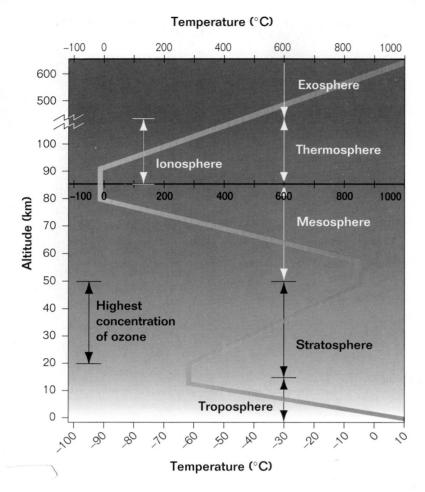

Figure 10-6 The division of the atmosphere into layers is based mainly on differences in temperature. **What is the temperature of the troposphere at a height of 10 km?**

Notice in **Figure 10-6** how the temperature of the atmosphere changes in different layers. Which layer is the coldest? Which layer is the warmest?

The Ozone Layer

Is the ozone layer in danger?

About 20 km above your head lies the ozone layer. The **ozone layer** is an atmospheric layer with a high concentration of ozone. This layer, located in the stratosphere, cannot be seen, yet your life depends on it. The ozone layer shields you from harmful energy from the sun.

Ozone is a form of oxygen. The oxygen we breathe has two atoms per molecule. An ozone molecule, however, binds three oxygen atoms together. The layer of ozone molecules absorbs most of the ultraviolet radiation that enters the atmosphere. **Ultraviolet radiation** is one of the many types of energy that comes to Earth from the sun. Too much exposure to ultraviolet radiation can damage the skin. Ultraviolet radiation can cause cancer and other health problems in many types of plants and animals.

Ozone Holes

Each year, more than 800 000 Americans develop skin cancer, and more than 9000 die from it. If the ozone layer disappeared, cancer rates might increase. **Figure 10-7** shows that the ozone layer is thinning and developing holes. In 1986, scientists found areas in the stratosphere with extremely low amounts of ozone. One very large hole opened over Antarctica. A smaller hole was discovered over the north pole. Since that time, these holes appear during certain seasons and disappear during others. The ozone layer changes due to natural processes such as seasons, sunspots, and volcanic eruptions, but pollutants may also be at fault.

CFCs

Some scientists hypothesize that pollutants in the environment are destroying the ozone layer. Blame has fallen on **chlorofluorocarbons** (CFCs), a group of chemical compounds used in refrigerators, aerosol sprays, and foam packaging. When these products are manufactured and used, CFCs enter the atmosphere. Recently, many governments have restricted the production and use of CFCs.

Chlorofluorocarbon molecules destroy ozone. Recall that an ozone molecule is composed of three oxygen atoms bonded together (O_3). When a chlorine atom from a chlorofluorocarbon molecule comes near a molecule of ozone, the ozone molecule breaks apart. It forms a regular two-atom molecule (O_2). This oxygen can't absorb ultraviolet radiation. The result is that more ultraviolet radiation reaches Earth's surface.

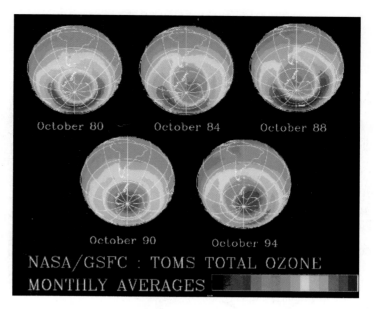

Figure 10-7 These images were produced using data from a NASA satellite. The purple color shows how the ozone hole has grown bigger over time.

Section Assessment

1. Explain why the temperature of the atmosphere does not increase or decrease steadily as you move from Earth's surface toward space.

2. What causes air pressure?

3. **Think Critically:** Imagine you're a football player running with the ball. Six players tackle you and pile on top—one on top of the other. Relate the pressure that you and each player above you feels to the pressure in the layers of the atmosphere.

4. **Skill Builder**
   Predicting Solar activity such as sun spots interact with Earth's atmosphere. Do the **Chapter 10 Skill Activity** on page 717 to predict when sun spots occur.

Science Journal
The names of the atmospheric layers end with the suffix *-sphere*. In these names, *sphere* means "layer." Use a dictionary to find out what *meso-*, *thermo-*, and *exo-* mean. In your Science Journal, write the meaning of these prefixes and explain why the layers are appropriately or inappropriately named.

Making a Barometer

Materials

- Small coffee can
- Drinking straw
- Large, rubber balloon
- Construction paper
- Transparent tape
- Scissors
- Rubber band

If you have flown in an airplane or zoomed to the top of a building in an elevator, you have experienced an air pressure change inside your ears. When you rapidly increased your altitude, air pressure outside your eardrums became lower than the pressure inside your eardrums. The air inside your ears pushed against your eardrums. In this activity, you'll see that a barometer reacts as your eardrums did when exposed to differences in pressure.

What You'll Investigate

How does a barometer react to a change in air pressure?

Goals

- **Make** a barometer.
- **Observe** the effects of weather changes on a barometer.

Procedure 🥽 ✋

1. **Cut** the balloon and **stretch** it tightly over the can. **Secure** it in place with the rubber band.

2. Using tape, **attach** a piece of construction paper vertically to the side of the coffee can as shown in the photo.

3. **Trim** one end of the straw to a point. **Tape** the other end of the straw to the balloon and **point** the trimmed end toward the paper.

4. Make a horizontal mark on the paper where the pointed end of the straw touches. **Write** *high* above this mark and *low* below it.

5. **Design** a data table to record your observations. **Record** the movement of the straw for a period of a week. Also **record** the weather conditions each day. **Plot** the movement of the straw on a graph.

Conclude and Apply

1. How did your barometer react to changes in air pressure?

2. **Analyze** your data to see what type of weather was associated with the pressures you recorded.

3. **Conclude** from your activity how a weather forecaster can use barometric pressure to help predict weather.

Where does river water come from?

Centuries ago, people noted that rivers flowed from mountains into the oceans. Because the oceans had not overflowed, they thought there must be a way for the water to pass through Earth and back up to the tops of mountains. In the Middle Ages, the years between 500 and 1500 A.D., some philosophers tried to explain this mechanism.

Many Explanations

One suggestion was that the water was somehow attracted upward, like iron filings to a magnet. Another theory was that spaces and cracks in Earth pulled in water vapor to avoid a vacuum. The vapors then condensed into water that later emerged as springs. Others thought that nature acted like a pump, with tides and strong winds putting pressure on the water at the sea bottom to force it up tunnels to the mountaintops.

Scientists during the Renaissance, the years between 1300 and 1600 A.D., concluded that the water in the rivers and streams came from rain and snow falling on the mountains. One scientist in the sixteenth century said that to understand rivers, it was more important to study nature than to study ancient philosophers' ideas about nature. He wrote that the sun's heat evaporates great amounts of water from the ocean into clouds. The water then falls as rain or snow. This water flows downhill as streams or sinks into Earth's crust until it meets impermeable rock and is forced back to the surface as springs. Fluids cannot pass through impermeable rock.

Observing the Alps

In 1715, an Italian scholar made a trip to the Alps to trace streams to their origins. He observed that water ran down slopes from the snowpack at the top. The rivers all came from melting snow and ice.

In another part of the Alps, he found great snowpacks but few streams. The local shepherds showed him where the water ran into cracks in the ground. He realized that this explained the origin of springs. Underground streams flowed from high in the Alps, seeped into the earth, and came to the surface as springs.

Science JOURNAL

Research the pros and cons associated with dam building. Predict the consequences that could result from damming a river. If you need help, refer to Predicting Consequences in the **Skill Handbook.**

Energy Transfer in the Atmosphere

In the future scenario, you return from work. You eat dinner and read the evening news transmitted on the computer network. You see that the Space Agency is still trying to create a hospitable atmosphere on Mars. It's studying the atmospheres of Earth and Venus to understand how they work and how an Earthlike atmosphere might be produced on Mars or Venus. The atmospheres of Earth and its neighboring planets of Venus and Mars are shown in **Figure 10-8.** The atmosphere on

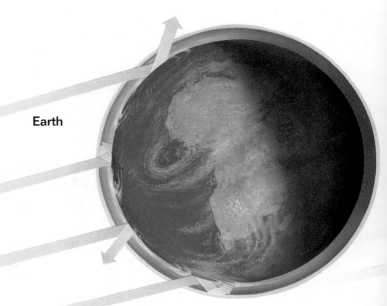

Figure 10-8 Most radiation entering Venus's atmosphere is trapped by thick gases and clouds. On Mars, a thin atmosphere allows much radiation to escape. Earth's atmosphere creates a delicate balance between energy received and energy lost.

Earth

Venus

Sun

What You'll Learn

▶ Three things that happen to the energy Earth receives from the sun
▶ The differences among radiation, conduction, and convection
▶ The water cycle

Vocabulary
radiation
conduction
convection
hydrosphere
water cycle

Why It's Important

▶ The sun is the source of most energy in our atmosphere.

Mars is currently too thin to support life or to hold much thermal energy from the sun. As a result, Mars is a cold, lifeless world. On the other hand, Venus's atmosphere is so dense that almost no thermal energy coming from the sun can escape. Venus is so hot that a living thing would instantly burn if it were put on Venus's surface.

In our solar system, nine planets circle the star we call the sun. Earth supports life, but the nearby planets, Mars and Venus, do not support life. How does the interaction between Earth's atmosphere and the sun provide an environment suitable for life?

The Sun

The sun is the source of all energy in our atmosphere. When Earth receives energy from the sun, three different things happen to that energy. Some energy is reflected back into space. Some is absorbed by the atmosphere and by land and water surfaces. The balance among these three events controls the characteristics of our atmosphere and the life that it supports. Let's take a look at what happens to the energy that reaches Earth.

Radiation

Mars

Energy from the sun reaches our planet in the form of radiant energy, or radiation. **Radiation** is the transfer of energy by electromagnetic waves. Radiation from the sun travels through empty space, as well as through our atmosphere. You experience radiation as light and heat. When the sun warms your face or when you sit by a fire and it warms the side of your body facing it, you experience radiant energy. You aren't in direct contact with the sun or the fire, but the energy still reaches you. ☑

Heat

When radiation from the fire reaches you, the molecules of your skin absorb the energy and you feel heat. Heat is energy that flows from an object with a higher temperature to an object with a lower temperature. Once objects at Earth's surface, such as asphalt roads, rocks, houses, or ocean water, absorb radiation, they heat up. These heated surfaces then radiate energy. Much of the radiation coming from the sun passes through the atmosphere. Most radiation coming from Earth's surface is absorbed and heats up our atmosphere.

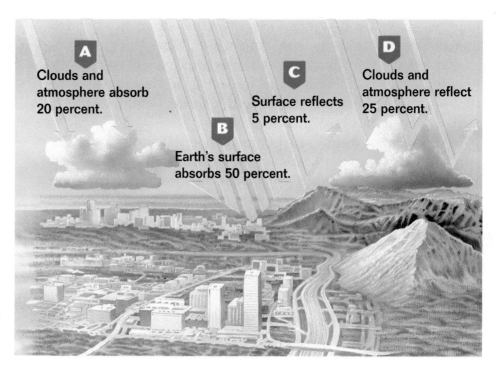

Figure 10-9 The sun is the source of energy in our atmosphere. Thirty percent of incoming solar radiation is reflected back into space. **How much is absorbed by Earth's surface?**

A Clouds and atmosphere absorb 20 percent.

B Earth's surface absorbs 50 percent.

C Surface reflects 5 percent.

D Clouds and atmosphere reflect 25 percent.

The ozone layer absorbs ultraviolet radiation. When ozone and other gases absorb radiation, the temperature of the atmosphere rises, as you saw in **Figure 10-6.**

On Venus, even less radiation is able to escape back to space, making Venus hotter than Earth. On Earth, a delicate balance exists between energy received from the sun and energy escaping back to space. In the future weather forecast at the beginning of this chapter, high temperatures were forecast. This may be because smog and other pollutants in the atmosphere are preventing radiation from returning to space. Air pollution can upset the balance of incoming and outgoing radiation on Earth.

Some radiation from the sun isn't absorbed by Earth's atmosphere or surface objects. Instead, it simply reflects off the atmosphere and surface, like a ball bouncing off a wall. **Figure 10-9** illustrates the percentages of radiation absorbed and reflected by Earth's surface and atmosphere.

Conduction

If you walk barefoot on hot asphalt, your feet heat up because of conduction. Radiation from the sun heated the asphalt, but direct contact with the asphalt heated your feet. In a similar way, Earth's surface transfers energy directly to the atmosphere. As air moves over warm land or water, air molecules are heated by direct contact. A warm layer of molecules on Earth's surface comes in direct contact with a layer of air molecules and transfers energy.

Conduction is the transfer of energy that occurs when molecules bump into one another. Molecules are always in motion, but molecules in hotter objects move more rapidly than those in cooler objects. When substances are in contact, energy is transferred from energized, fast-moving molecules to lower-energy molecules until all molecules are moving at about the same rate. **Figure 10-10** illustrates how the processes of heat transfer affect the atmosphere.

Convection

After the atmosphere is warmed by radiation or conduction, the heat is transferred throughout the atmosphere by a third process, convection. **Convection** is the transfer of heat by the flow of a heated material. Convection occurs in gases and liquids. Let's see how this works with air.

When air is warmed, the molecules move apart. This increases the volume of the air, which makes the air less dense. Air pressure decreases because fewer molecules are pressing in on each other. Cold temperatures affect the air in just the opposite way. In cold air, molecules move closer together. The air becomes more dense and air pressure increases. Because cold air is dense, it sinks. As the cold air falls toward Earth, it pushes up less-dense, warm air. A circular movement of air, called a convection current, results.

PHYSICS
INTEGRATION

Conduction
Infer which of the following would transfer heat by conduction the best: solids, liquids, or gases.

Figure 10-10 Heat is transferred within Earth's atmosphere by radiation, conduction, and convection.

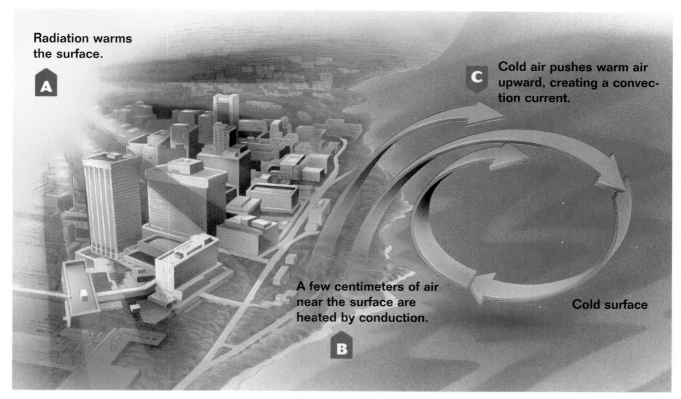

Radiation warms the surface.

A

Cold air pushes warm air upward, creating a convection current.

C

A few centimeters of air near the surface are heated by conduction.

B

Cold surface

Our Unique Atmosphere

Convection currents and other processes that transfer energy control our environment. As you have seen, radiation from the sun can escape back into space, be absorbed by the atmosphere, or be absorbed by bodies on Earth's surface. Once it's been absorbed, heat can be transferred by radiation, conduction, or convection. Just how much radiation is absorbed determines the type of life that can exist on this planet. Other planets in the solar system that are similar to Earth, such as Venus and Mars, don't absorb and lose the same amounts of radiation as Earth. Their atmospheres don't support life as we know it.

The Water Cycle

Another thing that allows our atmosphere to support life is water. All life as we know it needs water. Although most of Earth's water is in the oceans, it is also found in lakes, streams, rivers, groundwater, glaciers, and the atmosphere. All the water that is found at Earth's surface is the **hydrosphere.** Although there's a lot of water on Earth, 97 percent is salt water and only three percent is freshwater. Two-thirds of the freshwater is frozen in ice caps at the north and south poles. That leaves only one percent available for us to use. This one percent of freshwater is important because it is constantly moving between the atmosphere and Earth in the **water cycle,** as shown in **Figure 10-11.**

*inter***NET**
C O N N E C T I O N

Visit the Glencoe Science Web Site at **www.glencoe.com/ sec/science/fl** for more information about Earth's atmosphere.

Figure 10-11 Water moves from Earth to the atmosphere and back to Earth again. **How much of the water on Earth is fresh?**

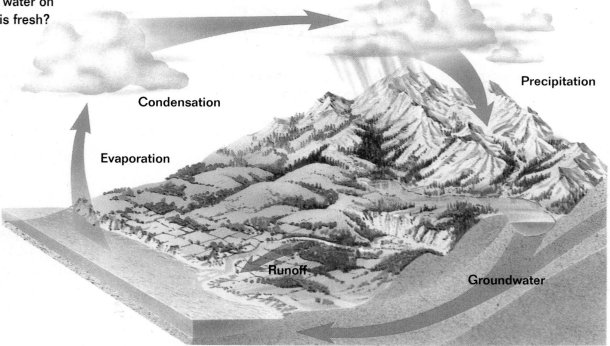

Condensation

Evaporation

Precipitation

Runoff

Groundwater

The sun provides the energy for the water cycle. Radiation from the sun causes water to change to a gas called water vapor. The process of water changing from a liquid state to a gas is called *evaporation*. Water evaporates from lakes, streams, and oceans and rises into Earth's atmosphere.

Forming Clouds

In the next step of the water cycle, water vapor rises in the atmosphere and cools. When it cools enough, it changes back into a liquid. This process of water vapor changing to a liquid is called *condensation*. When water vapor condenses, it forms clouds.

The third step in the water cycle is *precipitation*. Clouds are made up of millions of tiny water droplets that collide and form larger drops. When the drops grow so large that they can no longer stay suspended in the clouds, drops of water fall to Earth, and the water cycle continues. The moisture that falls from clouds is called precipitation. The forest in **Figure 10-12** is experiencing precipitation in the form of rain.

As you can see, many factors determine whether a planet will have an atmosphere capable of supporting life. How much energy is transferred to the atmosphere and how much energy escapes Earth's atmosphere are important to life on Earth. Learning about our atmosphere will help us protect it so it can continue to support life.

Figure 10-12 Rain is one form of precipitation. **Describe another form.**

Section Assessment

1. Pollution may be making our atmosphere more like that of Venus. How can that happen and how might it affect temperatures on Earth?

2. How does the sun transfer energy to Earth, and how does the atmosphere get heated?

3. **Think Critically:** Describe the role of the sun in the water cycle.

4. **Skill Builder**
   Concept Mapping Make a cycle concept map that explains what happens to energy that reaches Earth as radiant energy. If you need help, refer to Concept Mapping in the **Skill Handbook** on page 700.

Using Math

Earth is about 150 000 000 km from the sun. The radiation coming from the sun travels at 300 000 km/s. About how long does it take for the radiation from the sun to reach Earth?

The Heat Is On

Have you ever noticed how cool and refreshing a plunge in a pool or lake is on a hot summer day? Did you ever wonder why the land gets so hot when the water remains cool? At night, the water feels warmer than the land. Let's explore how water and land absorb heat.

Possible Materials

- Ring stand
- Soil
- Metric ruler
- Clear plastic boxes (2)
- Overhead light with reflector
- Thermometers (4)
- Water
- Masking tape
- Colored pencils (4)

Recognize the Problem

How do soil and water compare in their abilities to absorb and release heat?

Form a Hypothesis

Form a hypothesis to explain how soil and water compare in their abilities to absorb and release heat. Write another hypothesis about how air temperatures above soil and above water differ during the day and night.

Goals

- **Design** an experiment to compare the rates of heat absorption and of heat release of both soil and water.
- **Observe** how these differing rates of heat absorption and release affect the air above soil and above water.

Safety Precautions

CAUTION: *Be careful when handling the hot overhead light. Do not let the light or its cord make contact with water.*

Test Your Hypothesis

Plan

1. As a group, agree upon and write out your hypotheses.

2. **List** the steps that you need to take to test your hypotheses. Include in your plan how you will use your equipment to compare the rates of heat absorption and heat release of water and soil.

3. **Design** a data table in your Science Journal for both parts of your experiment—when the light is on and energy can be absorbed and when the light is off and energy is released.

Do

1. Make sure your teacher approves your plan and your data table before you proceed.

2. Carry out the experiment as planned.

3. During the experiment, **record** your observations and complete the data tables in your Science Journal.

4. Include in your measurements the temperatures of the soil and the water. Also **compare** the rate of release of heat by water and soil. Include in your measurements the temperatures of the air above both of the substances. Do each test for 14 minutes.

Analyze Your Data

1. Use your colored pencils and the information in your data tables to **make line graphs.** Show the rate of energy absorption and energy release for both soil and water. If you need help, refer to Making and Using Graphs in the **Skill Handbook** on page 683.

2. **Analyze** your graphs. When the light was on, which heated up faster, the soil or the water?

3. **Compare** how fast the air heated up over the water with how fast the air heated up over the land.

Draw Conclusions

1. Were your hypotheses supported or not? **Explain.**

2. **Infer** from your graphs which lost heat faster—the water or the soil.

3. **Compare** the temperatures of the air above the water and above the soil after the light was turned off. How do water and soil compare in their abilities to absorb and release heat?

Wind Formation

Have you ever watched a tree swaying in the breeze and wondered where wind comes from? Wind is caused by the uneven heating of Earth and its atmosphere. This uneven heating causes temperature differences that create areas of pressure differences in the atmosphere. Air moving from areas of high pressure to areas of lower pressure creates a general circulation of air around Earth. Wind is the movement of air from an area of high pressure to an area of lower pressure.

Heated Air

Temperature differences at Earth's surface are caused in part by Earth's curved surface. Areas of Earth receive different amounts of solar radiation. **Figure 10-13** illustrates why more radiation is received at the equator than at other latitudes. Air above the equator is heated more than at any other place on Earth. As you know, heated air has a low density, so it is pushed upward by denser, cold air. **Figure 10-14** shows this general pattern of air circulation.

Where does this cold, denser air come from? It comes from the poles, which receive less radiation from the sun, making air at the poles much cooler. This dense, high-pressure air

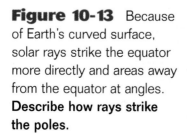

Figure 10-13 Because of Earth's curved surface, solar rays strike the equator more directly and areas away from the equator at angles. **Describe how rays strike the poles.**

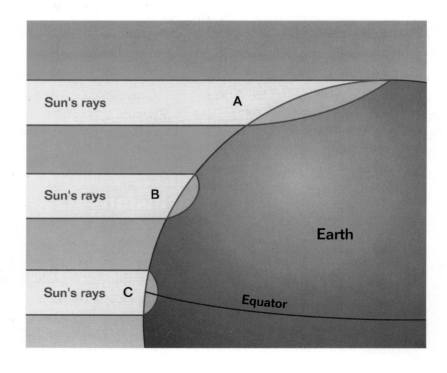

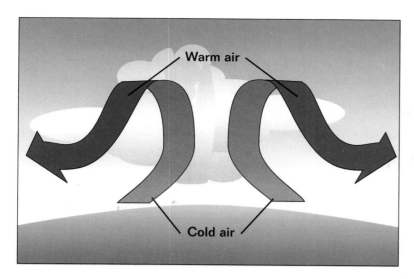

Figure 10-14 Wind develops from uneven heating on Earth. **As cold air sinks and moves under warm air, what happens to the warm air?**

Warm air

Cold air

sinks and moves along Earth's surface. However, as you read on, you'll see that cold, dense air pushing warmer, less-dense air upward cannot explain everything about wind.

The Coriolis Effect

The rotation of Earth creates the Coriolis effect. The **Coriolis effect** changes the direction of all free-moving objects such as air and water to the right north of the equator and left to the south. It causes air moving south in the northern hemisphere to turn westward. To someone at the equator, southbound air appears to move to the west as Earth turns east. The diagram of Earth in **Figure 10-15** shows this. The flow of air caused by differences in heating and by the Coriolis effect creates distinct wind patterns on Earth's surface. Not only do these wind systems influence the weather, but they also determine when and where ships and planes travel most efficiently.

Try at Home

MiniLab

Observing Convection Currents

Procedure

1. Fill a clear glass jar with hot water.
2. Place ice cubes on the water along with a few drops of food coloring and observe the motion of the food coloring.

Analysis

1. Describe the motion of the food coloring.
2. Compare and contrast the convection current that you made with convection currents in the atmosphere.

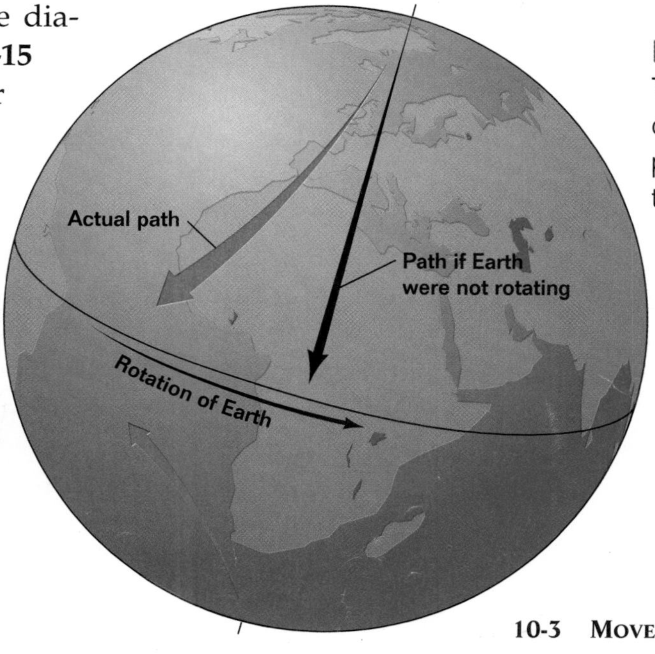

Figure 10-15 The Coriolis effect creates wind patterns across the world.

Actual path

Path if Earth were not rotating

Rotation of Earth

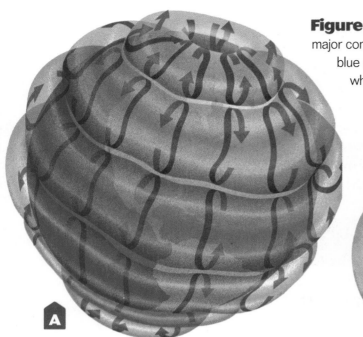

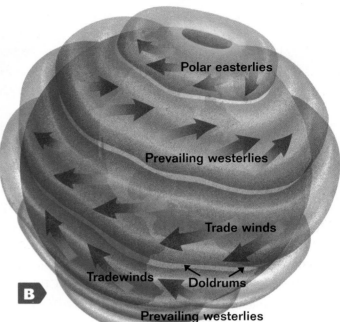

Figure 10-16 Uneven heating of Earth's surface produces major convection currents, shown by the purple arrows (A). The blue arrows (B) show the world's major wind systems created when the Coriolis effect deflects moving air westward.

Polar easterlies

Prevailing westerlies

Trade winds

Tradewinds   Doldrums

Prevailing westerlies

Polar easterlies

Wind Systems

Let's venture into the past to imagine sailing the oceans during the time of the great sailing ships. No motors propel the ship. You depend entirely on the winds for energy. That means you must avoid getting into the doldrums, which is the windless zone at the equator. In the doldrums, the air seems motionless. Actually, the air is moving almost straight up. Do you remember why this happens? ✔

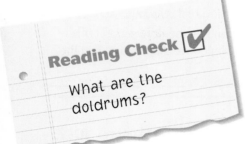

Reading Check ✔

What are the doldrums?

Surface Winds

A better place to sail is between the equator and 30° latitude north or south. In that area, air descending to Earth's surface creates steady winds that blow to the southwest in the northern hemisphere. In the southern hemisphere, they blow toward the northwest. These are the trade winds. In the days of the great sailing ships, the northern trade winds provided a dependable route for trade. **Figure 10-16** shows the major wind systems on Earth, along with convection currents. Sailing ships like the one in **Figure 10-17** were designed to use such winds.

Between 30° and 60° latitude north and south of the equator, winds blow in the opposite direction from the trade winds. These winds are called the prevailing westerlies.

Sailors use the prevailing westerlies to sail from the Americas to Europe. The prevailing westerlies blow from the southwest to the northeast in the northern hemisphere. They are responsible for much of the movement of weather across the United States and Canada. In the southern hemisphere, the prevailing westerlies blow from the northwest to the southeast.

The last major wind systems at Earth's surface are the polar easterlies. These winds blow from the northeast to the southwest near the north pole and from the southeast to the northwest near the south pole.

High-Altitude Winds

Winds also occur at higher altitudes. Narrow belts of strong winds, called **jet streams,** blow near the top of the troposphere. Two jet streams in each hemisphere blow from west to east at the northern and southern boundaries of the prevailing westerlies. These streams of air resemble fast-moving, winding rivers. Their speeds average between 97 and 185 km/h. Their positions in latitude and altitude change from day to day and season to season. They have a major effect on our weather.

Just as sailors seek the trade winds, prevailing westerlies, and polar easterlies to help propel their ships, jet pilots take advantage of jet streams. When flying eastward, planes save time and fuel. Going west, planes fly at different altitudes to avoid the jet streams.

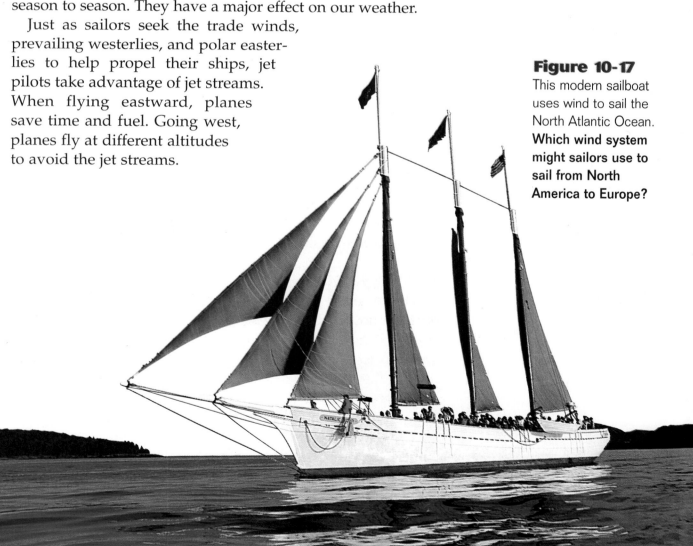

Figure 10-17
This modern sailboat uses wind to sail the North Atlantic Ocean. **Which wind system might sailors use to sail from North America to Europe?**

Daily and Seasonal Winds

The wind systems determine the major weather patterns for the entire globe. Smaller wind systems determine local weather. If you live near a large body of water, you're familiar with two such wind systems—land breezes and sea breezes.

Sea Breezes

Convection currents over areas where the land meets the sea cause sea breezes and land breezes. **Sea breezes** are created during the day because solar radiation warms the land more than the water. Air over the land is heated by conduction. This heated air becomes less dense and is forced upward by cooler, denser air moving inland from the ocean. A convection current results.

Land Breezes

At night, the land cools much more rapidly than the ocean water. Air over the land becomes cooler than the air over the ocean. The cool, dense air from the land moves out over the water, pushing the warm air over the water upward. Movements of air toward the water are called **land breezes. Figure 10-18** can help you understand how sea breezes and land breezes occur.

Mountain-valley wind is another wind that has a daily cycle. In the mountains, about three hours after sunrise, a valley wind starts flowing from the valley upward along the slope of the mountain. A few hours after sunset, a mountain wind begins to blow down the slope into the valley. This mountain-valley wind circulation comes from heating of the mountainsides during the day. At night, the mountain slopes cool quickly and the cooler, denser air drains into the valley.

Figure 10-18 These daily winds occur because a convection current changes its direction.

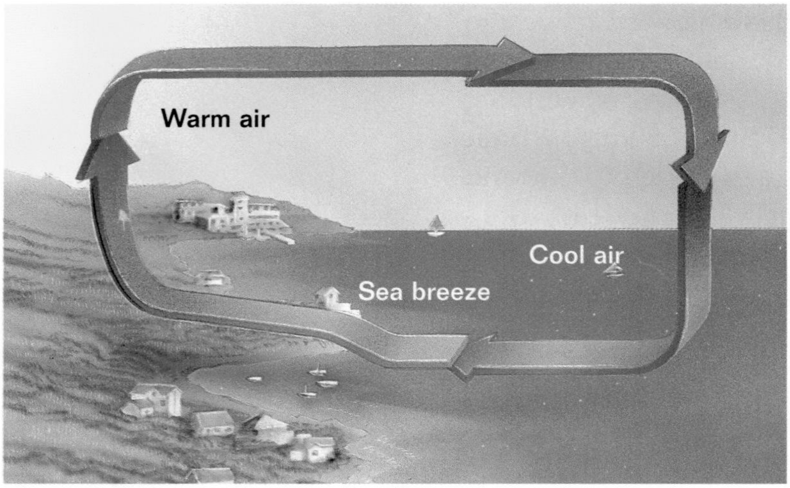

A During the day, cool air forces warm air over the land to rise, creating a sea breeze.

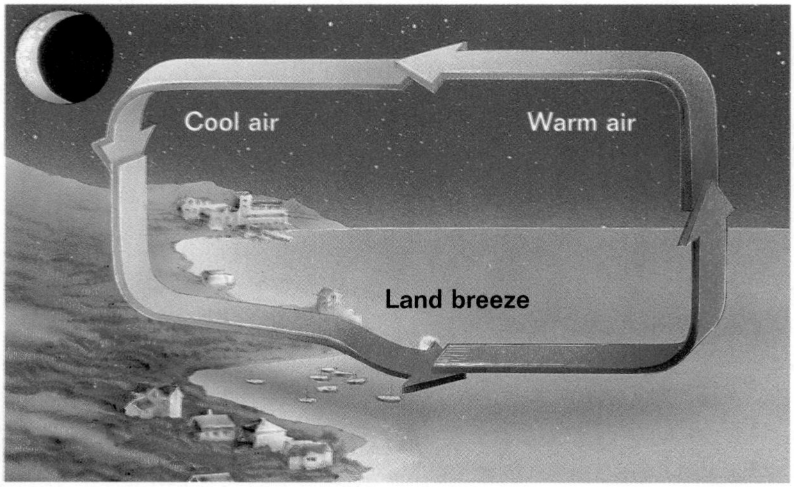

B At night, cold air over the land forces up the warmer air above the sea, creating a land breeze.

Figure 10-19

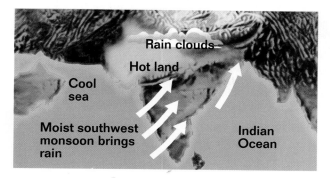

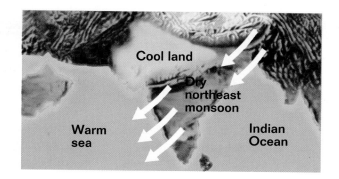

A When the land is intensely hot, the wet monsoon winds blow from the ocean onto the land, bringing rain.

B When the sun is not shining directly over the land, the air above the ocean has a lower pressure. Dry winds flow from the land out over the ocean, bringing the dry season.

Monsoons

Other winds change with the seasons. **Figure 10-19** shows monsoon winds that occur in tropical areas. During the winter, when land is cooler than the ocean, air flows away from the land. During the summer, when land is warmer, the air blows inland. Where the monsoon winds are strong, the summer monsoon blows moist, ocean air over the land and brings extremely heavy rain. The wind during the winter brings dry weather.

Section Assessment

1. Why do latitudes differ in the amount of solar energy they receive?

2. How does the Coriolis effect influence the general wind circulation of Earth?

3. **Think Critically:** Explain why a jet that flies from North Carolina to California uses more fuel and takes longer to complete its journey than a similar jet that flies from California to North Carolina.

4. **Skill Builder**
   Comparing and Contrasting
   Compare and contrast land and sea breezes and seasonal winds versus daily winds. If you need help, refer to Comparing and Contrasting in the **Skill Handbook** on page 686.

Using Computers

Graphics Use a computer graphics package and **Figure 10-16** to draw the wind systems on Earth. Make separate graphics of major wind circulation cells shown by purple arrows. On another graphic, show major surface winds. On another, draw the jet streams. Print your graphics and share them with your class. If you need help, refer to page 700.

For a **preview** of this chapter, study this Reviewing Main Ideas before you read the chapter. After you have studied this chapter, you can use the Reviewing Main Ideas to **review** the chapter.

The Glencoe MindJogger, Audiocassettes, and CD-ROM provide additional opportunities for review.

Section

10-1 EARTH'S ATMOSPHERE

The atmosphere is a thin blanket of air molecules that surrounds Earth. Its structure and composition are unique to our planet. Earth gets its thermal energy from the sun, but it's the atmosphere that transfers heat to all parts of the planet. Nitrogen and oxygen are the two most common gases in Earth's atmosphere. All gases in the atmosphere have mass, and thus, they push against one another, creating air pressure. Earth's atmosphere is classified into layers based on temperature differences. *Why do different layers of the atmosphere have different temperatures?*

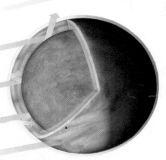

THE OZONE LAYER

The **ozone layer** protects Earth from too much **ultraviolet radiation.** When exposed to excessive amounts of ultraviolet radiation, humans can develop cancers and other health problems. *How does a molecule of chlorofluorocarbon destroy a molecule of ozone?*

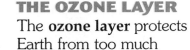

Reading Check ✓

Choose a major illustration from this chapter, such as **Figure 10-3.** List things you learned from this illustration.

Section

10-2 ENERGY FROM THE SUN

Some of the sun's energy that reaches Earth escapes back into space. Other energy is absorbed by Earth's air, land, and water. Solar energy fuels the water cycle between the atmosphere and Earth's surface. *How are the transfer of energy by convection and the water cycle similar?*

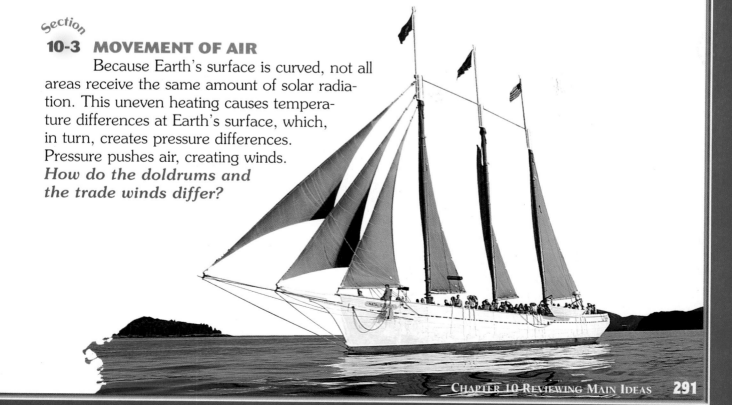

Precipitation

Condensation

Evaporation

Runoff

Groundwater

Section

10-3 MOVEMENT OF AIR

Because Earth's surface is curved, not all areas receive the same amount of solar radiation. This uneven heating causes temperature differences at Earth's surface, which, in turn, creates pressure differences. Pressure pushes air, creating winds. *How do the doldrums and the trade winds differ?*

Chapter 10 Assessment

Using Vocabulary

a. chlorofluoro-carbon
b. conduction
c. convection
d. Coriolis effect
e. hydrosphere
f. ionosphere
g. jet stream
h. land breeze
i. ozone layer
j. radiation
k. sea breeze
l. troposphere
m. ultraviolet radiation
n. water cycle

Use what you know about the above terms to answer the following questions.

1. How does a land breeze differ from a sea breeze?
2. What is the Coriolis effect?
3. Compare and contrast conduction and convection.
4. What are the layers of Earth's atmosphere?
5. Describe the water cycle.

Checking Concepts

Choose the word or phrase that best answers the question.

6. What is the most abundant gas in the air?
   A) oxygen   C) argon
   B) water vapor D) nitrogen
7. What is smog?
   A) conduction   C) pollution
   B) mud   D) wind
8. What is the uppermost layer of the atmosphere?
   A) troposphere C) exosphere
   B) stratosphere D) thermosphere
9. What is the warmest layer of air?
   A) troposphere C) mesosphere
   B) stratosphere D) exosphere

10. What protects living things from too much ultraviolet radiation?
    A) the ozone layer
    B) oxygen
    C) nitrogen
    D) argon
11. Where is air pressure greatest?
    A) troposphere
    B) stratosphere
    C) exosphere
    D) thermosphere
12. When objects are in contact, how is energy transferred?
    A) trade winds
    B) convection
    C) radiation
    D) conduction
13. What does a barometer measure?
    A) temperature   C) humidity
    B) air pressure D) wind speed
14. What type of wind is created by the movement of air toward water?
    A) sea breeze   C) land breeze
    B) doldrum   D) barometer
15. What are narrow belts of strong winds near the top of the troposphere called?
    A) doldrums   C) polar easterlies
    B) jet streams   D) trade winds

Thinking Critically

16. Why are there few or no clouds in the stratosphere?
17. It is thought that life could not have existed on land until the ozone layer formed about 2 billion years ago. Why does life on land require an ozone layer?
18. Explain how soup in a pan on a stove is heated by conduction and convection.
19. What happens when water vapor rises and cools?
20. Why does air pressure decrease with an increase in altitude?

Developing Skills

If you need help, refer to the **Skill Handbook.**

21. **Concept Mapping:** Complete the cycle concept map below using the following phrases to explain how air moves to form a convection current: *cool air pushes up warm air, cool air is warmed by conduction,* and *cool air sinks.*

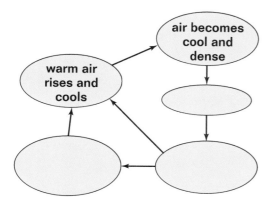

22. **Observing and Inferring:** In an experiment, a student measured the air temperature 1 m above the ground on a sunny afternoon and again one hour after sunset. The second reading was lower than the first. What can you infer from this?

23. **Hypothesizing:** Trees use carbon dioxide to photosynthesize. Carbon dioxide in the atmosphere prevents radiation from Earth's surface from escaping to space. Hypothesize how the temperature on Earth would change if many trees were cut down.

24. **Using Variables, Constants, and Controls:** Design an experiment to find out how plants are affected by differing amounts of ultraviolet radiation. In the design, use filtering film made for car windows. What is the variable you are testing? What are your constants? Your controls?

Test-Taking Tip

Cross It Out List the answer choice letters on scratch paper and cross out choices you've eliminated. You'll stop yourself from choosing an answer you've mentally eliminated.

Test Practice

Use these questions to test your Science Proficiency.

1. Early sailors avoided sailing into the doldrums. Why?
   A) Doldrums only blew from east to west.
   B) Doldrums only blew from west to east.
   C) Doldrums kept changing wind direction.
   D) Doldrums are a windless zone.

2. The upper part of the stratosphere is warmer than the upper part of the mesosphere. Which of the following **BEST** explains why?
   A) The stratosphere is closer to the sun than the mesosphere.
   B) The stratosphere is closer to Earth's surface than the mesosphere.
   C) The stratosphere has greater air pressure than the mesosphere.
   D) The stratosphere has gases that more easily absorb solar energy than the gases in the mesosphere.

Chapter Preview

Skills Preview

Skill Builders

- Recognize Cause and Effect
- Compare and Contrast

Activities

- Predict
- Use Numbers

MiniLabs

- Infer
- Make a Model

Reading Check ✓

Before beginning this chapter, read the What You'll Learn feature at the beginning of each section. Explain why each section could include this feature.

Explore Activity

Dark clouds, thunder, lightning, heavy rain—when you see any of these, take cover soon. You're about to experience some severe weather. Tornadoes are a type of severe weather event that comes with little or no warning. A tornado can roar through farms and cities, smashing everything in its path, leaving a trail of destruction. Winds in a tornado sometimes reach 500 km/hour —strong enough to flatten buildings and uproot trees. Updrafts in the center can act like a giant vacuum cleaner, sucking homes, cars, and even animals high into the air.

Model a Tornado

1. Obtain two 2-L plastic bottles.

2. Fill one about three-quarters full of water and add one drop of dish-washing soap to the water.

3. Put the empty bottle on top and tape the bottles securely, opening to opening.

4. Flip the bottles to put the one with water in it on top. Move the top bottle in a circular motion.

Science Journal

Describe what happens in the bottles. Use this description to compare this model of a tornado with a real tornado as you learn about the features of this weather phenomenon.

11•1 What is weather?

Factors of Weather

What You'll Learn

▶ The role of water vapor in the atmosphere and how it affects weather
▶ How clouds form and how they are classified
▶ How rain, hail, sleet, and snow develop

Vocabulary
weather
humidity
relative humidity
dew point
fog
precipitation

Why It's Important

▶ Your daily activities are affected by weather changes.

"What's the weather going to be today?" That's probably one of the first things you ask when you get up each day. Weather information can affect what you wear to school, how you get to and from school, and what you do after school.

Everyone discusses the weather. Can you explain what it is? **Weather** refers to the present state of the atmosphere. Weather describes current conditions such as air pressure, wind, temperature, and the amount of moisture in the air. One kind of weather is seen in **Figure 11-1.**

In the water cycle, the sun provides the energy to evaporate water into the atmosphere, where it forms clouds and eventually falls back to Earth.

The water cycle forms the basis of our weather. But, the sun does more than just evaporate water. It also heats air, causing the formation of the global winds. The interaction of air, water, and the sun causes weather.

Figure 11-1 The weather influences what you can do, especially outdoor activities such as a trip to the playground.

Humidity

The sun evaporates water into the atmosphere. How does this happen? How can the atmosphere hold water? The air of the atmosphere is somewhat like a sponge. The holes in a sponge enable it to hold water. The atmosphere holds water in a similar way. Water vapor molecules fit into spaces between the molecules that make up air. The amount of water vapor held in air is called **humidity.**

Humidity varies from day to day because the temperature of the air changes. The amount of water vapor that air can hold depends on the temperature. At cooler temperatures, molecules in air move more slowly. This slow movement in cool air allows water vapor molecules to join together (condense). At warmer temperatures, air and water vapor molecules move too quickly to join together.

If you look at **Figure 11-2,** you'll see that at 25°C, a cubic meter of air can hold a maximum of 22 g of water vapor. The same air cooled to 15°C can hold only about 13 g of water vapor. ✓

Try at Home
Mini Lab

Making Rain

Procedure
1. Pour a few centimeters of hot water into a tall, clear, widemouthed jar.
2. Put ice cubes in a small plastic bag. Suspend the bag from the top of the jar and let it hang down inside *above* the water level.

Analysis
1. In your Science Journal, describe what you see.
2. Describe what is happening to the water vapor in the jar.

Reading Check ✓

How does temperature affect humidity?

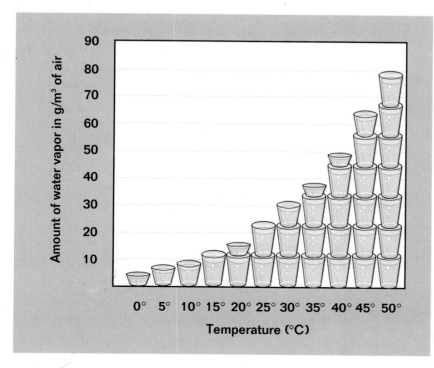

Figure 11-2 This graph shows the maximum amount of water vapor in air at various temperatures. **What happens to the amount of water vapor as the temperature decreases?**

Figure 11-3 When the air next to the glass cools to its dew point, condensation forms on the glass.

On hot summer days when the air seems damp and sticky, people often comment on the high humidity. When they mention humidity, they are actually talking about the relative humidity.

Relative Humidity

Have you ever heard a weather forecaster speak of relative humidity? **Relative humidity** is a measure of the amount of water vapor that air is holding compared to the amount it can hold at a specific temperature. When air contains as much moisture as possible at a specific temperature, it is saturated. If you hear a weather forecaster say the relative humidity is 50 percent, that means the air on that day contains 50 percent of the water needed for the air to be saturated.

As shown in **Figure 11-2,** air at 40°C is saturated when it contains about 50 g of water vapor per cubic meter of air. Air at 25°C is saturated when it contains 22 g of water vapor per cubic meter of air. If air at 25°C contains only 11 g of water vapor in each cubic meter of air, the relative humidity is 50 percent. Saturated air has a relative humidity of 100 percent.

When there is more water vapor than the air can hold, it will condense back to a liquid or freeze, depending on the temperature. The temperature at which air is saturated and condensation forms is the **dew point.** The dew point changes with the amount of moisture in the air.

You've probably seen water droplets form on the outside of a glass of cold milk, as in **Figure 11-3.** The cold glass cooled the air next to it to its dew point. The water vapor in the air condensed and formed water droplets on the glass. Dew on grass in the early morning forms the same way. When air near the ground is cooled to its dew point, water vapor condenses and forms droplets on the grass.

Cloud Formation

Why are there clouds in the sky? Clouds form as warm air is forced upward, expands, and cools, as shown in **Figure 11-4.** As the air cools, the amount of water vapor needed for saturation decreases and the relative humidity increases. When the relative

Determining Dew Point

Procedure

1. Partially fill a metal can with room-temperature water. Dry the outer surface of the can.
2. Slowly stir the water and add small amounts of ice.
3. In a data table in your Science Journal, note the exact water temperature at which a thin film of moisture first begins to form on the outside of the metal can.
4. Repeat steps 1–3 two more times.
5. The average of the three temperatures at which the moisture begins to appear is the dew point temperature of the air around the container.

Analysis

1. What factors determine the dew point?
2. Why does change in air temperature cause the dew point to change?

humidity reaches 100 percent, the air is saturated. Water vapor begins to condense in tiny drops around small particles such as dust, salt, and smoke in the atmosphere. These drops of water are so small they become suspended in the air. When millions of these drops collect, a cloud forms.

Cloud Classification

As you will see in the **Field Guide to Clouds** at the end of this chapter, many different types of clouds can be seen in the sky. Clouds are classified mainly by shape and by height. Some clouds stack up, reaching high into the sky, while others are low and flat. Some dense clouds bring rain or snow, while thin clouds appear on mostly sunny days. Refer to the Field Guide for more details.

Shape

The three main cloud types are stratus, cumulus, and cirrus. Cumulus clouds are masses of puffy, white clouds, often with flat bases. Some people refer to them as cauliflower clouds. They form when air currents rise. They may rise to great heights and can be associated with both fair weather and thunderstorms.

Stratus clouds form layers or smooth, even sheets in the sky. When layers of air cool below their dew point temperatures, stratus clouds appear. Stratus clouds usually form at low altitudes. Stratus clouds are associated with fair weather and precipitation. Sometimes, they form a dull, gray blanket that hangs low in the sky and brings drizzle.

Figure 11-4 Clouds form when moist air is pushed high enough to reach its dew point. The water vapor condenses, forming water droplets that group together.

A Clouds form when warm air is forced up in a convection current caused by solar radiation heating Earth's surface.

B Clouds form when warm, moist air is forced to rise over a mountain. The air cools and the water vapor condenses.

C Clouds form when two air masses meet. Warmer air is forced up over the cold air. As the warm air cools, the water vapor in it condenses. **Is the warm air on the left or the right?**

Figure 11-5 When water vapor in air collects on particles to form water droplets, the type of precipitation that is received on the ground depends on the temperature of the air.

A When the air near the ground is warm, water vapor forms raindrops that fall as rain.

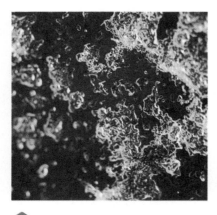

B When the air near the ground is cold, sleet, made up of many small ice pellets, falls.

C When the air is very cold, water vapor forms snowflakes.

D Hailstones are pellets of ice that form as the ice nuclei go up and down in the cloud.

When air is cooled to its dew point and condenses near the ground, it forms a stratus cloud called **fog. Figure 11-6** shows a stratus cloud fog in San Francisco.

Cirrus clouds appear fibrous or curly. They are high, thin, white, feathery clouds containing ice crystals. Cirrus clouds are associated with fair weather, but they may indicate approaching storms.

Height

Some prefixes of cloud names describe the height of the cloud base. The prefix *cirro-* describes high clouds, *alto-* describes middle-elevation clouds, and *strato-* refers to clouds at low elevations. Some clouds' names combine the altitude prefix with the term *stratus* or *cumulus*.

Cirrostratus clouds are high clouds that look like fine veils. They are made of ice crystals that appear to form halos around the moon or sun.

Altostratus clouds form at middle levels. They look like thick veils or sheets of gray or blue. If the clouds are not too thick, sunlight can filter through them. They produce light, continuous precipitation.

Rain Capacity

Nimbus clouds are dark clouds associated with precipitation. They are so full of water that no sunlight penetrates them. When a nimbus cloud is also a towering cumulus cloud, it is called a cumulonimbus cloud. Some cumulonimbus clouds grow huge, starting near Earth's surface and towering to nearly 18 000 m. Sudden, gigantic thunderstorms can be unleashed from them. Nimbostratus clouds are low, dark gray clouds that bring long, steady rain. They often have streaks that extend to the ground.

As long as the water drops in a cloud remain small, they stay suspended in the air. But when the water droplets combine and reach the size of 0.2 mm, they become too heavy and fall out of suspension in the form of precipitation.

Precipitation

Water falling from clouds is called **precipitation**. Air temperature determines whether the water droplets form rain, snow, sleet, or hail—the four main types of precipitation. **Figure 11-5** shows how the four types of precipitation form. Drops of water falling in temperatures above freezing come down as rain. Snow forms when the air temperature is below freezing and water vapor changes directly to a solid. Sleet forms when snow passes through a layer of warm air, melts, and then refreezes near the ground.

Figure 11-6 Fog surrounds the Golden Gate Bridge, San Francisco. Fog is a stratus cloud near the ground.

Problem Solving

Interpret When Dew Will Form

Sometimes in the early morning, you have probably noticed that some outdoor surfaces are wet and glisten in the sunlight. You are observing droplets of dew. In order for dew to form, the temperature must drop low enough to cause condensation in the air immediately above the ground. Dew will form on any solid surface such as grass, cobwebs, and even insect wings. Use **Figure 11-2** and the graph to the right to answer the following questions.

Think Critically: If the humidity on the day shown in the graph is 50 g of water vapor per cubic meter of air, at what time would you expect dew to form? At what hour will it disappear?

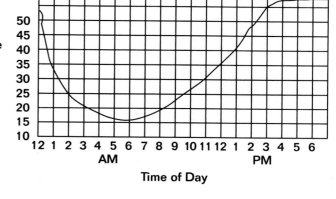

Air temperature in °C at 5 cm above ground

Time of Day

Figure 11-7 A large hail-stone appears to have a layered structure much like an onion.

Hail

Hail is precipitation in the form of lumps of ice as shown in **Figure 11-7.** Hail forms in cumulonimbus clouds of a thunderstorm when drops of water freeze in layers around a small nucleus of ice. Hailstones grow larger as they're tossed up and down by rising and falling convection currents. Most hailstones are smaller than 2.5 cm but can grow much larger. Hail can be the most damaging form of precipitation, especially if winds blow during a hailstorm. Falling hailstones can break windows and destroy crops.

By understanding the role of water vapor in the atmosphere, you can begin to understand weather. The relative humidity helps determine whether a location will have a dry day or some form of precipitation. The temperature of the atmosphere determines the form of precipitation. Studying clouds can add to your ability to forecast weather.

PHYSICS
INTEGRATION ➤

Section Assessment

1. When does water vapor in air condense?

2. How do clouds form?

3. What is the relationship between air temperature and the amount of water vapor that can be in the air?

4. **Think Critically:** How can the same cumulonimbus cloud produce both rain and hail?

5. **Skill Builder**
   Concept Mapping Make a network tree concept map that compares four clouds. Use these terms: *cirrus, cumulus, stratus, nimbus, feathery, fair weather, puffy, layered, precipitation, clouds, dark,* and *steady precipitation.* If you need help, refer to Concept Mapping in the **Skill Handbook** on page 680.

Using Math

Use the graph in **Figure 11-2** to determine the amount of water vapor air can hold when its temperature is 50°C.

The Heat Index

"It's not the heat, it's the humidity," people say, and they're right. High humidity affects your body's ability to cool itself, so you feel hotter. The "heat index" describes how your body feels at different levels of temperature and humidity. You can figure out the heat index using the chart below. For example, locate the air temperature of 90°F at the top of the chart. Then, locate the humidity of 70 percent. At this temperature and humidity, the heat index is 106°F.

Problem

What is the relationship between air temperature and relative humidity?

Heat Index Table

RELATIVE HUMIDITY	AIR TEMPERATURE (DEGREES FAHRENHEIT)										
	70°	75°	80°	85°	90°	95°	100°	105°	110°	115°	120°
	APPARENT TEMPERATURE (HEAT INDEX)										
0%	64	69	73	78	83	87	91	95	99	103	107
10%	65	70	75	80	85	90	95	100	105	111	116
20%	66	72	77	82	87	93	99	105	112	120	130
30%	67	73	78	84	90	96	104	113	123	135	148
40%	68	74	79	86	93	101	110	123	137	151	
50%	69	75	81	88	96	107	120	135	150		
60%	70	76	82	90	100	114	132	149			
70%	70	77	85	93	106	124	144				
80%	71	78	86	97	113	136					
90%	71	79	88	102	122						
100%	72	80	91	108							

Practice PROBLEMS

1. Make graphs by plotting actual air temperature versus apparent temperature (heat index) at 50 percent humidity and at 70 percent humidity.
2. Write a paragraph describing what happens to the heat index as the humidity rises. Give some specific examples to justify your ideas. You may want to make a new graph showing 20 percent, 50 percent, 70 percent, and 100 percent humidity all on the same graph. This will help you see any patterns.

Solution

1. Make a graph comparing the air temperature and the apparent temperature, or heat index, at a 20 percent humidity level.
2. On graph paper, draw a horizontal axis labeled "Actual Air Temperature" and a vertical axis labeled "Apparent Temperature (Heat Index)." Mark off a temperature scale on each axis, starting with 65°F, increasing in increments of five degrees.
3. In the table above, find 20 percent Relative Humidity in the light-blue area and move to the right. On your graph, locate 70° on the horizontal axis and 66° on the vertical axis. Make a dot at the intersection of the two grid lines. Continue to plot the data for the other temperatures in the table at 20 percent humidity.

11·2 Weather Patterns

Changes in Weather

Why do you ask about the weather in the morning when you get up? Isn't it safe to think that the weather is the same as it was the day before? Of course not! Weather is always changing because of the continuing movement of air and moisture in the atmosphere. These changes are generally related to the development and movement of air masses.

Air Masses

An **air mass** is a large body of air that has the same properties as Earth's surface over which it develops. For example, an air mass that develops over land is dry compared with one that develops over water. Also, an air mass that develops in the tropics is warmer than one that develops at a higher latitude. When you observe a change in the weather from one day to the next, it is due to the movement of air masses. **Figure 11-8** shows air masses that affect the United States.

Pressure Systems

You have heard weather forecasters mention high- and low-pressure systems. What are they? In the atmosphere, great masses of air molecules push down from above, creating atmospheric pressure at Earth's surface. Atmospheric pressure at sea level varies over the surface of Earth. The atmospheric

What You'll Learn

▶ What weather is associated with fronts and high- and low-pressure areas
▶ How low-pressure systems form at fronts
▶ How tornadoes develop from thunderstorms

Vocabulary
air mass
front
tornado
Doppler radar
hurricane

Why It's Important

▶ Air masses, pressure systems, and fronts cause weather to change constantly.

Figure 11-8 Six major air masses affect weather in the United States. Each air mass has the same characteristics of temperature and moisture content as the area over which it forms. **What air masses affect the weather in your region of the country?**

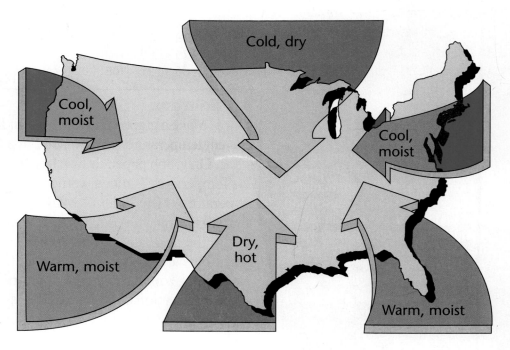

Cold, dry

Cool, moist

Cool, moist

Warm, moist

Dry, hot

Warm, moist

pressure is determined by three things: the temperature and density of the air and the amount of water vapor in the air.

Variation in atmospheric pressure affects the weather. Areas of high pressure at Earth's surface are regions of descending air. Section 11-1 explained that clouds form when air rises and cools. The sinking motion of high-pressure air masses makes it difficult for air to rise and clouds to form. That's why high pressure usually means good weather. Areas of low pressure usually have cloudy weather.

Fronts

Low-pressure systems form along the boundaries of air masses. The boundary between cold and warm air masses is called a **front.** All fronts involve both a warm and a cold air mass. Storms and precipitation occur at these fronts.

At a front, air at the surface moves from the high-pressure systems into the low-pressure systems. As the air flows into the low-pressure area, it flows under the less dense, warm air, forcing it upward. As the air in a low-pressure system rises, it cools. At a certain elevation, the air reaches its dew point and the water vapor in it condenses, forming clouds. **Figure 11-9** shows how a low-pressure system can develop at the boundary between cold and warm air.

At fronts where two different air masses meet, the air does not mix. Instead, the cold air mass moves under the warm air. The warm air rises. Winds begin. As surface winds blow from a high-pressure area into a low-pressure area, the Coriolis (kor ee OH lus) effect turns the winds. The Coriolis effect makes them circulate counterclockwise around a low-pressure area in the northern hemisphere and clockwise in the southern hemisphere.

Figure 11-9 These diagrams show how a low-pressure system occurs along a front.

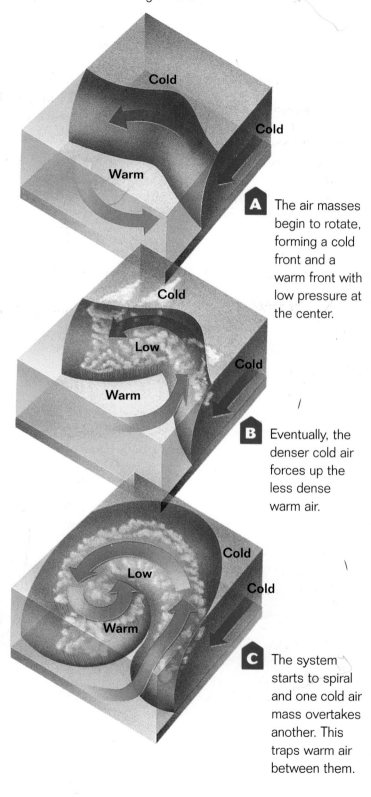

A The air masses begin to rotate, forming a cold front and a warm front with low pressure at the center.

B Eventually, the denser cold air forces up the less dense warm air.

C The system starts to spiral and one cold air mass overtakes another. This traps warm air between them.

Most changes in weather occur at one of four types of fronts—warm, cold, occluded, or stationary, as illustrated in **Figure 11-10.** Fronts usually bring a change in temperature and always bring a change in wind direction.

Figure 11-10 These diagrams show the structure of a warm, a cold, an occluded, and a stationary front.

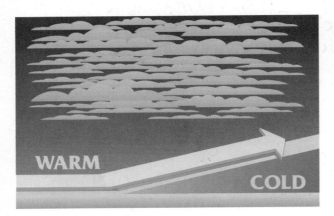

A A warm front develops when a less dense, warm air mass slides over a departing cold air mass. Precipitation occurs over a wide area. Look for high cirrus clouds to form as water vapor condenses. **What other clouds occur at a warm front?**

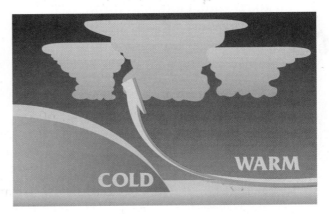

B In a cold front, a cold air mass pushes under a warm air mass and forces the warm air aloft along a steep front. This results in a narrow band of violent storms. Cold fronts often move at twice the speed of warm fronts. Cumulus and cumulonimbus clouds form along the front. **What kinds of weather do these clouds bring?**

C The faster-moving cold front overtakes the slower-moving warm front and forms an occluded front. The warm air is forced to rise off the ground. Strong winds and heavy precipitation may occur. **Why is the warm air forced up between the cold air masses?**

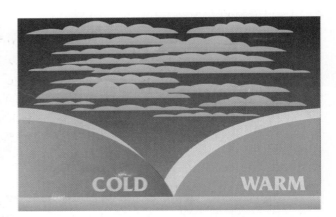

D A stationary front occurs when pressure differences cause a warm front or a cold front to stop moving. A stationary front may remain in the same place for several days. Light wind and precipitation occur across the entire frontal region. **What might happen if a stationary front remains for a long period of time?**

Severe Weather

Weather does affect you every day. Usually, you can still go about your business regardless of the weather. If it's raining, you can still go to school. Even if it snows a little, you can still get there. But, some weather conditions, such as those caused by blizzards, thunderstorms, and tornadoes, prevent you from going about your normal routine. Severe weather poses danger to people and animals.

Thunderstorms

In a thunderstorm, heavy rain falls, lightning flashes, thunder roars, and maybe hail falls. What forces cause such extreme weather conditions? Thunderstorms occur inside warm, moist air masses and at fronts. When the warm, moist air moves upward rapidly, cools, and condenses, it forms cumulonimbus clouds that can reach heights of 18 km. As the rising air reaches its dew point, water droplets and ice form and begin falling the long distance through the clouds toward Earth's surface. The falling droplets collide with other droplets and grow larger. The heavier raindrops fall, dragging down the air with them. This creates downdrafts of air that spread out at Earth's surface. These downdrafts cause the strong winds associated with thunderstorms.

Lightning

Thunderstorms also produce thunder and lightning. Lightning, like that in **Figure 11-11,** occurs when a rapid uplift of air builds up electric charges in the clouds. Some places in the clouds have a positive electrical charge and some have a negative electrical charge. When current flows between regions of opposite electrical charge, lightning flashes. Bolts of lightning can leap from cloud to cloud and from Earth to clouds.

Thunder results from the rapid heating of the air around a bolt of lightning. Lightning can reach temperatures of about 30 000°C, which is more than five times the temperature of the surface of the sun. This extreme heat causes the air around the lightning to expand rapidly. Then, it cools quickly and contracts. The rapid movement of the molecules forms sound waves heard as thunder.

Figure 11-11 This time-elapsed photo shows a thunderstorm over Arizona.

PHYSICS
INTEGRATION

Moving Air
The air over a city is usually warmer than the air over rural communities because of the concrete and asphalt in a city. Because of this difference, convection currents develop at the boundaries of cities and rural areas. Make a drawing of a city skyline in your Science Journal. Illustrate the drawing with arrows showing the direction the convection currents move in air.

Thunderstorms can cause a lot of damage. Their heavy rain sometimes causes flooding, and lightning can strike objects and set them on fire. Strong winds generated by thunderstorms also can cause damage. If a thunderstorm has winds traveling faster than 89 km/hour, it is classified as a severe thunderstorm. Hail from a thunderstorm can make dents in cars and the aluminum siding on houses. Although rain from thunderstorms helps crops grow, hail has been known to flatten and destroy a crop in a matter of minutes.

Tornadoes

Some of the most severe thunderstorms produce tornadoes. A **tornado** is a violent, whirling wind that moves in a narrow path over land. It usually moves from southwest to northeast. Most tornadoes form along a front. In severe thunderstorms, the wind at different heights blows in different directions and at different speeds. This difference in wind direction and speed is called *wind shear*. A strong updraft will tilt the wind shear and produce rotation inside the thunderstorm. A funnel cloud appears. **Figure 11-12** shows how a tornado funnel forms. Recall the tornado you made in the Explore Activity. ☑

Some tornado funnels do not reach Earth. When funnel clouds touch down, they pick up dirt and debris from the ground. This material gives the funnels their dark gray or black color. Sometimes, tornadoes strike Earth, go back up into the atmosphere, then dip down and strike another area.

When tornadoes touch the ground, their destructive winds rip apart

Reading Check ☑

What causes a tornado to form?

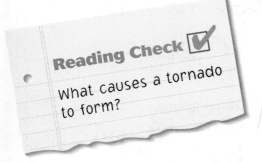

Figure 11-12 A funnel cloud, such as the one in this farm field (A), is formed by winds (B). The destructive winds of a tornado can reach up to 500 km/hour.

A

B

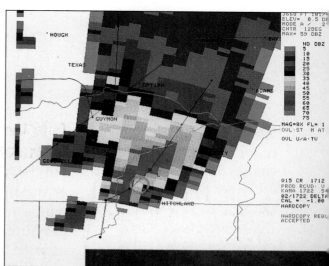

Figure 11-13 The hook-shaped image on the Doppler radar screen indicates a possible tornado in Texas. **Explain how you could determine the direction the storm is moving.**

buildings and trees. High winds can blow through broken windows. When winds blow inside a house, they can lift off the roof and blow out the walls, making it look as though the building exploded. The updraft in the center of a powerful tornado can lift animals, cars, and even houses into the air. Although tornadoes rarely exceed 200 m in diameter and usually last only a few minutes, they are often extremely destructive.

Tornadoes occur worldwide, but most tornadoes touch down in the United States—about 700 per year. Tornadoes most frequently strike the Midwest and South, usually in spring or early summer. Texas, Oklahoma, and Kansas report the most tornadoes.

NEXRAD and Doppler Radar

Tracking a tornado can help prevent loss of life. Thanks to Next Generation Weather Radar, or NEXRAD, severe storms that may evolve into tornadoes can be tracked. NEXRAD is a nationwide system of radar stations that use a specialized radar system called Doppler radar.

Doppler radar sends out repeated radio waves and monitors the reflected waves from distant storms. It can tell the direction a storm is moving.

If a storm is moving toward the radar, the reflected radio waves are squeezed and shift to a higher frequency. If a storm is moving away from the radar, the waves are lengthened and shift to a lower frequency. These frequency differences appear on the Doppler radar screen as different colors, as shown in **Figure 11-13.**

Bright green indicates winds coming toward the radar. Red indicates winds moving away from the radar. Where red and green are close together, rotation is occurring. This indicates a funnel cloud such as the one shown in **Figure 11-14.** If this cloud touches down, it becomes a tornado. Tornado advisories are issued by the National Weather Service. A tornado watch occurs when conditions are right for a tornado to form and a tornado warning is issued if a funnel cloud is observed by tornado spotters or Doppler radar. This usually provides time for people to get to safety.

Figure 11-14 This funnel cloud could become a tornado in a split second.

*inter***NET**
CONNECTION

Visit the Glencoe Science Web Site at **www.glencoe.com/ sec/science/fl** for more information about weather.

Hurricanes

The most powerful storm is the hurricane. A **hurricane** is a large, swirling, low-pressure system that forms over tropical oceans. It is like a machine that turns heat energy from the ocean into wind. A storm must have winds of at least 120 km/hour to be called a hurricane.

Hurricanes are similar to low-pressure systems on land, but they are much stronger. **Figure 11-15** illustrates the parts of the hurricane. In the North Atlantic, the southeast trade winds and the northeast trade winds sometimes meet. A low-pressure area develops in the middle of the swirl and begins rotating counterclockwise in the northern hemisphere. This usually happens between 5° and 20° north latitude, where the water is quite warm. Around the middle of the low-pressure area, warm, moist air is forced upward. As it rises to higher elevations, it cools and moisture condenses.

Figure 11-16 shows a hurricane hitting land. When a hurricane strikes land, the high winds, tornadoes, heavy rains, and high waves of the storm surge cause a lot of damage. Floods from the heavy rains can cause additional damage. The weather of the hurricane can destroy crops, demolish buildings, and kill people and animals. In 1998, Hurricane

Using Math

The locations of five of the deadliest hurricanes to strike the United States since 1900 are listed below.

Location	Year	Deaths
Galveston, TX	1900	8000
Florida	1928	1836
Southern TX	1919	600
New England	1938	600
Florida Keys	1935	498

Make a bar graph of these data, plotting the hurricane location on the *x*-axis and the number of deaths on the *y*-axis.

Figure 11-15

A In this hurricane cross section, the small red arrows indicate rising warm, moist air. This rising air forms cumulus and cumulonimbus clouds in bands around the eye. The blue arrows indicate cool, dry air sinking in the eye and between the cloud bands. The large, red arrows indicate the motion of the rising spiral cloud bands. The green arrow shows that the Coriolis effect then bends the flow.

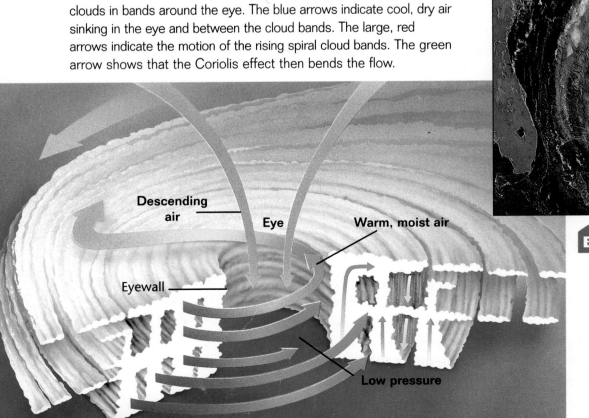

Descending air

Eye

Warm, moist air

Eyewall

Low pressure

B This photograph shows Hurricane Fran approaching Florida in September 1996.

Mitch hit Central America. In Honduras, more than 10 000 people were killed. Nearly 70 percent of the nation's crops were destroyed. Seventy percent of the nation's roads, water supplies, and bridges were severely damaged.

As long as a hurricane is over water, the warm, moist air rises and provides energy for the storm. When a hurricane reaches land, however, its supply of warm, moist air disappears and the storm loses power.

Most hurricanes in the United States strike along the Gulf of Mexico or along the Atlantic Coast. Mexico often sustains damage from hurricanes along its Pacific coast, as well as its Atlantic coast. Find out what happens to the islands of the Caribbean Sea during an average hurricane season.

Changes in weather affect your life. The interaction of air and water vapor causes constant change in the atmosphere. Air masses meet and fronts form, causing changes in weather. Severe weather can affect human lives and property.

Figure 11-16 Hurricanes can be destructive, killing people and destroying property.

Section Assessment

1. Why do high-pressure areas usually have clear skies?

2. Explain how a tornado develops from a thunderstorm.

3. How does Doppler radar determine the direction a storm is moving?

4. **Think Critically:** How do two converging fronts form a low-pressure area? Which front would bring the most severe weather?

5. **Skill Builder**
   Interpreting Scientific Illustrations For more practice in interpreting illustrations, do the **Chapter 11 Skill Activity** on page 718.

Using Computers

Spreadsheet Make a spreadsheet comparing warm fronts, cold fronts, stationary fronts, and occluded fronts. Indicate what kind of clouds and weather systems form with each. If you need help, refer to page 704.

Materials
- Magnifying glass or hand lens
- **Figure 11-19**
- Appendix I

Reading a Weather Map

Meteorologists use a series of symbols to provide a picture of local and national weather conditions. These symbols give information on the temperature, air pressure, cloud cover, and more. Let's see how you can interpret weather information from weather map symbols.

What You'll Investigate

How do you read a weather map?

Goals

- **Interpret** weather map symbols.
- **Predict** weather using weather map information.

Procedure

Use the information provided in the questions below and Appendix I to learn how to read a weather map.

Conclude and Apply

1. Locate the station models on the map for Tucson, Arizona, and Albuquerque, New Mexico. Find the dew point, cloud coverage, pressure, and temperature at each location.

2. Review information about the spacing of isobars and wind speed in Section 11-3 and determine whether the wind would be stronger at Roswell, New Mexico, or at Fort Worth, Texas. Record your answer.

3. Determine the type of front near Key West, Florida. Record your answer.

4. The triangles or half-circles on the weather front symbol are on the side of the line toward the direction the front is moving. In what direction is the cold front located over Colorado and Kansas moving?

5. **Locate** the pressure system over Winslow, Arizona. Review Section 11-3 and **describe** what would happen to the weather of Wichita, Kansas, if this pressure system were to move there.

6. Prevailing westerlies are winds responsible for the movement of much of the weather across the United States and Canada. Based on this, would you expect Charleston, South Carolina, to continue to have clear skies? **Explain** your answer.

7. Use the **Field Guide to Clouds** at the end of this chapter to **predict** the types of clouds that might be present over Tucson, Arizona; Key West, Florida; and Charleston, South Carolina.

Forecasting Weather

Weather Observations

You can determine current weather conditions by observing the temperature and looking to see if clouds are in the sky. You know if it's raining. You also have a general idea of the weather because you are familiar with the typical weather where you live. If you live in Florida, you probably don't worry about snow in the forecast. But, if you live in Maine, you assume it will snow every winter. What weather concerns do you have in your region?

A **meteorologist** (meet ee uh RAHL uh just) studies weather. Meteorologists take measurements of temperature, air pressure, winds, humidity, and precipitation. Meteorologists use weather satellites, Doppler radar, computers, and instruments attached to balloons to gather data such as shown in **Figure 11-17.** Instruments for observing weather improve meteorologists' ability to predict weather. Meteorologists use the information provided by weather instruments to make weather maps. They use these maps to make weather forecasts.

Weather Forecasts

Storms such as hurricanes, tornadoes, blizzards, and thunderstorms can be dangerous. When conditions show that severe weather may occur or when dangerous weather is observed, meteorologists at the National Weather Service issue advisories.

Figure 11-17 This tornado chaser uses a Doppler radar unit to obtain weather data about the severe storm.

What You'll Learn

► How data are collected for weather maps and forecasts
► The symbols used in a weather station model

Vocabulary
meteorologist
station model
isotherm
isobar

Why It's Important

► Reading a weather map allows you to interpret weather information and make predictions.

When they issue a weather watch, you should prepare for severe weather. Watches are issued for severe thunderstorms, tornadoes, floods, blizzards, and hurricanes. During a watch, stay tuned to a radio or television station reporting the weather. When a warning is issued, severe weather conditions already exist. You should take immediate action. During a severe thunderstorm warning, take shelter. During a tornado warning, go to the basement or a room in the middle of the house away from windows.

Weather Information

The National Weather Service depends on two sources for its information: meteorologists from around the world and satellites. Meteorologists take measurements in a specific location and give the data to the National Weather Service. The National Weather Service uses this information to make weather maps. The Service records the information on maps with a combination of symbols, forming a **station model.** A station model shows the weather conditions at one specific location, as shown in **Figure 11-18.** Weather satellites provide cloud maps, surface temperatures, photos of Earth, and other data. All this information is used to forecast weather and to issue warnings about severe weather.

Temperature and Pressure

In addition to station models, weather maps have lines that indicate atmospheric pressure and temperature. These lines connect locations of equal temperature or pressure. A line that connects points of equal temperature is called an **isotherm** (I suh thurm). *Iso* means "same" and *therm* means "temperature." You've probably seen isotherms on weather maps on TV or in the newspaper.

An **isobar** is a line drawn to connect points of equal atmospheric pressure. You can tell how fast wind is blowing in an area by noting how closely isobars are spaced. Isobars close together indicate a large pressure difference over a small area. A large pressure difference causes strong winds. Isobars

Figure 11-18

A station model shows the weather conditions at one specific location.

CALIFORNIA

Los Angeles

Type of high clouds

Type of middle clouds

Temperature (°C)

Barometric pressure in millibars with initial 9 or 10 omitted

188

20

Type of precipitation

12

Change in barometric pressure in last 3 hours (in tenths of millibars)

19

Dew point temperature

Wind speed and direction

Type of low clouds

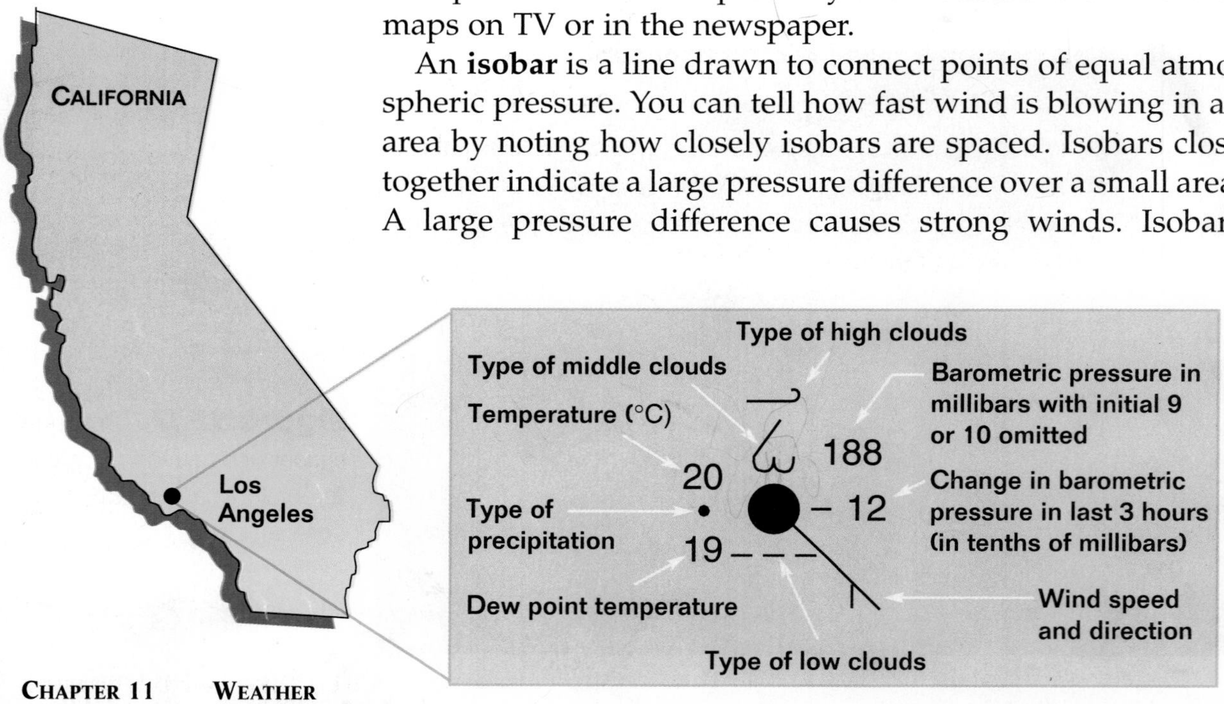

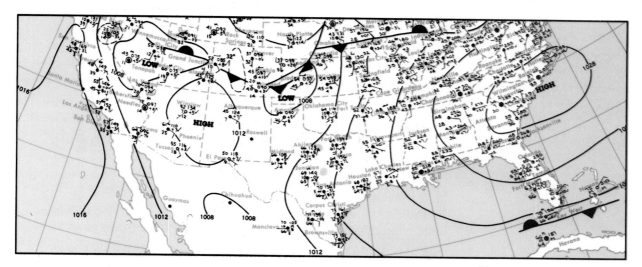

Figure 11-19 Highs, lows, isobars, and fronts on this weather
map help meteorologists forecast
the weather.

spread apart indicate a smaller difference in pressure. Winds
in this area are more gentle. Isobars also indicate the locations of high- and low-pressure areas. On a weather map like
the one in **Figure 11-19**, these areas are drawn as circles with
a *High* or a *Low* in the middle. ☑

When you watch the weather forecasts on television, notice
how weather fronts move across the United States from west to
east. This is a pattern that meteorologists depend on in forecasting the weather. However, weather forecasters cannot
always predict the exact weather because weather conditions
change rapidly. Local conditions also influence the weather.
However, improved technologies enable forecasters to be
increasingly more accurate.

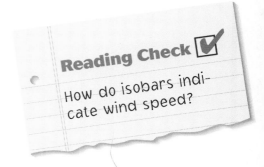

Reading Check ☑

How do isobars indi-
cate wind speed?

Section Assessment

1. What symbols are used in a station model?
2. What do the different lines on a weather map indicate?
3. **Think Critically:** Use Appendix I to analyze the station
   model shown in **Figure 11-18.** What is the temperature,
   type of clouds, wind speed and direction, and type of
   precipitation at that location?

4.  **Skill Builder**
   Comparing and Contrasting Contrast a
   weather watch and a weather warning. If you need help, refer
   to Comparing and Contrasting in the **Skill Handbook** on
   page 686.

*Science
Journal*
Weather affects
history. Research what
happened to American
troops at Valley Forge
during the War of
Independence in the win-
ter of 1777–1778. Imagine
that you were a soldier
there during that winter.
In your Science Journal,
describe your experiences.

On The Internet

Weather or Not

It's raining cats and dogs! Red sky at night, sailor's delight. These sayings are about the weather. You may check out the weather forecast to decide if a concert will be rained out or if you need to wear a coat to the park. Knowing what the weather will be like is important. But, how do scientists predict or forecast the weather? They collect weather data every day all over the country and try to find a pattern in the data.

Recognize the Problem

How can you use weather data to forecast the weather?

Form a Hypothesis

Think about what the weather was like yesterday and what it is like today. **Make a hypothesis** about what the weather will be like in your area for the next several days.

Goals

- **Organize** weather data available on the Glencoe Science Web Site, in newspapers, and on television.
- **Predict** the weather in your area based on the data.

Data Sources

Go to the Glencoe Science Web Site at **www.glencoe.com/sec/science/fl** for information about weather data. You also can find weather data on television news shows, in newspapers, or on the radio. Or, you can make your own weather station. You'll need a thermometer, a barometer, a rain gauge, and a wind vane.

Test Your Hypothesis

Plan

1. Make a data table like the one below in your Science Journal.

2. Collect data in your area every day for at least two weeks. Your weather data should include each of the items listed in the table.

3. You can post your weather data on the Glencoe Science Web Site and collect data from other schools around the country.

4. Use the data to make your own weather maps. Print the map from the Glencoe site or post your data on a large map of the United States, using an overlay of tissue paper or plastic.

Do

1. Make sure your teacher approves your plan and your data table before you proceed.

2. Carry out the experiment as planned.

3. While doing the experiment, **record** your observations and **complete** the data tables in your Science Journal.

Analyze Your Data

1. How close did your predictions come to actual weather? Was your hypothesis supported?

2. Were your forecasts for the first few days more accurate than the later day's forecasts? **Explain.**

Draw Conclusions

1. How could you make your predictions more accurate?

2. Would data from other areas help? Explain your answer.

Weather Data Collection Table					
Date					
Location					
Temperature					
Barometric Pressure					
Wind Speed					
Wind Direction					
Type of Precipitation					
Amount of Precipitation					
Cloud Cover					

FIELD GUIDE

to Clouds

FIELD ACTIVITY

For a week, use this field guide to help you identify the clouds in your area. Observe the clouds two to three times each day. In your Science Journal, record the date, time, types of clouds observed, and the general weather conditions. What relationships can you infer between the weather and the types of clouds that are present?

Clouds are like people—they come in many different sizes and shapes. Some tower thousands of meters into the sky. Others are like fragile wisps of cotton candy floating in the air. All clouds are formed by atmospheric conditions that in turn form our weather. Using this field guide, you can learn to identify different types of clouds and try your hand at weather forecasting.

How Clouds Are Classified

- Clouds are classified based on their shape and height.
- The height of a cloud is represented by the prefix used in its name. For example, a cirrocumulus (cirro + cumulus) cloud is a high cloud with a puffy shape.

High-level
clouds

Medium-level
clouds

Low-level
clouds

Key to Cloud Classification

The following symbols are used in this field guide to represent the height and shape of common clouds.

Height

symbol

prefix
Cirro
Describes high clouds with bases starting above 6000 m.

Alto
Describes middle clouds with bases between 2000 m to 6000 m.

Strato
Refers to low clouds below 2000 m.

Shape

symbol

prefix
Cirrus
Latin meaning: hair
Describes wispy, stringy clouds

Cumulus
Latin meaning: pile or heap
Describes puffy, lumpy-looking clouds

Stratus
Latin meaning: layer
Describes featureless sheets of clouds

Nimbus
Latin meaning: cloud
Describes low, gray rain clouds

Cirrus

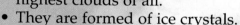

- Feathery cirrus clouds are the highest clouds of all.
- They are formed of ice crystals.
- They usually signal fair weather.
- They also can be a sign of changing weather.

Cirrostratus

- These thin, sheet-like clouds often form ahead of advancing storms, particularly if they're followed by middle clouds.

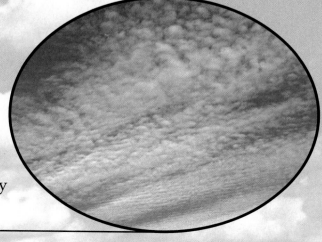

Cirrocumulus

- Cirrocumulus clouds are small, rounded, white puffs.
- They appear individually or in long rows.
- Their rippled pattern resembles the scales of fish. Hence, a sky full of cirrocumulus clouds is called a "mackerel sky."

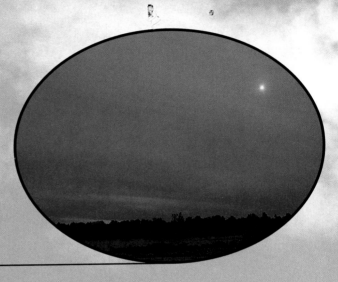

Altostratus

- Gray or blue-gray altostratus clouds—they're never white—often cover the entire sky.
- They are a sign of widespread, steady rain ahead.

Altocumulus

- These puffy, white or gray clouds look like rows of soft cotton balls.
- Randomly scattered altocumulus clouds may mean several days of fair weather.
- When the clouds resemble little castles, expect a thunderstorm by day's end.

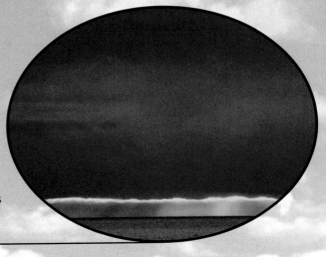

Nimbostratus

- Dark gray, wet-looking nimbostratus clouds are associated with steady rain or snow.
- The precipitation is light to moderate, never heavy.
- Nimbostratus clouds often have streaks that extend to the ground.

Stratus

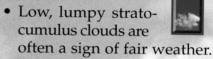

- Low-lying stratus clouds cover the sky in a blanket of gray.
- Light rain or drizzle usually accompanies these clouds.

Stratocumulus

- Low, lumpy strato-cumulus clouds are often a sign of fair weather.
- To distinguish them from altocumulus clouds, extend your arm toward the cloud.
- An altocumulus cloud will be roughly the size of your thumbnail. A stratocumulus cloud will be about the size of your fist.

Cumulus

- Small, scattered cumulus clouds with slight vertical growth signal fair weather.
- They have dome-shaped or tower-shaped tops, like cauliflowers.

Cumulonimbus

- These are thunder-storm clouds.
- They form near Earth's surface and grow to nearly 18 000 m.
- Lightning, thunder, and strong winds are associated with cumulonimbus clouds.

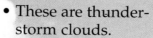

Chapter 11 Reviewing Main Ideas

For a **preview** of this chapter, study this Reviewing Main Ideas before you read the chapter. After you have studied this chapter, you can use the Reviewing Main Ideas to **review** the chapter.

The Glencoe MindJogger, Audiocassettes, and CD-ROM provide additional opportunities for review.

Section
11-1 WHAT IS WEATHER?

Humidity is created by water vapor in the air. When air cools to its **dew point,** water vapor condenses and forms clouds. **Precipitation** forms when the **relative humidity** reaches 100 percent, water condenses in drops around dust and other particles in the air, and the water droplets reach at least 0.2 mm in size. Rain, hail, sleet, and snow are types of precipitation. *What is the difference between humidity and relative humidity?*

Section
11-2 WEATHER PATTERNS

The temperature and the density of the air and the amount of water vapor in the air help determine the atmospheric pressure. High pressure brings clear skies and fair weather. Low-pressure areas are cloudy. Low-pressure systems form along the boundaries of **air masses.** *Why do clouds usually develop in a region that is experiencing low pressure?*

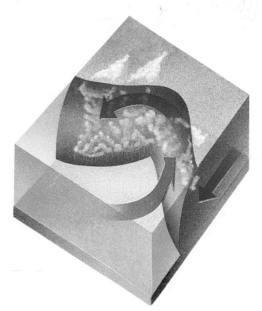

Reading Check ✓

Make up a new cloud type. Name it, using a prefix from the field guide. Describe when it would occur and what kind of weather it would bring.

SEVERE WEATHER

Fronts form at the boundary of two air masses. Warm fronts may produce precipitation over a wide area. Cold fronts produce a narrow band of violent storms. A stationary front produces weak winds and precipitation. Occluded fronts are sometimes associated with high winds and heavy precipitation. Thunderstorms, **tornadoes,** and **hurricanes** are examples of severe weather that can develop from low-pressure systems. All can result in loss of lives and destruction of property. Tornadoes are intense, whirling windstorms that can result from strong winds and low pressure in thunderstorms. *How do hurricanes form?*

Section
11-3 FORECASTING WEATHER

Meteorologists use information from radar, satellites, computers, and other instruments to make weather maps and forecasts. Symbols on a **station model** indicate the weather at a particular location. *Draw a station model to describe the weather conditions shown here.*

Chapter 11 Assessment

Using Vocabulary

a. air mass
b. dew point
c. Doppler radar
d. fog
e. front
f. humidity
g. hurricane
h. isobar
i. isotherm
j. meteorologist
k. precipitation
l. relative humidity
m. station model
n. tornado
o. weather

Using the list above, replace the underlined words with the correct key science term.

1. Severe weather often occurs at the <u>boundary between air masses</u>.

2. Thunderstorms may produce a <u>violent swirling storm moving in a narrow path</u>.

3. Low-pressure systems over oceans often produce a <u>large, swirling tropical storm</u>.

4. Weather forecasts can be gotten by checking <u>symbols that describe local weather conditions</u> on weather maps.

5. To determine the air pressure in an area, you can look at the <u>lines on a weather map that indicate points of equal pressure</u>.

Checking Concepts

Choose the word or phrase that best answers the question.

6. What is the condition of the air when water vapor condenses from it?
   A) hot
   B) temperate
   C) dry
   D) saturated

7. What is a large body of air that has the same properties as the area over which it formed?
   A) air mass
   B) station model
   C) front
   D) isotherm

8. What has been reached when water vapor in air condenses?
   A) dew point
   B) station model
   C) front
   D) isobar

9. What forms when water vapor changes directly into a solid?
   A) rain
   B) fog
   C) sleet
   D) snow

10. What are high, feathery clouds made of ice crystals called?
    A) cirrus
    B) nimbus
    C) cumulus
    D) stratus

11. What type of front forms when two cool air masses merge?
    A) warm
    B) cold
    C) stationary
    D) occluded

12. What increases when the temperature of air increases?
    A) humidity
    B) precipitation
    C) cloud cover
    D) weather

13. What is issued when severe weather conditions exist and immediate action should be taken?
    A) front
    B) watch
    C) station model
    D) warning

14. What term describes the amount of water vapor in the air?
    A) dew point
    B) precipitation
    C) humidity
    D) relative humidity

15. What is a stratus cloud near the ground called?
    A) cumulus
    B) dew
    C) cirrus
    D) fog

Thinking Critically

16. If you learn that there is 79 percent relative humidity, what does that mean?

17. How do water and the sun interact to cause our weather?

18. Why don't hurricanes form in polar regions?

19. If a barometer shows that the air pressure is dropping, what general weather prediction could you make?
20. What weather conditions would the tall, thick, anvil-shaped clouds indicate?

Developing Skills

If you need help, refer to the Skill Handbook.

21. **Comparing and Contrasting:** Compare and contrast tornadoes and severe thunderstorms.
22. **Observing and Inferring:** You take a hot shower. The mirror in the bathroom clouds up. Infer from this information what has happened.
23. **Interpreting Scientific Illustrations:** Use the cloud descriptions in the **Field Guide to Clouds** to describe the weather at your location today. Then, try to predict tomorrow's weather.
24. **Concept Mapping:** Construct events chains, one for each type of precipitation. Show the sequence from evaporation to falling precipitation. The number of events may vary.
25. **Interpreting Scientific Illustrations:** Describe the weather conditions shown on the station model below.

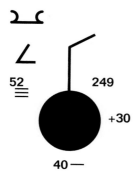

THE PRINCETON REVIEW

Test-Taking Tip

Your Answers Are Better Than the Test's When you know the answer, answer the question in your own words before looking at the answer choices. Often, more than one answer choice will look good, so arm yourself with yours before looking.

Test Practice

Use these questions to test your Science Proficiency.

1. If the actual amount of humidity in the air does not change, what is the cause-and-effect relationship of temperature and relative humidity?
   A) As temperature increases, relative humidity increases.
   B) As temperature decreases, relative humidity increases.
   C) As relative humidity increases, temperature increases.
   D) As relative humidity decreases, temperature increases.

2. Making long-range, accurate weather predictions is difficult. Why is this true?
   A) Weather instruments are not accurate.
   B) Weather instruments are not precise.
   C) Meteorologists do not communicate with one another.
   D) Atmospheric conditions are constantly changing.

Chapter Preview

Skills Preview

Skill Builders
- Compare and Contrast
- Form a Hypothesis

Activities
- Measure in SI
- Make a Model

MiniLabs
- Analyze Data
- Observe and Infer

Reading Check ✔

As you read this chapter, list five things you already knew about climate and ten things you are learning.

Explore Activity

Brrr... this penguin lives in Antarctica, where temperatures are cold year-round. Other places on Earth are almost always hot. Some areas are dry, while others are rainy. Why do temperature and precipitation vary so much from place to place? The amount of sun energy that a place receives plays an important part in weather patterns. Energy from the sun also creates wind. Wind systems distribute moisture and heat around the world, as you will see in the following activity.

Observe Deserts and Wind Systems

1. Obtain a world globe or atlas.

2. Locate several of the world's deserts.

3. Find the latitudes of these deserts.

4. Research major wind systems such as the trade winds and the prevailing westerlies to determine which winds affect these latitudes.

Many deserts are located next to mountain ranges. In your Science Journal, explain how mountains might affect precipitation patterns in different regions.

Climate

If you ever have a chance to travel around the world or around the United States, you'll experience a variety of climates. **Climate** is the pattern of weather that occurs in an area over many years. If you ever visit a rain forest, you'll find the climate there wetter than in a desert. The wettest rain forest averages 1168 cm of precipitation annually. A desert receives less than 25 cm of rain per year. Some places closer to the equator are much warmer than places near the poles. Temperatures on Earth range from –89.2°C to 57.8°C.

Climate is determined by averaging the weather of a region over a long period of time, such as 30 years. Scientists average temperature, precipitation, air pressure, humidity, and days of sunshine to determine an area's climate. Other factors that affect the climate of a region include latitude, landforms, location of lakes and oceans, availability of moisture, global wind patterns, ocean currents, and location of air masses.

Latitude Affects Climate

As you can see in **Figure 12-1,** latitudes close to the equator receive the most solar radiation. Latitude also affects climate. **Figure 12-2** shows a comparison of cities at different latitudes. The **Tropics,** the region between latitudes 23.5° N and 23.5° S, receive the most solar radiation because the sun shines almost directly overhead. Year-round temperatures in the tropics are always hot, except at high elevations. The **polar zones** extend from 66.5° north and south latitudes to the poles. Solar energy hits the polar zones at a low angle, spreading energy over a large area. Also, polar ice reflects some of this solar radiation back out to space. During winter, polar regions are tilted away from the sun and receive no solar radiation at all. Therefore, polar regions are never warm. Some are covered with ice year-round.

Between the tropics and the polar zones are the **temperate zones.** Temperatures in these zones are moderate. The United States, except for Alaska and Hawaii, is in a temperate zone.

Figure 12-1 The Tropics are warmer because they receive the most direct solar energy.

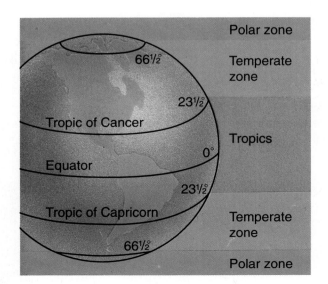

Polar zone

Temperate zone

66½

23½

Tropic of Cancer

Tropics

Equator

0°

23½

Tropic of Capricorn

Temperate zone

66½

Polar zone

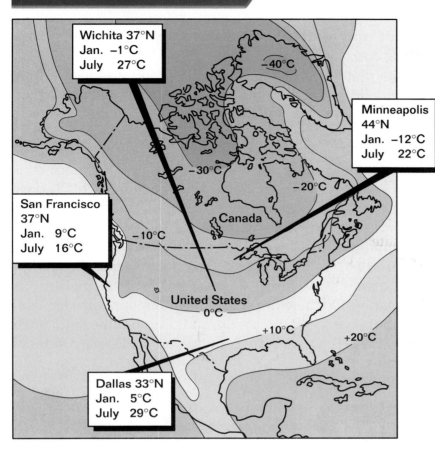

Wichita 37°N
Jan. −1°C
July 27°C

Minneapolis
44°N
Jan. −12°C
July 22°C

San Francisco
37°N
Jan. 9°C
July 16°C

Canada

United States
0°C

Dallas 33°N
Jan. 5°C
July 29°C

Figure 12-2 This map shows daily minimum temperatures (°C) in January and July throughout the United States.

A Minneapolis, Minnesota, at 44°N, receives less solar radiation than Dallas, Texas.

B San Francisco's climate is affected by the nearby ocean. **Compare these temperatures to those of Wichita, Kansas, on the same 37°N latitude line.**

C Dallas, Texas, at 33°N, receives more solar radiation than Minneapolis. **Compare the temperature range of Dallas to that of Minneapolis.**

Other Factors

There's more to climate than the general divisions of polar, temperate, and tropical. Within each zone, natural features, such as mountains and large bodies of water, affect climate. Large cities also change weather patterns, which can influence the local climate.

Large Bodies of Water

If you live near an ocean, you may have noticed that water heats up and cools down more slowly than land. Large bodies of water affect the climate of coastal areas. Many coastal regions are warmer in the winter and cooler in the summer than inland areas of similar latitude. Look at **Figure 12-2B** again. You can see the effect of an ocean by comparing the temperatures in a coastal city and a continental city, both at 37°N latitude.

Observing Solar Radiation

Procedure

1. Darken the room.
2. Hold a flashlight about 30 cm from a globe. Shine the light directly on the equator. With your finger, trace around the light.
3. Without moving the location of the light, tilt it to shine on 30°N latitude. The size of the illuminated area should increase. Repeat at 60°N latitude.

Analysis

1. How did the size and shape of the light beam change as you directed the light toward higher latitudes?
2. How does the tilt of Earth affect the solar radiation received by different latitudes?

Ocean currents also affect coastal climate. Warm currents begin near the equator and flow toward the higher latitudes, warming the regions they pass by. When the currents cool off and flow back toward the equator, they cool the air and climates of land nearby. Some warm currents move along our Atlantic coast. ☑

Winds blowing from the sea contain more moisture than those blowing from the land. Thus, coasts tend to have a wetter climate than places inland.

Reading Check ☑
How do ocean currents affect climate?

Mountains

At the same latitude, the climate is colder in the mountains than at sea level. When radiation absorbed by Earth's surface is reflected upward, there are fewer molecules in the air to absorb this heat at higher elevations.

Mountains also affect the climate of nearby areas, as shown in **Figure 12-3.** On the side of the mountain facing the wind—the windward side—air rises, cools, and drops its moisture as precipitation. On the other side of the mountain—the leeward side—the air descends, heats up, and dries out the land, often forming deserts. Deserts are common on the leeward sides of mountains.

Problem Solving

The Lake Effect

Depending on their temperature, ocean currents either warm or cool nearby coastal regions. Ocean breezes, filled with moisture, give coastal regions wetter climates than areas farther inland. If oceans modify the climate of nearby coastal areas, do you think large lakes do this, as well? The following data were collected from four different Ohio cities near Lake Erie. Examine the data and answer the questions.

Think Critically

1. How is the distance from Lake Erie related to frost-free days?

2. What is the relationship between distance from the lake and annual precipitation?

3. Is the climate of a city near Lake Erie affected by the lake? Explain.

4. Some fruit, such as grapes, need long growing seasons. Which of the four locations would be best for growing grapes?

Climate Data				
Location	A	B	C	D
Distance from the lake in kilometers	0	1.6	48.3	80.5
Average monthly range of temperature in °C	7.6	8.8	10.8	11.9
Frost-free days	205	194	162	154
Annual precipitation in centimeters	73.6	81.4	94.0	97.5

Large Cities

Large cities affect local climates. Solar radiation that strikes cities is absorbed by streets, parking lots, and buildings. These paved surfaces and structures heat up and radiate energy into the atmosphere. Automobile exhaust and other pollutants in the air trap this heat energy, creating what some people call a heat island effect. Summer temperatures in a city can be ten degrees higher than in surrounding rural areas.

In addition to raising temperatures, cities affect the climate in other ways. Skyscrapers act as small mountains and change local wind and precipitation patterns. A study of St. Louis, Missouri, found that 25 percent more rainfall, 45 percent more thunderstorms, and 31 percent more hailstorms occurred over the city than over the surrounding rural areas.

Figure 12-3 Climate differs on either side of a mountain range. This map shows the leeward and windward sides of the Andes, a mountain system between Chile and Argentina.

Section Assessment

1. What factors help determine the climate of a region?

2. How do mountains affect climate?

3. Explain how two cities located at the same latitude can have different climates.

4. **Think Critically:** Explain why types of plants and animals found on different sides of the same mountain range might differ.

5. **Skill Builder**
   Comparing and Contrasting Compare and contrast tropical, temperate, and polar climates. If you need help, refer to Comparing and Contrasting in the **Skill Handbook** on page 686.

Using Math

Using the data from the Problem Solving activity, predict the annual precipitation for a location 60 km from Lake Erie. Explain how you determined your answer.

Activity 12 • 1

Microclimates

A microclimate is a localized climate that differs from the main climate surrounding it. Buildings in a city, for instance, can affect the climate of the area surrounding the buildings.

Possible Materials

- Thermometers
- Psychrometer
- Paper strip or wind sock
- Large cans (4–5)
  * beakers or rain gauges (4–5)
- Piece of unlined paper

  *Alternate Materials

Recognize the Problem

Does your school building create microclimates?

Form a Hypothesis

Hypothesize how a building affects the climate of the area around it.

Goals

- **Observe** temperature, wind speed, relative humidity, and precipitation in areas outside your school.
- **Infer** how the building might affect these climate factors.

Safety Precautions

If a thermometer breaks, do not touch it. Have your teacher dispose of the glass safely. Do NOT use a mercury thermometer.

Relative Humidity										
Dry Bulb Temperature	**Dry Bulb Temperature Minus Wet Bulb Temperature, °C**									
	1	**2**	**3**	**4**	**5**	**6**	**7**	**8**	**9**	**10**
13°C	89	79	69	59	50	41	32	22	15	7
14°C	90	79	70	60	51	42	34	26	18	10
15°C	90	80	71	61	53	44	36	27	20	13
16°C	90	81	71	63	54	46	38	30	23	15
17°C	90	81	72	64	55	47	40	32	25	18
18°C	91	82	73	65	57	49	41	34	27	20
19°C	91	82	74	65	58	50	43	36	29	22
20°C	91	83	74	66	59	51	44	37	31	24
21°C	91	83	75	67	60	53	46	39	32	26
22°C	92	83	76	68	61	54	47	40	34	28
23°C	92	84	76	69	62	55	48	42	36	30
24°C	92	84	77	69	62	56	49	43	37	31
25°C	92	84	77	70	63	57	50	44	39	33

Test Your Hypothesis

Plan

1. As a group, agree upon and write out your hypothesis statement.

2. **List** the steps needed to test your hypothesis. Include in your plan how you will use your equipment to measure the temperature, wind speed, relative humidity, and precipitation at four or five sites around your school building.

3. To find relative humidity, you'll need to use a psychrometer. A psychrometer is an instrument with two thermometers, one wet and one dry. As moisture from the wet thermometer evaporates, it takes heat energy from its environment, and the environ-

ment immediately around the wet thermometer cools. The thermometer records a lower temperature. Relative humidity can be found by finding the difference between the wet thermometer and the dry thermometer and by using the chart on the previous page.

4. **Select** your test sites. Select a control site that is not affected by the building.

5. **Make a map** of the school building and the test sites.

6. **Design a data table** in your Science Journal to use as your group collects data.

Do

1. Make sure your teacher approves your plan and your data table before you proceed.

2. Carry out the experiment as planned.

3. While the experiment is going on, **record** your observations and **complete** the data table in your Science Journal.

Analyze Your Data

1. **Map** your data. Color code the areas to show which micro-climates had the highest and lowest temperatures, the greatest and least wind speed, the greatest and least relative humidity, and the greatest and least precipitation.

2. **Analyze** your data to find patterns.

Draw Conclusions

1. How did your test sites differ from your control site?

2. **Analyze** your hypothesis and the results of your experiment. Was your hypothesis supported?

Climate Classification

If your job were to classify climates, where would you begin? Climates can be classified in several ways. Climatologists, people who study climates, usually use a system developed in 1918 by Russian-German meteorologist and climatologist Wladimir Köppen. Köppen observed that the type of vegetation found in a region depended on the climate of the area. **Figure 12-4** shows differences Köppen might have observed. His classification system is based on his studies of temperature and precipitation.

Climate Types

The climate classification system shown in **Figure 12-5** divides climates into six groups: tropical, mild, dry, continental, polar, and high elevation. These groups are further divided into types. For example, the dry climate classification is divided into semiarid and arid.

Examine the map and count how many different climates are found in the United States. Why do so many different types of climates exist here? What climate exists where you live?

What You'll Learn

► A climate classification system
► How organisms adapt to particular climates

Vocabulary

adaptation
hibernation

Why It's Important

► Your climate differs from others on Earth.

Figure 12-4 The type of vegetation in a region depends on the climate.

A Short grasses grow in fairly dry climates.

B Ferns and trees draped with Spanish moss grow in climates that have heavy rainfall.

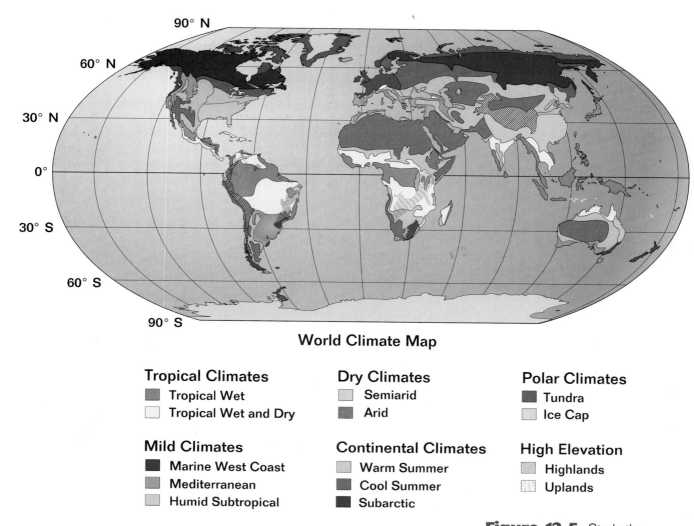

World Climate Map

Tropical Climates
- Tropical Wet
- Tropical Wet and Dry

Mild Climates
- Marine West Coast
- Mediterranean
- Humid Subtropical

Dry Climates
- Semiarid
- Arid

Continental Climates
- Warm Summer
- Cool Summer
- Subarctic

Polar Climates
- Tundra
- Ice Cap

High Elevation
- Highlands
- Uplands

Figure 12-5 Study the climate classification system shown on this map. Notice that most wet climates are located between latitudes 30° N and 30° S. **What other patterns do you see on this map?**

Organism Adaptations

Climates vary around the world, and as Köppen observed, the type of climate that exists in an area determines the vegetation found there. Fir trees aren't found in deserts, nor are cacti found in rain forests. In fact, all organisms have certain adaptations that allow them to survive in some climates but not in others. An **adaptation** is any structure or behavior that helps an organism survive in its environment. Adaptations develop in a population over a long period of time. Some adaptations are shown in **Figure 12-6** on the following page. Climatic factors that may limit where an organism can live are temperature, moisture, and amount of daylight.

Structural Adaptations

Some organisms have body structures that help them survive in certain climates. The fur of mammals insulates them from cold temperatures. A cactus has a thick, fleshy stem. This structural adaptation helps a cactus hold water. The waxy texture of the stem keeps water inside the plant from

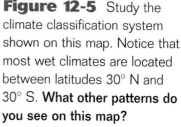

LIFE SCIENCE
◄INTEGRATION

evaporating. Instead of broad leaves, cactus plants have spiny leaves that further reduce water loss.

Behavioral Adaptations

Some organisms display behavioral adaptations that help them survive in certain climates. For example, rodents and certain other mammals undergo a period of inactivity in winter called **hibernation.** During hibernation, body temperature drops and body processes are reduced to a minimum. Animals hibernate, in part, because food is scarce during winter. ☑

Other animals have adapted differently. When it's cold, bees cluster together in a tight ball to keep from freezing. During hot, sunny days, desert snakes hide under rocks. At night, when it's cooler, they slither out in search of food. Instead of drinking water as turtles and lizards do in wet climates, desert turtles and lizards obtain the moisture they need from their food.

Reading Check ☑

What is hibernation?

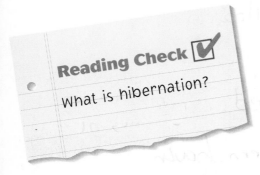

Figure 12-6 Organisms have structural and behavioral adaptations that help them survive in particular climates.

A Honeybees fan in fresh air to keep the hive cool. **How do bees keep warm?**

C A wolf's fur keeps it warm. Fur is hair. The spaces between the hairs trap air and heat and keep out the cold and rain.

B The needles and the waxy skin of a cactus reduce water loss.

Figure 12-7 People have adaptations that help them to survive in every climate.

Lungfish survive periods of intense heat by going through an inactive state called estivation. As weather gets hot and water begins evaporating, the fish burrows into mud and secretes a covering around itself. It lives this way until the warm, dry months pass.

Like other organisms, you have structural adaptations that help you adjust to climate. You can maintain a fairly constant body temperature, regardless of the outside temperature. In hot weather, your sweat glands release water onto your skin. The water evaporates. As a result, you become cooler. What other adaptations help the people in **Figure 12-7** adjust to climate?

Section Assessment

1. Use **Figure 12-5** and a world map to identify the climate type for each of the following locations: Cuba, North Korea, Egypt, and Uruguay.

2. What are some behavioral adaptations that allow animals to stay warm?

3. **Think Critically:** What special adaptations must plants and animals have to live in dry regions?

4. **Skill Builder**
   Forming a Hypothesis Some scientists think Earth is becoming hotter. Suppose this is true. Form a hypothesis about which adaptations will allow some present-day organisms to survive this change. If you need help, refer to Forming a Hypothesis in the **Skill Handbook** on page 688.

Science Journal
Research the ways people have adapted their behavior to survive in the six climate regions shown in **Figure 12-5.** Consider clothing, housing, and transportation. Write about these adaptations in your Science Journal.

12•3 Climatic Changes

Seasons

What You'll Learn

▶ What causes seasons
▶ How El Niño affects the climate
▶ Theories about climatic change

Vocabulary

season
El Niño
greenhouse effect
global warming
deforestation

Why It's Important

▶ Global warming is a serious, yet hotly debated environmental concern.

In temperate zones, weather generally changes with the season. **Seasons** are short-term periods of climate change caused by regular differences in daylight, temperature, and weather patterns. These differences are due to changes in the amount of solar radiation an area receives. **Figure 12-8** shows Earth revolving around the sun. Because Earth is tilted as it revolves, different areas of Earth receive changing amounts of solar radiation throughout the year. That affects wind patterns. In turn, wind patterns and natural features help create seasonal climatic changes.

Effects of Latitude

The middle latitudes or temperate zones often have warm summers and cool winters. Spring and fall are usually mild. Because of fairly constant solar radiation at the low latitudes near the equator, the Tropics do not have as much seasonal temperature change as the middle latitudes. But, tropical areas do experience dry and rainy seasons.

During the year, the high latitudes near the poles have great differences in temperature and number of daylight hours. As shown in **Figure 12-8,** during summer in the northern hemisphere, the north pole is tilted toward the sun. The north pole has 24 hours of daylight each day for six months. During that same time, the south pole experiences 24-hour days of darkness. At the equator, days are about the same length all year long.

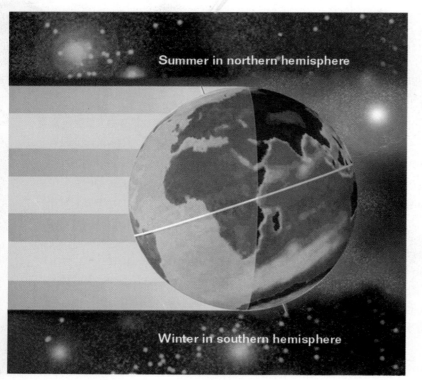

Summer in northern hemisphere

Winter in southern hemisphere

Figure 12-8 As Earth moves around the sun, different areas of Earth tilt toward the sun, bringing different seasons. In the southern hemisphere during winter, the south pole tilts away from the sun, making the sunlight less concentrated. At the same time in the northern hemisphere, the north pole tilts toward the sun. It's summer and days are long.

El Niño

Some climatic changes last longer than a season. **El Niño** (el·NEEN yoh) is a climatic event that starts in the tropical Pacific Ocean and sets off changes in the atmosphere. El Niño used to occur every three to seven years. Now, it happens more frequently, although scientists are not sure why. In El Niño, the Pacific Ocean warms along the equator. Near the equator, trade winds that blow east to west weaken and sometimes reverse. The change in the trade winds allows warm tropical water in the upper layers of the Pacific to flow eastward to South America. Ocean temperatures increase by 1°C to 7°C off the coast of Peru. The increase in temperatures causes the spaces around water molecules to expand, and sea level rises slightly.

El Niño does not directly cause unusual weather but instead affects the atmosphere and ocean, making stormy weather more likely. Warmer water brings more evaporation. Heavy rains fall over South America. During El Niño, one of the jet streams often splits. This changes the atmospheric pressure off California and wind and precipitation patterns around the world. Such changes can cause drought in Australia and Africa. They also affect dependable monsoon rains in Indonesia and cause storms in California, as shown in **Figure 12-9.**

LIFE SCIENCE INTEGRATION

Deadly El Niño?
During El Niño, some aquatic plants and animals living in waters off California die. Infer how El Niño may be the cause of their deaths.

Figure 12-9 The effects of El Niño are felt around the world. A strong El Niño occurred in 1998.

A A severe drought struck Indonesia.

B California was plagued by mudslides and floods.

Climatic Change

Although some years are warmer, colder, drier, or wetter than others, Earth's climate remains fairly constant. However, in Earth's past the climate was sometimes much colder or much warmer than it is today. Geological records show that in the past, the climate of different areas changed. Fossils of tropical plants and animals found in polar as well as temperate regions indicate warmer worldwide climates in the past. **Figure 12-10** illustrates how living things can be used to study climate changes. Glacial erosion and deposition around the world show that in the past 2 million years, glaciers covered large parts of Earth's surface. These periods of extensive glaciers are called ice ages. During Earth's past, ice ages have alternated with warm periods called interglacial intervals. Some ice ages lasted 60 000 years. Most interglacial periods lasted about 12 000 years. We are now in an interglacial interval, which began about 11 500 years ago. Ice cores drilled in Greenland show that cold spells, lasting 1000 years or more, changed rapidly to warm spells that lasted as long. **Figure 12-11** shows a scientist working with ice cores.

Figure 12-10 The length of growing seasons is recorded in tree rings. **Was Earth's climate always the same in the past? Explain.**

Climatic Change Theories

Research into the causes of climatic change suggests a variety of possibilities. Catastrophic events such as meteorite collisions and volcanic eruptions may have occurred, or perhaps the sun's output of energy isn't constant. It could be that when Earth's plates move, they change climate patterns, or perhaps Earth's movements in space cause climatic change.

Catastrophic events such as large meteorite collisions and volcanic eruptions put enormous volumes of dust, ash, and smoke into the atmosphere. These dust and smoke particles could have blocked so much solar radiation that they cooled the planet and changed the climate. **Figure 12-12** illustrates how a major volcanic eruption affects Earth's atmosphere.

Figure 12-11 By examining air bubbles trapped in ice cores, scientists learn about climates of past geologic eras.

Clouds

Evidence suggests that an increase in cloud cover can affect global temperatures. Thick clouds can block solar radiation from reaching Earth's surface. It is possible that an increase in cloud cover could lead to a cooling effect similar to that produced by volcanic ash. Clouds, however, also can absorb solar energy that has already reached Earth's surface. Thus, clouds have two effects—they both reflect and absorb solar energy. The reflection of solar energy can make Earth's climate cooler. The absorption of solar energy can make Earth's climate warmer.

Solar radiation provides Earth's energy. If the output of the radiation from the sun varies—regardless of cloud cover—this also could change Earth's climate.

Mini Lab

Analyzing Tree Rings

Procedure

1. As a tree grows, it adds layers of growth rings. When conditions for growth are good, growth rings occur far apart. When conditions are poor, growth rings appear close together.
2. Examine the growth rings of a cross section of wood. Note that the oldest wood is in the center.
3. Measure the thickness of several rings in your sample.

Analysis

1. How did the length of the growing seasons change as the tree grew older? Describe what evidence you found for this.
2. If scientists examine growth rings in petrified wood samples from different geologic times, what can they learn about climates of earlier geologic periods?

Figure 12-12 When Mount Pinatubo in the Philippines erupted in 1991, its volcanic ash cooled temperatures around the world.

interNET CONNECTION

Visit the Glencoe Science Web Site **www.glencoe.com/ sec/science/fl** for more information about climate changes.

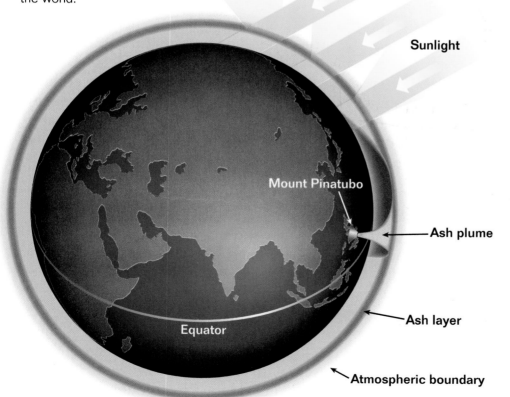

Sunlight

Mount Pinatubo

Ash plume

Ash layer

Equator

Atmospheric boundary

Figure 12-13 This glacier in Argentina is similar to those that covered large parts of North America during the last ice age. **What is an ice age?**

Earth Moves

Another possible explanation for major climatic change concerns the movement of the plates on Earth's crust. The movement of continents and oceans affects the transfer of heat on Earth's surface, which in turn affects wind and precipitation patterns. Through time, these altered patterns may change the climate.

Another theory relates to Earth's movements in space. Earth is currently tilted on its axis at 23.5° to the plane of its orbit around the sun. In the past, this tilt has increased to 25° and has decreased to 22°. When this tilt is at its maximum, the poles receive more solar energy. When the tilt is at its minimum, the poles receive less solar energy. Earth's tilt changes about every 41 000 years. Some scientists hypothesize that the change in tilt may affect climates.

Another Earth movement that may affect climatic change is the change in the shape of Earth's orbit around the sun. The shape of Earth's orbit changes over a 100 000-year cycle. When the orbit is more circular than at present, Earth is farther from the sun and temperatures are colder than those we are experiencing.

These movements of Earth may explain some of the variations in the most recent ice age. But, they do not explain why glaciers, such as the one shown in **Figure 12-13,** have occurred so rarely over the long span of geologic time.

As you've learned, many theories attempt to answer questions about why Earth's climate has changed through the ages. Probably all of these things play some role in changing climates. More study needs to be done before we can understand all the factors that affect climate.

Climatic Changes Today

Today, many newspaper and magazine headlines warn us about the greenhouse effect and global warming. The greenhouse effect and global warming are related, but they are not the same thing.

The **greenhouse effect** is natural heating caused when gases in our atmosphere trap heat. The greenhouse effect is illustrated in **Figure 12-14.** Carbon dioxide is the main greenhouse gas. Without the greenhouse effect, life as we know it would not be possible on Earth. Like Mars, Earth would be too cold.

Global Warming

Global warming means global temperatures are rising. One reason for global warming is the increase of greenhouse gases in our atmosphere. An increase in greenhouse gases increases the greenhouse effect. In the last 100 years, surface temperature on Earth has increased 0.5°C. This may be from global warming. ☑

If the mean temperature continues to rise, ice caps will melt. Low-lying areas might experience increased flooding. Already some ice caps are beginning to break apart and sea level is rising in certain areas. Some scientific studies show that these events are related to Earth's increased temperature.

You learned in the previous section that organisms are adapted to their environments. When environments change, can organisms adjust? In some tropical waters around the world, corals are dying. Are these deaths caused by warmer water? Many people think so.

Reading Check ☑

What is global warming?

Figure 12-14
The sun's radiation travels through our atmosphere and heats Earth's surface. Greenhouse gases in our atmosphere trap the heat. **How is this similar to the way a greenhouse works?**

When ice sheets melt, sea level rises. Between 1900 and 1970, sea level at New York City rose 23 cm. What was the average rise in sea level per year from 1900 to 1970? The present elevation of New York City is 396 cm above sea level. If sea level continues to rise at the same rate, when will New York City start to go under water?

Figure 12-15 When forests are cleared or burned, carbon dioxide levels increase in the atmosphere. **What can people do to help reduce CO_2 levels in the atmosphere?**

Some climate models show that in the future, Earth's temperatures will increase faster than they have in the last 100 years. Next, you will learn how people's activities may add to global warming, and you will find out what you can do to help lessen this problem.

Human Activities and Carbon Dioxide

Human activities affect the air in our atmosphere. Burning fossil fuels and removing vegetation add carbon dioxide to the atmosphere and contribute to global warming. Each year, the amount of carbon dioxide in our atmosphere continues to increase.

Burning Fossil Fuels

When natural gas, petroleum, and coal are burned for energy, the carbon in these fossil fuels is combined with oxygen. This increases the amount of carbon dioxide (CO_2) in our atmosphere.

Deforestation

Destroying and cutting down forests, called **deforestation,** also affects the amount of carbon dioxide in our atmosphere. Forests, such as the one shown in **Figure 12-15,** are cleared for mining, roads, buildings, and grazing cattle. Forests also are dying from the effects of pollution.

As they grow, trees take in carbon dioxide. When trees are removed, the carbon dioxide they could have removed from the atmosphere is left. Cut-down trees are often burned. Burning produces more carbon dioxide.

Ways to Reduce CO_2

What can we each do to help reduce the amount of CO_2 in the atmosphere? Conserving electricity is one answer. When we conserve electricity, we reduce the amount of fossil fuels that must be burned. One way to save fuel is to change daily activities that rely on energy from burning fossil fuels. Turn off the TV, for instance, when no one is watching it. Walk or ride a bike to the store, if possible, instead of driving a car. We also can use different energy sources to meet our energy needs, such as the wind farm shown in **Figure 12-16.**

Another way to reduce CO_2 is to plant vegetation. As you've learned, plants remove carbon dioxide from the atmosphere. Correctly planted vegetation also can shelter homes from cold winds or blazing sun and reduce the use of electricity.

Figure 12-16 This wind farm in California generates electricity without adding CO_2 to the atmosphere.

Section Assessment

1. What causes seasons?
2. In what way does El Niño change the climate?
3. **Think Critically:** How do we know that climates of earlier geologic eras were different from today's climates?
4. **Skill Builder**
   Interpreting Data Ice cores help scientists study Earth's past climate. Do the **Chapter 12 Skill Activity** on page 719 to determine how average global temperatures have changed over the last 165 000 years.

Using Computers

Word Processing
Design a pamphlet to inform people why Earth's climate changes. What are your predictions for the future? On what evidence do you base these predictions? Include this evidence in your pamphlet. If you need help, refer to page 698.

The Greenhouse Effect

Materials

- Identical large, empty glass jars (2)
- Lid for one jar
- Thermometers (3)

Have you ever climbed into a car on a warm day and burned yourself on the seat? Why was it so hot inside the car when it wasn't that hot outside? It was hotter in the car because the car functioned like a greenhouse. You experienced the greenhouse effect.

What You'll Investigate

How can you demonstrate the greenhouse effect?

Goals

- **Make a model** to demonstrate the greenhouse effect.
- **Measure** and **graph** temperature changes.

Safety Precautions

Be careful when you handle glass thermometers. If a thermometer breaks, do not touch it. Have your teacher dispose of the glass safely.

Procedure

1. Lay a thermometer inside each jar.

2. Place the jars next to each other by a sunny window. Lay the third thermometer between the jars.

3. **Record** the temperatures of the three thermometers. They should be the same.

4. Place the lid on one jar.

5. **Record** the temperatures of all three thermometers at the end of five, ten, and 15 minutes.

6. **Make a line graph** that shows the temperatures of the three thermometers for the 15 minutes of the experiment.

Conclude and Apply

1. **Explain** why you placed a thermometer between the two jars.

2. What were the constants in this experiment? What was the variable?

3. Which thermometer experienced the greatest temperature change during your experiment? Why?

4. **Analyze** what occurred in this experiment. How was the lid in this experiment like the greenhouse gases in the atmosphere?

5. **Infer** from this experiment why you should never leave a pet inside a closed car in warm weather.

Climate

Climate usually changes slowly over long periods of time. But, over the past few hundred years, scientists have learned that climate can sometimes change rapidly. The earliest climate records were written accounts of notable events, such as how much grain was harvested in a year. It wasn't until the 1800s that scientists began to draw conclusions about past climatic conditions based on their observations of the natural world.

Tree Rings

In the early 1900s, a unique method for obtaining information on climate was developed. Called dendrochronology, it is based on measuring the width of annual growth rings (see inset) in trees. In general, wet years produce wide rings while dry years produce narrow rings. By analyzing the annual rings of a large, old tree, wet and dry periods can be identified in the tree trunk. Climate records going as far back as 8000 years ago have been obtained from some of the world's oldest trees.

Ice Cores

Perhaps the most widely used method for obtaining climatic information measures the ratio of uncommon heavier types of water molecules to ordinary water molecules in the environment. When raindrops and snow crystals form, this ratio changes as the temperature changes. By measuring this ratio in ice cores from Greenland and Antarctica, temperature records as old as 100 000 years can be obtained. At left, a scientist saws an ice core sample. Such cores show that major climate changes sometimes occurred in just a few decades.

Other new techniques make use of ancient coral deposits, fossils, and sediments in lake and ocean beds. Data gathered from these sources help researchers explain the climate of today and better predict the climate of the future.

Science JOURNAL ▶

Imagine that you are living on a thick sheet of glacial ice during an ice age. In your Science Journal, describe what you would need to survive.

For a **preview** of this chapter, study this Reviewing Main Ideas before you read the chapter. After you have studied this chapter, you can use the Reviewing Main Ideas to **review** the chapter.

The Glencoe MindJogger, Audiocassettes, and CD-ROM provide additional opportunities for review.

Moist air

Dry air

Section

12-1 WHAT IS CLIMATE?

The **climate** of an area is the average weather over a long period of time, such as 30 years. The three main types of climate are tropical, polar, and temperate. In general, higher latitudes experience cooler climates than lower latitudes do. Natural features such as oceans, mountains, and even large cities affect climate. *In what ways do large cities affect the climate of nearby areas?*

Section

12-2 CLIMATE TYPES

Climates are classified by various characteristics, such as temperature, precipitation, and vegetation. Organisms have structural and behavioral **adaptations** that help them survive in particular climates. Adaptations develop in a population over a long period of time. *What are some adaptations of organisms that live in tropical, wet climates?*

Reading Check ✓

Is the greenhouse effect a fact or an opinion? How do you know? What are two facts related to climate? What are two opinions?

Section

12-3 CLIMATIC CHANGES

Seasons are caused by Earth's tilt on its axis as it revolves around the sun. **El Niño** disrupts the normal wind and precipitation patterns around the world. Geological records show that in the past, Earth's climate alternated between ice ages and warm periods called interglacial intervals. *Why are seasons and El Niño considered to be short-term climatic changes?*

GLOBAL WARMING

The **greenhouse effect** occurs naturally when certain gases trap Earth's heat. **Global warming** occurs when global temperatures rise because of an increased greenhouse effect. Many people feel that humans are contributing to global warming. *How does planting vegetation help decrease the amount of carbon dioxide in the atmosphere?*

Chapter 12 Assessment

Using Vocabulary

a. adaptation
b. climate
c. deforestation
d. El Niño
e. global warming
f. greenhouse effect
g. hibernation
h. polar zone
i. season
j. temperate zone
k. tropics

Explain the differences between the terms in each of the following sets.

1. global warming, greenhouse effect
2. polar zone, temperate zone
3. adaptation, hibernation
4. climate, season
5. deforestation, El Niño

Checking Concepts

Choose the word or phrase that best answers the question.

6. What is commonly found in places where warm air crosses a mountain and descends?
   A) lakes
   B) rain forests
   C) deserts
   D) glaciers

7. What do the fossils of tropical plants and animals found in polar regions tell scientists?
   A) the temperature of earlier geologic eras
   B) the relative length of growing seasons
   C) behavioral adaptations
   D) the amount of carbon dioxide in the air in prehistoric times

8. What is the main greenhouse gas in our atmosphere?
   A) helium
   B) carbon dioxide
   C) hydrogen
   D) oxygen

9. What latitude receives the most direct rays of the sun year-round?
   A) 60° N
   B) 90°
   C) 30° S
   D) 0°

10. What happens as you climb a mountain?
    A) temperature decreases
    B) temperature increases
    C) air pressure increases
    D) air pressure remains constant

11. Which of the following is true of El Niño?
    A) It occurs every ten to 20 years.
    B) It causes flooding in Australia.
    C) It cools the waters off Alaska.
    D) It sometimes reverses the direction of the trade winds.

12. What do changes in Earth's orbit affect?
    A) Earth's shape
    B) Earth's temperatures
    C) Earth's rotation
    D) Earth's tilt

13. The Köppen Climate Classification System is based on precipitation and what other factor?
    A) temperature
    B) air pressure
    C) winds
    D) latitude

14. Which of the following is an example of structural adaptation?
    A) hibernation
    B) migration
    C) fur
    D) estivation

15. How can people help reduce global warming?
    A) conserve energy
    B) burn coal
    C) produce methane
    D) remove trees

Thinking Critically

16. Why will global warming lead to the extinction of some organisms?

17. What can you infer if you find fossils of tropical plants in a desert?

18. On a summer day, why would a Florida beach be cooler than an orange grove 2 km away?

19. What would happen to global climates if the sun became larger?

20. Why would it be cooler if you climb to a higher elevation in a desert?

Developing Skills

If you need help, refer to the **Skill Handbook.**

21. **Interpreting Scientific Illustrations:** Study the graph below. How many years does it span?

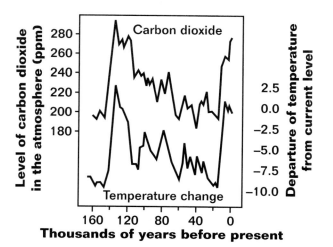

22. **Infer:** Explain how atmospheric pressure over the Pacific Ocean might affect the direction that the trade winds blow.

23. **Sequencing:** Make a chain-of-events chart to explain the effect of a major volcanic eruption on climate.

THE PRINCETON REVIEW

Test-Taking Tip

Investigate Ask what kinds of questions to expect on the test. Ask for practice tests so that you can become familiar with the test-taking materials.

Test Practice

The graph on this page shows long-term variations in atmospheric carbon dioxide levels and global temperature. Study this graph and answer the following questions. Use these questions to test your Science Proficiency.

1. Which of the following statements **BEST** describes the information on this graph?

   A) As carbon dioxide in the atmosphere has increased, so has global temperature.

   B) As carbon dioxide in the atmosphere has increased, global temperature has decreased.

   C) As global temperature has increased, carbon dioxide in the atmosphere has decreased.

   D) There is no relationship between carbon dioxide in the atmosphere and global temperatures.

2. Which of these statements is true according to the information in this graph?

   A) Earth's global-mean temperature has never been hotter than today.

   B) There has never been a higher level of carbon dioxide on Earth than today.

   C) The global-mean temperature 60 000 years ago was at its lowest point.

   D) The highest level of carbon dioxide in the atmosphere 80 000 years ago was 235 ppm.

Chapter Preview

Skills Preview

Skill Builders
- Map Concepts
- Compare and Contrast

Activities
- Observe

MiniLabs
- Observe
- Infer

Reading Check ✔

As you read about succession, record words and phrases that indicate a time sequence, such as *long ago*, *gradually*, and *as time passed*.

Explore Activity

Take a look at the land around you. Do you live in a part of the country with cactus and desert scrub? Or, is your home in a region of grassy prairies, sandy beaches, or mountain lakes? All life is found in the biosphere. In this chapter, you will learn what kinds of ecosystems exist in the biosphere, and you will find out why their biotic and abiotic factors differ. The following activity will help you get started.

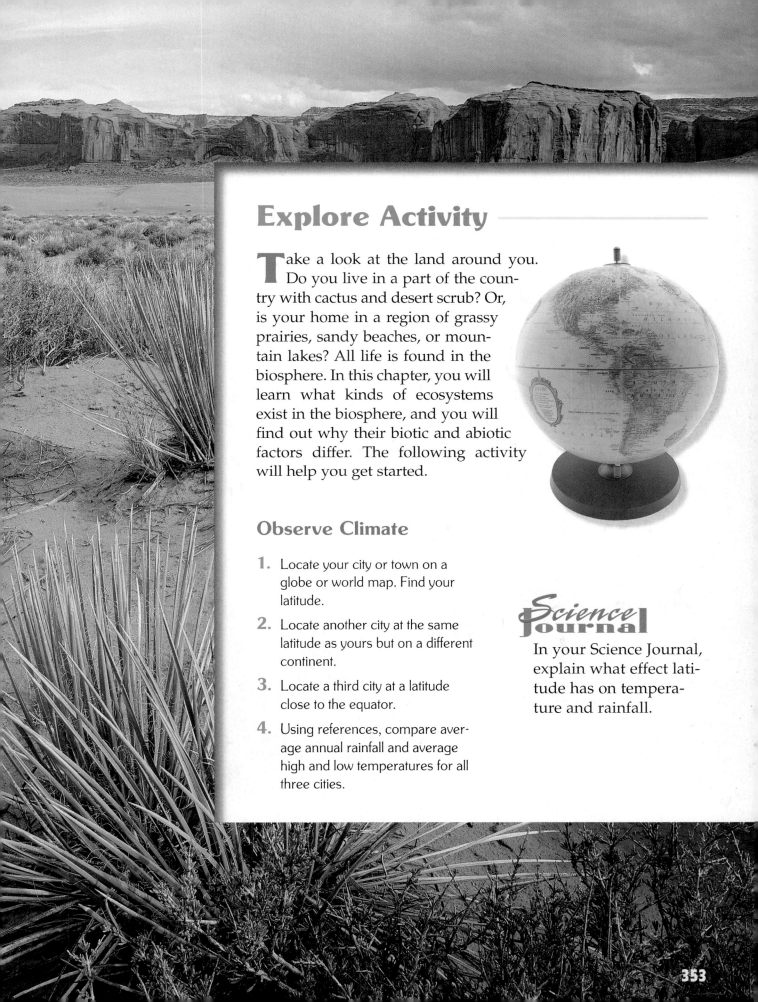

Observe Climate

1. Locate your city or town on a globe or world map. Find your latitude.

2. Locate another city at the same latitude as yours but on a different continent.

3. Locate a third city at a latitude close to the equator.

4. Using references, compare average annual rainfall and average high and low temperatures for all three cities.

Science Journal

In your Science Journal, explain what effect latitude has on temperature and rainfall.

13·1 How Ecosystems Change

What You'll Learn

▶ How ecosystems change over time
▶ How new communities arise in areas that were bare of life
▶ How to compare and contrast pioneer communities and climax communities

Vocabulary
ecological succession
primary succession
pioneer community
secondary succession
climax community

Why It's Important

▶ Your ecosystem is changing right now.

Ecological Succession

Imagine hiking through a forest. Huge trees tower over the trail. You know it can take many years for trees to grow this large, so it's easy to think of the forest as something that has always been here. But, this area has not always been covered with trees. Long ago, it may have been a pond full of fish and frogs surrounded by water-loving plants. As time passed, the decomposed bodies of plants and animals slowly filled in the pond until it eventually became a lush, green meadow full of grass and wildflowers. Gradually, over many more years, seeds blew in, trees began to grow, and a forest developed. The process of gradual change from one community of organisms to another is called **ecological succession.** The changes associated with succession usually take place in a fairly predictable order and involve animals, plants, and other organisms.

VISUALIZING Succession

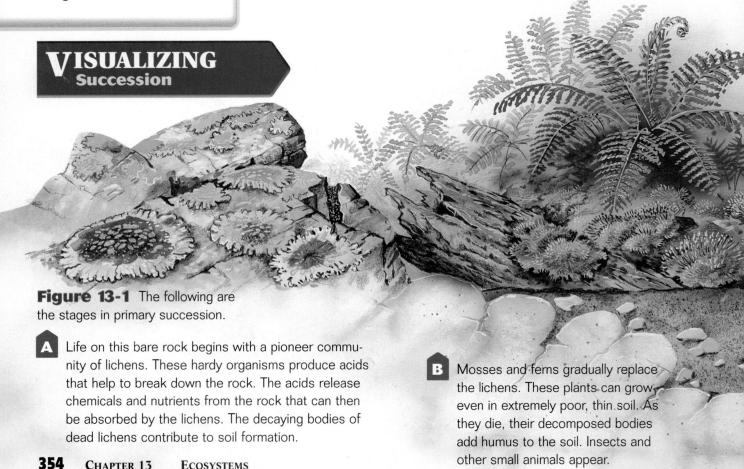

Figure 13-1 The following are the stages in primary succession.

A Life on this bare rock begins with a pioneer community of lichens. These hardy organisms produce acids that help to break down the rock. The acids release chemicals and nutrients from the rock that can then be absorbed by the lichens. The decaying bodies of dead lichens contribute to soil formation.

B Mosses and ferns gradually replace the lichens. These plants can grow even in extremely poor, thin soil. As they die, their decomposed bodies add humus to the soil. Insects and other small animals appear.

Primary Succession

Think about conditions around an erupting volcano. Incredibly hot, molten lava flows along the ground, destroying everything in its path. As the lava cools, it forms new land. Soil is formed from bare rock. Similar events happen to this newly formed land. Particles of dust and ash fall to the ground. The forces of weather and erosion break up the lava rock. A thin layer of soil begins to form. Birds, wind, and rain deposit more dust, along with bacteria, seeds, and fungal spores. Plants start to grow and decay. A living community has begun to develop.

Ecological succession that begins in a place that does not have soil is called **primary succession.** The first community of organisms to move into a new environment is called the **pioneer community,** as shown in **Figure 13-1.** Members of pioneer communities are usually hardy organisms that can survive drought, extreme heat and cold, and other harsh conditions. Pioneer communities change the conditions in their environments. These new conditions support the growth of other types of organisms that gradually take over.

CHEMISTRY
INTEGRATION

Freezing Water
Freezing temperatures are harmful to living organisms because water is the main component of cells. As water freezes, it expands. Infer what happens to cells if ice crystals form inside them.

C As the soil layer thickens, its ability to absorb and hold water improves. Grasses, wildflowers, and other plants that require richer, more moist soil begin to take over. Butterflies, bees, and caterpillars come to feed on the leaves and flowers. When these plants die, they also enrich the soil, which will become home to earthworms and other large soil organisms.

D Thicker, richer soil supports the growth of shrubs and trees. More insects, birds, mammals, and reptiles move into the area. After hundreds or thousands of years of gradual change, what was once bare rock has become a forest.

Figure 13-2 The tangled growth of weeds and grasses in untended yards and vacant lots, on abandoned farms, and along country roadsides is the beginning stage of secondary succession.

Reading Check

What is secondary succession?

Secondary Succession

What happens when a forest is destroyed by a fire or a city building is torn down? After a forest fire, nothing is left except dead trees and ash-covered soil. Once the rubble of a demolished building has been taken away, all that remains is bare soil. But, these places do not remain lifeless for long. The soil may already contain the seeds of weeds, grasses, and trees. More seeds are carried to the area by wind and birds. As the seeds germinate and plants begin to grow, insects, birds, and other wildlife move in. Ecological succession has begun again. Succession that begins in a place that already has soil and was once the home of living organisms is called **secondary succession,** shown in **Figure 13-2.**

Climax Communities

Succession involves changes in abiotic factors as well as biotic factors. You have already seen how lichens, mosses, and ferns change the environment by helping to form the rich, thick soil needed for the growth of shrubs and trees. Shrubs and trees also cause changes in abiotic factors. Their branches shade the ground beneath them, reducing the temperature. Shade also reduces the rate of evaporation, increasing the moisture content of the soil. Amount of sunlight, temperature, and moisture level determine which species will grow in soil.

The redwood forest shown in **Figure 13-3** is an example of a community that has reached the end of succession. As long as the trees are not cut down or destroyed by fire or widespread disease, the species that make up the redwood community tend to remain the same. When a community has reached the final stage of ecological succession, it is called a **climax community.** Because primary succession begins in areas with no life at all, it can take hundreds or even thousands of years for a pioneer community to develop into a climax community. Secondary succession is a shorter process, but it still may take a century or more.

Comparing Communities

As you have seen, pioneer communities are simple. They contain only a few species, and feeding relationships usually can be described with simple food chains. Climax communities are much more complex. They may contain hundreds of thousands of species, and feeding relationships usually involve complex food webs. Interactions among the many biotic and abiotic factors in a climax community create a more stable environment that does not change much over time. Climax communities are the end product of ecological succession. A climax community that has been disturbed in some way will eventually return to the same type of community, as long as all other factors remain the same. However, it may take a century or more for the community to return to its former state.

Figure 13-3 This forest of redwood trees in California is an example of a climax community. Redwoods live for hundreds of years. They create shade on the ground beneath them. Needles constantly fall from their branches. Eventually, they form an acidic soil that allows the growth of young redwoods but prevents the growth of many other types of plants.

Section Assessment

1. What is ecological succession?
2. What is the difference between primary and secondary succession?
3. What is the difference between pioneer and climax communities?
4. **Think Critically:** What kind of succession will take place on an abandoned, unpaved country road? Why?
5. **Skill Builder**
   Sequencing Describe the sequence of events in primary succession. Include the term *climax community.* If you need help, refer to Sequencing on page 680.

Science Journal
In your Science Journal, draw a food chain for a pioneer community of lichens and a food web for the climax community of an oak-maple forest. Write a short paragraph comparing the two communities.

Endangered and Threatened Species

A species becomes endangered when its numbers are so low that it is in danger of extinction in the near future. The list of threatened and endangered species in the United States and around the world is constantly growing due to a variety of reasons. In 1998, about 965 species in the United States were listed as endangered or threatened.

Recognize the Problem

What endangered or threatened species have been identified for your region of the country?

Form a Hypothesis

Form a hypothesis to explain some of the reasons why the organisms identified as threatened or endangered in your region are on the list.

Goals

- **Obtain** and **organize** data.
- **Infer** relationships between the plant or animal and its environment.
- **Use the Internet** to collect and compare data from other students.

Data Sources

Go to the Glencoe Science Web Site at **www.glencoe.com/sec/science/fl** to find links to information about endangered plants and animals around the country. You also will find information posted by other students` from around the country.

Species Data

Organism Genus species	Threatened or Endangered	Length of Time on List	Recovery Plan	General Information

Test Your Hypothesis

Plan

1. Find links to information on the Glencoe Science Web Site. You can also find information on endangered species at the local library or a local zoo.

2. Prepare a data table similar to the one below to record your findings.

3. If possible, observe one of the endangered or threatened species you've identified either in a zoo or in the wild.

Do

1. **Describe** the habitat and range of the organism you chose to study.

2. **Identify** any steps being taken to protect the organism. Outline the recovery plan written for one of the organisms in your region.

3. **Post** the information you collected in the table provided for this activity on the Glencoe Science Web Site.

4. **Check** the postings by other students for more information on your organism and on other organisms.

Analyze Your Data

1. Brainstorm possible reasons why your organism is threatened or endangered.

2. What factors were you able to identify as reasons for the organism becoming endangered?

3. Was your hypothesis supported by the information you collected? **Explain** your answer.

Draw Conclusions

1. What might help the organism you are studying survive the changes in conditions or other changes that have occurred in its range that caused its numbers to decrease.

2. How successful have any techniques established to protect the organism been?

3. Did you find more threatened or endangered species of plants or animals in your region? What explanation might there be for your findings?

4. What steps do you think should be taken, if any, to protect endangered or threatened species in your region? What objections might be raised for the steps taken to protect a species?

Factors That Determine Climate

What does a desert in Arizona have in common with a desert in Africa? They both have water-conserving plants with thorns, lizards, heat, little rain, and poor soil. How are the plains of the American West like the veldt of central Africa? Both regions have dry summers, wet winters, and huge expanses of grassland that support grazing animals such as elk and antelope. Many widely separated regions of the world have similar ecosystems. Why? Because they have similar climates. Climate is the general weather pattern in an area. The factors that determine a region's climate include temperature and precipitation.

Temperature

The sun supplies life on Earth not only with light energy for photosynthesis, but also with heat energy for warmth. The temperature of a region is regulated primarily by the amount of sunlight that reaches it. In turn, the amount of sunlight is determined by an area's latitude and elevation.

Latitude

As **Figure 13-4** shows, not all parts of Earth receive the same amount of energy from the sun. When you conducted the Explore Activity at the beginning of this chapter, you probably concluded that temperature is affected by latitude.

What You'll Learn

► How climate influences land environments
► The six biomes that make up land environments on Earth
► The adaptations of plants and animals found in each biome

Vocabulary

biome
tundra
taiga
temperate deciduous forest
tropical rain forest
grassland
desert

Why It's Important

► Resources that you need to survive are found in a variety of biomes.

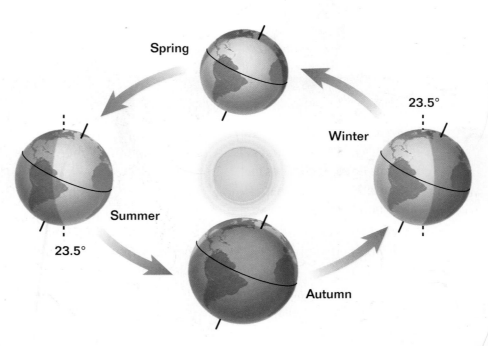

Figure 13-4 Because Earth is tilted on its axis, the angle of the sun's rays changes during the year. These changes create the seasons. The tilt of Earth's axis does not have as much of an effect on regions near the equator.

Spring
Winter
23.5°
Summer
23.5°
Autumn

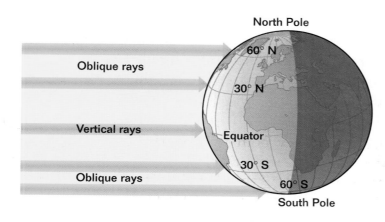

North Pole
60° N
30° N
Equator
30° S
60° S
South Pole

Oblique rays

Vertical rays

Oblique rays

Figure 13-5 Because Earth is curved, oblique rays of sunlight reaching higher latitudes near the poles are more spread out. These rays are therefore weaker than the sunlight reaching lower latitudes near the equator. Climates near the equator are warmer, and those near the poles are colder.

The nearer a region is to the north or south pole, the higher its latitude, the smaller the amount of energy it receives from the sun, as seen in **Figure 13-5,** and the colder its climate.

Seasonal changes in sunlight also have an effect on the temperature of a climate. Because Earth is tilted on its axis, the angle of the sun's rays changes as Earth moves through its yearly orbit. During winter in the northern hemisphere, regions north of the equator are tilted away from the sun. Rays of sunlight are spread over a larger area, reducing their warming effect. As a result, winter temperatures are colder than summer temperatures.

Elevation

A region's elevation, or distance above sea level, also has an influence on temperature. Earth's atmosphere acts as insulation that traps some of the heat that reaches Earth's surface. At higher elevations, the atmosphere is thinner, so more heat escapes back into space. As a result, the higher the elevation, the colder the climate. The climate on a mountain will be cooler than the climate at sea level at the same latitude. Higher elevations affect plant growth, as seen in **Figure 13-6.**

EARTH SCIENCE
◀ **INTEGRATION**

Using Math

Earth is tilted at an angle of 23.5°. Without using a protractor, sketch an angle that measures about 23.5°. Then, check your angle by measuring it with a protractor.

Figure 13-6 These Rocky Mountain bristlecone pines show the effects of higher elevations on plants. These trees are shaped by the wind and stunted by the cold, harsh conditions.

Precipitation

Water is one of the most important factors affecting the climate of an area. Precipitation (prih sihp uh TAY shun) is the amount of water that condenses and falls in the form of rain, snow, sleet, hail, and fog. Differences in temperature have an important effect on patterns of precipitation.

Have you heard the expression "Hot air rises"? Actually, hot air is pushed upward whenever cold air sinks. Cold air is more dense than hot air, so it tends to move toward the ground. This pushes warm air near Earth's surface upward. In warm tropical regions near the equator, the air, land, and oceans are constantly being heated by the direct rays of the sun. As the cooler air sinks, the warm air is pushed upward into the atmosphere. This warm air carries large amounts of water vapor from the oceans. When the air reaches a high enough altitude in the atmosphere, the water vapor it contains cools and condenses as rain. While the air rises, it also moves slowly toward either the north or south pole. The air loses virtually all of its moisture by the time it reaches a latitude of about 30°. Because of this pattern, deserts are common at latitudes near 30° in both the northern and southern hemispheres. Latitudes between 0° and 22° receive much larger amounts of rain.

The Rain Shadow Effect

The presence of mountain ranges also has an effect on rainfall patterns. As **Figure 13-7** shows, air that is moving toward a mountain range is forced upward by the shape of the land. As warm air is forced upward, it cools, condensing the water vapor it contains and creating rain or snow. By the time the air has passed over the mountains, it has lost its moisture. The region on the opposite side of the mountain range receives very little rain because it is in a "rain shadow" created by the mountains.

interNET CONNECTION

Little precipitation falls in the desert. Visit the Glencoe Science Web Site at **www.glencoe.com/sec/science/fl** for more information about how cacti thrive.

Figure 13-7 Moist air moving into California from the Pacific Ocean is forced upward when it reaches the Sierra Nevada Mountains. As air rises, it cools and loses its moisture in the form of rain or snow. By the time the air reaches Nevada and Utah, on the other side of the mountains, it is dry. This area is in the mountains' "rain shadow." It receives so little rain that it has become a desert.

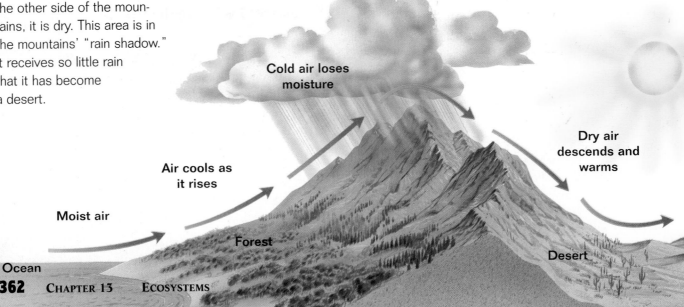

Cold air loses moisture

Dry air descends and warms

Air cools as it rises

Moist air

Forest

Desert

Ocean

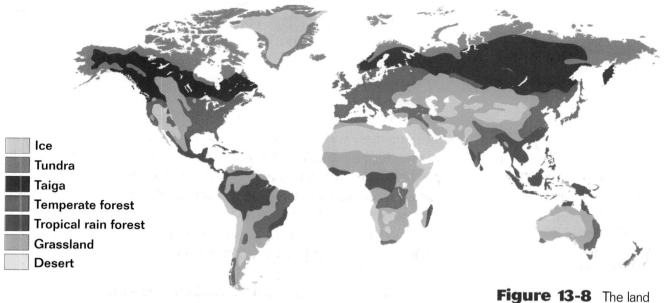

Ice
Tundra
Taiga
Temperate forest
Tropical rain forest
Grassland
Desert

Land Biomes

As you will see in the **Field Guide to Biomes** at the end of this chapter, regions with similar climates tend to have ecosystems with climax communities of similar structure. Tropical rain forests are climax communities found near the equator, where temperatures are warm and rainfall is plentiful. Coniferous forests grow where winter temperatures are cold and rainfall is moderate. Large geographic areas that have similar climates and ecosystems are called **biomes** (BI ohmz). The six most common biomes are mapped in **Figure 13-8.**

Tundra

At latitudes surrounding the north pole lies a biome that receives little precipitation but is covered with ice most of the year. The **tundra** (TUN dra) is a cold, dry, treeless region, sometimes called a cold desert, where winters are six to nine months long. For some of those months, the land remains dark because the sun never rises above the horizon. For a few days during the short, cold summer, the sun never sets. Precipitation averages less than 25 cm per year, and winter temperatures drop to −40°C, so water in the tundra soil remains frozen solid during the winter. During the summer, only the top few inches thaw.

Figure 13-8 The land portion of the biosphere can be divided into several biomes. Tundra, taiga, temperate forest, tropical rain forest, grassland, and desert are the most commonly known. **Which biome is most common in the United States?**

Try at Home

Mini Lab

Comparing Tundra and Taiga

Procedure

1. Compare the latitudes where tundra is found in the northern hemisphere with the same latitudes in South America.

2. Compare the latitudes where taiga is found in the northern hemisphere with the same latitudes in South America.

Analysis

Are either of these biomes found in South America? Explain why or why not.

Below the thawed surface is a layer of permanently frozen soil called permafrost. The cold temperatures slow down the process of decomposition, so the soil is also poor in nutrients.

Tundra plants are resistant to drought and cold. They include species of lichens known as reindeer moss, true mosses, grasses, and small shrubs, as seen in **Figure 13-9.** During the summer, mosquitoes, blackflies, and other biting insects are abundant. Many birds, including ducks, geese, various shorebirds, and songbirds, migrate to the tundra to nest during the summer. Hawks, snowy owls, mice, voles, lemmings, arctic hares, caribou, and musk oxen are also found there.

Taiga

Just below the tundra, at latitudes between about 50°N and 60°N, and stretching across Canada, northern Europe, and Asia, lies the world's largest biome. The **taiga** (TI guh), as shown in **Figure 13-10,** is a cold region of cone-bearing evergreen trees. This biome is also called the northern coniferous forest. Although the winter is long and cold, the taiga is warmer and wetter than the tundra. Precipitation is mostly snow and averages 35 cm to 100 cm each year.

Figure 13-9 Land is so flat in the tundra that water does not drain away. Because the frozen soil also prevents water from soaking into the soil, part of the tundra becomes wet and marshy during the summer. Frozen soil also prevents trees and other deep-rooted plants from growing in the tundra biome.

Figure 13-10 The climax community of the taiga is dominated by fir and spruce trees. Mammal populations include moose, black bears, lynx, and wolves.

No permafrost is found in a taiga. The ground thaws completely during the summer, making it possible for trees to grow. There are few shrubs and grasses, primarily because the forests of the taiga are so dense that little sunlight penetrates through the trees. Lichens and mosses grow on the forest floor.

Temperate Deciduous Forest

Temperate forests are found in both the northern and southern hemispheres, at latitudes below about 50°. Temperate regions usually have four distinct seasons each year. Precipitation ranges from about 75 cm to 150 cm and is distributed evenly throughout the year. Temperatures range from below freezing during the winter to 30°C or more during the warmest days of summer.

Many coniferous forests exist in the temperate regions of the world, particularly in mountainous areas. However, most of the temperate forests in Europe and North America are dominated by climax communities of deciduous trees, which lose their leaves every autumn. These forests, like the one in **Figure 13-11**, are called **temperate deciduous forests.** In the United States, they are found primarily east of the Mississippi River.

The loss of leaves in the fall signals a dramatic change in the life of the deciduous forest. Food becomes less abundant, and the leafless trees no longer provide adequate shelter for many organisms. Some animals, particularly birds, migrate to warmer regions during the winter. Other organisms reduce their activities and their need for food by going into hibernation until spring.

Reading Check ☑

Where are temperate deciduous forests found?

Figure 13-11 The mild climate and rich soil of the temperate deciduous forest support a wide variety of organisms. Animal life includes deer, foxes, squirrels, mice, snakes, and a huge number of bird and insect species. **Why do you think the temperate forests support a wide variety of organisms?**

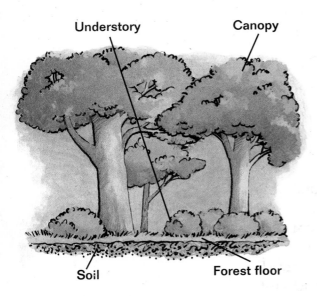

Figure 13-12 All forests are made up of layers with distinctly different biotic and abiotic factors.

Labels on figure: Understory, Canopy, Soil, Forest floor

Layers of Vegetation

Forests form layers of vegetation, as illustrated in **Figure 13-12.** At the top of the forest is the canopy, which consists of the leafy branches of trees. The *canopy* shades the ground below and provides homes for birds, insects, mammals, and many other organisms.

Beneath the canopy and above the forest floor is the shrub layer, or *understory*. The understory is made up of shorter plants that tolerate shade, along with organisms that depend on these plants for food and shelter.

The forest floor is dark and moist. It is home to many insects, worms, and fungi, as well as plants that can survive in dim light. Leaves, twigs, seeds, and the bodies of dead animals that fall to the forest floor either decompose or are eaten.

Problem Solving

Saving the Rain Forests

Many of the world's rain forests are being destroyed for economic reasons. Logging and farming provide income for people living in these areas. When a section of rain forest is cleared, trees that can be used as lumber are removed and sold. The remaining plants are cut down and burned, the ash is used to fertilize the soil, and food crops are planted. After a couple of years, the soil becomes too poor to produce a harvest, so the land is abandoned and another patch of forest is cleared.

People can make a living from the rain forest in other ways. Latex, a material used in surgical gloves, rubber bands, tires, and shoes, is the sap of rubber trees. Carefully tapping the trees provides a continual harvest without harming the forest. Many rain forest plants produce edible fruits, nuts, and oils that can be harvested year after year, without the need for clearing land. Harvesting these plants, rather than clearing land on which other crops can be grown for only a short time, could provide people with a sustainable income.

Think Critically: Suppose a family could earn the same amount of money in two different ways. One is to clear several hectares of rain forest, sell the timber, and grow food crops for two years. The other is to harvest latex and edible fruits and nuts from a larger area of rain forest for four years. Which course of action would you recommend? Why? Give reasons why the family might choose the other method.

Tropical Rain Forest

The most important climax community in the equatorial regions of the world is the lush, green plant growth of the **tropical rain forest.** Rainfall averages 200 cm to 225 cm each year, and some areas receive as much as 400 cm of rain annually. Temperatures are warm and stable, never varying much above or below about 25°C. The abundant rainfall and high temperatures combine to create a hot, humid environment that can be compared to the atmosphere inside a greenhouse.

Plants

The highest part of the rain forest canopy is formed by the leaves and branches of trees that may reach 30 m to 40 m in height. A rain forest may contain more than 700 species of trees and more than 1000 species of flowering plants. The canopy is so dense that it prevents much sunlight from filtering through to the regions below. Vines that are rooted in the soil grow up along tree trunks to reach the sun. Some types of plants such as orchids reach the light by anchoring themselves on tree trunks instead of in the soil. The understory is only dimly lit. Many of the plants growing here have huge leaves that catch what little sunlight is available. The forest floor is almost completely dark, with few plants other than ferns and mosses. Many of the tallest trees have support roots that rise above the ground. Most plants have shallow roots that form a tangled mat at the soil surface.

Animals

The rain forest is home to a huge number of animals. It is estimated that 1000 hectares (about 2500 acres) of rain forest in South America contain thousands of insect species, including 150 different kinds of butterflies. The same patch of forest also contains dozens of species of snakes, lizards, frogs, and salamanders, and hundreds of varieties of brightly colored birds, including parrots, toucans, cockatoos, and hummingbirds. Tree-dwelling mammals include monkeys, sloths, and bats. Ocelots and jaguars are tropical cats that prowl the forest floor in search of small mammals such as pacas and agoutis, or piglike peccaries, shown in **Figure 13-13.**

Using Math

Make a bar graph that shows the average yearly precipitation in each of the land biomes.

Grassland

Temperate and tropical regions that receive between 25 cm and 75 cm of precipitation each year and are dominated by climax communities of grasses are known as **grasslands.** Most grasslands have a dry season, when little or no rain falls, which prevents the development of forests. Virtually every continent has grasslands, like the one in **Figure 13-14,** and they are known by a variety of names. The prairie and plains of North America, the steppes of Asia, the veldts of Africa, and the pampas of South America are all grasslands.

Grass plants have extensive root systems, called sod, that absorb water when it rains and can withstand drought during long dry spells. The roots remain dormant during winter and sprout new stems and leaves when the weather warms in the spring. The soil is rich and fertile, and many grassland regions of the world are now important farming areas. Cereal grains such as wheat, rye, oats, barley, and corn, which serve as staple foods for humans, are types of grasses.

The most noticeable animals in grassland ecosystems are usually mammals that graze on the stems, leaves, and seeds of grass plants. Kangaroos graze in the grasslands of Australia. In Africa, common grassland inhabitants include wildebeests and zebras.

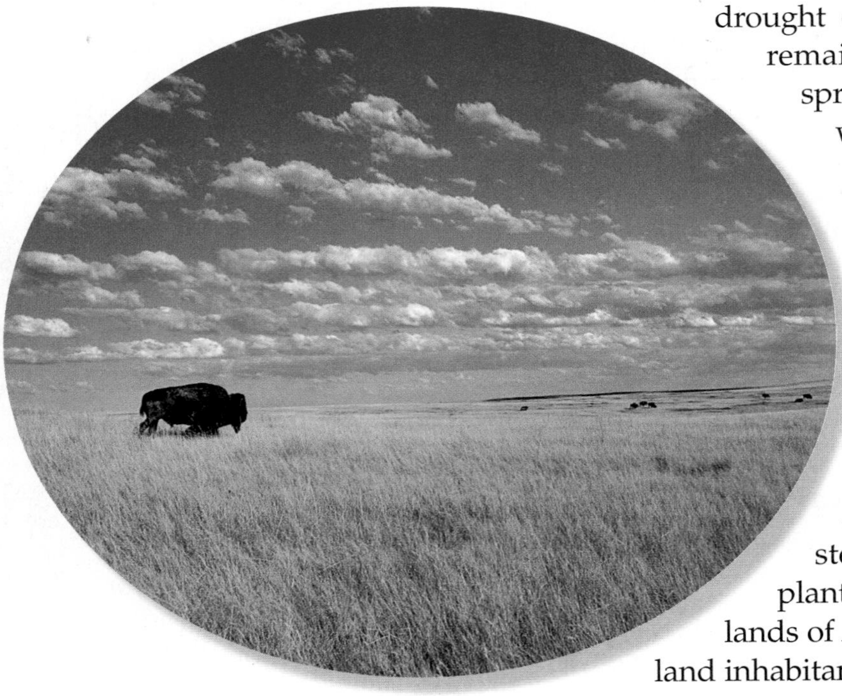

Figure 13-14 Grasslands, like this one in South Dakota, are hot and dry during the summer and cold and wet during the winter. They once supported huge herds of bison. Today, they are inhabited by pronghorn, gophers, ground squirrels, prairie chickens, and meadowlarks.

Desert

The **desert,** the driest biome on Earth, receives less than 25 cm of rain each year and supports little plant life. Some desert areas may receive no rain for years. When rain does come, it quickly drains away due to the sandy soil. Any water that remains on the ground evaporates rapidly, so the soil retains almost no moisture.

Because of the lack of water, desert plants are spaced widely apart, and much of the ground is bare. Some areas receive enough rainfall to support the growth of a few shrubs and small trees. Barren, windblown sand dunes are characteristic of the driest deserts, where rain rarely falls. Most deserts are covered with a thin, sandy or gravelly soil that contains little humus.

Adaptations of Desert Plants and Animals

Desert plants have developed a variety of adaptations for survival in the extreme dryness and hot and cold temperatures of this biome. Cactus plants, like the one in **Figure 13-15A,** with their reduced, spiny leaves, are probably the most familiar desert plants. Cacti have large, shallow roots that quickly absorb any water that becomes available.

Water conservation is important to all desert animals. Some, like the kangaroo rat, never need to drink water. They get all the moisture they need from the breakdown of food during digestion. Other adaptations involve behavior. Most animals are active only during the early morning or late afternoon, when temperatures are less extreme. Few large animals are found in the desert because there is not enough water or food to support them.

Figure 13-15 Desert organisms are adapted to hot, dry conditions.

 A Giant saguaro cacti expand to store water after it rains.

B Desert iguanas, common in deserts of the southwestern United States and Mexico, prefer temperatures above 100°F.

Section Assessment

1. Name two biomes that receive less than 25 cm of rain each year.

2. Compare the adaptations of tundra organisms to their environment with those of a desert organism to its environment.

3. **Think Critically:** Compare and contrast the canopies of temperate deciduous forests and tropical rain forests.

4. **Skill Builder**
   Observing and Inferring Animals adapt to their environments in order to survive. Do the **Chapter 13 Skill Activity** on page 720 to infer how some organisms adapt.

Using Computers

Database Create a database of information on Earth's land biomes. Include data on temperature range, precipitation, limiting factors, and descriptions of climax communities. If you need help, refer to page 699.

Materials

- Graph paper
- Thermometer
- Tape measure
- Hand lens
- Notebook
- Binoculars
- Pencil
- Field guides

Studying a Land Environment

An ecological study includes observation and analysis of living organisms and the physical features of the environment.

What You'll Investigate

How do you study an ecosystem?

Goals

- **Observe** biotic and abiotic factors of an ecosystem.
- **Analyze** the relationships among organisms and their environment.

Procedure

1. **Choose** a portion of an ecosystem near your school or home as your area of study. You might choose to study a pond, a forest area in a park, a garden, or another area.

2. **Decide** the boundaries of your study area.

3. Using a tape measure and graph paper, **make a map** of your study area.

4. Using a thermometer, **measure and record** the air temperature in your study area.

5. **Observe** the organisms in your study area. Use field guides to identify them. Use a hand lens to study small organisms. Use binoculars to study animals you cannot get near. Also, look for evidence (such as tracks or feathers) of organisms you do not see.

6. Record your observations in a table like the one shown. Make drawings to help you remember what you see.

7. Visit your study area as many times as you can and at different times of the day for four weeks. At each visit, be sure to make the same measurements and record all observations. Note how biotic and abiotic factors interact.

Conclude and Apply

1. **Identify** relationships among the organisms in your study area, such as predator-prey or symbiosis.

2. **Diagram** a food chain or food web for your ecosystem.

3. **Predict** what might happen if one or more abiotic factors were changed suddenly.

4. **Predict** what might happen if one or more populations were removed from the area.

Environmental Data				
Date	Time of Day	Temperature	Organisms Observed	Observations and Comments

Protecting Antarctica

The Coldest Place on Earth

Antarctica is a vast continent of rock covered with ice and surrounded by ocean. It is the least changed landmass in the world, in part because it is an environment hostile to humans. Winters are dark and long, with temperatures dipping to −90°C. During winter, shelves of ice extend from the land out over the ocean, essentially doubling the size of the continent. The yearly freezing and thawing of this ice has important effects on worldwide weather patterns and is a force that drives ocean currents.

Antarctica's Resources

Although the land is barren, seals and penguins, like the ones at left, use the shores as breeding grounds, and the waters of the Antarctic Ocean teem with life. Under the surface of Antarctica lie untouched mineral resources. Coal and oil probably exist in enormous quantities, as do other minerals that have already been discovered.

Antarctica and its remarkable natural resources are fully protected by a treaty that was drawn up in 1959 and signed by 12 nations—the United States, Great Britain, Argentina, Chile, France, Belgium, Norway, Australia, New Zealand, Japan, South Africa, and what was then the USSR. The Antarctic Treaty made the entire continent "a natural reserve, devoted to peace and science." Military activities, hunting, mining, and other actions that might harm the environment and its wild inhabitants are banned.

Since 1959, the Antarctic Treaty has been expanded to promote even greater environmental protection, international cooperation, and freedom for scientific research. Thanks to this agreement, Antarctica will remain an essentially undisturbed wilderness far into the future.

*inter*NET CONNECTION

Visit the Glencoe Science Web Site at **www.glencoe.com/sec/science/fl** to find out more about research in Antarctica.

13·3 Water Environments

What You'll Learn

▶ The difference between flowing freshwater and standing freshwater ecosystems

▶ Important seashore and deep-ocean ecosystems

Vocabulary
plankton
estuary
intertidal zone

Why It's Important

▶ You depend on water for your life processes.

Figure 13-16

A Freshwater streams are important in the ecosystem.

Freshwater Biomes

You've learned that temperature and precipitation are the most important factors determining which species can survive in a land environment. The limiting factors in water environments are the amount of salt in the water, dissolved oxygen, water temperature, and sunlight. The amount of salts dissolved in the water is called salinity. Freshwater contains little or no dissolved salts, and so has a low salinity. Earth's freshwater biomes include flowing water like these rivers and streams, as well as still or standing water, such as lakes and ponds.

Rivers and Streams

Flowing freshwater environments range from small, swiftly flowing streams, like the one in **Figure 13-16A,** to large, slow rivers. The faster a stream flows, the clearer its water tends to be and the higher its oxygen content. Swift currents quickly wash loose particles downstream, leaving a rocky or gravelly bottom. The tumbling and splashing of swiftly flowing water mixes in air from the atmosphere, increasing the oxygen content of the water.

Most of the nutrients that support life in flowing-water ecosystems are washed into the water from land. In areas where the water movement slows down, such as wide pools in streams or large rivers, debris settles to the bot-

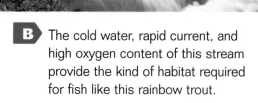

B The cold water, rapid current, and high oxygen content of this stream provide the kind of habitat required for fish like this rainbow trout.

Figure 13-17 Ponds and lakes differ in the types of communities inhabiting them. **What are some other differences between ponds and lakes?**

A The warm, sunlit waters of this pond are home to a large variety of organisms. Plants and algae form the basis of a food web that includes snails, insects, frogs, snakes, turtles, and fish.

tom. These environments tend to have higher nutrient levels and lower dissolved oxygen levels. They contain organisms such as freshwater mussels, minnows, and leeches that are not so well adapted for swiftly flowing water. They also tend to have more plant growth.

Lakes and Ponds

A lake or pond forms when a low place in the land fills with rainwater, snowmelt, or water from a stream. The waters of lakes and ponds hardly move at all. They contain more plant growth than flowing-water environments contain.

Ponds, like the one in **Figure 13-17A,** are smaller, shallow bodies of water. Because they are shallow, sunlight can usually penetrate all the way to the bottom, making the water warmer and promoting the growth of plants and algae. In fact, many ponds are almost completely filled with plant material, so the only clear, open water is at the center. Because of the lush growth in pond environments, they tend to be high in nutrients.

Lakes are larger and deeper than ponds. They tend to have more open water because most plant growth is limited to shallow areas along the shoreline. In fact, organisms found in the warm, sunlit waters of the lakeshore are often similar to those found in ponds.

Floating in the warm, sunlit waters near the surface of freshwater lakes and ponds are microscopic organisms known as plankton. **Plankton** includes algae, plants, and other organisms. If you were to dive all the way to the bottom, you would discover few, if any, plants or algae growing. Colder temperatures and lower light levels limit the types of organisms that can live in deep lake waters. Most lake organisms are found along the shoreline and in the warm water near the surface. ☑

B The population density of the warm, shallow water of the lakeshore is high. Fewer types of organisms live in the deeper water.

Reading Check ☑

What is plankton?

Saltwater Biomes

Figure 13-18 These Canada geese are swimming in an estuary of the Chesapeake Bay.

About 95 percent of the water on the surface on Earth contains high concentrations of salts. The saltwater biomes include the oceans, seas, and a few inland lakes, such as the Great Salt Lake in Utah.

Estuaries

Virtually every river on Earth eventually flows into the ocean. The area where a river meets the ocean and contains a mixture of freshwater and salt water is called an **estuary.** Estuaries are located near coastlines and border the land. Salinity changes with the amount of freshwater brought in by rivers and streams, and with the amount of salt water pushed inland by the tides.

Estuaries like the one in **Figure 13-18** are extremely fertile, productive environments because freshwater streams bring in tons of nutrients from inland soils. Nutrient levels in estuaries are higher than those in freshwater or other saltwater ecosystems. Estuarine organisms include many species of algae, a few salt-tolerant grasses, shrimp, crabs, clams, oysters, snails, worms, and fish. Estuaries serve as important nursery grounds for many species of ocean fish.

Seashores

All of Earth's landmasses are bordered by ocean water. The fairly shallow waters along the world's coastlines contain a variety of saltwater ecosystems, all of which are influenced by the tides and by the action of waves. The gravitational pull of the sun and moon causes the tides to rise and fall twice each day in most parts of the world. The **intertidal zone** is the portion of the shoreline that is covered with water at high tide and exposed to the air during low tide. Organisms living in the intertidal zone must not only be adapted to dramatic changes in temperature, moisture, and salinity, but also be able to withstand the force of wave action. Two kinds of intertidal zones are shown in **Figure 13-19.**

Mini Lab

Modeling Freshwater Environments

Procedure

1. Cover the bottom of a 2-L bottle with about 2 cm of gravel, muck, and other debris from the bottom of a pond. If plants are present, add one or two to the bottle. Use a dip net to capture small fish, insects, or tadpoles.

2. Carefully pour pond water into the bottle until it is about two-thirds full. Seal the bottle.

3. Keep the bottle indoors at room temperature and out of direct sunlight.

Analysis

1. Using a hand lens, observe as many organisms as possible. Record your observations. After two or three days, return your sample to the original habitat.

2. Write a short paper describing the organisms in your sample ecosystem and explaining their interactions.

Figure 13-19 Organisms living in intertidal zones have adaptations to survive in these changing environments.

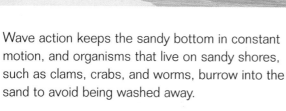

A Wave action keeps the sandy bottom in constant motion, and organisms that live on sandy shores, such as clams, crabs, and worms, burrow into the sand to avoid being washed away.

B Algae, mussels, barnacles, snails, and other organisms adapted for clinging to the rocks are typically found on rocky shores. These organisms must be able to tolerate the heavy force of breaking waves.

Open Ocean

Life abounds in the open ocean, where there is no land. The ocean can be divided into life zones based on the depth to which sunlight can penetrate the water. The lighted zone of the ocean is the upper 200 m or so. It is the home of the plankton that make up the foundation of the food chain in the open ocean. Below about 200 m, where sunlight cannot reach, is the dark zone of the ocean. Animals living in this region feed on material that floats down from the lighted zone, or they feed on each other.

Section Assessment

1. What are the similarities and differences between a lake and a stream?

2. What biotic or abiotic factor limits life on the floor of a tropical rain forest and the bottom of the deep ocean? Why?

3. Think Critically: Why do few plants grow in the waters of a swift-flowing mountain stream?

4. 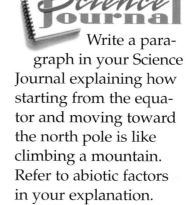 **Skill Builder**
Comparing and Contrasting Compare and contrast the effects of (1) temperature in the tundra and desert and (2) sunlight in deep-lake and deep-ocean waters. If you need help, refer to Comparing and Contrasting in the **Skill Handbook** on page 686.

Science Journal Write a paragraph in your Science Journal explaining how starting from the equator and moving toward the north pole is like climbing a mountain. Refer to abiotic factors in your explanation.

FIELD GUIDE to BIOMES

FIELD ACTIVITY

Research the average monthly rainfall, high temperature, and low temperature for each month of the past year for the area where you live. Prepare a graph of data using the example below. Based on your findings, which biome graph most closely matches your data? What biome do you live in? What type of plant and animal life do you expect to find in your biome?

Have you ever wondered why you do not find polar bears in Florida or palm trees in Alaska? Organisms are limited to where they can live and survive due to temperature, amount of rainfall, and type of soil found in a region. A biome's boundaries are determined by climate more than anything else. Climate is a way of categorizing temperature extremes and yearly precipitation patterns. Use this field guide to identify some of the world's biomes and to determine which biome you live in.

Interpreting Land Biome Climates

The following graphs represent the climates of six different biomes. To read each biome graph, use the following information. Axis *A* shows the months of the year. Axis *B* shows the average amount of precipitation for each month. Axis *C* shows the average high and low temperature for each month.

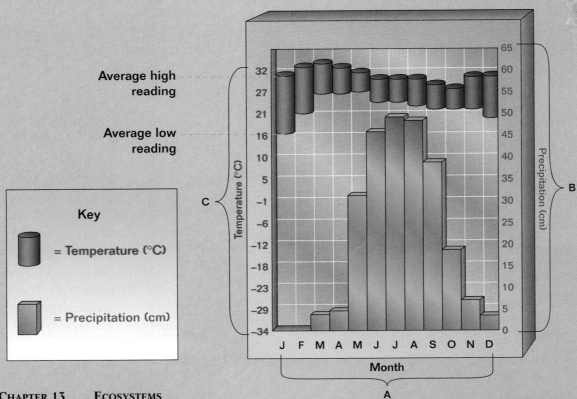

Average high reading

Average low reading

Key

⬤ = Temperature (°C)

▬ = Precipitation (cm)

Temperature (°C): 32, 27, 21, 16, 10, 5, −1, −6, −12, −18, −23, −29, −34

Precipitation (cm): 65, 60, 55, 50, 45, 40, 35, 30, 25, 20, 15, 10, 5, 0

Month: J F M A M J J A S O N D

A   B   C

Biome: Tundra

- Seasons: long, harsh winters; short summers; very little precipitation
- Plants: mosses, lichens, grasses, and sedges
- Animals: weasels, arctic foxes, snowshoe hares, snowy owls, and hawks

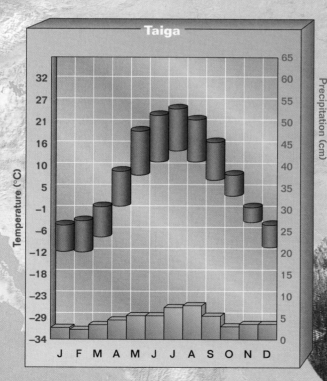

Biome: Taiga

- Seasons: cold, severe winters with much snow; short growing seasons
- Plants: conifers such as spruces, firs, and larches
- Animals: caribou, wolves, moose, bear, and summer birds

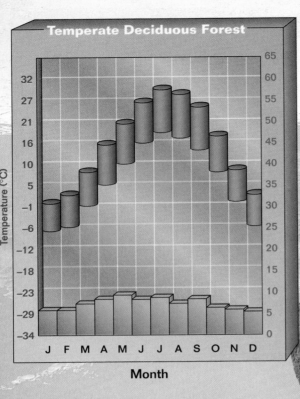

Temperate Deciduous Forest

Biome: Temperate Deciduous Forest

- Seasons: cold winters, hot summers, and moderate precipitation
- Plants: deciduous trees such as oak, hickory, and beech, which lose their leaves every autumn
- Animals: wolves, deer, bears, small mammals, and birds

Biome: Grassland

- Seasons: cold winters, hot summers with little precipitation
- Plants: grasses and a few trees
- Animals: grazing animals, wolves, prairie dogs, foxes, ferrets, snakes, lizards, and insects

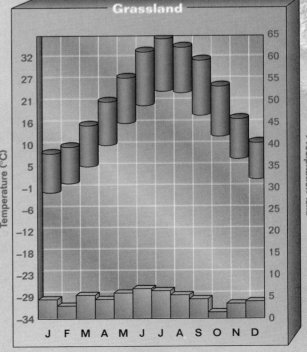

Grassland

Biome: Desert

- Seasons: warm to hot in daytime, cool in the evening, little precipitation
- Plants: cacti, yuccas, Joshua trees, and bunchgrasses
- Animals: small rodents, jackrabbits, birds of prey, and snakes

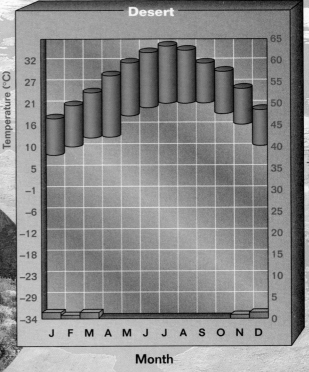

Desert

Temperature (°C): 32, 27, 21, 16, 10, 5, −1, −6, −12, −18, −23, −29, −34

Precipitation (cm): 65, 60, 55, 50, 45, 40, 35, 30, 25, 20, 15, 10, 5

Month: J F M A M J J A S O N D

Biome: Tropical Rain Forest

- Seasons: hot all year with precipitation almost every day
- Plants: trees and orchids
- Animals: birds, reptiles, insects, monkeys, and sloths

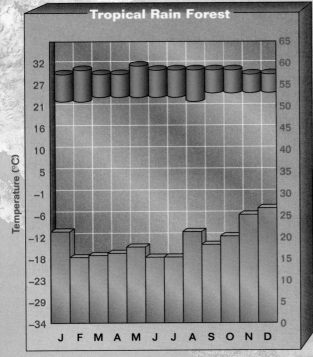

Tropical Rain Forest

Temperature (°C): 32, 27, 21, 16, 10, 5, −1, −6, −12, −18, −23, −29, −34

Precipitation (cm): 65, 60, 55, 50, 45, 40, 35, 30, 25, 20, 15, 10, 5, 0

Month: J F M A M J J A S O N D

For a **preview** of this chapter, study this Reviewing Main Ideas before you read the chapter. After you have studied this chapter, you can use the Reviewing Main Ideas to **review** the chapter.

The Glencoe MindJogger, Audiocassettes, and CD-ROM provide additional opportunities for review.

Section
13-1 HOW ECOSYSTEMS CHANGE
The process of gradual change from one community of organisms to another is **ecological succession.** It involves changes in both abiotic and biotic factors. Succession can be divided into **primary** and **secondary succession. Pioneer communities** are the first to move into an environment, and **climax communities** are the final organisms to move in. *How can you explain that lawns usually do not go through succession?*

Section
13-2 LAND ENVIRONMENTS
Climate is the general weather pattern in an area. The factors that determine a region's climate are temperature and precipitation. Large geographic areas with similar climates and climax communities are biomes. The six major biomes are the **tundra, taiga, temperate deciduous forests, tropical rain forests, grasslands,** and **deserts.** *How does climate influence the type of biomes?*

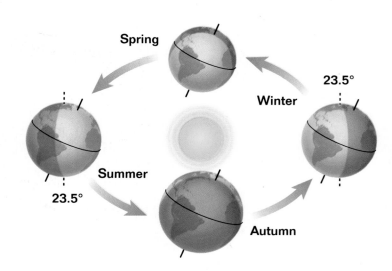

Spring

23.5°

Winter

Summer

23.5°

Autumn

Reading Check ✔

Diagram changes in an ecosystem as a series of causes and effects. You might start with this cause: an ecosystem's soil is thin and poor. What is a possible effect?

Section 13-3 WATER ENVIRONMENTS

The limiting factors in water environments include the amount of salt in the water, dissolved oxygen, water temperature, and sunlight. Freshwater ecosystems include rivers, streams, lakes, and ponds. Saltwater ecosystems include the oceans, seas, and a few inland lakes. An area where a river meets the ocean is called an **estuary.** All land on Earth is surrounded by ocean water. The **intertidal zone** is the portion of the shoreline that is covered with water at high tide and exposed to the air during low tide. The open ocean is divided into life zones based on the depth to which sunlight can penetrate the water. *Describe where estuaries form. How are they important?*

Chapter 13 Assessment

Using Vocabulary

a. biome
b. climax community
c. desert
d. ecological succession
e. estuary
f. grassland
g. intertidal zone
h. pioneer community
i. plankton
j. primary succession
k. secondary succession
l. taiga
m. temperate deciduous forest
n. tropical rain forest
o. tundra

Each of the following sentences is false. Make the sentence true by replacing the italicized word with a word from the list above.

1. *Primary succession* has occurred when one community of organisms replaces another.
2. *Plankton* are the first organisms to inhabit an area.
3. An *estuary* is a region with similar climate and climax communities.
4. A *biome* is an equatorial region that receives large amounts of rainfall.
5. A *tropical rain forest* is where freshwater mixes with salt water.

Checking Concepts

Choose the word or phrase that best answers the question.

6. What determines the climate of an area?
   A) plankton
   B) succession
   C) limiting factors
   D) abiotic factors

7. What are tundra and desert examples of?
   A) ecosystems
   B) biomes
   C) habitats
   D) communities

8. What is a treeless, cold, and dry biome called?
   A) taiga
   B) tundra
   C) desert
   D) grassland

9. Which is **NOT** a grassland?
   A) pampas
   B) veldts
   C) steppes
   D) estuaries

10. Mussels and barnacles have adapted to the wave action of what?
    A) sandy beach
    B) rocky shore
    C) open ocean
    D) estuary

11. Which biome contains the largest number of species?
    A) taiga
    B) temperate deciduous forest
    C) tropical rain forest
    D) grassland

12. What is the end result of succession?
    A) pioneer community
    B) limiting factor
    C) climax community
    D) permafrost

13. Which biome does **NOT** have trees as a climax community?
    A) tundra
    B) taiga
    C) tropical rain forest
    D) grassland

14. Which does **NOT** contain freshwater?
    A) lakes
    B) ponds
    C) rivers
    D) oceans

15. Which does **NOT** have flowing water?
    A) ponds
    B) rivers
    C) seashores
    D) streams

Thinking Critically

16. Would a soil sample from a temperate deciduous forest contain more or less humus than soil from a tropical rain forest? Explain.

17. A grassy meadow borders an oak-maple forest. Is one of these ecosystems undergoing succession? Why?

18. Describe how ecological succession eventually results in the layers of vegetation found in forests.

19. Why do many tropical rain forest plants make good houseplants?

Developing Skills

If you need help, refer to the **Skill Handbook.**

20. **Concept Mapping:** Make a concept map for water environments. Include these terms: *saltwater ecosystems, freshwater ecosystems, intertidal zone, lighted zone, dark zone, lake, pond, river, stream, flowing water,* and *standing water.*

21. **Making and Using Graphs:** Make a bar graph of the amount of rainfall per year in each biome.

Rainfall Amounts

Biome	Rainfall/Year
Deciduous forests	100 cm
Tropical rain forests	225 cm
Grasslands	50 cm
Deserts	20 cm

22. **Hypothesizing:** Make a hypothesis as to what would happen to succession in a pond if the pond owner removed all the cattails and reeds from around the pond edges every summer.

23. **Comparing and Contrasting:** Compare and contrast the adaptations of organisms living in swiftly flowing streams and organisms living in the rocky intertidal zones.

24. **Recognizing Cause and Effect:** Devastating fires, like the one in Yellowstone National Park in 1988, cause many changes to the land. Determine the effect of a fire to an area that has reached its climax community.

THE PRINCETON REVIEW

Test-Taking Tip

Where's the fire? Slow down! Go back over reading passages and double check your math. Remember that doing most of the questions and getting them right is always better than doing all the questions and getting lots of them wrong.

Test Practice

Use these questions to test your Science Proficiency.

1. What determines whether a land supports a deciduous forest or a grassland?
   A) temperature
   B) latitude
   C) precipitation
   D) length of growing season

2. What causes the vertical distribution of plants in a deep lake?
   A) color of the water
   B) depth that light can penetrate
   C) kind of plants in the lake
   D) kind of animals in the lake

3. How are primary succession and secondary succession similar?
   A) both begin where no soil is present
   B) both end in climax communities
   C) both begin with a pioneer community
   D) both develop where lava has cooled

4. What is the layer of vegetation that shades the ground below and provides homes for birds, insects, and mammals called?
   A) soil
   B) understory
   C) canopy
   D) forest floor

5

Classifying Life

What's Happening Here?

Life comes in an astonishing variety of sizes and shapes. Giant sea kelp (left) grows to a hundred meters long. Air bladders help the leafy blades float up toward the light. A one-celled diatom (below, magnified 55 times) displays its beautiful symmetry. Kelp and diatoms are both algae and belong to the protist kingdom, a unique group among the six kingdoms of life. Some protists move about the way animals do, and others make their own food the way plants do—and some protists do both! How can such different forms of life belong to the same kingdom? What other kingdoms make up the rest of life? These are some of the questions answered in this unit.

inter**NET**
CONNECTION

Explore the Glencoe Science Web Site at **www.glencoe.com/sec/ science/fl** to find out more about topics found in this unit.

CHAPTER

14

The Structure of Organisms

Chapter Preview

Section 14-1
Cells—The Units of Life

Section 14-2
Cell Organization

Section 14-3
Viruses

Skills Preview

Skill Builders
- Map Concepts
- Interpret Scientific Illustrations

Activities
- Compare and Contrast
- Use Numbers

MiniLabs
- Observe and Infer
- Make a Model

Reading Check ✓

Different types of microscopes are presented at the beginning of this chapter. As you read, think about how these inventions helped scientists separate fact from fiction. Why was this important?

Explore Activity

In the photograph to the left are many things. Some are alive, and others are not. Living things are called organisms and are many shapes, sizes, and colors. They live on land, in water, or both. Some fly, some swim—others move fast, or just creep. But, a photograph cannot show all the organisms in an environment. Some organisms, such as bacteria, are so small that you can only see them under a microscope. In the following activity, you will compare the traits of two organisms.

Compare and Contrast Two Organisms

1. Choose an organism in the large photograph and make a list of its traits in your Science Journal.

2. Now look at the smaller photo. These organisms are magnified 5000 times. They are soil bacteria, and each rod-shaped structure is an entire organism. Does it look like something that is alive? In your Science Journal, make a list of its traits.

3. Compare and contrast the two organisms.

Infer why you and something as small as a bacterium are both considered organisms.

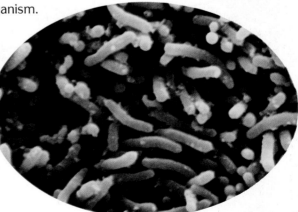

Magnification: 5000×

14·1 Cells—The Units of Life

What You'll Learn

▶ The history leading to the cell theory
▶ The differences between the compound light microscope and the electron microscope
▶ The importance of the cell theory

Vocabulary
compound light microscope
electron microscope
cell theory

Why It's Important

▶ We are like other living things because we are all made of cells.

The Microscope

The number of living things in your environment that you can't see is much greater than those that you can see. Many of these things are just one cell in size. Larger living things are made of many cells. We need to use a magnifying glass or a microscope to see most of these cells.

Trying to see separate cells in a leaf, like one in **Figure 14-1,** is like trying to see individual bricks in a wall from three blocks away. If you start to walk toward the wall, it becomes easier to see individual bricks. When you get right up to the wall, you can see each brick in detail and many of the small features of each brick. A microscope performs a similar function. A microscope has one or more lenses that make an enlarged image of an object. Through these lenses, the leaf is brought closer to you, and you see the individual cells that carry on life processes.

Magnification: 500×

Figure 14-1 Individual cells become visible when the ivy leaf is viewed with a microscope.

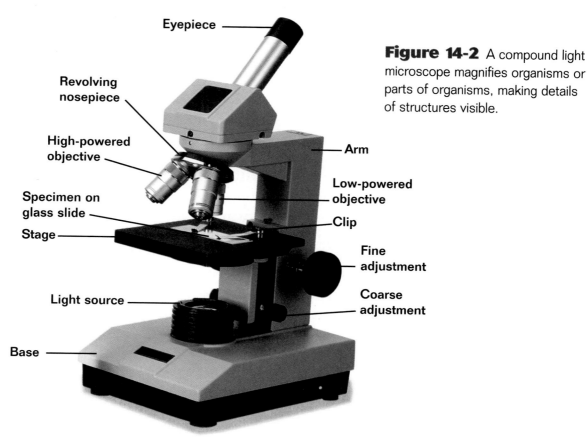

Eyepiece

Revolving nosepiece

High-powered objective

Specimen on glass slide

Stage

Light source

Base

Arm

Low-powered objective

Clip

Fine adjustment

Coarse adjustment

Figure 14-2 A compound light microscope magnifies organisms or parts of organisms, making details of structures visible.

Early Microscopes

Microscopes are simple or compound, depending on how many lenses they contain. A simple microscope is similar to a magnifying glass. It has only one lens. In 1590, a Dutch maker of reading glasses, Zacharias Janssen, put two magnifying glasses together in a tube. The result was the first crude compound microscope. By combining two lenses, he got an image that was larger than an image made by only one lens. These early compound microscopes weren't satisfactory, however. The lenses would make an image larger, but it wasn't always sharp or clear.

In the mid 1600s, Anton Van Leeuwenhoek, a Dutch fabric merchant, made a simple microscope with a tiny glass bead for a lens. With it, he reported seeing things in pond water that no one had ever imagined before. His microscope could magnify up to 270 times. Another way to say this is that his microscope could make the image of an object 270 times larger than its actual size. Today, we would say his lens had a power of 270×.

PHYSICS INTEGRATION

Convex Lenses
A magnifying glass is a convex lens. All microscopes use one or more convex lenses. In your Science Journal, diagram a convex lens and describe its shape. Use the illustration to explain how it magnifies.

The Compound Light Microscope

The microscope you will use in studying life science is a compound light microscope similar to the one in **Figure 14-2.** In a **compound light microscope,** light passes through and around an object and then through two or more lenses.

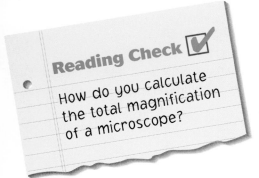

Reading Check ☑

How do you calculate the total magnification of a microscope?

Lenses enlarge the image and bend the light toward your eye. It has an eyepiece lens and objective lenses. An eyepiece lens usually has a power of 10×. An objective lens may have a power of 43×. Together, they have a total magnification of 430× (10× times 43×). Some compound microscopes have more powerful lenses that can magnify an object up to 2000 times (2000×) its original size. ☑

The Stereomicroscope

Your classroom may have stereoscopic (stereo) light microscopes. Stereomicroscopes have lenses for each eye that give you a three-dimensional image of an object. They are used to look at objects that are too thick for light to pass through or too large to fit in the stage of a compound light microscope. You may look at whole insects, leaves, or your fingertips with a stereomicroscope.

Electron Microscopes

PHYSICS
INTEGRATION ➤

Things that are too small to be seen with a light microscope can be viewed with an electron microscope. Instead of using lenses to bend beams of light, an **electron microscope** uses a magnetic field to bend beams of electrons. Electron microscopes can magnify images up to 1 million times. **Figure 14-3** shows the kind of detail that can be seen with an electron microscope. Electron microscope images must be photographed or electronically produced.

There are several kinds of electron microscopes. One is the transmission electron microscope (TEM), which is used to study parts inside a cell. The object has to be sliced thin and placed in a vacuum. A vacuum has no air. As a result, only dead cells and tissues can be observed this way. A scanning electron microscope (SEM) is used to see the surfaces

Figure 14-3 Electron microscopes reveal details that cannot be seen using a compound light microscope.

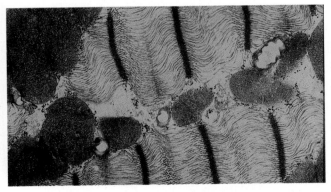

Magnification: 75 625×

A Transmission electron microscopes (TEM) provide images that show great detail. This TEM image shows a thin cross section of a bee's skeletal muscle.

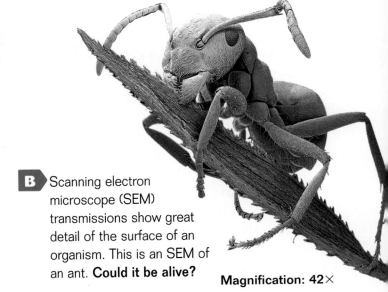

B Scanning electron microscope (SEM) transmissions show great detail of the surface of an organism. This is an SEM of an ant. **Could it be alive?**

Magnification: 42×

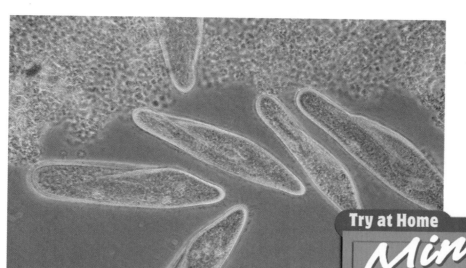

Magnification: 98×

Figure 14-4 This is an image of paramecia, one-celled organisms found in pond water.

Try at Home

Mini Lab

Observing Magnified Objects

Procedure

1. Look at a newspaper through both the curved side and the flat bottom of an empty clear glass.
2. Look at the newspaper through a clear glass bowl filled with water and then look at the newspaper with a magnifying glass.

Analysis

1. In your Science Journal, compare how well you can see the newspaper through each of the objects.
2. What did early scientists learn by using such tools?

of whole objects. An SEM called the Environmental SEM allows images of some living things to be produced. From the time of Van Leeuwenhoek until the present, the microscope has been a valuable tool for studying cells. You will see how it was used to develop the cell theory.

The Cell Theory

During the seventeenth century, when explorers were discovering new lands, scientists were discovering the microscopic world. They examined blood and scrapings from their own teeth. In mud from ponds and drops of rainwater, they discovered organisms like the ones in **Figure 14-4.**

Cells weren't discovered until the microscope was improved. In 1665, Robert Hooke, an English scientist, cut a thin slice of cork and looked at it under his microscope. To Hooke, the cork seemed to be made up of little empty boxes, which he called cells. **Figure 14-5** is an image of cells observed and sketched by Robert Hooke more than 300 years ago. Actually, Hooke was not aware of the importance of what he was seeing.

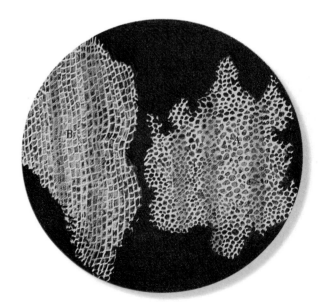

Figure 14-5 Robert Hooke made these drawings of cork cells.

Development of the Cell Theory

In the 1830s, Matthias Schleiden, a German scientist, used a microscope to study plant parts. He concluded that all plants are made of cells. Just a year later, another German scientist, Theodor Schwann, after observing many different animal cells, concluded that all animals are made up of cells. Together, they became convinced that all living things are made of cells.

Several years later, a German doctor, Rudolf Virchow, hypothesized that new cells don't form on their own. Instead, cells divide to form new cells. This was a startling idea. Remember that at that time people thought earthworms fell from the sky when it rained. People thought that life came about spontaneously. What Virchow said was that every cell that is or ever has been came from a cell that already existed.

The **cell theory** is one of the major theories in science. It is not based on the hypotheses and observations of only one person, but results from the discoveries of many scientists. Today, it serves as the basis for scientists who study the parts of cells, how cells are organized, and how cells and organisms reproduce and change through time. The cell theory is summarized in **Figure 14-6.**

Figure 14-6 The observations and conclusions of many scientists became known as the cell theory. The major ideas of the cell theory are as follows:

The Cell Theory

1. All organisms are made up of one or more cells.

2. Cells are the basic units of structure and function in all organisms.

3. All cells come from cells that already exist.

Section Assessment

1. Explain why the invention of the microscope was important in the study of cells.

2. Why is the cell theory important?

3. What is the difference between a simple and a compound light microscope?

4. **Think Critically:** Why would it be better to look at living cells rather than dead cells?

5. **Skill Builder**
   Concept Mapping Using a network tree concept map, show the differences between compound light microscopes and electron microscopes. If you need help, refer to Concept Mapping in the **Skill Handbook** on page 680.

Using Math

Calculate the total low-power and high-power magnification of a microscope that has an 8× eyepiece, a 10× objective, and a 40× high-power objective.

Using Decimals in Division

Problem

Decimal division can help you better visualize the size of small cells and organisms seen through a microscope. A red blood cell (like those magnified at left) is about seven ten-thousandths of a centimeter (0.0007) in diameter. How many red blood cells could be placed across the diameter of a dime?

Solution

1. Measure the diameter of a dime in centimeters. It should be about 1.8 cm.

2. To find how many red blood cells will fit across a dime, divide the diameter of the dime by the diameter of one red blood cell.

$$1.8 \text{ cm} \div 0.0007 \text{ cm}$$

3. In order to do this division, the divisor (the number you divide by) must be a whole number. The divisor in this problem is 0.0007. To make it a whole number, move the decimal point to the right four places. The divisor now equals 7. Moving the decimal point four places to the right is the same as multiplying by 10 000. In division problems, whatever you do to the divisor must also be done to the dividend (the number you divide into). So, you multiply 1.8 by 10 000 to get 18 000. The problem becomes 18 000 cm ÷ 7 cm or

```
       2571
   7)18000
     14
      40
      35
      50
      49
      10
       7
       3
```

Because the remainder of 3 is less than half the divisor of 7, do not round the quotient up to 2572. Thus, the answer to the problem is that you could place about 2571 red blood cells across the diameter of a dime.

Practice
PROBLEMS

1. Suppose you are 150 cm tall. A particular alga is about 0.0001 cm in length. How many of these algae could be placed end-to-end to span your height?

2. A certain bacterium with a length of about 0.00015 mm is the smallest known living organism. In a book, a picture of this bacterium measures 2.4 cm. How many times has the picture been magnified?

Design Your Own Experiment

Activity 14•1

Comparing Light Microscopes

Possible Materials

- A compound light microscope
- A stereoscopic light microscope
- Any 8 items from the classroom; include some living or once-living items
- Microscope slides and coverslips
- Plastic petri dishes
- Distilled water
- Dropper

You're a technician in a police forensic laboratory. You use stereoscopic and compound light microscopes in the laboratory. A detective just returned from a crime scene with bags of evidence. You must examine each piece of evidence under a microscope. How do you decide which microscope is the best tool to use?

Recognize the Problem

Microscopes are useful tools for scientists. Stereoscopic and compound light microscopes are used for many tasks. What things are better viewed with a compound light microscope? What things are better viewed with a stereoscopic microscope?

Form a Hypothesis

Compare the items to be examined under the microscopes. Which microscope will be used for each item?

Goals

- **Learn** how to use a stereoscopic microscope and a compound light microscope.
- **Compare** the uses of the stereoscopic and compound light microscopes.

Safety Precautions

Thoroughly wash your hands when you have completed this experiment.

Test Your Hypothesis

Plan

1. As a group, **decide** how you will test your hypothesis.

2. **List** the steps that you will need to complete this experiment. Be specific, describing exactly what you will do at each step. Make sure the steps are in a logical order. Remember that you must place an item in the bottom of a plastic petri dish to **examine** it under the stereoscopic microscope. You must **make a wet mount** of any item to be examined under the compound light microscope.

3. If you need a data or observation table, **design** one in your Science Journal.

Do

1. Make sure your teacher approves the objects you'll examine, your plan, and data table before you proceed.

2. **Carry out** the experiment as planned.

3. While doing the experiment, **record** your observations and **complete** the data table.

Analyze Your Data

1. **Compare** the items you examined with those of your classmates.

2. Based on this experiment, **classify** the eight items you observed.

Draw Conclusions

1. **Infer** which microscope a scientist might use to examine a blood sample, fibers, and live snails.

2. If you examined an item under both microscopes, how would the images differ?

3. **List** five careers that require people to use a stereomicroscope. **List** five careers that require people to use a compound light microscope. Enter the lists in your Science Journal.

14•2 Cell Organization

What **You'll Learn**

► The names and functions of each part of a plant cell and an animal cell

► How important a nucleus is in a cell

► What tissues, organs, and organ systems are and how they compare

Vocabulary

cell	Golgi body
membrane	mitochondria
nucleus	lysosome
chromatin	cell wall
cytoplasm	chloroplast
organelle	tissue
endoplasmic	organ
reticulum	
ribosome	

Why **It's Important**

► If you know how your cells work, it's easier to understand how you can do what you do.

An Overview of Cells

In contrast to the dry cork boxes that Hooke saw, living cells are dynamic and have several things in common. They all have a membrane and a gel-like material called cytoplasm inside the membrane. In addition, they all have hereditary material that controls the life of the cell.

How Cells Differ

Cells come in a variety of sizes. A single nerve cell in your leg may be a meter in length. A human egg cell, on the other hand, is no bigger than a dot on this i. Going a step further, a human red blood cell is about one-tenth the size of a human egg cell.

The shape of a cell may also tell you something about the job the cell does. The nerve cell in **Figure 14-7** with its fine extensions sends impulses through your body. Look at its shape in contrast to the white blood cell, which can change shape. Some cells in plant stems are long and hollow with holes. They transport food and water through the plant. Human red blood cells, on the other hand, are disk-shaped and have to be small and flexible enough to move through tiny blood vessels.

Figure 14-7 Often, the shape of a cell tells you something about the job it performs.

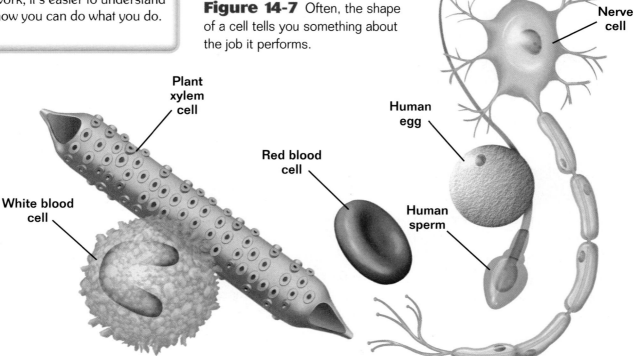

White blood cell

Plant xylem cell

Red blood cell

Human egg

Human sperm

Nerve cell

Figure 14-8 Pond scum is made up of prokaryotic cells. **Where do most of its chemical reactions take place?**

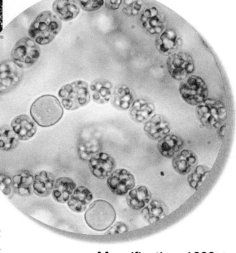

Magnification: 1000×

Cell Types

Scientists have found that there are two basic types of cells. Cells that have no membrane around their hereditary material are prokaryotic cells. Bacteria and cells that form pond scum, like those in **Figure 14-8,** are prokaryotic cells. A eukaryotic cell has a nucleus, which is hereditary material surrounded by a membrane. The animal and plant cells in this chapter are eukaryotic cells.

Bacterial Cells

Bacteria, such as those in **Figure 14-9,** and other prokaryotes exist as one-celled organisms. Most prokaryotes have an outer, protective cell wall. Inside the cell wall is the cell membrane. The cell membrane forms a container for the gelatinlike cytoplasm. The hereditary material and other cell substances are in the cytoplasm. Most of the chemical reactions that the cell needs to survive happen in the cytoplasm.

Magnification: 11 408×

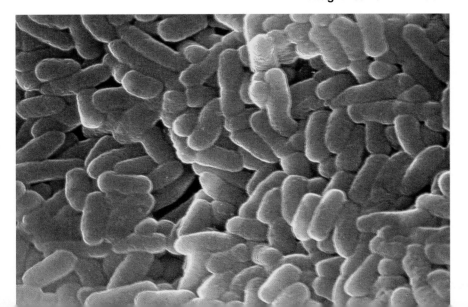

Figure 14-9 A bacterial cell is a one-celled organism. It does not have a membrane around its nucleus. These bacteria cause tuberculosis in humans.

Figure 14-10 Animal cells are typical eukaryotic cells. Refer to this diagram as you read about cell parts and their jobs.

A The cell membrane is made up of a double layer of phospholipids, which are fatlike molecules.

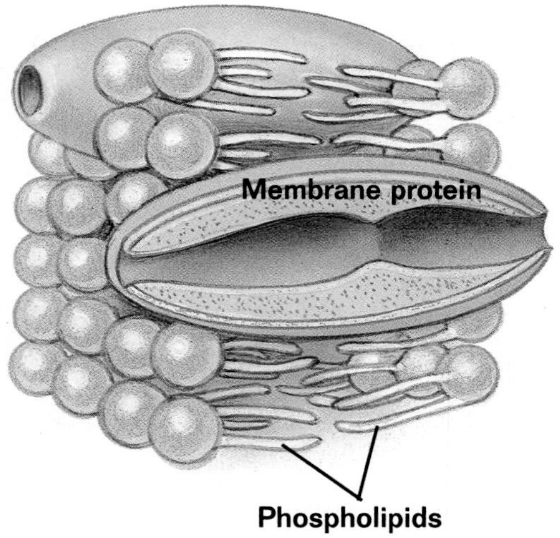

Membrane protein

Golgi bodies

Lysosome

Nuclear membrane

Chromatin — Nucleus

Nucleolus

Cell membrane

Phospholipids

B Below is the image of an animal cell. The parts of the cell are labeled in the diagram to the left.

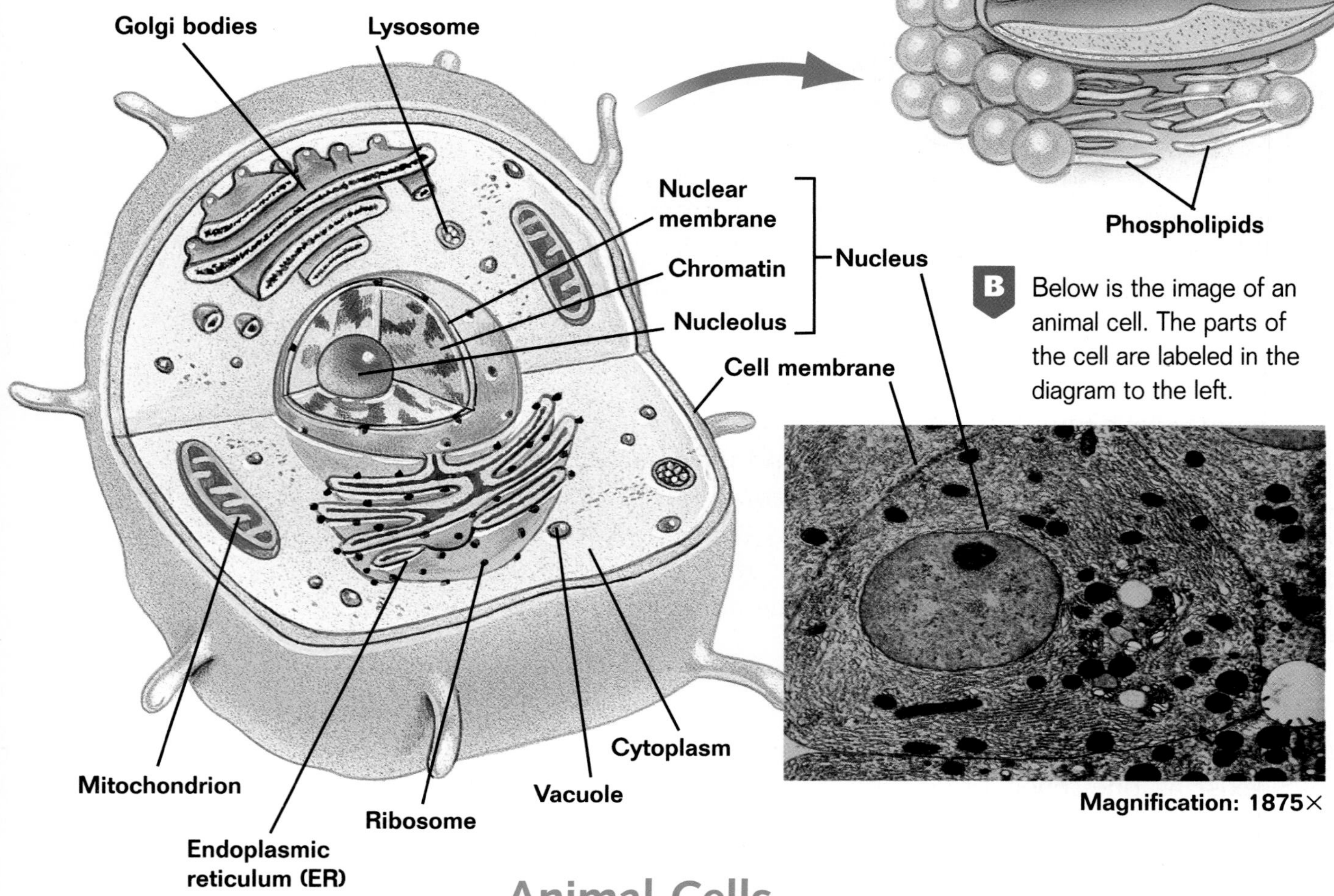

Nucleus

Mitochondrion

Endoplasmic reticulum (ER)

Ribosome

Vacuole

Cytoplasm

Magnification: 1875×

Animal Cells

Each cell in your body is constantly active and has a specific job to do. The activities in your cells might be compared to a business that operates 24 hours a day making dozens of different products. A business operates inside a building. A cell is similar. It functions inside a structure called the cell membrane. Materials that are needed to make specific products are brought into the building. Finished products are shipped out. Similarly, substances move into a cell and products and wastes move out.

Cell Membrane

The **cell membrane** is a structure that forms the outer boundary of the cell and allows only certain materials to move into and out of the cell. The membrane, as shown in **Figure 14-10**, is flexible. It is made up of a double layer of molecules with some proteins and other large molecules scattered throughout. The cell membrane helps to maintain a chemical balance between materials inside and outside the cell. Food and oxygen move into the cell through the membrane. Waste products also leave through the membrane. Many substances enter and leave the cell in different ways.

Nucleus

The largest structure in the cytoplasm of a eukaryotic cell is the nucleus. The **nucleus** directs all the activities of the cell. The nucleus, shown in **Figure 14-11,** is like a manager who directs everyday business for a company and passes on information to employees. A nucleus is separated from the cytoplasm by a nuclear membrane. Materials enter and leave the nucleus through openings in the membrane. The nucleus contains the instructions that direct all of the cell's functions. These instructions are found on long threadlike chromatin. **Chromatin** is a form of hereditary material. It is made of proteins and DNA. DNA is the chemical that is the blueprint for the cell's structure and activities. When a cell begins to divide, the chromatin tightly coils and takes on the form of chromosomes, which are easier to see. A structure called a nucleolus is also found in the nucleus.

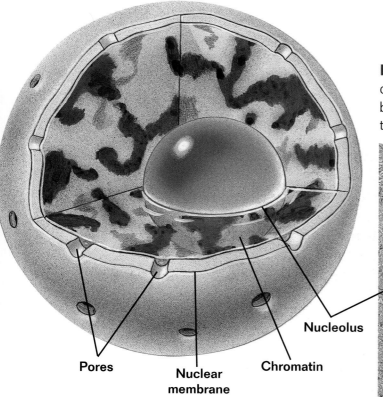

Pores

Nuclear membrane

Chromatin

Nucleolus

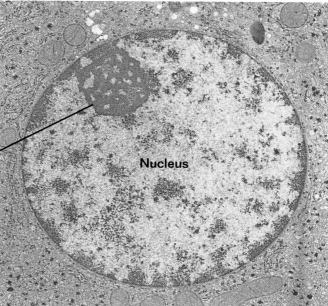

Figure 14-11 The nucleus of a cell is surrounded by a double membrane. DNA in the nucleus controls the activities in the cell.

Magnification: 20 500×

Nucleus

Mini Lab

Modeling Cytoplasm
Procedure 🚫 🥽 🧤

1. Fill a beaker with 100 mL of water.
2. Add unflavored gelatin and stir.
3. Shine a flashlight through the beaker.

Analysis

1. Describe what you see.
2. How does a model help you understand what a real thing looks like?

Cytoplasm

Cytoplasm is the gelatinlike mixture inside the cell membrane. Cytoplasm contains many chemicals including a large amount of water. Within the cytoplasm are structures that carry out the life processes for the cell. Cytoplasm constantly moves or streams.

The structures within the cytoplasm of eukaryotic cells are **organelles.** Each one has a specific job or jobs. Some organelles break down food molecules. Others move wastes to be expelled from the cell. Still others store materials. Most organelles are surrounded by membranes. The nucleus is an organelle.

Organelles in the Cytoplasm

The **endoplasmic reticulum (ER),** illustrated in **Figure 14-12,** is a folded membrane that moves materials around in the cell. The ER extends from the nucleus to the cell membrane and takes up a lot of space in some cells. The ER is like a system of conveyor belts in a business along which materials are moved from one place to another.

One chemical that takes part in nearly every cell activity is protein. Proteins are part of cell membranes. Other proteins are needed for chemical reactions that take place in the cytoplasm. Cells make their own proteins on small, two-part structures

Figure 14-12 Endoplasmic reticulum (ER) is a complex series of membranes in the cytoplasm of the cell. If ribosomes are present on the endoplasmic reticulum, then the endoplasmic reticulum is referred to as *rough ER*. Proteins are made on these ribosomes. **What would smooth ER look like?**

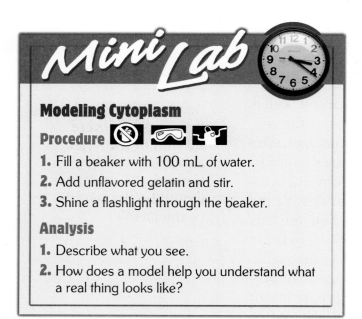

Magnification: 63 548×

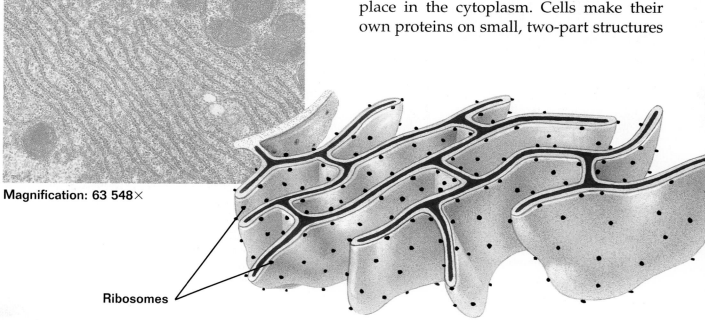

Ribosomes

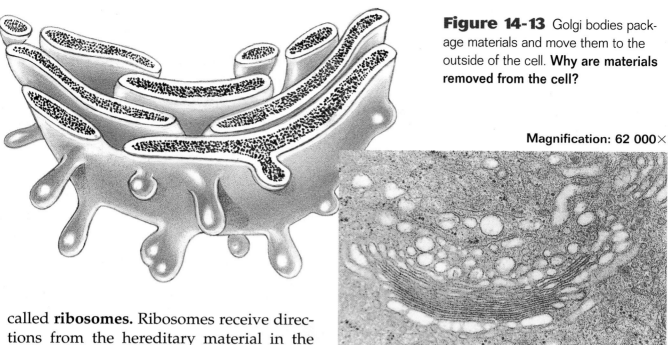

Magnification: 62 000×

called **ribosomes.** Ribosomes receive directions from the hereditary material in the nucleus on how and when to make specific proteins. Some ribosomes are scattered in the cytoplasm. Others are attached to the ER. Ribosome parts are made in the nucleolus.

In a business, products are made, packaged, and moved to loading docks to be carried away. In cells, stacks of membrane-covered sacs called **Golgi bodies** package proteins to be moved outside of the cell. When something is moved to the outside of a cell, the cell secretes it. **Figure 14-13** illustrates Golgi bodies.

Cells require a continuous supply of energy. Energy is stored in molecules that can power cell reactions. Just as a power plant supplies energy to a business, mitochondria

Figure 14-14 Mitochondria are known as the "powerhouses of the cell." In these organelles, food molecules are broken down, and energy is released. **What types of cells may contain many mitochondria?**

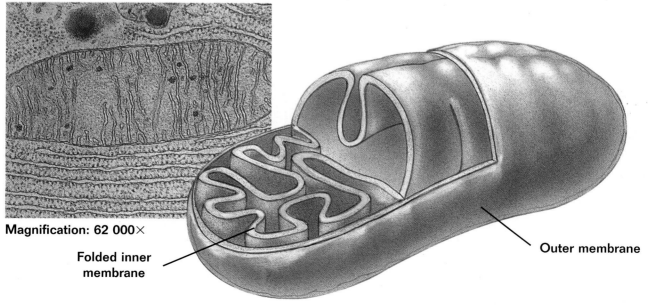

Magnification: 62 000×

Folded inner membrane

Outer membrane

release energy for the cell. **Mitochondria,** such as the one pictured in **Figure 14-14,** are organelles where food molecules are broken down and energy is released. Some types of cells are more active than others. Muscle cells, which are always moving in some way, have large numbers of mitochondria. Why would active cells have more or larger mitochondria?

An active cell constantly breaks down and recycles substances. In animal cells, organelles called **lysosomes** contain digestive chemicals that break down food molecules, cell wastes, and worn out cell parts. In a healthy animal cell, chemicals are released only when needed. When a cell dies, a lysosome's membrane disintegrates. This releases digestive chemicals that quickly break down the cell's contents for reuse by the organism. In plant cells, the large vacuole releases digestive chemicals.

Vacuoles and vesicles are storage organelles in cells. Vacuoles are larger than vesicles. Either structure may store water, waste products, food, and other cellular materials. In plant cells, the vacuole may take up most of the cell's volume.

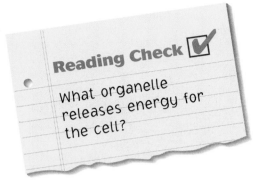

Reading Check

What organelle releases energy for the cell?

Problem Solving

Using Numbers to Find the Surface Area and Volume of Cells

The cells in mice, elephants, and humans are about the same size. More than 10 trillion cells make up the human body. If 1000 of these cells were lined up, they would total less than 2 cm in length—about the width of a thumbnail.

Why are most cells microscopic? In order to survive, a cell must take in nutrients and remove wastes. Substances move into and out of a cell by passing through the cell membrane. This fact limits the size to which a cell can grow. Why?

Solve the Problem

1. Assume that a cell is like a cube.

2. Find the surface area of each cube illustrated below. Surface area is width × length × 6. (A cube has six faces.)

3. Calculate the volume of each cube. The volume of a cube is length × width × height.

4. Find the ratio of surface area to volume for each cube by dividing the surface area by the volume.

Think Critically

1. What happens to the surface area-to-volume ratio as the size of the cube increases?

2. If a cell doubled its volume, how much bigger would its cell membrane be?

3. How can a large cell solve its low surface area-to-volume ratio?

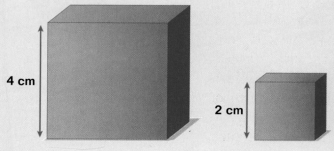

4 cm

2 cm

1 cm

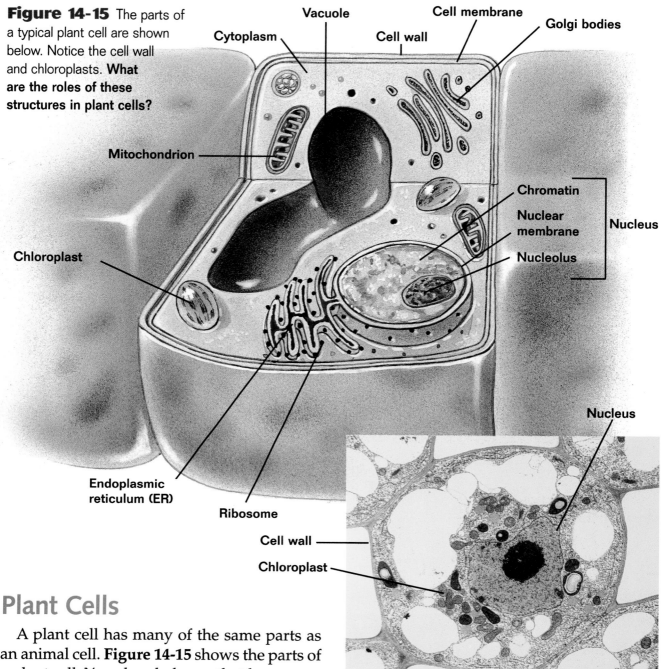

Figure 14-15 The parts of a typical plant cell are shown below. Notice the cell wall and chloroplasts. **What are the roles of these structures in plant cells?**

Vacuole

Cytoplasm

Cell membrane

Cell wall

Golgi bodies

Mitochondrion

Chloroplast

Chromatin

Nuclear membrane

Nucleolus

Nucleus

Endoplasmic reticulum (ER)

Ribosome

Cell wall

Chloroplast

Nucleus

Magnification: 1750×

Plant Cells

A plant cell has many of the same parts as an animal cell. **Figure 14-15** shows the parts of a plant cell. You already know that lysosomes are found only in animal cells. Another difference between a plant cell and an animal cell is that a plant cell has a cell wall outside the cell membrane. The **cell wall** is a rigid structure that supports and protects the plant cell and is made of bundles of tough cellulose fibers. Sometimes, other substances made by the cell are part of the cell wall.

Unlike animal cells, many plant cells have the ability to make their own food, a sugar. It is made in the **chloroplasts,** the green organelles found in the cytoplasm. Chloroplasts contain chlorophyll, a green pigment that traps light energy. As a result of many chemical reactions, light energy is changed into chemical energy and stored in sugar molecules.

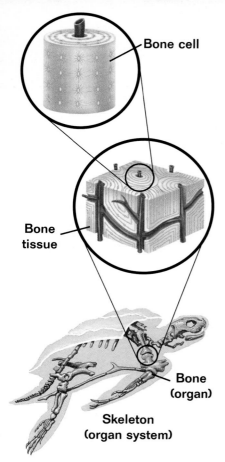

Bone cell

Bone tissue

Bone (organ)

Skeleton (organ system)

Turtle (organism)

Figure 14-16 In a many-celled organism, different types of tissues are organized into organs and systems.

Organizing Cells

A one-celled organism like a bacterium may perform all its life functions by itself. Cells in a many-celled organism, however, do not work alone. Instead, each cell depends in some way on other cells as the organism carries out its functions. This interaction helps the whole organism stay alive.

In **Figure 14-16,** you can see a single bone cell. You also see a group of the same type of bone cells that together form a tissue. In many-celled organisms, cells are organized into **tissues,** which are groups of similar cells that work together to do one job. Each tissue cell does its part to keep the tissue alive.

Tissues are organized into organs. An **organ** is a structure made up of different types of tissues that work together to do a particular job. Your heart is an organ made up of muscle, nerve, and blood tissues. Several different tissues make up a plant leaf, an organ of the plant in which food is made.

A group of organs working together to do a certain job is an organ system. Your heart and blood vessels make up your cardiovascular system. What other systems can you think of?

In a many-celled organism, several systems work together. Roots, stems, and leaves in a plant work together to keep the plant alive. Name three systems in your body that work together.

Each cell in a many-celled organism carries on its own life functions. Although cells in an organism may differ in appearance and function, all the cells working together keep the organism alive.

Section Assessment

1. Explain the importance of the cell nucleus in the life of a cell.

2. Give an example of an organ system in an animal and name the parts that make up the organ system.

3. **Think Critically:** How is the cell of a one-celled organism different from the cells in many-celled organisms?

4. **Skill Builder**
   Interpreting Scientific Illustrations
   Illustrations provide the reader with important information. Do the **Chapter 14 Skill Activity** on page 721 to learn about cells and cell organelles by interpreting the scientific illustrations.

Your textbook compared cell functions to that of a business. In your Science Journal, write an essay that explains how a cell is like your school or town.

Activity 14•2

Comparing Plant and Animal Cells

If you were to compare a goldfish to a rose bush, you would find the two to be very different. However, when the individual cells of these organisms are compared, will they be so different? Try this activity to see how plant and animal cells compare.

Materials

- Microscope
- Microscope slide
- Coverslip
- Forceps
- Dropper
- *Elodea* plant
- Prepared slide of human cheek cells

What You'll Investigate

In this exercise, you will observe an animal cell, a human cheek cell, and a plant cell, *Elodea*, under a compound light microscope.

Goals

- **Compare and contrast** an animal cell and a plant cell.

Procedure

1. **Copy** the data table in your Science Journal. Check off the cell parts as you observe them.

2. Follow the directions for using low- and high-power objectives on your microscope and for making a wet-mount slide.

3. Using forceps, **make** a wet-mount slide of a young leaf from the tip of an *Elodea* plant.

4. **Observe** the leaf on low power. Focus on the top layer of cells. Carefully focus down through the top layer of cells to observe other layers of cells.

5. Switch to high power and focus on one cell. Does the center of the cell appear empty? This is the central vacuole that contains water and stores cell products. **Observe** the chloroplasts in the cytoplasm, which are the green disk-shaped objects moving around the central vacuole. Try to find the cell nucleus. It looks like a clear ball.

6. Make a drawing of the *Elodea* cell. **Label** the cell wall, cytoplasm, chloroplasts, central vacuole, and nucleus. Return to low power and remove the slide.

7. Place a prepared slide of cheek cells on the microscope stage. Locate the cells under low power.

8. Switch to high power and **observe** the cell nucleus. **Draw and label** the cell membrane, cytoplasm, and nucleus.

Conclude and Apply

1. How many cell layers could you see in the *Elodea* leaf?

2. **Compare and contrast** the shape of the cheek cell and the *Elodea* cell.

3. What can you conclude about the differences between plant and animal cells?

Cell Observations		
Cell Part	*Elodea*	**Cheek**
cytoplasm		
nucleus		
chloroplasts		
cell wall		
cell membrane		

14·3 Viruses

Characteristics of Viruses

Imagine something that doesn't grow or eat, yet reproduces. This something is a virus. A **virus** is nonliving and consists of a core of hereditary material surrounded by a protein coat. Viruses are so small that scientists must use extremely powerful microscopes to see them.

Viruses are unlike living things. They can reproduce only inside a living cell. Some viruses can be made into crystals and stored in a jar on a shelf for years. Then, if they enter an organism, they may quickly reproduce. This may cause new infections and damage the organism. Viruses, therefore, have the potential to greatly impact the living world.

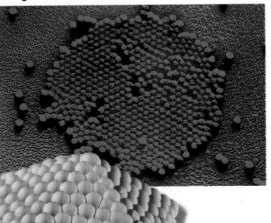
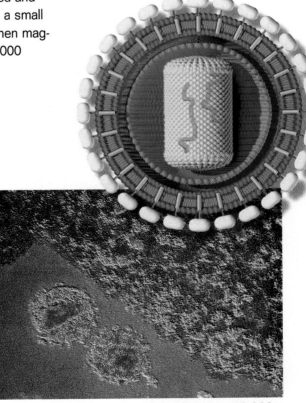

Figure 14-17 Viruses, from a Latin word for *poison*, come in a variety of shapes and are responsible for many diseases. On these pages are photos and computer models of several types of viruses.

Magnification: 20 000×

A The polio virus is many sided and looks like a small crystal when magnified 20 000 times.

B The AIDS virus, HIV, is spherical in shape and is studded with projections. **How might this structure enable the virus to infect cells?**

Magnification: 46 000×

What You'll Learn

► The structure of a virus and how viruses reproduce and cause disease
► The benefits of vaccines
► Some helpful uses of viruses

Vocabulary
virus
host cell
vaccine

Why It's Important

► Viruses affect nearly all organisms.

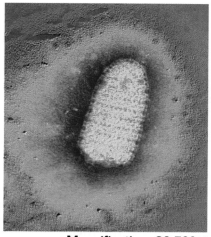

Magnification: 36 700×

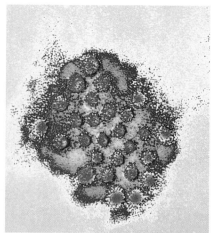

Magnification: 35 000×

Figure 14-18 Many viruses are named for the disease they cause or where they were first found. The rabies virus, shown on the left, is named for the disease it causes in animals. The virus on the right is named for where it was first found. It is the Norwalk virus named for Norwalk, Ohio.

Classification of Viruses

Viruses, as illustrated in **Figure 14-17,** may be classified by their shape, the kind of hereditary material they have, the kind of organism they infect, or their method of reproduction. The protein coat of a virus gives it its shape. As shown in **Figure 14-18,** viruses are often named for the diseases they cause, such as the polio virus, the organ or tissue they infect or where they were first found.

Magnification: 95 000×

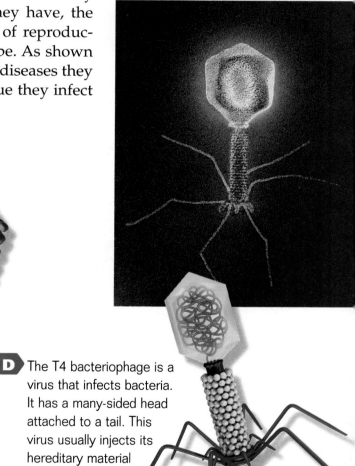

C The tobacco-mosaic virus is rod shaped and has a coat of proteins that spiral around a single strand of hereditary material. It causes tobacco plants to become stunted and the leaves to become discolored and blotchy.

D The T4 bacteriophage is a virus that infects bacteria. It has a many-sided head attached to a tail. This virus usually injects its hereditary material into a cell through the tail, much like a hypodermic needle.

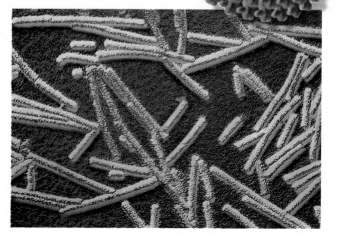

Magnification: 220 000×

Reproduction of Viruses

When most people hear the word *virus,* they relate it to a cold sore, a cold, or HIV, the virus that causes AIDS. Mumps, measles, and chicken pox are also diseases caused by viruses. A virus must be inside a living cell to reproduce. The cell in which a virus reproduces is called a **host cell.** Once a virus is in a host cell, the virus can act in two ways. It can either be active, as shown below, or it can become latent, an inactive stage.

Active Viruses

When a virus enters a cell and is active, it causes the host cell to make new viruses, which destroy the host cell. Follow the steps in **Figure 14-19** to see how an active virus reproduces itself inside a bacterial cell.

VISUALIZING
An Active Virus

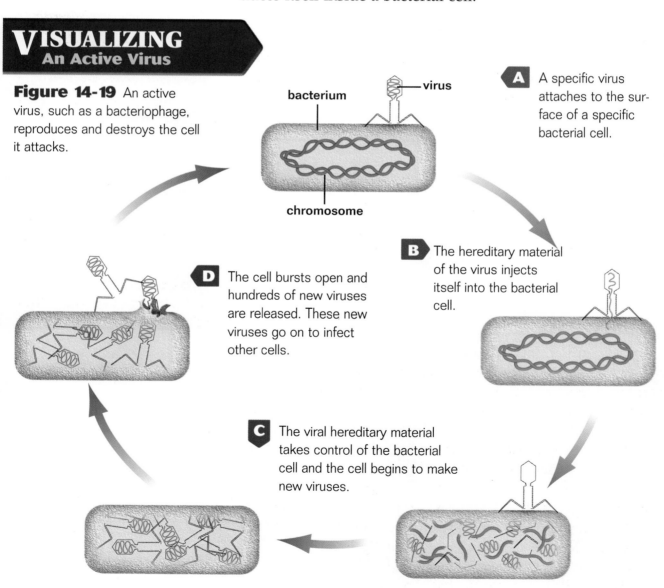

Figure 14-19 An active virus, such as a bacteriophage, reproduces and destroys the cell it attacks.

A A specific virus attaches to the surface of a specific bacterial cell.

B The hereditary material of the virus injects itself into the bacterial cell.

C The viral hereditary material takes control of the bacterial cell and the cell begins to make new viruses.

D The cell bursts open and hundreds of new viruses are released. These new viruses go on to infect other cells.

bacterium

virus

chromosome

A A specific virus attaches to the surface of a specific bacterial cell. The hereditary material of the virus injects itself into the cell.

B The viral hereditary material may become part of the bacterial cell's chromosome.

C The bacterial cell divides. The virus is now part of two cells instead of one.

F The bacterial cell breaks open and releases the viruses, thereby destroying the host bacterial cell.

D The virus becomes active.

E New viruses are made.

Figure 14-20 A latent virus may not immediately destroy the cell it attacks.

Latent Viruses

Some viruses may be latent viruses. A latent virus enters a cell and its hereditary material may become part of the cell's hereditary material. It does not immediately destroy the cell or make new viruses. Latent viruses may appear to hide inside host cells for many years. Then, at any time, the virus can become active. Stress, or too much sun or cold, may cause a virus to become active. Follow **Figure 14-20** as it outlines the reproduction cycle of latent viruses. ☑

If you have ever had a cold sore, you've been infected by a virus that has gone from its latent phase into its active phase. The appearance of a cold sore on your lip is a sign that the virus is active and destroying cells in your lip. When the cold sore disappears, the virus has become latent again. The virus is still in your body's cells, but you just don't realize it.

Reading Check ☑

What is a latent virus?

Table 14-1

Viral Diseases in Humans		
Disease	**Caused by**	**Vaccine**
AIDS	HIV	No
Chicken pox	*Varicella zoster*	Yes
Common cold	more than 200 rhinoviruses	No
Influenza	flu types A, B, and C	Yes
Measles	rubella-*Rubivirus* rubeola-paramyxovirus	Yes
Mumps	paramyxovirus	Yes
Polio	*Poliovirus hominis*	Yes
Rabies	rhabdovirus	Yes
Smallpox	orthopoxvirus	Yes

Viral Diseases

Viruses may cause diseases in plants, animals, fungi, bacteria, and protists. There are no antibiotic medications to *cure* viral diseases. But some viral diseases can be *prevented* by vaccines. A **vaccine** is made from damaged virus particles that can't cause disease anymore. **Table 14-1** lists many viral diseases found in humans. The availability of vaccines to fight such infections is also indicated.

Vaccines

Edward Jenner, an English doctor, is credited with developing a vaccine in 1796. Jenner developed a vaccine for smallpox, a disease that was greatly feared even into the twentieth century. Jenner noticed that people who milked cows and came down with a disease called cowpox didn't get smallpox. He prepared a vaccine from the sores of milkmaids who had cowpox. When injected into healthy people, the cowpox vaccine seemed to protect them from smallpox. Did Jenner know he was fighting a virus? No. At that time, no one understood what caused disease or how the body fought disease.

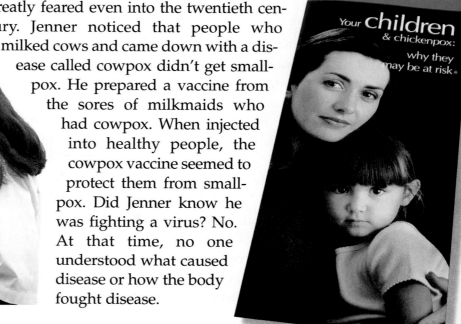

Figure 14-21 Modern vaccination procedures help prevent many childhood and adult diseases. **What other common vaccinations are given?**

Vaccinations are an important step in maintaining health. **Figure 14-21** shows a child receiving a vaccination by receiving a shot.

Studies Using Viruses

Most of what you hear about viruses might make you think that viruses always act in a harmful way. However, there are some cases where, through research, scientists are discovering uses for viruses that may make them helpful.

One experimental method, called gene therapy, involves substituting normal hereditary material for a cell's defective hereditary material. The normal hereditary material is enclosed in a virus. The virus may then "infect" targeted cells, taking the new strand of hereditary material into the cells to replace the defective hereditary material.

Using gene therapy, scientists hope to help people with genetic disorders. For example, some people have the genetic disorder sickle-cell anemia. Because of a defective gene, abnormal hemoglobin causes changes in red blood cells. They cannot function normally which causes many problems. With the help of a virus, a repaired gene was allowed to infect blood cells in a mouse, and the mouse blood cells began to produce the correct substance. Researchers are hoping to use similar techniques for humans with sickle-cell disease or cancer.

interNET CONNECTION

Scientists have determined that Marburg virus, Ebola Zaire, and Ebola Reston all belong to the virus family Filoviridae. Visit the Glencoe Science Web Site at **www.glencoe.com/sec/science/fl** for more information about the Marburg and Ebola viruses.

Section Assessment

1. Describe the structure of viruses and explain how viruses reproduce.

2. How are vaccines beneficial?

3. How may some viruses be helpful?

4. **Think Critically:** Explain why a doctor might not give you any medication if you had a viral disease.

5. **Skill Builder**
   Concept Mapping Make an events-chain concept map to show what happens when a latent virus becomes active. If you need help, refer to Concept Mapping in the **Skill Handbook** on page 680.

Using Computers

Spreadsheet Enter the following data in a spreadsheet and make a line graph. How does temperature affect viruses? At 36.9°C, there are 1.0 million viruses; at 37.2°C, 1.0 million; at 37.5°C, 0.5 million; at 37.8°C, 0.25 million; at 38.3°C, 0.10 million; and at 38.9°C, 0.05 million. If you need help, refer to page 704.

For a **preview** of this chapter, study this Reviewing Main Ideas before you read the chapter. After you have studied this chapter, you can use the Reviewing Main Ideas to **review** the chapter.

The Glencoe MindJogger, Audiocassettes, and CD-ROM provide additional opportunities for review.

Section

14-1 CELLS—THE UNITS OF LIFE

The first compound microscope was made in 1590. In the mid 1600s, a simple microscope was developed that could make an image of an object 270 times larger than the actual size of the object. As scientists learned more about lenses, **compound light microscopes** were made. Compound light microscopes use light and lenses to make images. Things that are too small to be seen with a light microscope can be viewed with an **electron microscope.** An electron microscope bends beams of electrons in a magnetic field. Images can be seen only when they are photographically or electronically produced.

With the help of the microscope, scientists concluded that all living things were made of cells. According to the cell theory, the cell is the basic unit of life. Organisms are made of one or more cells, and all cells come from other cells.

What are the similarities and differences between a compound light microscope and an electron microscope?

Reading Check ✓

Inside a circle, write the word *virus*. Around the circle write facts you know about viruses. Underline those that you knew before reading this chapter.

Section 14-2 CELL ORGANIZATION

There are two basic types of cells, prokaryotic cells and eukaryotic cells. A prokaryotic cell has no membrane around its hereditary material. A eukaryotic cell has a **nucleus,** hereditary material surrounded by a membrane. In both cell types, the hereditary material controls all cell functions. All cells are surrounded by a **cell membrane.** Inside the cell membrane is a gelatinlike mixture called **cytoplasm.** The hereditary material is in the cytoplasm along with other cell structures. Eukaryotic cells have structures called **organelles** that do specific jobs. All cell parts work together to keep a cell alive. There are differences among animal, plant, and bacterial cells. Animal cells do not have cell walls. Plant cells have cell walls and chloroplasts. Bacteria have no membrane-covered organelles.

Many-celled organisms are organized to perform all the jobs necessary to keep them alive. Most have tissues, organs, and organ systems. *What feature distinguishes a prokaryotic cell from a eukaryotic cell?*

Section 14-3 VIRUSES

A virus is a structure containing hereditary material surrounded by a protein coat. It can only reproduce when inside a living host cell. An active virus enters a cell, reproduces, and then destroys the cell. A latent virus enters a cell and may become a part of the cell's hereditary material. Latent viruses may hide inside host cells for many years before becoming active. Viruses cause diseases in animals, plants, fungi, and bacteria. Vaccines prevent some viral diseases. *Why don't scientists consider viruses living organisms?*

Using Vocabulary

a. cell membrane
b. cell theory
c. cell wall
d. chloroplast
e. chromatin
f. compound light microscope
g. cytoplasm
h. electron microscope
i. endoplasmic reticulum
j. Golgi body
k. host cell
l. lysosome
m. mitochondria
n. nucleus
o. organ
p. organelle
q. ribosome
r. tissue
s. vaccine
t. virus

Using the vocabulary words, give two examples of each of the following.

1. a tool to view cells and microorganisms
2. made from more than one cell
3. an organelle where energy is converted
4. part of all cells
5. involved in moving cellular products

Checking Concepts

Choose the word or phrase that best completes the sentence.

6. Which of the following is a viral disease ?
   A) tuberculosis   C) smallpox
   B) anthrax   D) tetanus
7. Which microscope uses lenses to magnify?
   A) compound light microscope
   B) scanning electron microscope
   C) transmission electron microscope
   D) atomic force microscope
8. Which microscope magnifies up to 1 million times or more ?
   A) compound light microscope
   B) stereoscopic microscope
   C) transmission electron microscope
   D) atomic force microscope

9. Which scientist gave the name *cells* to structures he viewed?
   A) Hooke   C) Schleiden
   B) Schwann   D) Virchow
10. What organelle helps to recycle old cell parts?
    A) chloroplast   C) lysosome
    B) centriole   D) cell wall
11. What structure allows only certain things to pass in and out of the cell?
    A) cytoplasm   C) cell wall
    B) cell membrane   D) nuclear envelope
12. What are structures in the cytoplasm of the eukaryotic cell called?
    A) organs   C) organ systems
    B) organelles   D) tissues
13. What is made of folded membranes that move materials around inside the cell?
    A) chromatin   C) Golgi body
    B) cytoplasm   D) endoplasmic reticulum
14. Which of the following is part of a bacterial cell?
    A) a cell wall   C) mitochondria
    B) lysosomes   D) a nucleus
15. What do groups of different tissues form (such as the heart)?
    A) organ   C) organ system
    B) organelle   D) organism

Thinking Critically

16. Why is it difficult to get rid of viruses?
17. What type of microscope would be best to use to look at a piece of moldy bread? Give reasons to support your choice.
18. What would happen to a plant cell that suddenly lost its chloroplasts?
19. What would happen to an animal cell if it didn't have ribosomes?
20. How would you decide whether an unknown cell was an animal cell, a plant cell, or a bacterial cell?

Developing Skills

If you need help, refer to the **Skill Handbook.**

21. **Interpreting Scientific Illustrations:** Use the illustrations of cells in Section 14-2 to describe how the shape of a cell may be related to its function.

22. **Concept Mapping:** Complete the following concept map of the basic units of life.

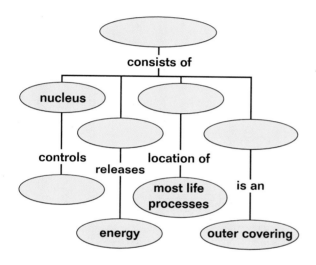

23. **Sequencing:** Sequence the following from simple to complex: *small intestine, circular muscle cell, human,* and *digestive system.*

24. **Making and Using Tables:** List the cell structures and their functions in a table.

25. **Comparing and Contrasting:** In a table, compare and contrast the structures of a virus, a bacterial cell, and a eukaryotic cell.

26. **Making a Model:** Make a timeline to show the development of the cell theory. Begin with the development of the microscope in 1590 and end with Virchow's statement in the 1850s. Include the contributions of Van Leeuwenhoek, Hooke, Schleiden, and Schwann.

Test-Taking Tip

Plan Your Work and Work Your Plan
Set up a study schedule for yourself well in advance of your test. Plan your workload so that you do a little each day rather than a lot all at once. The key to retaining information is to repeatedly review and practice it.

Test Practice

Use these questions to test your Science Proficiency.

1. A cell wall is found in plant cells but not in animal cells. Which of the following statements would indicate the presence of a cell wall in plant cells?
   A) Plant fibers are used for weaving fabrics like cotton and linen.
   B) Plants are food producers.
   C) Plants and plant products are often used as medicines.
   D) Crushed leaves, stems, and other plant parts may be used as dyes.

2. Mitochondria are more numerous in active cells like liver cells and muscle cells. Which of the following explains why these cells need more mitochondria?
   A) Mitochondria are surrounded by two membranes.
   B) Mitochondria have their own DNA.
   C) Mitochondria are sites where food molecules are broken down and energy is released.
   D) New mitochondria are produced only when existing ones grow and divide.

3. What is the cell structure that acts as the control center of a eukaryotic cell?
   A) cell membrane   C) mitochondrion
   B) chloroplast   D) nucleus

CHAPTER

15 Classifying Living Things

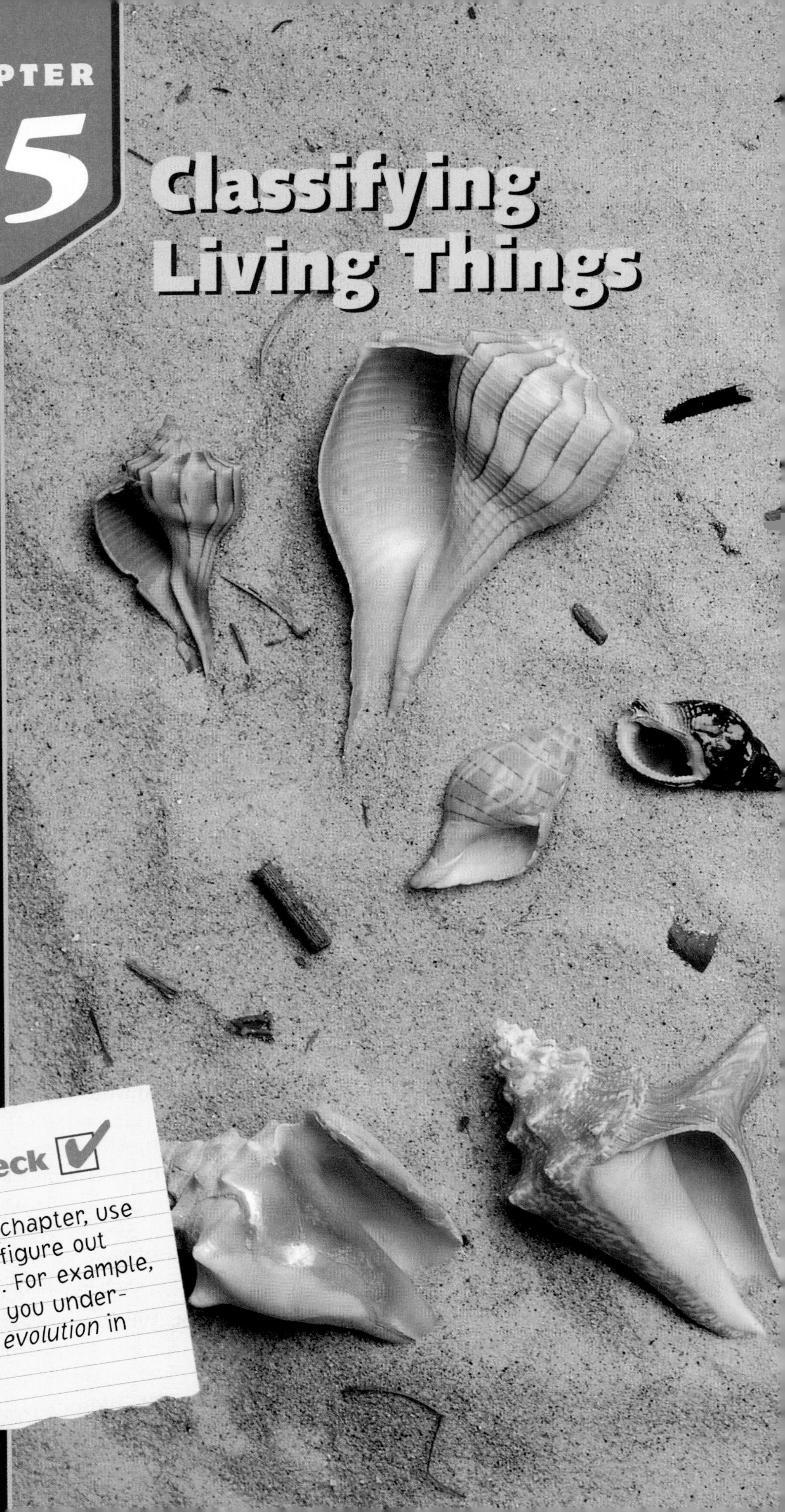

Chapter Preview

Section 15-1
- What is classification?

Section 15-2
- Modern Classification

Section 15-3
- Identifying Organisms

Skills Preview

Skill Builders
- Observe and Infer
- Map Concepts

MiniLabs
- Classify
- Communicate

Activities
- Form a Hypothesis
- Use a Key

Reading Check

As you read this chapter, use context clues to figure out unfamiliar terms. For example, what clues help you understand the term *evolution* in Section 15-2?

Explore Activity

How many plants and animals are discovered each year? You might think that the answer would be a small number, or perhaps none at all, but that would not be right. Life scientists discover, describe, and name hundreds of organisms every year. How do they decide if a certain plant belongs to the iris or orchid family of flowering plants? Or, if an insect is more like a grasshopper or a beetle? Think about how scientists might make these distinctions.

Classify Things

1. Observe the seashells pictured on these two pages. They were once parts of living organisms.

2. Notice the features that are the same and those that are different.

3. Make a list of their similarities and differences.

4. Separate the objects into two groups.

5. To which group does this snail belong?

Science Journal

In your Science Journal, predict how this activity models how biologists categorize living things.

What You'll Learn

▶ Why classification systems are needed

▶ Aristotle's system of classification

▶ Linnaeus's system of classification

Vocabulary
classify
taxonomy
kingdom
binomial nomenclature
genus
species

Why It's Important

▶ Classification helps you to find the connections among the differences in nature.

Classifying

When you go into a grocery store, do you go to one aisle to get milk, to another to get margarine, and to a third to get yogurt? Most grocery stores group similar items together. You would find the dairy products mentioned above in one area. When you place similar items together, you classify them. To **classify** means to group ideas, information, or objects based on their similarities. The science of classifying is called **taxonomy** (tak SAHN uh mee).

Classification is an important part of your life. Grocery stores, bookstores, and department stores group similar items together. In what other places is classification important?

Early History of Classification

More than 2000 years ago, Aristotle, a Greek philosopher, developed a system to classify living things. Aristotle thought that all living things on Earth could be placed in either the plant kingdom or the animal kingdom.

Figure 15-1 Aristotle's system of classification did not work for some organisms. For example, frogs can live in water and on land. **What other organisms don't fit into Aristotle's classification system? Why don't they fit?**

In taxonomy, a **kingdom** is the first and largest category. Aristotle began his classification of animals by grouping them according to their physical traits. Then, he used such things as where they lived, the presence or absence of blood, how they reproduced, and wing types to sort them into smaller groups.

Eventually, scientists began to criticize Aristotle's system because it had too many exceptions. Animals were classified according to where they lived, but what about frogs? Frogs spend part of their lives in water and part on land, as shown in **Figure 15-1**. His method of classifying included philosophical ideas that added to the confusion.

Scientific Naming

By the mid-eighteenth century, the classifications of Aristotle had changed and new systems had been developed. However, a lot of confusion remained. Sometimes, an organism had a different name in each country it lived in. Sometimes, it was known by different names in the same country.

Another problem was the length of names for organisms. By this time, many plants, animals, and other organisms had been identified and named. To avoid confusion, scientists gave organisms names that described them in great detail. The name often consisted of several words. For example, the

Problem Solving

Classifying an Organism

Laquitia and her family were on vacation in southern Arizona. One evening, they were driving through a national park just as the sun was setting. Suddenly, a tawny, heavily marked cat with a long tail ran across the road and disappeared into the dense brush. The cat's spots included rings, speckles, slashes, and bars. Laquitia and her family were startled to see such a beautiful animal. No one in the car knew what it was.

Solve the Problem:

1. What important characteristics might be needed to identify an animal?

2. Would Laquitia need other information to be able to determine the animal's species?

Think Critically: How would you begin to figure out what cat Laquitia saw?

interNET CONNECTION

Visit the Glencoe Science Web Site at **www. glencoe.com/sec/ science/fl** for more information about the rules for naming or renaming organisms.

Figure 15-2 *Scabiosa caucasica* is also called the pincushion flower. During the fifteenth century, it was made into a medicine to treat scabies, a skin problem caused by mites. That's why the genus is named *Scabiosa.* The specific name means that the plant came from the Caucasus Mountains in Russia.

Reading Check

What is the smallest, most precise classification category?

spearmint plant was named *Mentha floribus spicatis, foliis oblongis serratis.* This name means, more or less, "a member of the mint genus that has its flowers in a spike arrangement, and oblong, serrated leaves." These long names were difficult for scientists to work with. Can you imagine asking for "a member of the mint genus that has its flowers in a spike arrangement, and oblong, serrated leaves, chewing gum?" Carolus Linnaeus, a Swedish physician and naturalist, created a way to give each organism a simpler, unique name.

Binomial Nomenclature

Linnaeus's system, called **binomial nomenclature** (bi NOH mee ul•NOH mun klay chur), gives a two-word name to every organism. Binomial means "two names." The two-word name is commonly called the organism's scientific name. The first word of an organism's scientific name is the genus, and the second is the specific name. A **genus** (JEE nus) is a group of different organisms that have similar characteristics. Together, the genus name and the specific name make up the scientific name of a particular species, as shown in **Figure 15-2.** A **species** (SPEE sheez) is the smallest, most precise classification category. Organisms belonging to the same species can mate to produce fertile offspring. ☑

Mini Lab

Using Binomial Nomenclature

Procedure

1. Make a model of a fictitious organism.
2. Give your organism a scientific name.
3. Make sure that your name is Latinized and supplies information about the species.

Analysis

1. Present your organism to the class. Ask them to guess its name.
2. Why do scientists use Latin when they name organisms?

An example of a two-word name, or species, is *Canis famil-iaris*. This is a domesticated dog. Notice that the first word, the genus name, always begins with a capital letter. The second word, the specific name, begins with a lowercase letter. Both words in a scientific name are written in italics or underlined. Linnaeus's naming system uses Latin because when he developed it, Latin was the language used at European universities and understood by nearly all educated people. Today, it provides an international understanding of all scientific names. In Linnaeus's system, no two organisms have the same scientific name. Because of Linnaeus's system and the use of Latin, scientists around the world recognize the name *Canis familiaris* as a domesticated dog and not a gray wolf, *Canis lupus*. You can see the differences among a dog, a gray wolf, and a coyote in **Figure 15-3.**

Figure 15-3 The photo on the left shows a dog, *Canis familiaris*. Other members of the genus Canis are the coyote, *Canis latrans* (middle), and the gray wolf, *Canis lupus* (right). Notice that they are all different species. **Why are they placed in the same genus?**

Section Assessment

1. What is the purpose of classification?
2. What were the contributions of Aristotle and Linnaeus to taxonomy?
3. **Think Critically:** List two examples of things that are classified based on their similarities.
4. **Skill Builder**
   Observing and Inferring To learn how to classify organisms by observing them, do the **Chapter 15 Skill Activity** on page 722.

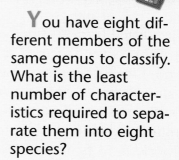

Using Math

You have eight different members of the same genus to classify. What is the least number of characteristics required to separate them into eight species?

Species Diversity

Human Footprints

Are there any places on Earth untouched by humans? The old-growth forests of the northwestern United States as well as the rain forests of South America and Asia—previously untouched areas—are increasingly under pressure from human demands. Loggers and lumber companies want to harvest old-growth timber. Farmers want to clear the rain forest to grow crops.

What is species diversity?

Rain forests, coral reefs, and other environments provide homes to hundreds of thousands of organisms. In a hectare (about 10 sq km) of rain forest, for example, there may be 200 species of plants and more than 1000 species of animals. This great variety of plants, animals, and other organisms makes up species diversity. An ecosystem that has a high diversity of species is more stable than one with fewer species.

How is species diversity changed?

In the past, because humans have entered into undisturbed areas, particular species, such as the Carolina parakeet and the passenger pigeon, have become extinct. Extinction reduces species diversity and the stability of ecosystems. Even though extinction is a natural process, humans are contributing to extinction today at a far greater rate than has ever occurred before.

Every minute, more than 20 hectares of rain forest are cut for timber or are cleared for farming or mining. Some areas of old-growth forests in the United States are protected from cutting because the northern spotted owl (right), an endangered species, lives there. Protecting an entire forest because of one endangered species is one way to prevent a decrease in species diversity, but it is a controversial method. International organizations, communities, and individuals concerned about species diversity are working to figure out how best to protect and develop these areas.

*inter*NET
CONNECTION

The Smithsonian Institution created a biodiversity program in 1986 that focuses on problems associated with maintaining global forest diversity. Visit the Glencoe Science Web Site at **www.glencoe.com/sec/science/fl** for more information on the Smithsonian Institution's program.

Modern Classification

15·2

Six-Kingdom System

How do the classification systems used today differ from those of the past? Aristotle and Linnaeus developed their systems of classification using only those characteristics of organisms that they could see. Today, scientists use those and other traits to classify organisms. For example, they may look at the chemical and genetic makeup of organisms. By studying fossils, they examine and compare ancestors to existing organisms. They may compare body structures or early stages of development. By studying all of these things and more, scientists can determine an organism's phylogeny. The **phylogeny** (fi LAH jon nee) of an organism is its evolutionary history or how it has changed over time. Phylogeny tells scientists who the ancestors of an organism were. Today, classification of organisms is based on phylogeny.

The classification system most commonly used today separates organisms into six kingdoms. These kingdoms are animal, plant, fungi, protists, eubacteria, and archaebacteria. Organisms are placed into a kingdom based on several characteristics. These characteristics include cell type, whether it is single celled or many celled, ability to make food, and others. The organisms in **Figure 15-4** all belong to the Kingdom Fungi.

What **You'll Learn**

► The names of the six kingdoms of living things
► How to identify characteristics and members of each kingdom
► The groups within each kingdom

Vocabulary

phylogeny   class
phylum   order
division   family

Why **It's Important**

► Modern classification helps you understand how living things are related.

Figure 15-4 Fungi have common characteristics. One characteristic is that they cannot make their own food.

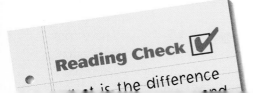

Figure 15-5 Classification systems change as new information is learned about organisms. One proposed system groups all organisms into three domains and then into kingdoms.

DOMAIN
Bacteria

KINGDOM
Eubacteria

DOMAIN
Eukarya

KINGDOMS
Animalia

Plantae

Fungi

Protista

DOMAIN
Archaea

KINGDOMS
Euryarchaeota

Crenarchaeota

Prokaryotes and Eukaryotes

Cell type separates two kingdoms from the other four kingdoms. The archaebacteria and eubacteria kingdoms contain organisms that are just one prokaryotic (proh kair ee AH tik) cell in size—a cell without a nucleus. Protists, fungi, plants, and animals have one or more eukaryotic (yew kair ee AH tik) cells—cells with a nucleus. **Table 15-1** lists information about each of the six kingdoms. Some scientists propose that before organisms are grouped into kingdoms, they should be placed in larger groups called domains. One proposed domain classification system is shown in **Figure 15-5.**

Groups Within Kingdoms

Suppose you go to a music store at the mall to buy a new CD. Will you look through all the CDs in the store until you find the one you're looking for? No, the CDs are separated into categories of similar types of music such as rock, soul, classical, country, and jazz. Within each category, the CDs are divided by artists, and then by specific titles. Because of this classification system, you can easily find the CD you want.

Scientists classify organisms into groups in the same way. Every organism is placed into a kingdom. Then, an organism is assigned to a **phylum** (FI lum), the next smallest group. In the plant kingdom, the word **division** is used in place of phylum. Each phylum or division is separated into **classes.** Classes are separated into **orders,** and orders are separated into **families.** A genus is a group within a family. A genus can have one or more species. ✓

Scientists use these categories to classify

Reading Check ✓

at is the difference

Design Your Own

Activity 15 • 1

Test Your Hypothesis

Plan

1. As a group, list the steps that you need to take to classify seeds. Be specific, and describe exactly what you will do at each step. List your materials.

2. **Classify** your seeds by making a model.

3. Make a plan to identify your seeds.

4. Read over your entire experiment to make sure that all steps are in logical order.

Do

1. Make sure your teacher approves your model before you proceed.

2. Carry out the experiment as planned.

3. While you are working, write down any observations that you make that would cause you to change your model.

4. **Complete** the plan.

Analyze Your Data

1. **Compare** your key and model with those made by other groups.

2. Check your key by having another group use it.

Draw Conclusions

1. In what ways can groups of different types of seeds be classified?

2. Why is it an advantage for scientists to use a standardized system to classify organisms? What observations did you make to support your answer?

Identifying Organisms

What You'll Learn

► Why scientific names are more useful to scientists than common names
► The function of a dichotomous key
► How to use a dichotomous key

Vocabulary
dichotomous key

Why It's Important

► It is easy to identify organisms if you can use a dichotomous key.

Common Names and Scientific Names

Have you heard anyone call the bird in **Figure 15-7A** a *Turdus migratorius?* In much of the United States, this bird is commonly called a robin, or a robin redbreast. However, people who live in England call the bird in **Figure 15-7B** a robin. In much of Europe, the same bird is also called a redbreast. If you lived in Australia, you'd call the bird in **Figure 15-7C** a robin, or a yellow robin. Are these the same species of bird? No, these birds are obviously different from one another.

Figure 15-7 These three robins have the same common name but are three different species.

Figure 15-8 Common names can be misleading. Sea horses (A) are fish, but starfish (B) are not fish. Prairie dogs (C) are more closely related to squirrels than to dogs. **Do you know a misleading common name?**

Yet, they all have the same or a similar common name. **Figure 15-8** gives other examples of some common names that are confusing.

What would happen if life scientists used only common names when they communicated with others about organisms? There would be many misunderstandings. The system of binomial nomenclature developed by Linnaeus gives each bird a unique scientific name. The scientific names for the birds in **Figure 15-7** are: **A**, *Turdus migratorius*; **B**, *Erithacus rubecula*; and **C**, *Eopsaltria australis*.

Functions of Scientific Names

Scientific names serve four functions. First, they help scientists avoid errors in communication. A life scientist who studied the yellow robin, *Eopsaltria australis*, would not be confused by information he or she read about *Turdus migratorius*,

Try at Home

Mini Lab

Communicating Ideas

Procedure

1. Find a picture in a magazine of a piece of furniture that you could both sit or lie down on.

2. Show the picture to ten people and ask them to tell you what they call the piece of furniture.

3. Keep a record of the answers in your Science Journal.

Analysis

1. In your Science Journal, infer how using common names can be confusing when communicating with others.

2. How does using scientific names make communication between scientists easier?

Using Math

1. Make a bar graph for the frequency of answers of your Try at Home MiniLab on the previous page.
2. Compile a list of all answers given to your classmates for the same MiniLab.
3. Make a bar graph for the frequency of responses of the compiled list.
4. Compare the two bar graphs.

Reading Check

where could you find the scientific name of an organism?

the American robin. Second, organisms with similar evolutionary histories are classified together. Because of this, you know that organisms with the same genus name are related. Third, scientific names give descriptive information about the species. What can you tell from the species name *Turdus migratorius*? It tells you that this bird migrates from place to place. Fourth, scientific names allow information about organisms to be organized and found easily and efficiently. Such information may be in a field guide, a book, or a pamphlet that lists related organisms and gives their scientific names.

Tools for Identifying Organisms

You've been asked to identify the organism in **Figure 15-9.** What do you do? The easiest thing would be to ask someone. You could contact a professor at a university, an exterminator, a county extension specialist, an expert at a natural history museum, or any knowledgeable person. However, no one knows or is expected to know all members of any taxonomic group. The person would probably tell you that the organism is a tick. He or she might look in a field guide to find its scientific name. If you were to use a field guide, you might be able to identify the organism. ☑️

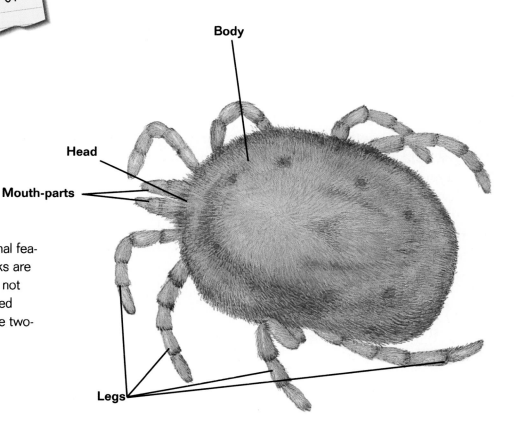

Body

Head

Mouth-parts

Legs

Figure 15-9 Two external features used for identifying ticks are eight legs and a body that is not in sections. Other eight-legged arthropods, like spiders, have two-section bodies.

Many kinds of field guides have been written like those in **Figure 15-10** and the field guide at the end of this chapter. Field guides about plants, fungi, fish, and nearly every other kind of organism are available. Most field guides have descriptions, illustrations of organisms, and information about habitats to help with identification. You can identify species from around the world by using the appropriate field guide.

Figure 15-10 Field guides are useful when trying to identify things.

Using Dichotomous Keys

A **dichotomous** (di KAH toh mus) **key** is a detailed list of characteristics used to identify organisms and includes scientific names. Dichotomous keys are arranged in steps with two descriptive statements at each step. Look at the dichotomous key for mites and ticks in **Table 15-2**. Notice that at each numbered step, the descriptions are labeled "a" and "b." To use the key, you must always begin with a choice from the first pair of descriptions. Notice that the end of each description is either the name of a species or directions to go to another step. If you use the dichotomous key properly, you will eventually end up with the correct name for your species.

Let's identify the soft tick in **Table 15-2**. Start at 1 of the key. Your tick is brown, so you go to 3. You measure your tick and find it is more than 5 mm in length, so you go on to 4. Your tick is brown with an oval, flattened body, so you choose "b."

Table 15-2

Key to Some Mites and Ticks of North America

Actual size: 5 mm

1. Animal color
  a. red, go to 2
  b. not red, go to 3

2. Body texture
  a. smooth; body globular and somewhat elongated; red freshwater mite, *Limnochares americana*
  b. dense velvety hair; body oval to rounded rectangle; velvet mite, *Trombidium* species

3. Body length
  a. 0.5 mm or less; two-spotted spider mite, *Tetranychus uriticae*
  b. more than 0.5 mm, go to 4

4. Body coloration
  a. dark brown with a small, whitish, patterned shield near the head; American dog tick, *Dermacentor* species
  b. brown; body is a flattened oval with a soft plate on the back; mammal soft tick, *Ornithodoros* species

Figure 15-11 Each of these animals is a different species of mite or tick. **What things do they have in common?**

A Actual size: 3.2 mm

B Actual size: 3 mm

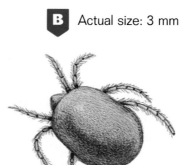

C Actual size: 0.5 mm

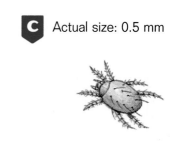

EARTH SCIENCE
INTEGRATION ➤

The dichotomous key tells you that your tick is an example of an *Ornithodoros* species, which are mammal soft ticks.

Keys are useful in a variety of ways. It is important to know if a rock is igneous, metamorphic, or sedimentary when classifying fossils, for example. Minerals can be classified using a key that describes characteristics such as hardness, luster, color, streak, and cleavage. Why might you need to know several characteristics to classify a mineral or a living thing?

Section Assessment

1. List four reasons biologists use scientific names instead of common names in their communications.

2. Why can common names cause confusion?

3. What is the function of a dichotomous key?

4. **Think Critically:** Why would you infer that two species that look similar share a common evolutionary history?

5. **Skill Builder**
   Classifying Classify the ticks and mites marked A, B, and C in **Figure 15-11,** using the dichotomous key in **Table 15-2.** If you need help, refer to Classifying in the **Skill Handbook** on page 679.

Science Journal
Select a field guide for grasses, trees, insects, or mammals. Select two organisms in the field guide that closely resemble each other. Compare them and explain how they differ using labeled diagrams.

Activity 15•2

Using a Dichotomous Key

Materials
- Paper and pencil

Scientists who classify organisms have made many keys that allow you to identify unknown organisms. Try this activity to see how it is done.

What You'll Investigate

How a dichotomous key can be used to identify native cats in the United States.

Goals

- **Learn** to use a dichotomous key.
- **Identify** two native cats of North America.

Procedure

1. **Observe** the cats pictured below.

2. Begin with 1 of the key to the right. **Identify** the cat labeled A.

3. On your paper, write the common and scientific name for the cat and list all of its traits given in the key.

4. Use the same procedure to **identify** the species of the cat labeled B.

Conclude and Apply

1. According to the key, how many species of native cats reside in North America?

2. How do you know that this key doesn't contain all the species of native cats in the world?

3. **Infer** why you couldn't identify a lion using this key.

4. **Explain** why it wouldn't be a good idea to begin in the middle of a key instead of with the first step.

Key to Native Cats of North America

1. Tail length
   a. short, go to 2
   b. long, go to 3

2. Cheek ruff
   a. no cheek ruff; long ear tufts tipped with black; coat distinctly mottled; lynx, *Lynx canadensis*
   b. broad cheek ruffs; ear tufts short; coat with indistinct spots; bobcat, *Lynx rufus*

3. Coat
   a. plain colored, go to 4
   b. patterned, go to 5

4. Coat color
   a. yellowish to tan above with white to buff below; mountain lion, *Felis concolor*
   b. all brown or black; jaguarundi, *Felis yagouaroundi*

5. Coat pattern
   a. lines of black-bordered brown spots; ocelot, *Felis pardalis*
   b. irregular tan and black, go to 6

6. Animal size
   a. large cat; rows of black rosettes or rings unevenly distributed; jaguar, *Panthera onca*
   b. small cat; four dark-brown stripes on the back and one on the neck; some irregularly shaped spots; margay, *Felis wiedii*

A   **B**

FIELD GUIDE

to Insects

FIELD ACTIVITY

For a week, use this field guide to help you identify insect orders. Look in different places and at different times of day for insects. In your Science Journal, record the order of insect found, along with the date, time, and place. *Why do you think there are so many kinds of insects?*

It's brown and creepy, and has wings and six legs. If you call it a bug, you may be correct, but if you said it was an insect, you definitely would be correct. Insects belong to a large group of animals called the arthropods. They are related to shrimp, spiders, lobsters, and centipedes. There are more insect species than all other animal species on Earth. Insects are found from the tropics to the tundra. Some are aquatic all or part of their lives. There are even insects that live inside other animals. Insects play important roles in the environment. Many are helpful, but others are destructive.

How Insects Are Classified

An insect's body is divided into three parts: head, thorax, and abdomen. The head has a pair of antennae and eyes and paired mouthparts. Three pairs of jointed legs and, sometimes, wings are attached to the thorax. They have a hard covering over their entire body. Some insects shed this covering so that they can grow. Insects are classified into smaller groups called orders. By observing an insect and recognizing certain features, you can identify the order it belongs to. This field guide presents ten insect orders.

Insect Orders

Dermaptera Earwigs

- A pair of pincerlike structures extends from the end of the abdomen.
- They are usually active at night and hide under litter or in any dark, protected place during the day.
- Earwigs may damage plants.

Common Earwig

Coleoptera Beetles

- A pair of thick, leathery, sometimes-knobby wings meets in a straight line and covers another pair of wings, the thorax, and all or most of the abdomen.
- Most beetles are considered serious pests, but some feed on other insects and others are scavengers.

This is the largest order of insects. There are many sizes, shapes, and colors of beetles. Not all beetles are called beetles. For example, ladybugs, fireflies, June bugs, and weevils are beetles.

Convergent Ladybug Beetle

Male Stag Beetle

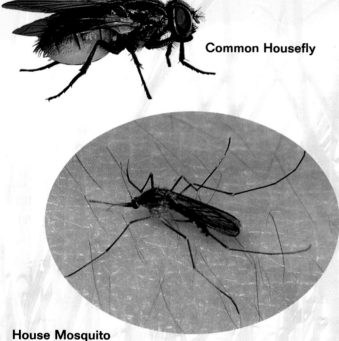

Common Housefly

Diptera Flies—Mosquitoes

- They are small insects with large eyes.
- They have two pair of wings but only one pair is visible.
- Mouths are adapted for piercing and sucking, or scraping and lapping

Many of these insects are food for larger animals. Some spread diseases, others are pests, and some eat dead and decaying things. They are found in many different environments.

House Mosquito

Odonata Dragonflies—Damselflies

- They have two pairs of transparent, many-veined wings that are nearly equal in size and never folded against the insect's body.
- A pair of large eyes are on its head.
- They have a long, thin abdomen.

These insects are usually seen near bodies of water. All members of this group catch small insects, such as mosquitoes, while in flight.

Twelve Spotted Skimmer Dragonfly

Isoptera **Termites**

- Adults are small, dark brown or black, and may have wings.
- Immature forms are small, soft-bodied, pale yellow or white, and wingless.
- Termites live in colonies in the ground or in wood.

The adults are sometimes confused with ants. The thorax and abdomen of a termite look like one body part, but a thin waist separates the thorax and abdomen of an ant. Although most people consider termites to be destructive insects, they play an important role in recycling trees and other woody plants. Termites can digest wood because certain bacteria and protists live in their digestive tracts.

Pacific Coast Termi

Dictyoptera **Cockroaches—Mantises**

- They have long, thin antennae on the he
- The front wings are smaller than back wings are thin and fanlike when opened
  - Front legs of a mantis for grasping; the other legs are similar to tho roach.

Praying mantises are call insects because they eat harmful, insects. Cockroac wherever humans live.

Carolina Praying Mantis

American Cockroach

Hymenoptera

Ants—Bees—Wasps

- They have two pairs of transparent wings, if present.
- They are found in many different environments, either in colonies or alone.

Members of this order may be so small that they can be seen only with a magnifier. Others may be nearly 35 mm long. They are important because they pollinate flowers, and some prey on harmful insects. Honeybees make honey and wax. Despite common beliefs, not all bees and wasps can sting.

American Bumble Bee

Black

Pa

Ideas

Reading Check ☑

• All organisms can be classified using only three features. Why can't these features be used to classify dogs? What features could you use to classify dogs?

DERN CLASSIFICATION

are classified into six **kingdoms**
everal characteristics. Cell
organisms into two
okaryotes and eukary-
g other characteristics
isms into smaller and smaller
The last level of classification is the
hich kingdoms contain prokary-
which contain eukaryotes?

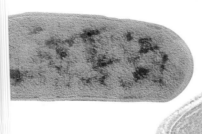

3 IDENTIFYING ORGANISMS

Scientific names give descriptive information about species.
n species has its own unique name. Species names are used world-
e. Communication among scientists and others is easier and
clearer with scientific names. Field guides and
dichotomous keys are used to identify specific organisms. Identification of organisms
is important in the study of living organisms. *Why do you*
always start
with the number
one entry of a
dichotomous key?

on the

• An ad

Chapter 15 Assessment

Using Vocabulary

a. binomial nomenclature
b. class
c. classify
d. dichotomous key
e. division
f. family
g. genus
h. kingdom
i. order
j. phylogeny
k. phylum
l. species
m. taxonomy

Distinguish between the terms in each of the following sets.

1. kingdom, species
2. division, phylum
3. dichotomous key, binomial nomenclature
4. classify, taxonomy
5. class, family

Checking Concepts

Choose the word or phrase that best answers the question.

6. Which group has the most members?
   A) family   C) genus
   B) kingdom   D) order

7. In what category do the most similar organisms belong?
   A) family   C) genus
   B) class   D) species

8. Which of the following are all many-celled organisms?
   A) animals   C) fungi
   B) bacteria   D) protists

9. What is the closest relative of *Canis lupus*?
   A) *Quercus alba*   C) *Felis tigris*
   B) *Equus zebra*   D) *Canis familiaris*

10. What does the first word in a two-word scientific name of an organism identify?
    A) kingdom   C) phylum
    B) species   D) genus

11. To which kingdom do mushrooms belong?
    A) animal   C) fungi
    B) eubacteria D) plant

12. What is the evolutionary history of an organism?
    A) taxonomy   C) phylogeny
    B) biology   D) chemistry

13. What are the simplest eukaryotes?
    A) animals   C) eubacteria
    B) fungi   D) protists

14. What are trees and flowers?
    A) animals   C) fungi
    B) plants   D) protists

15. What are cells without a nucleus?
    A) eukaryotes C) species
    B) phylogeny   D) prokaryotes

Thinking Critically

16. Explain what binomial nomenclature is and why it is important.

17. Name each of the six kingdoms, and identify a member of each kingdom.

18. Write a sh
    identify
    such t
    and
    an
    na

19. D
    a
    F

20

Developing Skills

[n]eed help, refer to the **Skill Handbook**.

[Co]ncept Mapping: Using information in [sec]tions 15-1 and 15-2, make an events [cha]in concept map to show events from [Ari]stotle to modern classification.

[Co]mparing and Contrasting: Compare [the] number and variety of organisms in [a k]ingdom and in a genus.

[Cla]ssifying: Use the Key to Native Cats [of] North America to identify these cats.

[Ma]king and Using Graphs: Make a [circ]le graph using the data listed in the [tab]le below.

[Num]ber of Species of Organisms	
[King]dom	Number of Species
[Plan]ts	51 000
	100 000
	285 000
[Anim]als	2 000 000

THE PRINCETON REVIEW

Test-Taking Tip

You Are Smarter Than You Think
Nothing on the science tests that you will take this year is so difficult that you can't understand it. You can learn to master any of it. Be self-confident and just keep practicing your test-taking skills.

Test Practice

Use these questions to test your Science Proficiency.

1. You are examining a cell under a micro-scope. Which of the following observa-tions lets you know that the cell is **NOT** from the Kingdom Eubacteria?
   A) Its nucleus is surrounded by a membrane.
   B) The cell has a wall.
   C) The cell is small.
   D) Flagella are attached to the cell wall.

2. Two organisms look different from each other, but a taxonomist suspects they are members of the same species. Why would the taxonomist come to this con-clusion?
   A) They fight with each other.
   B) They come from the same country.
   C) They seem to get along well.
   D) They mate and produce fertile offspring.

3. The blue jay, *Cyanocitta cristata*, is most closely related to which of the following birds?
   A) green jay, *Cyanocorax yncas*
   B) Stellar's jay, *Cyanocitta stelleri*
   C) eastern bluebird, *Sialia sialis*
   D) bluethroat, *Luscinia svecica*

Chapter Preview

Skills Preview

Skill Builders
- Hypothesize
- Map Concepts

Activities
- Design an Experiment
- Organize Data

MiniLabs
- Recognize Cause and Effect
- Infer

Reading Check ✔

As you read this chapter, find out the differences among the meanings of the prefixes *a-*, *anti-*, and *ana-*. List and define two words that begin with each prefix.

Explore Activity

What would it be like to have millions of cells like those shown on these pages living inside you? It isn't hard to imagine such a situation, because all of us have huge populations of cells living in our small intestines all the time! These cells are bacteria called *Escherichia coli.* You can find out what some other bacteria look like by doing the following activity. Then, in this chapter, learn more about these cells and why they are so important to the existence of life on Earth.

Observe Bacteria

Magnification: 400×

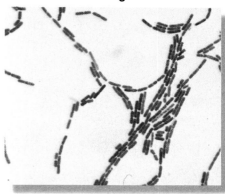

1. Mix a small drop of yogurt with ten drops of water in a small dish.

2. Add a drop of crystal violet. The crystal violet stains the bacteria so that you can see them.

3. After 30 s, dip a toothpick into the mixture and then touch the tip of the toothpick onto a glass slide. Let the slide dry.

4. Observe the bacteria under low and then high magnifications

Science Journal

In your Science Journal, describe and draw what the bacteria look like. Compare your drawing to the above photo.

Two Kingdoms of Bacteria

What are bacteria?

When most people hear the word *bacteria*, they probably associate it with sore throats or other illnesses. However, very few bacteria cause illness. Most are important for other reasons. Bacteria are almost everywhere—in the air you breathe, the food you eat, the water you drink, and even at great ocean depths. A shovelful of soil contains billions of them. Millions of bacteria live on and in your body. Many are beneficial to you.

There are two types of cells—prokaryotic and eukaryotic. Bacteria are prokaryotes because they have no true nucleus. Organelles in bacteria are not surrounded by membranes. The nuclear material of a bacterial cell is made up of one or more circular chromosomes. Bacteria have cell walls and cell membranes and also contain ribosomes.

Types of Bacteria

Bacteria are grouped into two kingdoms—eubacteria (yoo bak TIHR ee uh) and archaebacteria (ar kee bak TIHR ee uh). Some eubacteria, such as the cyanobacteria in **Figure 16-1,** contain chlorophyll, which enables them to make their own food. They obtain their energy from the sun by photosynthesis. Most eubacteria do not make their own food. Some break down dead organisms to obtain energy. Others live as parasites and absorb nutrients from living organisms. Archaebacteria live in habitats where few organisms can live and obtain energy in other ways.

Figure 16-1 These cyanobacteria make their own food. **What do cyanobacteria contain that enables them to make food?**

Magnification: 1250×

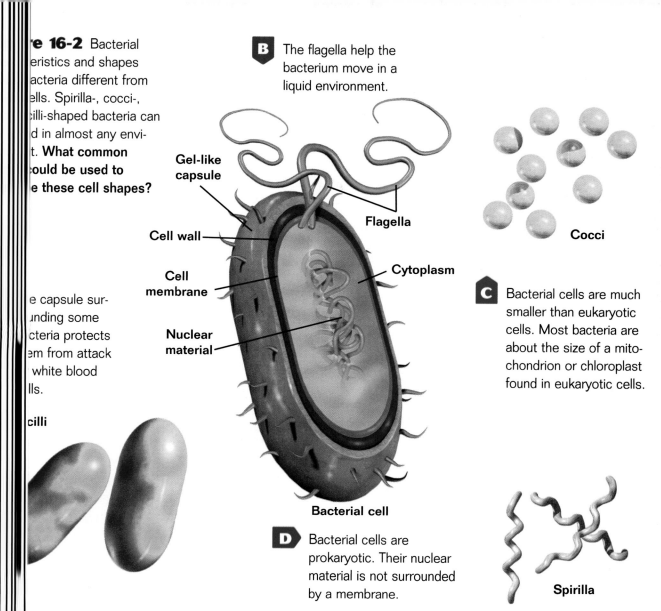

e 16-2 Bacterial
eristics and shapes
acteria different from
ells. Spirilla-, cocci-,
cilli-shaped bacteria can
d in almost any envi-
t. **What common
ould be used to
e these cell shapes?**

Gel-like
capsule

Cell wall

Cell
membrane

Nuclear
material

e capsule sur-
nding some
cteria protects
m from attack
white blood
lls.

cilli

B The flagella help the
bacterium move in a
liquid environment.

Flagella

Cytoplasm

Bacterial cell

D Bacterial cells are
prokaryotic. Their nuclear
material is not surrounded
by a membrane.

Cocci

C Bacterial cells are much
smaller than eukaryotic
cells. Most bacteria are
about the size of a mito-
chondrion or chloroplast
found in eukaryotic cells.

Spirilla

erial Shapes

bacteria that normally inhabit your home and body
hree basic shapes—spheres, rods, and spirals. Sphere-
d bacteria are called *cocci* (sing. *coccus*), rod-shaped bac-
re called *bacilli* (sing. *bacillus*), and spiral-shaped bacteria
led *spirilla* (sing. *spirillum*). The general characteristics of
ia can be seen in the bacillus shown in **Figure 16-2**. It con-
ytoplasm surrounded by a cell membrane and wall.
ial chromosomes are not located in a membrane-bound
s but are found in the cytoplasm. Some bacteria have a
gel-like capsule around the cell wall. The capsule helps
cterium stick to surfaces. How does a capsule help a
ium to survive?
y bacteria float freely in the environment on air and
currents, your hands, your shoes, and even the family
cat. Many that live in moist conditions have whiplike
lled **flagella** to help them move. ☑

Reading Check ☑

What are flagella?

Observing Bacterial Growth

Procedure

1. Obtain two or three dried beans.
2. Break them into halves and place the halves into 10 mL of distilled water in a glass beaker.
3. Observe how many days it takes for the water to become cloudy and develop an unpleasant odor.
4. Use methylene blue to dye a drop of water from the beaker and observe it under the microscope.

Analysis

1. How long did it take for the water to become cloudy?
2. What did you observe on the slide that would make the water cloudy?
3. What do you think the bacteria were feeding on?

Eubacteria

Eubacteria is the larger of the two bacterial kingdoms. It contains so many organisms that it is hard to classify. All bacteria except archaebacteria, which you will learn about later in this chapter, are considered to be eubacteria, or "true bacteria." These organisms live in much less harsh environments than archaebacteria. As illustrated in **Figure 16-3,** eubacteria include many diverse groups, from species that live off other organisms to those that can make their own food.

Cyanobacteria

One type of eubacteria is known as cyanobacteria. Cyanobacteria are eubacteria that are producers. They make their own food using carbon dioxide, water, and energy from sunlight. Cyanobacteria contain chlorophyll and another pigment that is blue. This pigment combination gives cyanobacteria their common name, blue-green bacteria. However, some cyanobacteria are yellow, black, or red. The Red Sea gets its name from red cyanobacteria.

Figure 16-3 Bacteria are divided into two main groups—archaebacteria and eubacteria. **Which group contains the largest variety of organisms?**

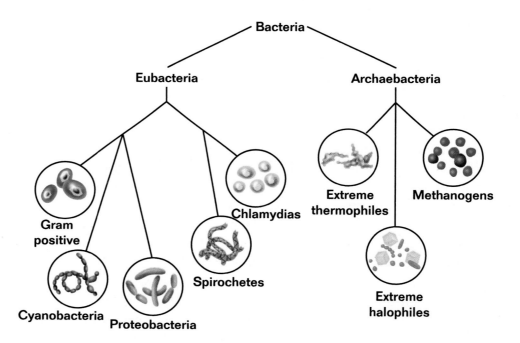

species of cyanobacteria are one-celled organisms.
...ver, some of these organisms live together in long
... or filaments. Look again at **Figure 16-1.** Many are cov-
...with a gel-like substance. This adaptation enables
...bacteria to live in globular groups called colonies.
...bacteria are important for food production in lakes and
.... Since cyanobacteria make food from carbon dioxide,
... and the energy from sunlight, fish in a healthy pond
...t them and use the energy released from that food.
...e you ever seen a pond covered with smelly, green,
...y slime? When large amounts of nutrients enter a pond,
...bacteria increase in number and produce a matlike
...h called a bloom. Available resources are quickly con-
...l and the cyanobacteria die. Bacteria feed on them and
... all the oxygen in the water. As a result, fish and other
...sms die.

Using Math

Figure 16-4 shows a bacterium that is dividing into two cells. Measure the length of one of the new cells in millimeters. Determine the actual size of the cell by dividing the measured length by the magnification.

Problem Solving

...ntrolling Bacterial Growth

...antibiotic is a substance produced by one organ-
...to inhibit or kill another organism. Many anti-
...cs are produced by molds and fungi. While trying
...row bacteria in a dish, a scientist discovered mold
...growing on the dish. The area around this mold
...free of bacteria. This event led to the discovery of
...icillin, a common antibiotic. Streptomycin, another
...mon antibiotic, was first discovered in soil fungi.
...soil fungi was observed to prevent the growth of
...eria. Other substances that prevent or inhibit bac-
...l growth include alcohol, hydrogen peroxide,
...ch, and ammonia.

...ertisers proclaim that their mouthwash products
...fight bad breath by killing the bacteria that cause
...ow could you test a mouthwash sample for anti-
...c action?

...ve the Problem

...Describe an experiment that you could do to
...determine if your mouthwash is effective at killing
...bacteria.

2. What controls would you use in your experiment?

Think Critically: Read the ingredients label on a bottle of mouthwash. Which of the ingredients appear to be effective against bacteria? What other ingredients are present? What role do colored dyes play?

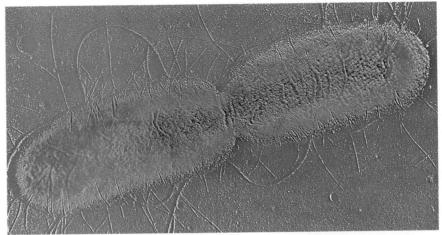

Figure 16-4 In this color-enhanced electron micrograph, a bacterium is shown undergoing fission.

Magnification: 14 400×

Reproduction

Bacteria reproduce by fission, as shown in **Figure 16-4.** **Fission** produces two cells with genetic material identical to that of the parent cell. It is the simplest form of asexual cell reproduction. Some bacteria exchange genetic material through a process similar to sexual reproduction. Two bacteria line up beside each other and exchange DNA through a fine tube. This results in cells with different genetic material than their parents. As a result, the bacteria may have variations that give them an advantage for surviving in changing environments.

Most bacteria live in places where there is a supply of oxygen. An organism that uses oxygen for respiration is called an **aerobe** (AY rohb). You are an aerobic organism. In contrast, some organisms, called **anaerobes** (AN uh rohbz), have variations that allow them to live without oxygen.

Figure 16-5 Bacteria that live in mineral hot springs like Morning Glory Pool, shown below, are anaerobes. **What problems would bacteria have to overcome to live in conditions such as these?**

...aebacteria

...gdom Archaebacteria contains certain kinds of anaero-
...acteria, which, like eubacteria, are thought to have
...d for billions of years. They are found in extreme con-
...s, such as the hot springs shown in **Figure 16-5,** salty
... muddy swamps, the intestines of cattle, and near deep
...vents where life exists without sunlight. The conditions
...ich archaebacteria live today may resemble conditions
... on early Earth.

...haebacteria are divided into three groups, based on
... they get energy. There are
...anogens, halophiles, and thermo-
...les. The methanogens use carbon
...xide for energy and produce the me-
...ane gas that bubbles up out of swamps
...d marshes. The extreme halophiles live
... salty environments such as the Great
...alt Lake in Utah and the Dead Sea. Some
...f them require a habitat ten times saltier
...han seawater to grow. The last group of
...archaebacteria is the extreme ther-
...nophiles that survive in hot areas like the
one shown in **Figure 16-6.**

Figure 16-6

Section Assessment

1. What are the characteristics of bacteria?
2. How do aerobic and anaerobic organisms differ?
3. How do bacteria reproduce?
4. **Think Critically:** A mat of cyanobacteria is found growing on a lake with dead fish floating along the edge. What has caused these events to occur?
5. **Skill Builder**
   Interpreting Data Do the **Chapter 16 Skill Activity** on page 723 to interpret the data to determine which substance best prevents bacterial growth.

Using Math

Some bacteria may reproduce every 20 minutes. Suppose that one bacterium is present at the beginning of a timed period. How long would it take for the number of bacteria to increase to more than 1 million?

Observing Cyanobacteria

You can obtain many species of cyanobacteria from ponds. When you look at these organisms under a microscope, ...t they have many similarities but that they are also ...ach other in important ways. In this activity, you ...d contrast species of cyanobacteria.

Materials

Observe photos or prepared slides, if available, of *Gloeocapsa* and *Anabaena*. If using slides, observe under the low and high power of the microscope. Notice the difference in the arrangement of the cells. In your Science Journal, draw and label a few cells of each species of cyanobacterium.

Observe photos of *Nostoc* and *Oscillatoria*. In your Science Journal, draw and label a few cells of each.

Indicate whether each cyanobacterium sample is in colony form or filament form. Write a *yes* or *no* for the presence or absence of each characteristic in each type of cyanobacterium.

onclude and Apply

1. How does the color of cyanobacteria compare with the color of leaves on trees? What can you infer from this?

2. How can you tell by **observing** them that cyanobacteria belong to Kingdom Eubacteria?

3. **Describe** the general appearance of cyanobacteria.

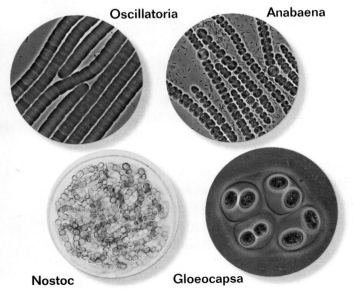

Oscillatoria

Anabaena

Nostoc

Gloeocapsa

Cyanobacteria Observations				
Structure	**Ana-baena**	**Gloe-ocapsa**	**Nostoc**	**Oscill-atoria**
Filament or colony				
Nucleus				
Chlorophyll				
Gel-like layer				

Bacteria in Your Life

Beneficial Bacteria

Have you had any bacteria for lunch lately? Any time you eat cheese or yogurt, you eat some bacteria. Bacteria break down substances in milk to make many everyday products. Cheese-making is illustrated in **Figure 16-7.** If you have eaten sauerkraut, you ate a product made with cabbage and a bacterial culture. Vinegar is also produced by a bacterium.

What **You'll Learn**

► Some ways bacteria are helpful
► The importance of nitrogen-fixing bacteria
► How some bacteria cause disease

Vocabulary
saprophyte
nitrogen-fixing bacteria
pathogen
antibiotic
vaccine
toxin
endospore

Why **It's Important**

► Discovering the ways bacteria affect your life can help you understand biological processes.

Figure 16-7 Bacteria that break down proteins in milk are used in production of various kinds of cheese.

A Bacteria such as *Streptococcus lactis* added to milk cause the milk to curdle, or separate into curds (solids) and whey (liquids).

B Other bacteria are added to the curds. Curds are then allowed to ripen into cheese. Which type of cheese is made depends on the bacterial species added to the curds.

Uses of Bacteria

Bacteria called saprophytes (SAP ruh fitz) help maintain nature's balance. A **saprophyte** is any organism that uses dead material as a food and energy source. Saprophytes digest dead organisms and recycle nutrients so that they are available for use by other organisms. Without saprophytic bacteria, there would be layers of dead material deeper than you are tall spread over all of Earth. ☑

Reading Check ☑
What is a saprophyte?

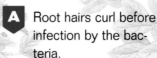
Figure 16-8 Root nodules, which form on the roots of peanuts, peas, and other legumes, contain nitrogen-fixing bacteria.

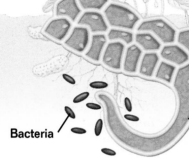

A Root hairs curl before infection by the bacteria.

B Bacteria enter the roots through an infection thread, which carries the bacteria into the root.

Infection thread

Root hair

Bacteria

The roots of plants such as peanuts and peas contain nitrogen-fixing bacteria in growths called nodules, illustrated in **Figure 16-8**. These **nitrogen-fixing bacteria** change nitrogen from the air into forms useful for plants and animals. Both plants and animals need nitrogen for making needed proteins and nucleic acids. It is estimated that nitrogen-fixing bacteria save U.S. farmers millions of dollars in fertilizer costs every year.

Many industries rely on bacteria. Biotechnology is putting bacteria to use in making medicines, enzymes, cleansers, adhesives, and other products. The ability of bacteria to digest oil has been extremely important in helping to clean up the extensive oil spills in Alaska, California, and Texas.

Harmful Bacteria

Some bacteria are pathogens. A **pathogen** is any organism that produces disease. If you have ever had strep throat, you have had firsthand experience with a bacterial pathogen. Other pathogenic bacteria cause anthrax in cattle, and diphtheria, tetanus, and whooping cough in humans. Bacterial diseases in humans and animals are usually treated effectively with antibiotics. An **antibiotic** is a substance produced by one organism that inhibits or kills another organism. Penicillin, a well-known antibiotic, works by preventing bacteria from making cell walls. Without cell walls, bacteria cannot survive.

Some bacterial diseases can be prevented by vaccines. A **vaccine** is made from damaged particles taken from bacterial

*inter***NET**
CONNECTION

Visit the Glencoe Science Web Site at **www.glencoe. com/sec/science/fl** for more information about toxin-producing bacteria.

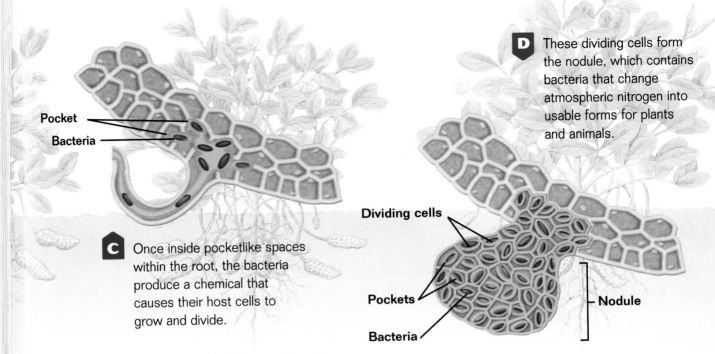

Pocket

Bacteria

C Once inside pocketlike spaces within the root, the bacteria produce a chemical that causes their host cells to grow and divide.

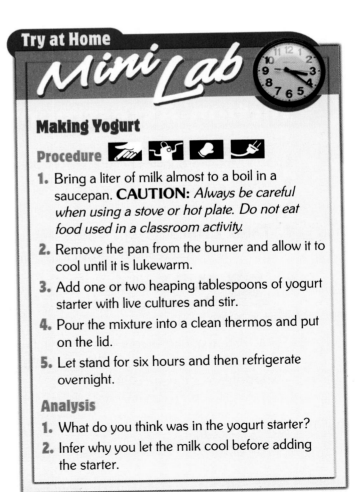

D These dividing cells form the nodule, which contains bacteria that change atmospheric nitrogen into usable forms for plants and animals.

Dividing cells

Pockets

Bacteria

Nodule

cell walls or from killed bacteria. Once injected, the white blood cells in the body learn to recognize the bacteria. If the particular bacteria then enter the body at a later time, the white blood cells immediately attack and overwhelm them. Vaccines have been produced that are effective against many bacterial diseases.

Some pathogens produce poisons. The poison produced by a bacterial pathogen is called a **toxin.** Botulism, a type of food poisoning, is caused by a toxin that can cause paralysis and death. The bacterium that causes botulism is *Clostridium botulinum.* Many bacteria that produce toxins are able to produce thick walls around themselves when conditions are unfavorable. This thick-walled structure is called an **endospore,** illustrated in **Figure 16-9.** Endospores can exist for hundreds of years before they begin to grow again. Botulism endospores must be exposed to heat for a long time to be destroyed. Once the endospores are in canned food, the bacteria can change back to regular cells and start producing toxins. Botulism bacteria are able to grow inside cans because they are anaerobes and do not need oxygen to live.

Try at Home

Mini Lab

Making Yogurt

Procedure

1. Bring a liter of milk almost to a boil in a saucepan. **CAUTION:** *Always be careful when using a stove or hot plate. Do not eat food used in a classroom activity.*
2. Remove the pan from the burner and allow it to cool until it is lukewarm.
3. Add one or two heaping tablespoons of yogurt starter with live cultures and stir.
4. Pour the mixture into a clean thermos and put on the lid.
5. Let stand for six hours and then refrigerate overnight.

Analysis

1. What do you think was in the yogurt starter?
2. Infer why you let the milk cool before adding the starter.

Figure 16-9 Bacteria sometimes form endospores when conditions become unfavorable. These structures can survive harsh winters, dry conditions, and heat. In this photo, the blue in the center of each structure is the endospore. The golden part is the cellular material. **How can botulism endospores be destroyed?**

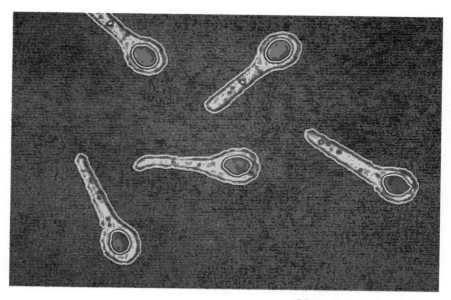

Magnification: 15 000×

PHYSICS
INTEGRATION

Vacuum Packing
A vacuum is a space from which all gas molecules have been removed. Vacuum-packed foods have most of the air removed from around the food. How would this prevent food from spoiling?

Pasteurization

Pasteurization, a process of heating food to a temperature that kills harmful bacteria, is used in the food industry. You are probably most familiar with pasteurized milk, but some fruit juices are also pasteurized. The process is named for Louis Pasteur, who first formulated the process for the wine industry during the nineteenth century in France.

Section Assessment

1. Why are saprophytes helpful and necessary?
2. Why are nitrogen-fixing bacteria important?
3. What makes penicillin an effective antibiotic?
4. **Think Critically:** Why is botulism associated with canned foods and not fresh foods?
5. **Skill Builder**
   Measuring in SI Air may have more than 3500 bacteria per cubic meter. How many bacteria might be in your classroom? If you need help, refer to Measuring in SI in the **Skill Handbook** on page 694.

Using Computers

Spreadsheet Create a spreadsheet that includes: Disease Name, Disease Organism, Method of Transmission, and Symptoms. Enter information for the following diseases: whooping cough, tuberculosis, tetanus, diphtheria, and scarlet fever. Sort your data using Method of Transmission. If you need help, refer to page 704.

Bioremediation

Each year, tons of pollutants are released into ecosystems because of human activities. Many of these pollutants are both poisonous and long lasting. Soil, surface, and groundwater contamination results from the buildup of these harmful compounds. Traditional methods of cleaning up damaged ecosystems, such as the use of landfills and toxic-waste dumps, can be costly and ineffective as long-term solutions.

An Unusual Solution

One approach to cleaning up polluted ecosystems is bioremediation—the use of living microorganisms to change pollutants into harmless compounds. Some microorganisms naturally have the ability to break down harmful compounds. Scientists find and isolate these organisms, often stimulating them to clean up polluted areas. Other times, it is necessary to genetically engineer a microorganism to break down specific pollutants. Archaebacteria and eubacteria are the main organisms used in bioremediation efforts. These microorganisms break down polluting substances—even oil and gasoline—and change them into less damaging compounds, such as carbon dioxide and water. At left, technicians spray a fertilizer mix on an oil-soaked shore to promote the growth of oil-eating bacteria. Although bioremediation is not a complete cure, it is a new way to help repair damaged ecosystems.

Uses and Advantages of Bioremediation

About five to ten percent of all industrial, agricultural, and municipal wastes are being treated by bioremediation. To clean water, for example, bacteria are placed in lagoons or large containers. Then, wastewater is pumped through these sites, and the bacteria break down the pollutants in the water into harmless compounds. In another technique, pollutants are mixed into soil and broken down by microorganisms found there. An advantage of bioremediation is that it can eliminate hazardous waste where it occurs, rather than at a distant treatment site. Bioremediation has proven to be safe and effective, and it costs 60 to 90 percent less than many traditional methods.

interNET CONNECTION

Use the Glencoe Science Web Site at **www.glencoe.com/sec/ science/fl** to research local waste treatment companies. Do more companies use traditional methods or bioremediation? Try to find out why a company uses a particular method.

Activity 16·2

Are there bacteria in foods?

Materials

- 6 test tubes
- 6 stoppers
- test-tube rack
- felt-tip marker
- 3 droppers
- 3 craft sticks
- Milk, buttermilk, cottage cheese, yogurt, sour cream, water
- bromothymol blue solution (150 mL)

You've learned that bacteria are too small to be seen without a microscope, but is there some way that you can tell if they are present in foods? Because bacteria produce carbon dioxide like other living things, a chemical test that indicates the presence of carbon dioxide can be used to tell if bacteria are growing in foods you eat.

What You'll Investigate

Is there bacteria in the food you eat?

Goals

- **Observe** color changes in test tubes containing food.
- **Determine** which foods contain the most bacteria.

Procedure

1. Use the marker to label the test tubes 1 through 6 and place them in the test tube rack.

2. Add 25 mL of bromothymol blue—indicator solution to each test tube.

3. Using a different dropper each time, add four drops of water to tube 1, four drops of milk to tube 2, and four drops of buttermilk to tube 3. Be careful not to let the drops go down the sides of the tubes.

4. Using a different craft stick each time, add an amount of yogurt about the size of a green pea to tube 4, the same amount of cottage cheese to tube 5, and the same amount of sour cream to tube 6.

5. Loosely place a stopper in each tube and record the color of the contents of each tube in a data table.

6. Leave the tubes undisturbed until the end of the class period. Record the color of the contents of the tubes in the data table.

7. The next time you arrive in class, record the color of the contents of the tubes again.

Conclude and Apply

1. Why was water added to tube 1?

2. What color does bromothymol turn if carbon dioxide is present?

3. Using strength of the color change as a guide, judge which tubes contain the most bacteria.

Data Table for Test of Bacteria in Food						
Tube	Contents	Color at Start	Color at End of Class	Color One Day Later	Test + or −	Bacteria Present?
1	Water					
2	Milk					
3	Buttermilk					
4	Yogurt					
5	Cottage Cheese					
6	Sour Cream					

For a **preview** of this chapter, study this Reviewing Main Ideas before you read the chapter. After you have studied this chapter, you can use the Reviewing Main Ideas to **review** the chapter.

The Glencoe MindJogger, Audiocassettes, and CD-ROM provide additional opportunities for review.

Section

16-1 TWO KINGDOMS OF BACTERIA

Bacteria are prokaryotic cells that usually reproduce by **fission.** All bacteria contain DNA, ribosomes, and cytoplasm but lack membrane-bound organelles. Bacteria are placed into one of two kingdoms—eubacteria and archaebacteria. The eubacteria are considered to be true bacteria and contain a great variety of organisms. Archaebacteria are bacteria that exist in extreme conditions, such as deep-sea vents and hot springs. Most bacteria break down cells of other organisms to obtain food, but cyanobacteria make their own food. **Anaerobes** are bacteria that are able to live without oxygen, whereas **aerobes** need oxygen to survive. *How do prokaryotic cells differ from eukaryotic cells?*

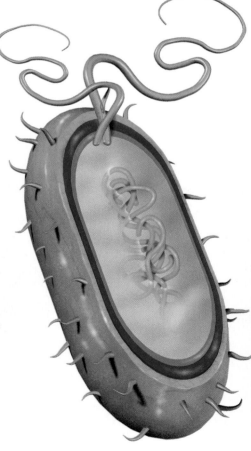

Reading Check ☑

Review **Figure 16-8.** Then, describe the nitrogen-fixing process in your own words, using numbered steps. You will probably have more than four steps.

Section
16-2 BACTERIA IN YOUR LIFE

Bacteria may be helpful or harmful. They may aid in recycling nutrients, fixing nitrogen, or helping in food production. They can even be used to break down harmful pollutants. Other bacteria are harmful because they can cause disease in the organisms they infect. Pasteurization is one process that can prevent harmful bacteria in food. *What are some diseases caused by harmful bacteria?*

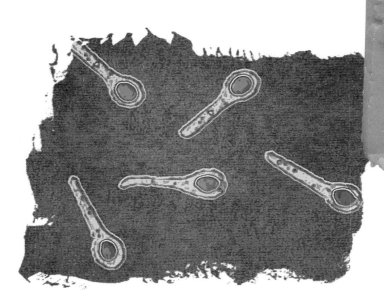

 *Career*
CONNECTION

Alice Arellano, Wastewater Operator

Alice Arellano is a wastewater control-room operator responsible for cleaning wastewater in Austin, Texas. Wastewater from peoples' homes in Austin is discharged into the Colorado River, but it first has to be treated. Treatment is a complex process that involves screening, filtering, and chemical treatment. Part of treatment involves using microorganisms, like bacteria, to break down harmful bacteria that live in the wastewater. *How can understanding the way bacteria live help design water-treatment processes?*

Chapter 16 Assessment

Using Vocabulary

a. aerobe
b. anaerobe
c. antibiotic
d. endospore
e. fission
f. flagella
g. nitrogen-fixing bacteria
h. pathogen
i. saprophyte
j. toxin
k. vaccine

Each phrase below describes a science term from the list. Write the term that matches the phrase describing it.

1. organism that decomposes dead organisms
2. structure by which some organisms move
3. heat-resistant structure in bacteria
4. substance that can prevent, not cure, a disease
5. any organism that produces disease

Checking Concepts

Choose the word or phrase that best answers the question.

6. What is a way of cleaning up an eco-system using bacteria to break down harmful compounds?
   A) landfills
   B) toxic waste dumps
   C) waste storage
   D) bioremediation

7. What do bacterial cells contain?
   A) nuclei
   B) DNA
   C) mitochondria
   D) no chromosomes

8. What do bacteria that make their own food have?
   A) chlorophyll
   B) lysosomes
   C) Golgi bodies
   D) mitochondria

9. Which of the following describes most bacteria?
   A) anaerobic
   B) pathogens
   C) many-celled
   D) beneficial

10. What is the name for rod-shaped bacteria?
    A) bacilli
    B) cocci
    C) spirilla
    D) colonies

11. What structure(s) allow(s) bacteria to stick to surfaces?
    A) capsule
    B) flagella
    C) chromosome
    D) cell wall

12. What causes blooms in ponds?
    A) archaebacteria
    B) cyanobacteria
    C) cocci
    D) viruses

13. How are nutrients and carbon dioxide returned to the environment?
    A) producers
    B) flagella
    C) saprophytes
    D) pathogens

14. Which of the following is caused by a pathogenic bacterium?
    A) an antibiotic
    B) nitrogen fixation
    C) cheese
    D) strep throat

15. Which organisms do not need oxygen to survive?
    A) anaerobes
    B) aerobes
    C) humans
    D) fish

Thinking Critically

16. What would happen if nitrogen-fixing bacteria could no longer live on the roots of plants?

17. Why are bacteria capable of surviving in all environments of the world?

18. Farmers often rotate crops such as beans, peas, and peanuts with other crops such as corn, wheat, and cotton. Why might they make such changes?

19. One organism that causes bacterial pneumonia is called pneumococcus. What is its shape?

20. What precautions can be taken to prevent food poisoning?

Developing Skills

If you need help, refer to the **Skill Handbook.**

21. **Concept Mapping:** Use the events chain to sequence the events following a pond bloom.

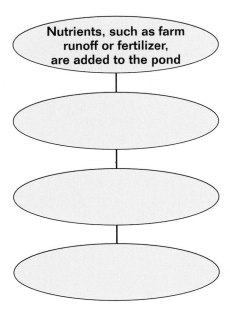

Nutrients, such as farm runoff or fertilizer, are added to the pond

22. **Making and Using Graphs:** Graph the data from the table below. Using the graph, determine where the doubling rate would be at 20°C.

Bacterial Reproduction Rates

Temperature (°C)	Doubling Rate per Hour
20.5	2.0
30.5	3.0
36.0	2.5
39.2	1.2

23. **Interpreting Data:** What is the effect of temperature in question 22?

24. **Design an Experiment:** How could you decide if a kind of bacteria can grow anaerobically?

THE PRINCETON REVIEW

Test-Taking Tip

Investigate Ask what kinds of questions to expect on the test. Ask for practice tests so that you can become familiar with the test-taking materials.

Test Practice

Use these questions to test your Science Proficiency.

1. One group of bacteria are known as extremophiles, which literally means "lovers of the extreme." Which group of organisms would **BEST** fit this name?
A) eubacteria
B) archaebacteria
C) cyanobacteria
D) aerobes

2. Bioremediation has been shown to have several advantages over traditional methods of ecosystem cleanup. Which of the following is **NOT** an advantage of bioremediation?
A) It is less time consuming.
B) It is less costly.
C) It is more effective.
D) It can be done at the site of the pollution.

3. Many bacteria are considered beneficial organisms. Which of the following is **NOT** a reason they are considered beneficial?
A) They change nitrogen in the air to a form useful for plants.
B) They cause anthrax in cattle.
C) They are used in food production.
D) They are the source of some medicines.

CHAPTER

17

Protists and Fungi

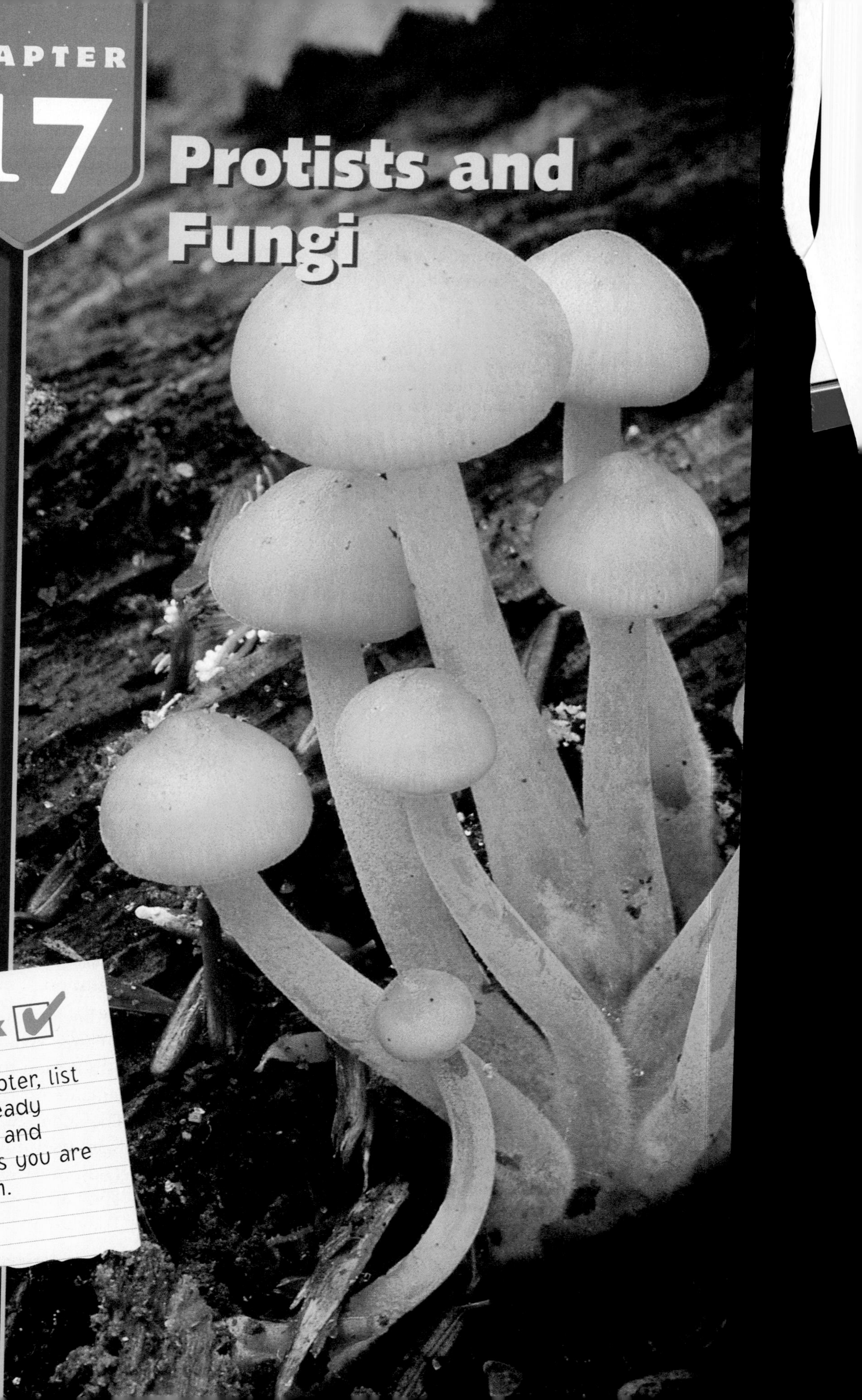

Chapter Preview

Section 17-1
Kingdom Protista

Section 17-2
Kingdom Fungi

Skills Preview

Skill Builders

- Compare and Contrast
- Use Variables, Constants, and Controls

Activities

- Observe
- Compare

MiniLabs

- Predict
- Estimate

Reading Check

As you read this chapter, list three things you already knew about protists and fungi, and ten things you are learning about them.

Explore Activity

Would you eat the mushrooms on the facing page? If you did, you would be sorry because they do not taste good. It is hard to tell by their appearance which mushrooms are good to eat and which are not. Some mushrooms are even poisonous. Though the mushrooms on the opposite page are not edible, there are many mushrooms that are. Edible mushrooms are sought after by gourmets for salads, casseroles, pizza, and other dishes. Morel mushrooms, for example, are so highly prized that those who search for them will keep their whereabouts a secret for fear that others will find their treasure. Do the activity below to learn about the parts of mushrooms.

Dissect a Mushroom

1. Look at a whole edible mushroom from the produce section of a grocery store.

2. Using a magnifying glass, observe the underside of the mushroom cap where the stalk is connected to it. Then, carefully pull off the cap and observe gills on which will form of thousands of tin structures calle

3. Use your f apart le proc sm

17-1 Kingdom Protista

What You'll Learn

- The characteristics shared by all protists
- How to describe the three groups of protists
- How to compare and contrast the protist groups

Vocabulary

protist
algae
protozoans
pseudopods
cilia

Why It's Important

- Kingdom Protista shows the importance of variety in the environment.

What is a protist?

Look at the organisms in **Figure 17-1.** Do you see any similarities among them? As different as they appear, all of these organisms belong to the protist kingdom. A **protist** is a single- or many-celled organism that lives in moist or wet surroundings. All protists have a nucleus and are therefore eukaryotic. Despite these similarities, the organisms in Kingdom Protista (proh TIHS tuh) vary greatly. Some protists contain chlorophyll and make their own food, and others don't. Protists are plantlike, animal-like, and funguslike.

Evolution of Protists

Not much evidence of the evolution of protists can be found because many lack hard parts and, as a result, few fossils of these organisms have been found. However, by studying the genes of modern protists, scientists are able to trace their ancestors. Scientists hypothesize that the common ancestor of all protists was a one-celled organism with a nucleus, mitochondria, and other cellular structures. The cellular structures of this organism may have been different from those found in modern protists. Evidence suggests that protists that can't make their own food evolved differently from protists that do make their own food. Some scientists suggest that a cyanobacterium, a bacterium that contains chlorophyll, was taken up by a one-celled organism with mitochondria. As this organism changed over time, the cyanobacterium became the organism's chloroplast, the organelle where food is produced. Plantlike protists probably developed from this kind of organism.

EXAMPLES OF Protists

Figure 17-1 Kingdom Protista is made up of a variety of organisms. **Using what you see in the art, write a description of a protist.**

Plantlike Protists

Plantlike protists are known as **algae** (AL jee). Some species of algae are one-celled and others are many-celled. All algae can make their own food because they contain the pigment chlorophyll in their chloroplasts. Even though all algae have chlorophyll, not all of them look green. Many have other pigments that cover up their chlorophyll. Species of algae are grouped into six main phyla according to their structure, pigments, and the way in which they store food.

Euglenoids

Algae that belong to the phylum Euglenophyta (yoo GLEE nuh fi tuh) have characteristics of both plants and animals. A typical euglenoid, the Euglena, is shown in **Figure 17-2.** Like plants, these one-celled algae have chloroplasts and produce carbohydrates as food. When light is not present, euglenas feed on bacteria and protists. Although euglenas have no cell walls, they do have a strong, flexible layer inside the cell membrane that helps them move and change shape. Many move by using whiplike tails called flagella. Another animal-like characteristic of euglenas is that they have an adaptation called an eyespot that responds to light.

Diatoms

Diatoms, shown in **Figure 17-3,** belong to the phylum Bacillariophyta (buh sih law ree oh FI tuh) and are found in both freshwater and salt water. Diatoms are photosynthetic, which means they can make their own food. These one-celled algae store food in the form of oil. They have a golden-brown pigment that masks the green chlorophyll. For this reason, they are sometimes referred to as gold-brown algae.

Diatoms reproduce in extremely large numbers. When the organisms die, their small cell walls sink to the floor of the

Figure 17-2 How are Euglenas similar to both plants and animals?

Magnification: 130×

Figure 17-3 The cell walls of diatoms contain silica, the main element in glass. The body of a diatom is like a small box with a lid. Diatoms are covered with markings and pits that form patterns.

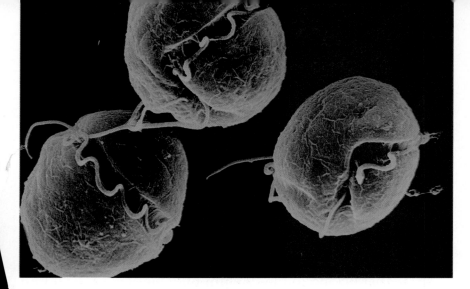

Figure 17-4 Dinoflagellates usually live in the sea. Notice the groove that houses one of the two flagella that mark all members

body of water and collect in deep layers. Ancient deposits of diatoms are mined with power shovels and used in insulation, filters, and road paint. The cell walls of diatoms produce the sparkle that makes some road lines visible at night and the crunch you feel when you use toothpaste to brush your teeth.

Dinoflagellates

Phylum Dinoflagellata contains species of one-celled algae called dinoflagellates that have red pigments. Because of their color, they are known as fire algae. The name *dinoflagellate* means "spinning flagellates." One of the flagella moves the cell, and the other circles the cell, causing it to spin with a motion similar to a top. Dinoflagellates, shown in **Figure 17-4,** store food in the form of starches and oils.

VISUALIZING
Green Algae

Figure 17-5 There are many different shapes among the species of green algae.

A *Chlamydomonas* is an example of a one-celled green alga. It is found in freshwater ponds and in moist soil.

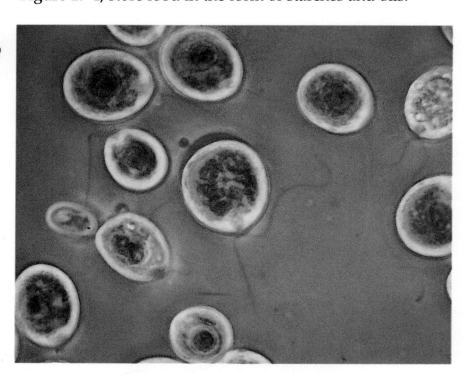

Magnification: 700✕

Almost all dinoflagellates live in salt water. They are important food sources for many saltwater organisms. Some dinoflagellates, however, do live in freshwater and are suspected to have caused health problems for humans and other organisms on the East Coast.

Green Algae

Seven thousand species of green algae form the phylum Chlorophyta (klaw RAHF uh duh), giving it the most variety of any group of protists. The presence of chlorophyll in green algae tells you that they undergo photosynthesis and produce food in the form of starch. They are important because nearly half of the oxygen we consume is a result of the photosynthesis of green algae.

Although most green algae live in water, others can live in many other environments, including tree trunks and other organisms. Green algae can be one-celled or many-celled. **Figure 17-5** shows different forms of green algae.

EXAMPLES OF Green Algae

- River moss
- *Chlamydomonas*
- *Volvox*
- *Spirogyra*
- *Ulva*

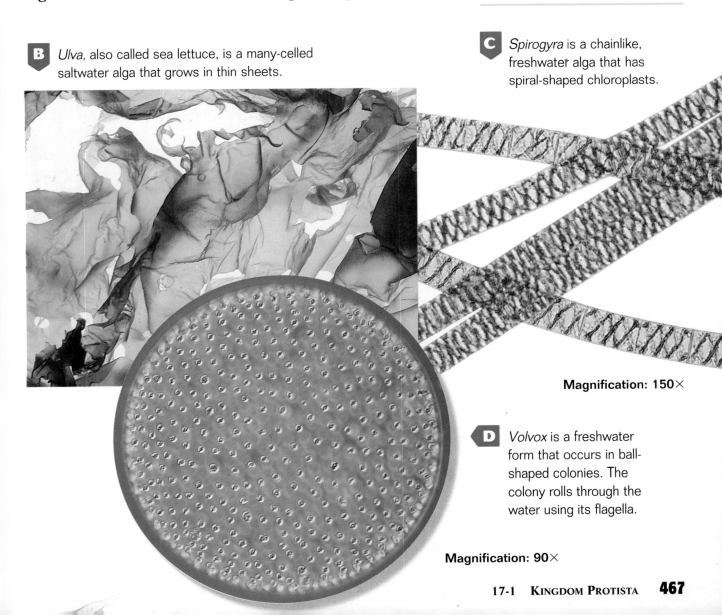

B *Ulva*, also called sea lettuce, is a many-celled saltwater alga that grows in thin sheets.

C *Spirogyra* is a chainlike, freshwater alga that has spiral-shaped chloroplasts.

Magnification: 150×

D *Volvox* is a freshwater form that occurs in ball-shaped colonies. The colony rolls through the water using its flagella.

Magnification: 90×

Figure 17-6 Carrageenan, a substance extracted from the red algae Irish moss, gives some puddings their smooth, creamy texture.

Reading Check

What are some common household items that contain red algae?

Red Algae

Red algae belong to the phylum Rhodophyta (roh DAHF uh duh). *Rhodo-* means "red" and describes the color of members of this phylum. Pudding and toothpaste are made with red algae. Carrageenan is found in red algae, such as the Irish moss shown in **Figure 17-6.** It gives toothpaste and pudding their smooth, creamy textures. Most red algae are many-celled. Some species of red algae can live up to 175 m deep in the ocean. Their red pigment allows them to absorb the limited amount of light that penetrates to those depths and enables them to produce the starch on which they live. ☑

Brown Algae

Brown algae make up the phylum Phaeophyta (fee AHF uh duh). Members of this phylum are many-celled and vary greatly in size. They are mostly found growing in cool, saltwater environments. Kelp, shown in **Figure 17-7,** is an important food source for many fish and invertebrates. They form a dense mat of stalks and leaflike blades where small fish and other animals live. Giant kelp are the largest organisms in the protist kingdom.

People in many parts of the world eat brown algae. The thick texture of foods such as ice cream and marshmallows is produced by algin, which is found in these algae. Brown algae also are used to make fertilizer. **Table 17-1** summarizes the different phyla of plantlike protists.

Figure 17-7 Giant kelp may be as much as 100 m long and can form forests like this one located off the coast of California. **What are some practical uses for brown algae?**

Table 17-1

The Plantlike Protists			
Phylum	**Example**	**Pigments**	**Other Characteristics**
Euglenophyta Euglenoids		Chlorophyll	One-celled alga that moves with flagella; has eyespot to detect light.
Bacillariophyta Diatoms		Golden Brown	One-celled alga with body made of two halves. Cell walls contain silica.
Dinoflagellata Dinoflagellates		Red	One-celled alga with two flagella. Flagella cause cell to spin. Some species cause red tide.
Chlorophyta Green Algae		Chlorophyll	One- and many-celled species. Most live in water; some live out of water, in or on other organisms.
Rhodophyta Red Algae		Red	Many-celled alga; carbohydrate in red algae is used to give some foods a creamy texture.
Phaeophyta Brown Algae		Brown	Many-celled alga; most live in salt water; important food source in aquatic environments.

Animal-Like Protists

One-celled, animal-like protists are known as **protozoans.** These complex organisms live in water, soil, and in both living and dead organisms. Many types of protozoans are parasites. A parasite is an organism that lives in or on another organism. Protozoans contain special vacuoles for digesting food and getting rid of excess water. Protozoans are separated into groups—rhizopods, flagellates, ciliates, and sporozoans—by how they move. **Figure 17-8** is an example of one type of protozoan.

TRAITS OF Animal-like Protists

- One-celled
- Many are parasites
- Grouped by how they move

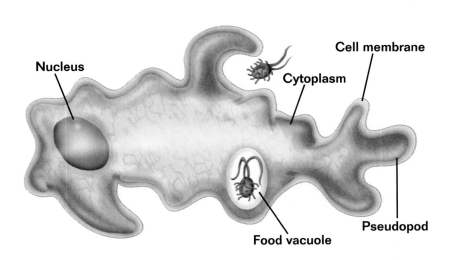

Nucleus
Cell membrane
Cytoplasm
Food vacuole
Pseudopod

Figure 17-8 An amoeba constantly changes shape as it extends its cytoplasm to capture food and move from place to place. Many areas of the world have a species of amoeba in the water that causes the condition dysentery. Dysentery leads to a severe form of diarrhea. **Why is an amoeba classified as a protozoan?**

Figure 17-9 Many saltwater rhizopods have skeletons made out of calcium carbonate, the material that makes up chalk.

A The White Cliffs of Dover in England are made almost entirely of the shells of billions of rhizopods.

B Rhizopod shells come in a variety of shapes.

Magnification: 100×

Figure 17-10 *Trypanosoma*, responsible for African sleeping sickness, is spread by the tsetse fly in Africa. This flagellate is the gray organism in the photo below. The red disks are blood cells. The disease causes fever, swollen glands, and extreme sleepiness.

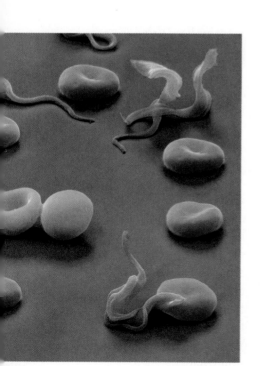

Magnification: 4000×

Rhizopods

The first protozoans were probably similar to members of the phylum Rhizopoda. The amoeba shown in **Figure 17-8** is a typical member of this phylum. Rhizopods move about and feed using temporary extensions of their cytoplasm called **pseudopods** (SEWD uh pahdz). The word *pseudopod* means "false foot." An amoeba extends the cytoplasm of a pseudopod on either side of a food particle such as a bacterium. Then, the pseudopod closes and the particle is trapped. A vacuole forms around the food and it is digested. Members of the phylum Rhizopoda, as shown in **Figure 17-9,** are found in freshwater and saltwater environments, and certain types are found in animals as parasites.

Flagellates

Protozoans that move using flagella are called flagellates and belong to the phylum Zoomastigina (zoe uh mas tuh JINE uh). All of the flagellates have long flagella that whip through a watery environment, moving the organism along. Many species of flagellates live in freshwater, though some are parasites.

Trypanosoma, shown in **Figure 17-10,** is a flagellate that causes African sleeping sickness in humans and other animals. Another flagellate lives in the digestive system of termites. The flagellates are beneficial to the termites because they produce enzymes that digest the wood the termites eat. Without the flagellates, the termites would not be able to digest the wood.

Cell membrane
Cilia
Food vacuole
Oral groove
Micronucleus
Macronucleus
Anal pore
Contractile vacuole

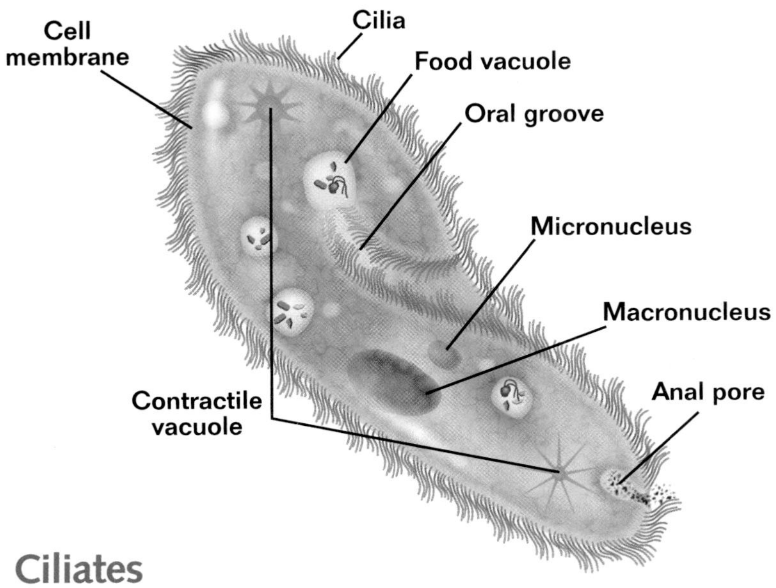

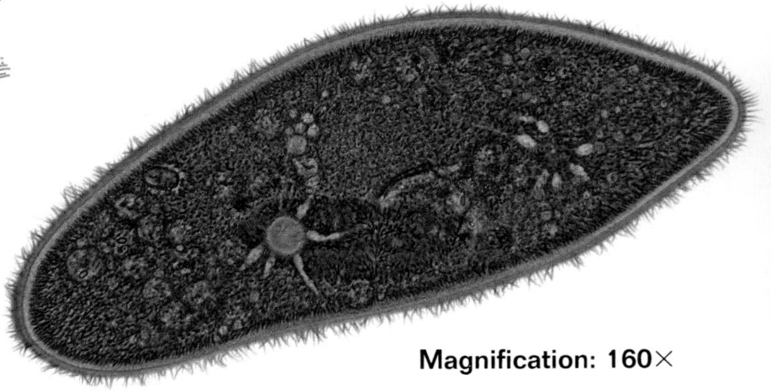

Figure 17-11 *Paramecium* is a typical ciliate found in many freshwater environments. These rapidly swimming protists consume bacteria. **Can you find the contractile vacuoles in the photo below? What is their function?**

Magnification: 160×

Ciliates

The most complex protozoans belong to the phylum Ciliophora. Members of this phylum move by using cilia. **Cilia** (SIHL ee uh) are short, threadlike structures that extend from the cell membrane. Ciliates may be covered with cilia or have cilia grouped in specific areas of the cell. Cilia beat in an organized way that allows the organism to move swiftly in any direction.

A typical ciliate is *Paramecium*, shown in **Figure 17-11**. In *Paramecium*, you can see another characteristic of the ciliates: each has two nuclei—a macronucleus and a micronucleus. The macronucleus controls the everyday functions of the cell. The micronucleus is used in reproduction. Paramecia usually feed on bacteria swept into the oral groove by the cilia. Once the food is inside the cell, a food vacuole forms and the food is digested. Wastes are removed through the anal pore. As the name implies, a contractile vacuole contracts and excess water is ejected from the cell.

Sporozoans

The phylum Sporozoa contains only parasitic organisms. Sporozoans have no way of moving on their own. All are parasites that live in and feed on the blood of humans and other animals, as shown in **Figure 17-12**.

Using Math

A paramecium may be about 0.1 cm long. Giant kelp, a kind of brown algae, may be as much as 100 m long—about the same length as a football field. Using these measurements, how many times larger is a giant kelp than a paramecium?

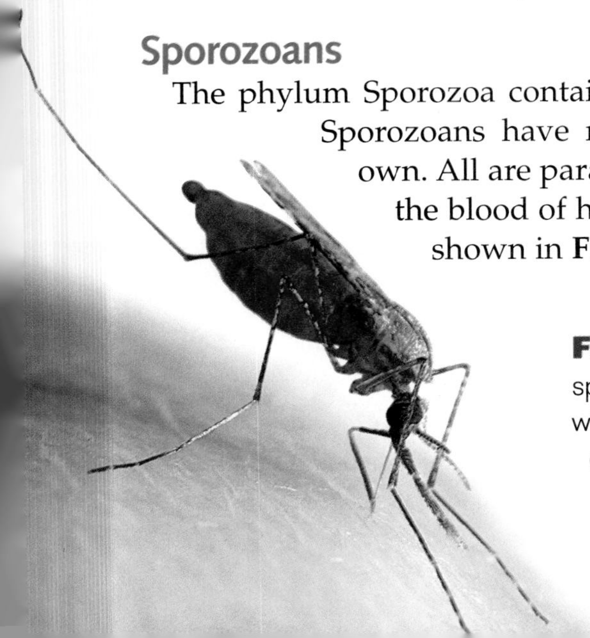

Figure 17-12 Only female *Anopheles* mosquitoes spread the sporozoan that causes malaria. Malaria is spread when an infected mosquito bites a human. This disease still causes about 1 million deaths each year worldwide.

Funguslike Protists

Funguslike protists include several small phyla that have features of both protists and fungi. Slime molds and water molds are funguslike protists. They get energy by breaking down organic materials. Examples of slime molds are illustrated in **Figure 17-13.**

Slime Molds

Slime molds are much more attractive than their name sounds. Many are brightly colored. They form a delicate, weblike structure on the surface of their food supply. Slime molds have some protozoan characteristics. During part of their life cycle, the cells of slime molds move by means of pseudopods and behave like amoebas. Slime molds reproduce with spores the way fungi do. You will learn about reproduction in fungi in the next section.

Although most slime molds live on decaying logs or dead leaves in moist, cool, shady woods, one common slime mold is sometimes found crawling across lawns and mulch. It creeps along feeding on bacteria and decayed plants and animals. When conditions become less favorable, reproductive structures form on stalks and spores are produced.

Figure 17-13 Slime molds come in many different forms and colors ranging from brilliant yellow or orange to rich blue, violet, pink, and jet black. **How are slime molds similar to both protists and fungi?**

Blue slime mold

Pretzel slime mold

Pink slime mold

Water Molds and Downy Mildews

Water molds, downy mildews, and white rusts make up another phylum of funguslike protists. Most members of this large and diverse group live in water or moist places. Most water molds appear as fuzzy, white growths on decaying matter. They are called funguslike protists because they grow as a mass of threads over a plant or animal, digest it, and then absorb the organism's nutrients. Water molds have cell walls as do fungi, but their relatively simple cells are more like protozoans. Unlike fungi, they produce reproductive cells with flagella at some point in their reproductive cycles. Some water molds are parasites of plants while others feed on dead organisms. **Figure 17-14B** shows a parasitic water mold that grows on decaying fish. If you have an aquarium, you may see water molds attack a fish and cause its death.

Another important member of this phylum is a downy or powdery mildew that causes a disease on the leaves of many plants when days have been warm and nights become cooler and moist. In fact, the most well-known member of this phylum is the downy mildew, pictured in **Figure 17-14A,** that caused the Irish potato famine in the 1840s. Potatoes were

*inter*NET
CONNECTION

Visit the Glencoe Science Web Site at **www.glencoe.com/ sec/science/fl** for more information about funguslike protists.

Problem Solving

Puzzled About Slime

At one time, slime molds were classified as fungi. This is because at times, when conditions are unfavorable, they dry up and look like tiny mushrooms. Now, they are classified as protists because they move like protists and have characteristics similar to protists.

Slime molds, such as the scrambled egg slime mold, can be found covering moist wood as in the photograph shown below. They may be white or bright red, yellow, or purple. If you looked at a piece of slime mold on a microscope slide, you would see that the cell nuclei move back and forth as the cytoplasm streams along. This is the method slime mold uses to creep over the wood.

Think Critically: What characteristics do slime molds share with protists? In what ways are slime molds similar to amoebas and fungi? In what ways are they different?

Scrambled egg slime mold

Figure 17-14 The potato plant (A) and the fish (B) show the effects of fungus like protists.

Ireland's main crop and the primary food source for its people. When the potato crop became infected with downy mildew, potatoes rotted in the fields, leaving many people with no food. Nearly 1 million people died in the resulting famine. Many others left Ireland and emigrated to the United States. This downy mildew continues to be a problem for potato growers, even in the United States.

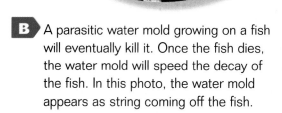

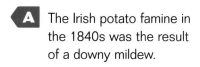

A The Irish potato famine in the 1840s was the result of a downy mildew.

B A parasitic water mold growing on a fish will eventually kill it. Once the fish dies, the water mold will speed the decay of the fish. In this photo, the water mold appears as string coming off the fish.

Section Assessment

1. What are the main characteristics of all protists?
2. Compare and contrast the three groups of protists.
3. How are plantlike protists classified into different phyla?
4. **Think Critically:** Why aren't there many fossils of the different groups of protists?
5. **Skill Builder**
   Making and Using Tables Do the **Chapter 17 Skill Activity** on page 724 and compare and contrast the protist groups.

Using Computers

Spreadsheet Use a spreadsheet to make a table that compares the characteristics of the four phyla of protozoans. Include phylum, example species, method of transportation, and other characteristics. If you need help, refer to page 704.

Comparing Algae and Protozoans

Algae and protozoan cells have characteristics that are similar enough to place them within the same kingdom. However, the variety of forms within Kingdom Protista is great. In this activity, you can observe many of the differences that make organisms in Kingdom Protista so diverse.

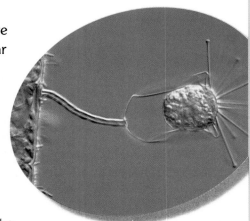

Materials
- Cultures of *Paramecium, Amoeba, Euglena,* and *Spirogyra*
  ***prepared slides of above organisms**
- Prepared slide of slime mold
- Coverslips (5)
- Microscope
  ***stereomicroscope**
- Dropper
- Microscope slides (5)
  ***Alternate Materials**

What You'll Investigate
What are the differences between algae and protozoans?

Goals
- **Draw and label** the organisms you examine.
- **Observe** the differences between algae and protozoans.

Safety Precautions
🚫 🥽 🧤 Make sure to wash your hands after handling algae and protozoans.

Procedure
1. **Design** a data table in your Science Journal for your drawings and observations.
2. **Make** a wet mount of the *Paramecium* culture. If you need help doing this, refer to Appendix D.

3. **Observe** the wet mount first under low and then under high power. Draw and label the organism.
4. Repeat steps 2 and 3 with the other cultures. Return all preparations to your teacher and wash your hands.
5. **Observe** the slide of slime mold under low and high power. Record your observations.

Conclude and Apply
1. For each organism that could move, **label** the structure that enabled the movement.
2. Which protists make their own food? **Explain** how you know that they make their own food.
3. **Identify** those protists with animal characteristics.

Protist Observations				
	Paramecium	**Amoeba**	**Euglena**	**Spirogyra**
Drawing				

What are fungi?

Do you think you can find members of Kingdom Fungi in a quick trip around your house or apartment? You can find fungi in your kitchen if you have mushroom soup or fresh mushrooms. Yeasts are a type of fungi used to make bread and cheese. You also may find mold, a type of fungus, growing on an old loaf of bread, or mildew, another fungus, growing on your shower curtain.

As important as fungi seem in the production of different foods, they are most important in their role as organisms that decompose or break down organic materials. Food scraps, clothing, dead plants, and animals are all made of organic material. Fungi work to decompose, or break down, all these materials and return them to the soil. The materials returned to the soil are then reused by plants. Fungi, along with bacteria, are nature's recyclers. They keep Earth from becoming buried under mountains of waste materials.

Characteristics of Fungi

Fungi were once classified as plants because, like plants, they grow anchored in soil and have cell walls. But, unlike plants, fungi do not make their own food or have the specialized tissues and organs of plants, such as leaves and roots. Most species of fungi are many-celled. The body of a fungus is usually a mass of many-celled, threadlike tubes called **hyphae** (HI fee), as illustrated in **Figure 17-15**.

Fungi don't contain chlorophyll and therefore cannot make their own food. Most fungi feed on dead or decaying tissues. Organisms that obtain food in this way are called *saprophytes*. A fungus gives off enzymes that break down food outside of

Hyphae

Figure 17-15 Most hyphae grow underground, though they also may form reproductive structures such as the mushrooms pictured here.

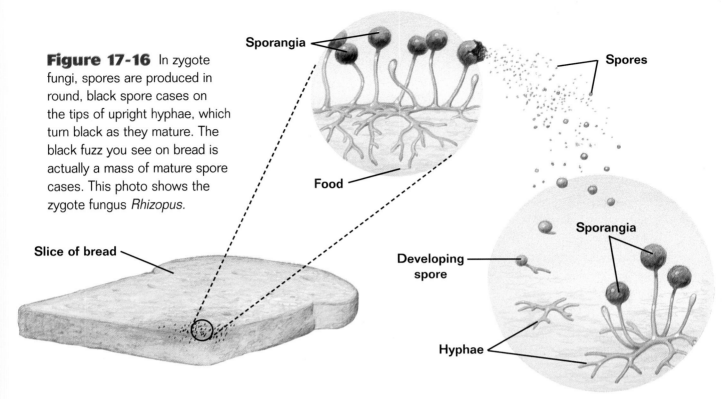

Figure 17-16 In zygote fungi, spores are produced in round, black spore cases on the tips of upright hyphae, which turn black as they mature. The black fuzz you see on bread is actually a mass of mature spore cases. This photo shows the zygote fungus *Rhizopus*.

itself. Then, the fungus cells absorb the digested food. Fungi that cause athlete's foot and ringworm are parasites. They obtain their food directly from living things.

Fungi grow best in warm, humid areas, such as tropical forests or the spaces between your toes.

A **spore** is a reproductive cell that forms new organisms without fertilization. The structures in which fungi produce spores are used to classify fungi into one of four phyla.

Zygote Fungi

The fuzzy black mold that you sometimes find growing on an old loaf of bread or perhaps a piece of fruit is a type of zygote fungus. Fungi that belong to this division, the phylum Zygomycota, produce spores in round spore cases called sporangia (spuh RAN jee uh) on the tips of upright hyphae, as illustrated in **Figure 17-16.** When each sporangium splits open, hundreds of spores are released into the air. Each spore will grow into more mold if it lands where there is enough moisture, a warm temperature, and a food supply.

Sac Fungi

Yeasts, molds, morels, and truffles are all examples of sac fungi. The spores of these fungi are produced in a little saclike structure called an ascus. The phylum Ascomycota (ahs coh my COH tuh) is named for these sacs. The ascospores are released when the tip of an ascus breaks open.

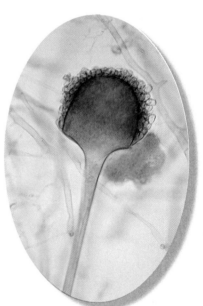

Magnification: 100×

Immature Rhizopus spore

Interpreting Spore Prints

Procedure

1. Obtain several mushrooms from the grocery store and let them age until the undersides look brown.
2. Remove the stems and arrange the mushroom caps with the gills down on a piece of unlined white paper.
3. Let the mushroom caps sit undisturbed overnight and remove them from the paper the next day.

Analysis

1. Draw and label a sketch of the results in your Science Journal.
2. Describe the marks on the page and what made them.
3. How could you estimate the number of new mushrooms that could be produced from one mushroom cap?

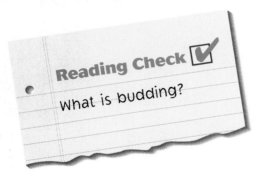

Reading Check ✓
What is budding?

Many sac fungi are well known by farmers because they destroy plant crops. Diseases caused by sac fungi are Dutch elm disease, apple scab, and ergot disease of rye.

Yeast is an economically important sac fungus. Yeasts don't always reproduce by forming spores. They also reproduce asexually by budding, as illustrated in **Figure 17-17. Budding** is a form of asexual reproduction in which a new organism grows off the side of the parent. Yeasts are used in the baking industry. As yeasts grow, they use sugar for energy and produce alcohol and carbon dioxide as waste products. The carbon dioxide causes bread to rise. ✓

Imperfect Fungi

The so-called imperfect fungi, phylum Deuteromycota, are species of fungi in which a sexual stage has never been observed. When a sexual stage of one of these fungi is observed, the species is immediately classified as one of the other three phyla. Instead, imperfect fungi reproduce asexually, most through the use of spores. *Penicillium* is one example from this group. Penicillin, an antibiotic, is an important product of this fungus. Other examples of imperfect fungi are species that cause ringworm and athlete's foot. Because changes in classification now allow asexual fungi to be included in other phyla, *Penicillium* is sometimes considered a sac fungus.

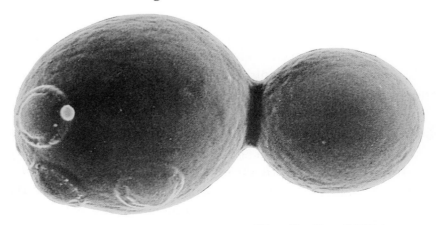

Figure 17-17 Yeasts can reproduce by forming buds off the side of the parents. The bud pinches off and forms an identical cell. **What are yeasts used for?**

Magnification: 6100×

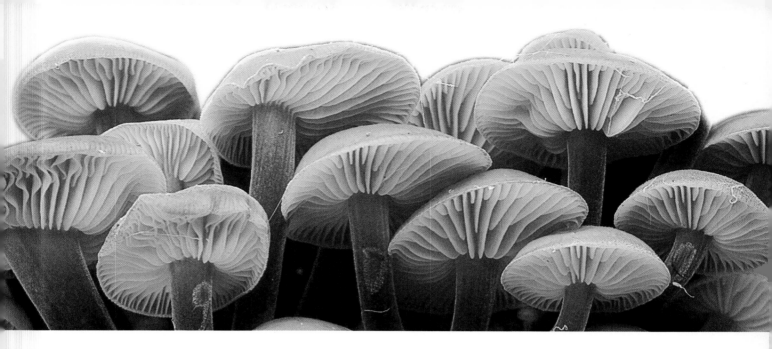

Figure 17-18 A mushroom is the spore-producing structure of a club fungus. The gills are thin sheets of tissue found under the mushroom cap. Spores are contained in many club-shaped structures that line the gills. **What are these club-shaped structures called?**

Club Fungi

The mushrooms shown in **Figure 17-18** are members of the phylum Basidiomycota. These fungi are commonly known as club fungi. The spores of these fungi are produced in a club-shaped structure called a basidium. The spores you observed on the gills of the mushroom in the MiniLab on the previous page were produced in the basidia.

Many of the club fungi are economically important. Rusts and smuts cause billions of dollars worth of damage to food crops each year. Cultivated mushrooms are an important food crop, but you should never eat a wild mushroom because many are poisonous.

Lichens

The colorful organisms in **Figure 17-19** are lichens. A **lichen** (LI kun) is an organism that is made of a fungus and either a green alga or a cyanobacterium. When two organisms live together, they often have a relationship in which both organisms benefit. The cells of the alga live tangled up in the threadlike strands of the fungus. The alga gets a moist, protected place to live, and the fungus gets food made by the green alga or cyanobacterium. Lichens are an important food source for many animals, including caribou and musk oxen.

CHEMISTRY
INTEGRATION

pH

The measurement of how much acid or base a substance contains is its pH. Acids are measured on a pH scale that ranges from 1 to 14. Substances that have a pH lower than 7 are considered acidic. Acids become stronger as the pH decreases. The acids produced by lichens are weak, but given enough time, they can erode sedimentary rock. Look up the pH for some common acids, such as stomach acid, lemon juice, and battery acid. In your Science Journal, compare these to the pH of lichen.

Figure 17-19 Lichens can grow upright, appear leafy, or look like a crust on bare rock. All three forms may grow near each other. **Can you think of one way that lichens might be classified?**

Rocks crumble as they weather. Lichens are important in the weathering process because they are able to grow on bare rock. Lichens release acids as part of their metabolism. The acids break down the rock. As bits of rock accumulate and lichens die and decay, soil is formed. This soil supports the growth of other species. Organisms, such as the lichens seen in **Figure 17-19,** that grow on bare rock are called pioneer species because they are the first organisms to appear in a barren area.

Earth scientists also use lichens to monitor pollution levels because many species of lichens quickly die when they are exposed to pollution. When the lichen species return to grow on tree trunks and buildings, it is an indication that the pollution has been cleaned up.

Crusty lichen

British soldier lichen

Leafy lichen

Section Assessment

1. How do fungi obtain food?
2. What common characteristics are shared by fungi?
3. What are some important functions of lichens?
4. **Think Critically:** If an imperfect fungus were found to produce basidia under some circumstances, how would the fungus be reclassified?
5. **Skill Builder**
   Comparing and Contrasting
   Organize information about fungi in a table. Use this information to compare and contrast the characteristics of the four divisions of fungi. Include information on lichens as a fifth division in your table. If you need help, refer to Comparing and Contrasting in the **Skill Handbook** on page 686.

Using Math

Of the 100 000 species of fungi, approximately 30 000 are sac fungi. From this information, estimate the percent of sac fungi as a part of the total fungi kingdom.

Monitoring Red Tides

What is a red tide?

Imagine a humpback whale dying and washing up on a beach. Then multiply this death by 14. Add to this grisly scene tons of dead fish littering beaches from Florida to Massachusetts. Such events actually happened in 1987. The cause was a single species of dinoflagellate, a type of microscopic algae (see inset). At times, certain kinds of dinoflagellates reproduce rapidly to form extremely dense populations, or "blooms," that turn the ocean surface red—a condition known as a red tide (see photo at left). Pigments in the dinoflagellates are responsible for the red color. It is not unusual for a red tide to stretch hundreds of kilometers along a coastline. Red tides often occur in warm, shallow parts of the ocean, or where runoff from the land adds nutrients to seawater.

Red tides can be deadly because some dinoflagellates produce poisonous substances called toxins. When a red tide occurs, the algae are so numerous that the amount of toxin in the water is concentrated enough to kill fish and marine mammals such as whales. Toxins also accumulate in the tissues of filter-feeding shellfish such as clams and mussels, making them poisonous. People who eat shellfish contaminated by a red tide can become ill and may die.

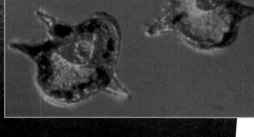

How are red tides monitored?

In the past, scientists monitored red tides by sampling seawater and shellfish for the presence of dinoflagellates. Wherever large numbers of dinoflagellates were detected, researchers would alert the public not to eat seafood from those areas. This method of monitoring red tides was not always effective, however, because only small stretches of ocean could be tested at any one time, and red tides often developed before scientists became aware of them.

More recently, satellites equipped with infrared cameras have been used to monitor red tides from space. Satellite images reveal sea-surface temperatures over huge areas of ocean and give scientists clues as to where red tides are most likely to occur. Predicting red tides before they develop can help save lives.

interNET CONNECTION

Visit the Glencoe Science Web Site at **www.glencoe.com/sec/science/fl** for more information about red tides. Determine whether there is an area or time of year in which red tides occur with noticeable frequency.

Materials

- Cultures of fungi (bread mold, mushrooms, yeasts, lichens, or *Penicillium*)
- Cellophane tape
- Microscope
- Microscope slides
- Coverslips
- Magnifying lens

Comparing Types of Fungi

Fungi differ mainly in their reproductive structures. The diversity of these structures allows scientists to classify fungi as zygote fungi, club fungi, sac fungi, or imperfect fungi. In this activity, you will compare the reproductive structures in cultures of fungi.

What You'll Investigate

How do reproductive structures of fungi compare?

Goals

- **Observe** the appearance of fungi colonies.
- **Compare** the reproductive structures of fungi cultures.
- **Draw, label, and identify** different types of fungi.

Safety Precautions

Make sure to wash your hands after handling fungi.

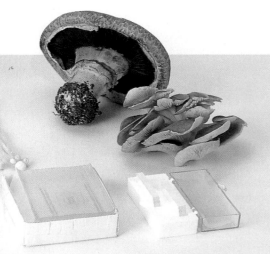

Procedure

1. **Design** a data table like the one below in your Science Journal with columns labeled *Fungus, Colony Appearance, Reproductive Structures,* and *Fungi Division.*

2. **Compare and contrast** the cultures of fungi in drawings that you label.

3. Your teacher will demonstrate how to collect the reproductive structures of fungi with cellophane tape by gently touching the tape to your samples.

4. Place the tape, adhesive side up, on a microscope slide and cover it with a coverslip. If you need help making a wet mount, see **Appendix D.**

5. Draw and label the reproductive structures.

6. Repeat this procedure for each culture of fungus.

7. Fill in the data table you designed. One column has been done for you below.

Conclude and Apply

1. Write a description of the reproductive structures you observed. Include relative numbers, shape of cells, and size.

2. From your descriptions, explain why fungi are classified based on their reproductive structures.

3. List the four divisions of fungi, and give an example of each division.

Fungi Observations			
Fungus	**Colony Appearance**	**Reproductive Structures**	**Fungi Division**
mushrooms	rounded stalks with clublike caps	basidia	club fungi

For a **preview** of this chapter, study this Reviewing Main Ideas before you read the chapter. After you have studied this chapter, you can use the Reviewing Main Ideas to **review** the chapter.

The Glencoe MindJogger, Audiocassettes, and CD-ROM provide additional opportunities for review.

Section

17-1 KINGDOM PROTISTA

Protists are one- or many-celled eukaryotic organisms. They are thought to have evolved from a one-celled organism with a nucleus, mitochondria, and other cellular structures. The protist kingdom has members that are plantlike, animal-like, and funguslike. Plantlike protists are classified by their structure, their pigments, and the way in which they store food. Animal-like protists are separated into groups by how they move. Funguslike protists have characteristics of both protists and fungi.

What common names are given to each group of protists?

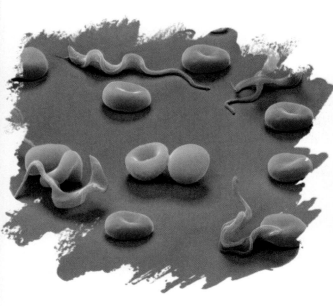

Reading Check ✓

Review "Other Charac-
teristics" in Table 17-1.
How could you break the
information under this
heading into at least two
columns?

Section

17-2 KINGDOM FUNGI

Fungi are organisms that reproduce using **spores.** They are saprophytes, or parasites, which means they feed off other things because they cannot make their own food. One of the most important roles of fungi is to decompose organic material and return the nutrients to the soil. There are four groups of fungi: zygote fungus, sac fungus, club fungus, and imperfect fungus. Fungi are placed into one of these groups according to the structures in which they produce spores. *Why are imperfect fungi given that name?*

Career
CONNECTION

Dr. Regina Benjamin, Family Practice Physician

Dr. Benjamin runs a family practice in Bayou La Batre, Alabama. She's the only doctor in town, and about 80 percent of her patients live below the poverty level. Dr. Benjamin sees a lot of skin infections caused by fungi because the environment is humid, which promotes the growth of fungus. Fungal infections can be difficult to treat. *Why is classifying protists and fungi important for health care professionals?*

Chapter 17 Assessment

Using Vocabulary

a. algae
b. budding
c. cilia
d. hyphae
e. lichen
f. protist
g. protozoans
h. pseudopods
i. spore

Each phrase below describes a science term from the list. Write the term that matches the phrase describing it.

1. reproductive cell of a fungus
2. eukaryotic organism that is animal-like, plantlike, or funguslike
3. threadlike structures used for movement
4. plantlike protists
5. organism made up of a fungus and an alga or a cyanobacterium

Checking Concepts

Choose the word or phrase that best answers the question.

6. Which of the following is an example of one-celled algae?
   A) paramecia   C) amoeba
   B) lichen   D) diatom

7. What color are members of phylum Bacillariophyta?
   A) green   C) golden-brown
   B) red   D) brown

8. Which of the following organisms cause red tides when found in large numbers?
   A) *Euglena*   C) *Ulva*
   B) diatoms   D) dinoflagellates

9. What phylum do brown algae belong to?
   A) Rhodophyta   C) Phaeophyta
   B) Dinoflagellata D) Euglenophyta

10. Which of the following moves using cilia?
    A) *Amoeba*   C) *Trypanosoma*
    B) *Paramecium*   D) *Euglena*

11. Where would you most likely find funguslike protists?
    A) on decaying logs
    B) in bright light
    C) on dry surfaces
    D) on metal surfaces

12. Decomposition is an important role of which organisms?
    A) protozoans   C) plants
    B) algae   D) fungi

13. Which of the following organisms are monitors of pollution levels?
    A) club fungus   C) slime mold
    B) lichen   D) imperfect fungus

14. What produce the spores in mushrooms?
    A) sporangia   C) asci
    B) basidia   D) hyphae

15. Which of the following is an example of an imperfect fungus?
    A) mushroom   C) *Penicillium*
    B) yeast   D) lichen

Thinking Critically

16. What kind of environment is needed to prevent fungal growth?

17. Look at **Figure 17-5C** again. Why is *Spirogyra* a good name for this green alga?

18. Compare and contrast one-celled, colonial, chain, and many-celled algae.

19. Why do scientists find it difficult to trace the origin of fungi? Explain your answer.

20. Explain the adaptations of fungi that enable them to get food.

Developing Skills

If you need help, refer to the **Skill Handbook.**

21. **Observing and Inferring:** Match the prefix of each alga, *Chloro-, Phaeo-,* and *Rhodo-,* with the correct color: brown, green, and red.

22. **Concept Mapping:** Complete the following concept map on a separate sheet of paper.

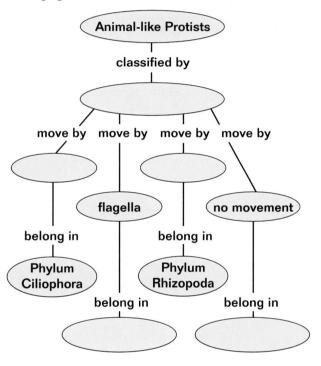

23. **Comparing and Contrasting:** Make a chart comparing and contrasting sac fungi, zygote fungi, club fungi, and imperfect fungi.

24. **Classifying:** Classify the following organisms based on their method of movement: *Euglena,* water molds, *Amoeba,* dinoflagellates, *Paramecium,* slime molds, *Trypanosoma,* and *Volvox.*

25. **Design an Experiment:** You find a new and unusual fungus growing in your refrigerator. Design an experiment to determine what phylum it belongs to.

THE PRINCETON REVIEW

Test-Taking Tip

Where's the Fire? Slow down! Double-check your math, and go back over reading passages. Remember that doing most of the questions and getting them right is always better than doing all the questions and getting lots of them wrong.

Test Practice

Use these questions to test your Science Proficiency.

1. Algae and plants have some characteristics in common. Which of the following **BEST** represents differences between algae and plants?
   A) Algae have cell walls, but plants do not.
   B) Plants have chlorophyll, but algae do not.
   C) Algae have cell membranes and nuclei, but plants do not.
   D) Plants have roots, stems, and leaves, but algae do not.

2. At one time, some protists were classified as animals because they moved and engulfed food. Which of the following protists are most like animals?
   A) protozoans
   B) algae
   C) slime molds and water molds
   D) zygote fungi

3. Fungi are classified according to how they produce sexual spores. Which of the following groups of fungi are **NOT** known to ever produce sexual spores?
   A) zygote fungi
   B) imperfect fungi
   C) club fungi
   D) sac fungi

6

Plants & Animals

What's Happening Here?

A peacock fans its spectacular feathers (left) to attract a mate. Why must it find a mate? To produce more peacocks (and peahens). Plant reproduction occurs in many different ways. Bromeliad berries develop from flowers that grow on a stem with brilliantly colored, petal-like structures (below). Birds feed on the berries. As birds visit other plants, they excrete the seeds of the berries, thereby planting bromeliads. Thus, animals help plants by scattering seeds, and plants help animals, including humans, by providing food. In this unit, you'll learn how plants make this important contribution to all life, and you'll explore the differences within the animal kingdom.

interNET CONNECTION

Explore the Glencoe Science Web Site at **www.glencoe.com/sec/science/fl** to find out more about topics found in this unit.

Chapter Preview

Section 18-1
Characteristics
of Plants

Section 18-2
Seedless Plants

Section 18-3
Seed Plants

Skills Preview

Skill Builders
- Hypothesize
- Map Concepts

Activities
- Predict
- Compare and Contrast

MiniLabs
- Measure in SI
- Observe and Infer

Reading Check ✔

As you read, list terms that describe parts of both plants and people, such as *vascular tissue*, *cuticle*, and *epidermis*. Define the terms as they relate to plants and to people.

Explore Activity

Plants are all around—in parks and gardens, by streams and on rocks, in houses, and even on dinner plates. Do you eat salads? Salads are made up of edible plants. What plants would you choose for a salad? Do you know what plant parts you would be eating? In the following activity, find out which plant parts are edible. Then, in the chapter, learn about plant life.

Infer Which Plant Parts Are Edible

1. Make a list of five foods that you might eat during a typical day.

2. Decide whether the foods contain any plant parts.

3. Infer what plant parts were used to make your five foods.

Science Journal

Plants provide many nutrients. List the nutrients from a package of dried fruit in your Science Journal. As a class, compare the nutrients in the dried fruits each student selected.

18·1

18·1 Characteristics of Plants

18·1

What You'll Learn

▶ The characteristics of plants
▶ What plant adaptations make it possible for plants to survive on land
▶ Similarities and differences between vascular and nonvascular plants

Vocabulary

cellulose
cuticle
vascular plant
nonvascular plant

Why It's Important

▶ Plants produce food and oxygen for most organisms on Earth. Without plants, there would be no life.

What is a plant?

Do you enjoy walking along nature trails in parks like the one shown in **Figure 18-1?** Maybe you've taken off your shoes and walked barefoot on soft, cool grass. Perhaps you've climbed a tree to see what your world looks like from high in its branches. In every instance, members of the plant kingdom surrounded you.

Now look at **Figure 18-2.** These organisms, mosses and liverworts, have characteristics that identify them as plants, too. What do they have in common with grasses, trees, and ferns? What makes a plant a plant?

Characteristics of Plants

All plants are made of eukaryotic cells that have cell walls. Cell walls provide structure and protection for plant cells. Many plant cells contain the green pigment chlorophyll. Plants range in size from microscopic water ferns to giant sequoia trees that are sometimes more than 100 m in height. They have roots or rootlike structures that hold them in the ground or onto something. Plants have successfully adapted to nearly every environment on Earth. Some grow in frigid, ice-bound polar regions and others grow in hot, dry deserts. Many plants must live in or near water.

About 285 000 plant species have been discovered and identified. Scientists think many more are still to be found, mainly in tropical rain forests. If you were to make a list of all

Figure 18-1 All plants are many celled and nearly all contain chlorophyll. Grasses, trees, and ferns all are members of Kingdom Plantae.

Figure 18-2 Plants include liverworts (A) and mosses (B).

the plants you could name, you probably would include vegetables, fruits, and field crops like wheat, rice, or corn. These plants are important food sources to humans and other consumers. Without plants, most life on Earth as we know it would not be possible.

Origin and Evolution of Plants

Where did the first plants come from? Like all life, early plants probably came from the sea, evolving from plantlike protists. What evidence is there that this is true? Both plants and green algae, a type of protist, have the same types of chlorophyll and carotenoids (KER uh tuh noydz) in their cells. Carotenoids are red, yellow, or orange pigments found in some plants and in all cyanobacteria.

Fossil Record

One way to understand the evolution of plants is to look at the fossil record. Unfortunately, plants usually decay before they form fossils. The oldest fossil plants are from the Silurian period and are about 420 million years old. Fossils of early plants are similar to the plantlike protists. Fossils of *Rhynia major*, illustrated in **Figure 18-3,** represent the earliest land plants. Scientists hypothesize that these kinds of plants evolved into some plants that exist today.

Cone-bearing plants, such as pines, probably evolved from a group of plants that grew about 350 million years ago. Fossils of these plants have been dated to the Paleozoic era, 300 million years ago. Flowering plants did not exist until the Cretaceous period, about 120 million years ago. The exact origin of flowering plants is not known.

Using Math

Fossil evidence shows that the first land plants lived about 420 million years ago. If Earth is 4.6 billion years old, what percent of Earth's age was Earth without land plants?

Figure 18-3 Fossils of *Rhynia major*, an extinct, small land plant, show that it had underground stems but no true roots or leaves.

Adaptations to Land

Imagine life for a one-celled green alga, a protist, floating in a shallow pool. The water in the pool surrounds and supports it. The alga can make its own food through the process of photosynthesis. Materials enter and leave the cell through the cell membrane. The alga has everything it needs to survive.

Now, imagine a summer drought. The pool begins to dry up. Soon, the alga is on damp mud and is no longer supported by the pool's water, as shown in **Figure 18-4.** It won't starve because it still can make its own food. As long as the soil stays damp, the alga can move materials in and out through the cell membrane. But, what will happen if the drought continues, and the soil becomes drier and drier? The alga will continue to lose water because water diffuses through the cell membrane from where there is more water to where there is less water. Without water in its environment, the alga will dry up and die.

Protection and Support

What adaptations would make it possible for plants to survive on land? Losing water is a major problem for plants. What would help a plant conserve water? Plant cells have cell membranes, but they also have rigid cell walls outside the membrane. Cell walls contain **cellulose** (SEL yuh lohs), an organic compound made up of long chains of glucose molecules. Some woody plants, such as oaks and pines, are as much as 50 percent cellulose. Cell walls provide structure and support and help reduce water loss.

Figure 18-4 Algae must have water to survive.

A Each green alga produces its own food and moves materials in and out through the cell membrane. **By what process do algae make food?**

B If a pond completely dries up, the algae in it will die.

Figure 18-5 A waxy cuticle is an adaptation that enables plants to survive on land.

A Rain beads up on the leaves of some plants because of the cuticle. This reduces the amount of moisture on plant surfaces.

B A waxy cuticle prevents moisture loss from this prickly pear cactus. **Why is this important for a cactus?**

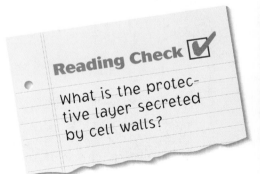

C Waxy cuticles are often found on flowers such as this orchid.

Covering the stems, leaves, and flowers of some land plants is a cuticle. The **cuticle** (KYEWT ih kul) is a waxy, protective layer secreted by the cell walls. It slows down the evaporation of water from a plant. After it rains, go outside and see how raindrops bead up on some plant surfaces, as illustrated in **Figure 18-5A.** Removing water from plant surfaces is important because too much moisture on a plant may affect cell functions. Too much surface moisture also may lead to fungal diseases. The cuticle is an adaptation that enabled plants to live on land. ☑

Life on land meant that plant cells could not depend on water to support them or to move substances from one cell to the next. Support came with the evolution of stems and substances that strengthen the cell walls. Eventually, plants developed tissues that distribute materials.

Reproduction

The move to land by plants not only meant changes to reduce water loss and increase support, but it also meant a change in plant reproduction. Plants evolved from organisms that reproduced in water. They completely depended on water for reproduction and survival. Some plants still require water to reproduce, but others do not. The development of cones and flowers that produce seeds allowed these plants to survive on land.

Reading Check ☑

What is the protective layer secreted by cell walls?

Life on Land

Life on land has some advantages for plants. There is more sunlight and carbon dioxide for plants on land than in water. Plants use sunlight and carbon dioxide for the food-making process, photosynthesis. During photosynthesis, plants give off oxygen. As more and more plants adapted to life on land, the amount of oxygen in Earth's atmosphere increased. This paved the way for the evolution of organisms that depend on oxygen. In some cases, it meant that some organisms evolved together. For example, some flowering plants provided animals with food, and the animals pollinated the plant's flowers.

Classification of Plants

Today, the plant kingdom is classified into major groups called divisions, as illustrated in **Figure 18-6.** A division is the same as a phylum in other kingdoms, as listed in Appendix E of this book. A less formal way to group plants is as vascular or nonvascular plants. **Vascular plants** have tissues that make up the organ system that carries water, nutrients, and other substances throughout the plant. **Nonvascular plants** have no vascular tissue and use other ways to move water and substances.

interNET CONNECTION

Visit the Glencoe Science Web Site at **www.glencoe.com/ sec/science/fl** for more information about plants that are sources of medicines. In your Science Journal, list five medicines that come from plants.

Problem Solving

Cause and Effect in Nature

People in all cultures have used and still use plants as medicine. Some Native American cultures used willow bark to cure headaches. Heart problems were treated with foxglove in England and sea onions in Egypt. In Peru, the bark of the cinchona tree was used to treat malaria. Scientists have found that many native cures are medically sound. Willow bark contains salicylates, the main ingredient in aspirin. Foxglove, as seen in the photo to the right, is still the main source of digitalis, a drug prescribed for heart problems. Cinchona bark contains quinine, an anti-malarial drug.

Think Critically: Predict how the destruction of the rain forests might affect research for new drugs from plants.

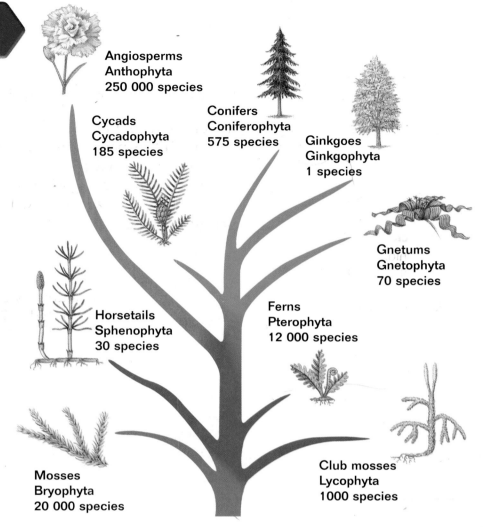

VISUALIZING
The Plant Kingdom

Figure 18-6 The diversity of Kingdom Plantae is represented by a branching tree, composed of different divisions. All of these plant groups are related but have differences that separate them. **What differences can you detect among the plant divisions in this illustration?**

Angiosperms
Anthophyta
250 000 species

Cycads
Cycadophyta
185 species

Conifers
Coniferophyta
575 species

Ginkgoes
Ginkgophyta
1 species

Gnetums
Gnetophyta
70 species

Horsetails
Sphenophyta
30 species

Ferns
Pterophyta
12 000 species

Mosses
Bryophyta
20 000 species

Club mosses
Lycophyta
1000 species

Section Assessment

1. List the characteristics of plants.
2. Compare vascular and nonvascular plants.
3. Name three adaptations that allow plants to survive on land.
4. **Think Critically:** If you left a board lying on the grass for a few days, what would happen to the grass underneath the board? Why?
5. **Skill Builder**
   Forming a Hypothesis From what you have learned about adaptations necessary for life on land, make a hypothesis as to what types of adaptations land plants might have if they had to survive submerged in water. If you need help, refer to Forming a Hypothesis in the **Skill Handbook** on page 688.

Science Journal The oldest surviving plant species is *Ginkgo biloba*. Research the history of this species, then write about it in your Science Journal.

18•2 Seedless Plants

Seedless Nonvascular Plants

If you were asked to name the parts of a plant, you probably would list roots, stems, leaves, and perhaps flowers. You also may know that many plants grow from seeds. But, did you know that some plants do not have all of these parts? **Figure 18-7** shows some common types of nonvascular plants.

Liverworts and Mosses (Bryophytes)

The bryophytes (BRI uh fites)—liverworts and mosses—are small, nonvascular plants that are usually just a few cells thick and only 2 cm to 5 cm in height. They have stalks that look like stems and leafy green growths. The threadlike roots of bryophytes are called **rhizoids.** Water is absorbed and distributed directly through their cell walls. Bryophytes grow in damp environments such as the forest floor, the edges of ponds and streams, and near the ocean. Bryophytes usually reproduce by spores because they do not have flowers to produce seeds.

Liverworts get their name because to some people, one type looks like a liver. It is a rootless plant that has a flattened, leaflike body. Liverworts usually have one-celled rhizoids. In the ninth century, liverworts were thought to be useful in treating diseases of the liver. The ending, -*wort*, means "herb," so the word *liverwort* means "herb for the liver." Of approximately 20 000 species of nonvascular plants, most are classified as mosses. Have you ever seen mosses growing on tree trunks, rocks, or the ground in damp or humid areas? Mosses have green, leaflike

What You'll Learn

► Characteristics of seedless nonvascular plants and seedless vascular plants

► The importance of some nonvascular and vascular plants

Vocabulary
rhizoid
pioneer species

Why It's Important

► Seedless plants are often the first to grow in damaged or disturbed environments.

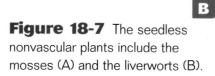

Figure 18-7 The seedless nonvascular plants include the mosses (A) and the liverworts (B).

EARTH SCIENCE
INTEGRATION

Soil Formation
Soil is a mixture of weathered rock and decaying organic matter (plant and animal). Infer what roles pioneer species such as lichens, mosses, and liverworts play in building soil.

---

growths in a spiral around a stalk. Their threadlike rhizoids are only a few cells in length.

The Importance of Bryophytes

Mosses and liverworts are important in the ecology of many areas. Although mosses require moist conditions to grow and reproduce, many of them can withstand long, dry periods. Often, they are among the first plants to grow in new environments, such as lava fields as shown in **Figure 18-8,** or disturbed environments, such as forests destroyed by fire.

When a volcano erupts, lava covers the land and destroys the plants living there. After the lava cools, spores of mosses and liverworts are carried by the wind to the new rocks. The spores will grow into plants if enough water is available and other growing conditions are right. Organisms that are the first to grow in new or disturbed areas like these are called **pioneer species.** As pioneer plants grow and die, decaying plant material builds up. This, along with the breakdown of rocks, begins the formation of soil. Pioneer plants change environmental conditions so that other plants can grow.

Mini Lab

Measuring Water Absorption by a Moss

Procedure
1. Place a few teaspoons of *Sphagnum* moss on a piece of cheesecloth. Twist the cheesecloth to form a ball and tie it securely.
2. Weigh the ball.
3. Put 200 mL of water in a container and add the ball.
4. Predict how much water the ball will absorb.
5. Wait 15 minutes. Remove the ball and drain the excess water back into the container.

Analysis
1. Weigh the ball and measure the amount of water left in the container.
2. In your Science Journal, calculate how much water the *Sphagnum* moss absorbed.

Seedless Vascular Plants

The plants in **Figure 18-9** are like mosses because they are seedless plants that reproduce by spores. They are different from mosses because they have vascular tissue. The vascular tissue in the seedless vascular plants is made up of long, tubelike cells. These cells carry water, minerals, and nutrients to cells throughout the plant. Why is having cells like these an advantage to a plant? Remember that bryophytes are only a few cells thick. Each cell absorbs water directly from its environment. As a result, these plants cannot grow large. Vascular plants, on the other hand, can grow bigger and thicker because the vascular tissue distributes water and nutrients. ☑

Types of Seedless Vascular Plants

Seedless vascular plants include the ground pines, spike mosses, horsetails, and ferns. Today, there are about 1000 species of ground pines, spike mosses, and horsetails. Ferns are more abundant, with at least 12 000 species known. Many species of seedless vascular plants are known only from fossils. They flourished during the warm, moist Paleozoic era. Fossil records show that some horsetails grew 15 m tall, unlike modern species that only grow 1 m to 2 m tall.

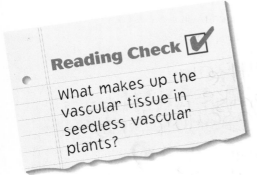

Reading Check ☑

What makes up the vascular tissue in seedless vascular plants?

Figure 18-9 The seedless vascular plants include ground pines, spike mosses, horsetails, and ferns. **Why can these plants grow taller than mosses and liverworts?**

Ferns

Horsetails

Spike moss

Ground pine

Figure 18-10 Club mosses such as ground pines (A) and spike mosses (B) produce spores at the end of stems in tiny, conelike structures. Photographers once used the dry, flammable spores of club mosses as flash powder. It burned rapidly and produced the light to take photographs.

Ground Pines and Spike Mosses

The photographs in **Figure 18-10** show ground pines and spike mosses. Both groups of plants are often called club mosses. They are seedless vascular plants with needlelike leaves. Spores are produced at the end of the stems in structures that look like tiny pine cones. Ground pines are found from arctic regions to the tropics, but never in large numbers. In some areas, they are endangered because they have been overcollected to make wreaths and other decorations.

Spike mosses resemble ground pines. One species of spike moss, the resurrection plant, is adapted to desert conditions. When water is scarce, the plant curls up and seems dead. When water becomes available, the resurrection plant unfurls its green leaves and begins making food again. The plant can repeat this process whenever necessary.

Horsetails

Horsetails have a stem structure unique among the vascular plants. Their stems are jointed and have a hollow center surrounded by a ring of vascular tissue. At each joint, leaves grow around the stem. In **Figure 18-11,** you can see these joints easily. If you pull on a horsetail stem, it will pop apart in sections. Like the club mosses, spores from horsetails are produced in a conelike structure at the tips of some stems.

Figure 18-11 The spores of horsetails are found in conelike structures on the tips of some stems.

Figure 18-12 Most ferns produce spores in special structures on the leaves, but the spores of the cinnamon fern are on a separate stalk.

The stems of the horsetails contain silica, a gritty substance found in sand. For centuries, horsetails have been used for polishing objects, sharpening tools, and scouring cooking utensils. Another common name for horsetails is scouring rush.

Ferns

Ferns belong to the largest group of seedless vascular plants. Ferns, like those in **Figure 18-12,** have stems, leaves, and roots. They also have characteristics of both nonvascular and vascular plants.

Like the bryophytes, ferns produce spores, and they have vascular tissue like vascular plants. Today, thousands of species of ferns grow on Earth, but once there were many more. From clues left in rock layers, scientists know that during the Carboniferous period of the Paleozoic era, much of Earth was tropical. Steamy swamps covered large areas, as illustrated in **Figure 18-13.** The tallest plants were species of ferns. The ancient ferns grew as tall as 25 m—much taller than any fern species alive today. The tallest, modern tree ferns are about 3 m to 5 m in height.

Formation of Fuel

When ferns and other plants of the Carboniferous period died, many of them became submerged in water and mud before they could decompose. This plant material built up, became compacted and compressed, and eventually turned into coal. This process took millions of years.

Today, a similar process is taking place in bogs. A bog is a poorly drained area of land that contains decaying plants. The decay process is slow because waterlogged soils do not

interNET
CONNECTION

Visit the Glencoe Science Web Site at **www.glencoe.com/ sec/science/fl** for more information about which ferns are native to your state. In your Science Journal, list three of these ferns and describe their

EARTH SCIENCE
INTEGRATION▶

contain oxygen. The plants in bogs are mostly seedless plants like mosses and ferns. Peat, the remains of peat mosses, is mined from bogs in some countries for a low-cost fuel. Scientists hypothesize that over time, if additional layers of soil bury, compact, and compress the peat, it will become coal.

Figure 18-13 Many more species of club mosses, horsetails, and ferns grew in carboniferous swamp forests than are alive today.

Section Assessment

1. Compare and contrast the mosses and ferns.

2. What do fossil records tell us about seedless plants?

3. Under what conditions would you expect to find pioneer plants?

4. **Think Critically:** List ways seedless plants affect your life each day. (HINT: Where do electricity and heat for homes come from?)

5. 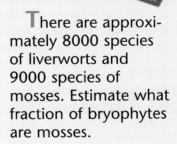 **Skill Builder**
   Concept Mapping Make a concept map showing how seedless nonvascular and seedless vascular plants are related. Include these terms in the concept map: *plant kingdom, bryophytes, seedless nonvascular plants, seedless vascular plants, ferns, ground pines, horsetails, liverworts, mosses,* and *spike mosses.* If you need help, refer to Concept Mapping in the **Skill Handbook** on page 680.

Using Math

There are approximately 8000 species of liverworts and 9000 species of mosses. Estimate what fraction of bryophytes are mosses.

Materials

One living example of each of these plants:
- Moss
- Liverwort
- Club moss
- Horsetail
- Fern
  - *detailed photographs of the above plant types*
  - *Alternate Material*

Comparing Seedless Plants

Liverworts, mosses, ferns, horsetails, and club mosses have at least one common characteristic—they reproduce by spores. But, do they have other things in common? In this activity, discover their similarities and differences.

What You'll Investigate

How are seedless plants alike and how are they different?

Goals

- **Observe** types of seedless plants.
- **Compare and contrast** seedless plants.

Procedure

1. Copy the Plant Observations table into your Science Journal.

2. Examine each plant and fill in the table using the following guidelines:
   Color—green or not green
   Growth—mostly flat and low or mostly upright
   Root Type—small and fiberlike or rootlike
   Leaf Form—needlelike, scalelike, or leaflike

Conclude and Apply

1. **Observe and infer** what characteristics seedless plants have in common.

2. **Hypothesize** about the differences in growth.

3. **Compare and contrast** the seedless plants.

Plant Observations				
Plant	**Color**	**Growth**	**Root Type**	**Leaf Form**
Moss				
Liverwort				
Club moss				
Horsetail				
Fern				

How it Works

Preservation in Peat Bogs

A bog is a wetland, characterized by wet, spongy, poorly drained ground. It typically contains a thin layer of living plants overlying a thick layer of partially decomposed plant material called peat. One of the major types of peat is moss peat. It is formed mostly from *Sphagnum* moss. Peat bogs are acidic, low in minerals, and lack oxygen. These conditions provide a unique environment. When some types of organisms become trapped and buried in a peat bog, they do not decay. In Europe and North America, the well-preserved bodies of humans and other animals have been found in peat bogs.

STEP BY STEP

1 Mosses and other wetland plants grow on the surface of a bog.

2 Over time, a layer of partially decayed plant matter accumulates. Eventually, this becomes a thick layer of peat.

3 A substance in the cell walls of *Sphagnum* moss reacts with, and ties up, certain nutrients. These nutrients are essential for the survival of decay-causing bacteria. Without these nutrients, the bacteria cannot live in a bog.

4 When an animal is buried in a bog, its soft tissues, such as skin and internal organs, are not destroyed by decay. But, the animal's bones are dissolved away because of the acidic environment.

5 The skin of animals buried in a peat bog undergoes a sort of tanning process. Human skin becomes leatherlike and coffee colored, as seen in the photograph below.

Think Critically

1. What kinds of information might scientists gain by studying bog-preserved ancient humans?

2. Another type of peat is fuel peat. What property of peat do you think makes it usable as a fuel?

Career CONNECTION

Archaeologists have found hundreds of preserved animals in peat bogs. An archaeologist studies ancient peoples, their remains, and their culture. Pretend you are an archaeologist. Imagine what it must be like for archaeologists to discover human remains.

18·3 Seed Plants

What You'll Learn

- ► The characteristics of seed plants
- ► The structures and functions of roots, stems, and leaves
- ► The main characteristics of gymnosperms and angiosperms and their importance
- ► Similarities and differences of monocots and dicots

Vocabulary

xylem	gymnosperm
phloem	angiosperm
cambium	monocot
stomata	dicot
guard cell	

Why It's Important

- ► Understanding seed plants will help you appreciate how much you depend on them.

What is a seed plant?

Have you ever eaten vegetables like the ones shown in **Figure 18-14?** All of these foods come from seed plants. What fruits and vegetables have you eaten today? If you had an apple, a peanut butter and jelly sandwich, or a glass of orange juice for lunch, you ate foods that came from seed plants.

Nearly all the plants you are familiar with are seed plants. Seed plants have roots, stems, leaves, and vascular tissue and produce seeds. A seed usually contains an embryo and stored food. The stored food is the source of energy for growth of the embryo into a plant. More than 250 000 species of seed plants are known in the world today. Seed plants are generally classified into two major groups: the gymnosperms and the angiosperms.

Figure 18-14 The products of plants, like these being sold at a market in Ecuador, provide food for humans. **How are plants an important part of the world's food supply?**

Figure 18-15 The vascular tissue of some seed plants includes xylem, phloem, and cambium.
Which of these tissues transports food throughout the plant?

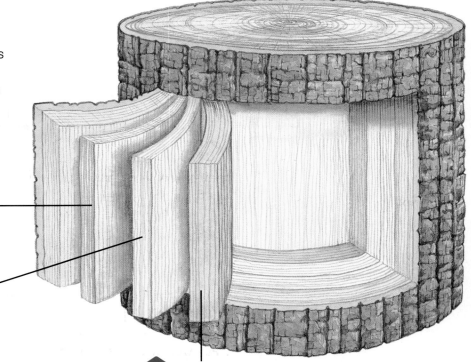

A Phloem transports dissolved sugar throughout the plant.

B Cambium produces xylem and phloem as the plant grows.

C Xylem transports water and dissolved substances throughout the plant.

Vascular Tissue

Three tissues usually make up the vascular system in a seed plant. **Xylem** (ZI lum) tissue is made up of tubular vessels that transport water and dissolved substances up from the roots throughout the plant. **Phloem** (FLOH em) is a plant tissue made up of tubular cells. Phloem moves food from where it is made to other parts of the plant where it is used or stored. In some plants, a cambium is between xylem and phloem. **Cambium** (KAM bee um) is a tissue that produces new xylem and phloem cells. All three tissues are illustrated in **Figure 18-15.**

Stems

Did you know that the trunk of a tree is really its stem? Stems are usually above ground and support the branches, leaves, and flowers. The stem also allows movement of materials between leaves and roots. Some stems store food. Potatoes and onions are underground stems that store food. Sugarcane has an aboveground stem that stores large quantities of food. Stems of cacti are adapted to carry on photosynthesis and make food for the rest of the plant.

Observing Water Moving in a Plant

Procedure

1. Into a clear container, about 10 cm tall and 4 cm in diameter, pour water to a depth of 1.5 cm. Add 15 drops of red food coloring to the water.
2. Put the root end of a whole green onion in the colored water in the container. Do not cut the onion in any way.
3. Let the onion stand overnight.
4. The next day, examine the outside of the onion. Peel off the layers of leaves and examine them.

Analysis

1. In your Science Journal, compare the appearance of the onion before and after it was in the colored water.
2. Describe the location of red color inside the onion.
3. Infer how the red color inside the onion might be related to vascular tissue.

Figure 18-16 The root system of a dandelion is longer than the plant is tall. When you pull up a dandelion, you often pull off the top portion of the plant. The root quickly produces new leaves, and another dandelion grows.

Plant stems are either herbaceous (hur BAY shus) or woody. Herbaceous stems usually are soft and green, like the stems of peppers, corn, and tulips. Oak, birch, and other trees and shrubs have hard, rigid, woody stems.

Roots

Imagine a large tree growing alone on top of a hill. What is the largest part? Maybe you said the trunk or the branches. Did you consider the roots? The root systems of most plants are as large or larger than the aboveground stems and leaves, like the dandelion in **Figure 18-16.**

Roots are important to plants. Water and other substances enter a plant through its roots. Roots have vascular tissue to move water and dissolved substances from the ground up through the stems to the leaves. Roots also anchor plants. If they didn't, plants could be blown away by wind or washed away by water. Each root system must support the plant parts that are above the ground—the stem, branches, and leaves of a tree, for example. Sometimes, part or all of roots are above ground, too.

Roots may store food. When you eat carrots or beets, you eat roots that contain stored food. Root tissues also may perform special functions such as absorbing oxygen that is used in the process of respiration.

Leaves

Have you ever rested in the shade of a tree's leaves on a hot, summer day? Leaves are the organs of the plant that usually trap light and make food through the process of photosynthesis. Leaves come in many shapes, sizes, and colors.

Using Math

The roots of some cacti are shallow but grow horizontally as much as 15 m in all directions from the stem. How much soil surface area do these roots cover?

Leaf Structure

Look at the structure of a typical leaf shown in **Figure 18-17.** The epidermis is a thin layer of cells that covers and protects both the upper and lower surfaces of a leaf. A waxy cuticle that protects and reduces water loss covers the epidermis of many leaves. A feature of most leaves is stomata. **Stomata** are small pores in the leaf surfaces that allow carbon dioxide, water, and oxygen to enter and leave a leaf. The stomata are surrounded by **guard cells** that open and close the pores. The cuticle, stomata, and guard cells all are adaptations that help plants survive on land. ☑

Reading Check ☑

What is the role of stomata in a leaf?

Leaf Cells

A typical leaf is made of different layers of cells. Covering the upper and lower surfaces of a leaf is the epidermis. Just below the upper epidermis is the palisade layer. It consists of closely packed, long, narrow cells that usually contain many chloroplasts. Most of the food produced by plants is made in the palisade cells. Between the palisade layer and the lower epidermis is the spongy layer. It is a layer of loosely arranged cells separated by air spaces. In a leaf, xylem and phloem are in the spongy layer.

Figure 18-17 The structure of a typical leaf is adapted for photo-synthesis. **Why do cells in the palisade layer have more chloroplasts than cells in the spongy layer?**

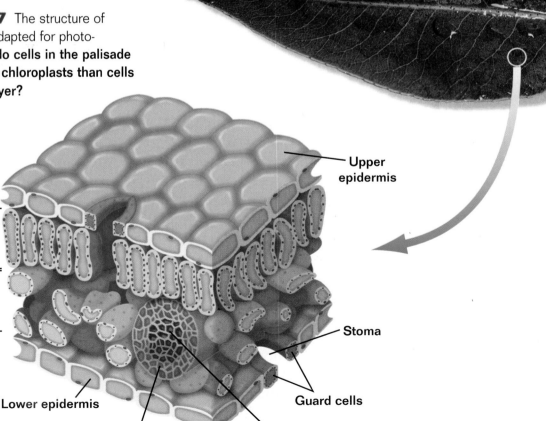

Palisade layer

Spongy layer

Upper epidermis

Stoma

Guard cells

Lower epidermis

Phloem

Xylem

A Conifers are the largest, most diverse division of the gymnosperms. Most conifers are evergreen plants, such as this blue spruce.

B About 100 species of cycads exist today. Only one genus grows naturally in the United States. This sago palm comes from Java, an island in Indonesia.

Figure 18-18 The gymnosperms include conifers (A), cycads (B), ginkgoes (C), and gnetophytes (D).

EXAMPLES OF
Gymnosperms

- Pine
- Hemlock
- Spruce
- Sago Palm
- Ginkgo
- Joint Fir

Gymnosperms

The oldest trees alive today are gymnosperms (JIHM nuh spurmz). A bristlecone pine tree in the White Mountains of eastern California is estimated to be 4900 years old. **Gymnosperms** are vascular plants that produce seeds on the surface of the female reproductive structure. The word *gymnosperm* comes from the Greek language and means "naked seed." Seeds of gymnosperms are not protected by a fruit. Gymnosperms do not produce flowers. Leaves of most gymnosperms are needlelike or scalelike. Gymnosperms are often called evergreens because most keep their leaves for more than one year.

Four divisions of plants—conifers, cycads, ginkgoes, and gnetophytes—are classified as gymnosperms. **Figure 18-18** shows examples of the four divisions. You are probably most familiar with the division Coniferophyta, the conifers. Pines, firs, spruces, redwoods, and junipers belong to this division. It contains the greatest number of gymnosperm species. All conifers produce two types of cones, the male and female reproductive structures. These are usually on the same plant. Seeds develop on the female cone.

D The 70 species of gnetophytes are classified into three genera. More than half of the species, such as this joint fir, are in one genus, another genus has just one species, and the rest of the species are in the third genus.

C Today, the ginkgoes are represented by only one living species. Ginkgoes lose their leaves in the fall. **How is this different from most gymnosperms?**

Angiosperms

When people are asked to name a plant, most people name an angiosperm (AN jee uh spurm). Angiosperms are familiar plants no matter where you live. They grow in parks, fields, forests, jungles, deserts, freshwater, salt water, cracks of sidewalks, or dangling from wires or other plants. One species of orchid even grows underground. Angiosperms make up the plant division Anthophyta. More than half the plant species known today belong to this division.

An **angiosperm** is a vascular plant that flowers and has a fruit that contains seeds. The fruit develops from a part or parts of one or more flowers. The flowers of angiosperms vary in size, shape, and color. Duckweed, an aquatic plant, has a flower that is only 0.1 mm long. A plant in Indonesia has a flower that is nearly 1 m in diameter and can weigh 9 kg. Nearly every color can be found in some flower, although some people would not include black. Multi-colored flowers are common. Some plants have flowers that are not easily recognized as flowers, such as those found on oak and birch trees.

EXAMPLES OF
Angiosperms

- **Grasses and grains**
- **Cacti**
- **Palms**
- **Garden flowers**
- **Vegetables**
- **Fruits**
- **Nuts** (except pine nuts)
- **Leafy trees** (except ginkgoes)

Figure 18-19 By observing a monocot and a dicot, their plant characteristics can be determined.

Monocots

Seed   **Seedling**

A Monocots, such as these lilies, have flower parts in multiples of three. If you had cereal for breakfast, you ate part of a monocot. Corn, rice, oats, and wheat are monocots.

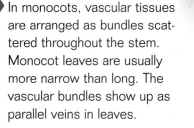

B In monocots, vascular tissues are arranged as bundles scattered throughout the stem. Monocot leaves are usually more narrow than long. The vascular bundles show up as parallel veins in leaves.

Monocots and Dicots

The two classes of angiosperms are the monocots and the dicots. The terms *monocot* and *dicot* are shortened forms of the words *monocotyledon* and *dicotyledon*. The prefix *mono* means "one," and *di* means "two." A cotyledon is a seed leaf inside a seed. Therefore, **monocots** have one seed leaf inside their seeds and **dicots** have two. **Figure 18-19** compares the characteristics of monocots and dicots.

Importance of Seed Plants

Imagine that your class is having a picnic in the park. You cover the wooden picnic table with a red-checked, cotton tablecloth and pass out paper cups and plates. Your lunch includes hot dogs, potato chips, and apple cider. Perhaps you collect leaves or flowers for a science project. Later, you clean up and put leftovers in paper bags.

Now, let's imagine this scene if there were no seed plants on Earth. There would be no wooden picnic table and no

Dicots

D In dicot stems, vascular bundles occur in rings. These bundles of rings are the annual rings in woody stems. The vascular bundles are the network of veins in dicot leaves.

C Dicots, such as the hibiscus, have flower parts in multiples of four or five. Oaks, maples, and many other trees are dicots. Most vegetables and fruits are dicots, as are many garden flowers.

Seed   **Seedling**

pulp to make paper products such as cups, plates, and bags. The hot dog came from the meat of animals that eat only plants. Bread for buns, apples for cider, and potatoes for chips all come from plants. The tablecloth is made from cotton, a plant. Without seed plants, there would be no picnic.

Uses of Gymnosperms and Angiosperms

Conifers are the most economically important gymnosperms. Most of the wood used for construction, as in **Figure 18-20,** and for paper production, comes from conifers such as pines and spruces. Resin, a waxy substance secreted by conifers, is used to make chemicals found in soap, paint, varnish, and some medicines.

Figure 18-20 The wood from conifers, such as pines, is commonly used in construction. Resin is used to make household products.

Figure 18-21 Cotton is a flowering plant that yields long fibers that can be woven into a wide variety of fabrics. **What chemical compound makes up these fibers?**

The most common plants on Earth are the angiosperms. They are important to all life because they form the basis for the diets of most animals. Grains such as barley and wheat and legumes such as peas and lentils were among the first plants ever grown by humans. Angiosperms also are the source of many of the fibers used in clothing. Cotton fibers, as seen in **Figure 18-21,** grow from the outer surface of cotton-seeds. The fibers of the flax plant are processed and woven into linen fabrics. The production of medicines, rubber, oils, perfumes, pesticides, and some industrial chemicals uses substances found in angiosperms.

Section Assessment

1. What are the characteristics of a seed plant?

2. Compare and contrast the characteristics of gymnosperms and angiosperms.

3. You are looking at a flower with five petals, five sepals, one pistil, and ten stamens. Is it from a monocot or dicot plant?

4. **Think Critically:** The cuticle and epidermis of leaves are transparent. If they were not transparent, what might be the result?

5. **Skill Builder**
   Classifying Conifers have needlelike or scalelike leaves. Do the **Chapter 18 Skill Activity** on page 725 to learn how to use this characteristic to classify conifers.

Using Computers

Word Processing Use a word-processing program to outline the structures and functions that are associated with roots, stems, and leaves. If you need help, refer to page 678.

Comparing Monocots and Dicots

Materials
- Monocot and dicot flowers
- Monocot and dicot seeds
- Scalpel
- Forceps
- Iodine solution

You have read that monocots and dicots are similar because they are both groups of flowering plants. However, you also have learned that these two groups are different. Try this activity to compare and contrast monocots and dicots.

What You'll Investigate

How do the characteristics of monocots and dicots compare?

Goals

- **Observe** similarities and differences between monocots and dicots.
- **Classify** plants as monocots or dicots based on flower characteristics.
- **Infer** what type of food is stored in seeds.

Procedure

1. Copy the Plant Data table in your Science Journal.

2. **Observe** the leaves on the stem of each flower. In your Science Journal, describe the monocot and the dicot leaves.

3. **Examine** the monocot and the dicot flower. For each flower, remove and count the sepals and petals. Enter these numbers on the table.

4. Inside each flower, you should see a pistil(s) and several stamens. **Count** each type and enter these numbers as "Other Observations."

5. **Examine** the two seeds. **Cut** the seeds lengthwise, **observe** each half, and **identify** the embryo and cotyledon(s).

6. Place a drop of iodine on different parts of the seed. A blue-black color indicates the presence of starch. **CAUTION:** *Iodine is poisonous. It will stain and can burn your skin.*

Conclude and Apply

1. **Compare** the numbers of sepals and petals of monocot and dicot flowers.

2. What characteristics are the same for monocot and dicot flowers?

3. Distinguish between a monocot and a dicot seed.

4. What type of food is stored in monocot and in dicot seeds?

Plant Data				
	Number of Sepals	**Number of Petals**	**Number of Cotyledons**	**Other Observations**
Monocot				
Dicot				

For a **preview** of this chapter, study this Reviewing Main Ideas before you read the chapter. After you have studied this chapter, you can use the Reviewing Main Ideas to **review** the chapter.

The Glencoe MindJogger, Audiocassettes, and CD-ROM provide additional opportunities for review.

Section

18-1 CHARACTERISTICS OF PLANTS

Plants are made up of eukaryotic cells. They usually have some form of leaves, stems, and roots. Plants vary greatly in size and shape. Most plants are adapted to live on land. As plants evolved from aquatic to land forms, changes in structure and function occurred. The changes included how they reproduced, supported themselves, and moved substances from one part of the plant to another. The plant kingdom is classified into groups called divisions. *What are some plant adaptations for living on land?*

Section

18-2 SEEDLESS PLANTS

Seedless plants include **nonvascular** and **vascular** types. Bryophytes—mosses and liverworts—are seedless **nonvascular plants.** They have no true leaves, stems, roots, or vascular tissues and live in moist environments. For bryophytes, reproduction usually is by spores. Bryophytes may be considered **pioneer species** because they are some of the first plants to grow in new or disturbed environments. They change the environment so that other plant species may grow there. Club mosses, horsetails, and ferns are seedless **vascular plants.** They have vascular tissues, a pipeline that moves substances throughout the plant. Like bryophytes, these plants may reproduce by spores. When ancient forms of these plants died, they underwent a process that, over time, resulted in the formation of coal. *How are bryophytes and ferns alike?*

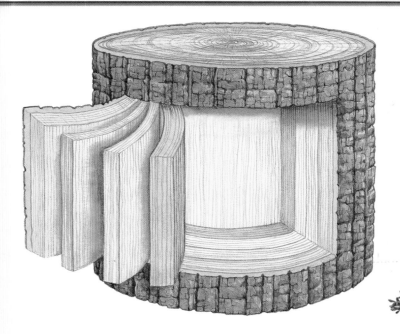

Reading Check ✓

Choose a topic in this chapter that interests you. Look it up in a reference book, an encyclopedia or on a CD. Think of a way to share what you learn.

Section 18-3 SEED PLANTS

Seed plants are what most people think of when they hear the word *plants*. These plants have adapted to survive in nearly every environment on Earth. Seed plants produce seeds and have vascular tissue, stems, roots, and leaves. Vascular tissues transport food, water, and dissolved substances in the roots, stems, and leaves. The two major groups of seed plants are gymnosperms and angiosperms. **Gymnosperms** generally have needlelike leaves and some type of cone. **Angiosperms** are plants that flower and are classified as **monocots** or **dicots.** Seed plants provide food, shelter, clothing, and many other products. *What structures are common to all seed plants?*

Using Vocabulary

a. angiosperm
b. cambium
c. cellulose
d. cuticle
e. dicot
f. guard cell
g. gymnosperm
h. monocot
i. nonvascular plant
j. phloem
k. pioneer species
l. rhizoid
m. stomata
n. vascular plant
o. xylem

Explain the differences between the terms in each of the following sets.

1. xylem, phloem, cambium
2. angiosperm, dicot, monocot
3. guard cell, stomata
4. cuticle, cellulose
5. vascular plant, gymnosperm

Checking Concepts

Choose the word or phrase that best answers the question.

6. Which of the following is a seedless, vascular plant?
   A) moss   C) horsetail
   B) liverwort   D) pine

7. What are the small openings in the surface of a leaf surrounded by guard cells?
   A) stomata   C) rhizoids
   B) cuticles   D) angiosperms

8. What is the plant structure that anchors the plant?
   A) stem   C) roots
   B) leaves   D) guard cell

9. What kind of plants have structures that move water and other substances?
   A) vascular   C) nonvascular
   B) protist   D) moneran

10. What division has plants that are only a few cells thick?
    A) Anthophyta   C) Pterophyta
    B) Cycadophyta   D) Bryophyta

11. Where is new xylem and phloem produced?
    A) guard cells   C) stomata
    B) cambium   D) cuticle

12. Which of the following is **NOT** part of an angiosperm?
    A) flowers   C) cones
    B) seeds   D) fruit

13. In what part of a leaf does most photosynthesis happen?
    A) epidermis   C) stomata
    B) cuticle   D) palisade layer

14. Which of these is an advantage to life on land for plants?
    A) more direct sunlight
    B) less carbon dioxide
    C) greater space to grow
    D) less competition for food

15. What do ferns **NOT** have?
    A) fronds   C) spores
    B) rhizoids   D) vascular tissue

Thinking Critically

16. What might happen if a land plant's waxy cuticle were destroyed?

17. Well-preserved human remains have been found in peat bogs. Explain why this occurs.

18. Plants called succulents store large amounts of water in their leaves, stems, and roots. In what environments would you expect to find succulents growing naturally?

19. Explain why mosses are usually found on moist areas.

20. How do pioneer species change environments so that other plants may grow there?

Developing Skills

If you need help, refer to the **Skill Handbook.**

21. **Concept Mapping:** Complete this map for the seedless plants of the plant kingdom.

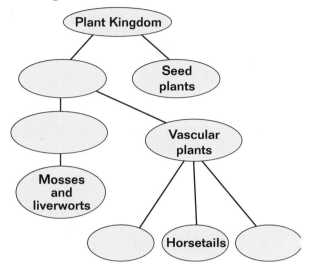

22. **Interpreting Data:** What do the data in this table tell you about where gas exchange occurs in each plant leaf?

Stomata (per mm²)		
	Upper Surface	**Lower Surface**
Pine	50	71
Bean	40	281
Fir	0	228
Tomato	12	13

23. **Making and Using Graphs:** Make two circle graphs using the table in question 22.

24. **Interpreting Scientific Illustrations:** Using **Figure 18-19,** compare and contrast the *number of seed leaves, bundle arrangement in the stem, veins in leaves,* and *number of flower parts* for monocots and dicots.

Test-Taking Tip

You Are Smarter Than You Think
Nothing on the science tests that you will take this year is so difficult that you can't understand it. You can learn to master any of it. Be confident and just keep practicing your test-taking skills.

Test Practice

Use these questions to test your Science Proficiency.

1. What does the cuticle found on the surface of many plant cells help to do?
   A) increase the carbon dioxide released
   B) change the method of reproduction
   C) reduce water loss for the plant
   D) keep the surface area as small as possible

2. What is one explanation for why bryophytes grow just a few centimeters tall?
   A) They lack reproductive structures.
   B) Their rhizoids are not real roots.
   C) Many creatures trample them on the forest floor.
   D) They do not have vascular tissues.

3. What is one feature that gymnosperms and flowering plants have in common?
   A) reproduce naturally from seeds
   B) have leaves that stay on the plant for more than one year
   C) produce the same types of fruit
   D) are nonvascular plants

CHAPTER 18 ASSESSMENT 519

Plant Processes

Chapter Preview

Skills Preview

Skill Builders
- Compare and Contrast
- Observe and Infer

Activities
- Predict
- Design an Experiment

MiniLabs
- Observe and Infer
- Measure in SI

Reading Check ✓

Before you read the chapter, make a list of all the vocabulary words. Next to each word, write what you think it means. Then, as you read, change your definitions if necessary.

Explore Activity

Plants are similar to other living things. They are made of cells, reproduce, make and use substances, and need water. If someone forgot to water the petunias shown in the photograph, what do you think would happen? From your own experience, you probably know they would wilt. Do the following activity to discover the relationship between plants and water. Find out how water goes in and out of a plant. In this chapter, you will learn about other plant processes.

Observe Plants

1. Obtain a resealable plastic bag and a small potted plant from your teacher.
2. Place the potted plant in the plastic bag.
3. Seal the bag and place it in a sunny window.
4. Look at the plant at the same time every day for a few days.

Science Journal

In your Science Journal, describe what happens in the bag. If enough water is lost by a plant and not replaced, predict what will happen to the plant.

19·1 Photosynthesis and Respiration

What You'll Learn

► How plants take in and give off gases
► Why photosynthesis and respiration are important
► Why photosynthesis and respiration are related

Vocabulary
stomata
transpiration
photosynthesis
respiration

Why It's Important

► Understanding photosynthesis and respiration in plants will help you understand their importance to life on Earth.

Gas Exchange in Plants

When you breathe, you take in and release mixtures of gases. You inhale air, a mixture of nitrogen, oxygen, carbon dioxide, and other gases. The mixture of gases that you exhale is mostly nitrogen, carbon dioxide, and water vapor. Gas exchange is one of the ways living cells obtain raw materials and get rid of waste products. For most organisms, carbon dioxide and water vapor are waste products of cell processes.

In plants, water and carbon dioxide are two of the raw materials needed for survival. Plant roots or rootlike structures absorb most of the water and it moves up through the plant to where it is needed. Water leaves a plant as water vapor. It may leave cells by diffusion and then be released through openings called **stomata** (sing., *stoma*). Stomata are on the surface(s) of a leaf or leaflike structure.

Stomata

How does carbon dioxide enter a leaf? Each stoma is surrounded by two guard cells that control the size of the opening. Water moves into and out of guard cells by osmosis. As water moves into guard cells, they swell and change shape,

Figure 19-1 Stomata open when guard cells absorb water (A). They close when water is lost (B). **Would a build-up of salt in the soil around a plant make the stomata open or close?**

Magnification: 300×

Magnification: 300×

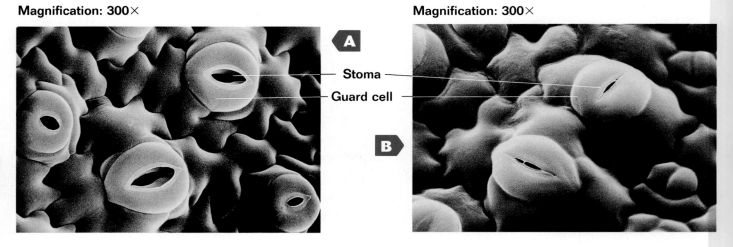

A

B

Stoma
Guard cell

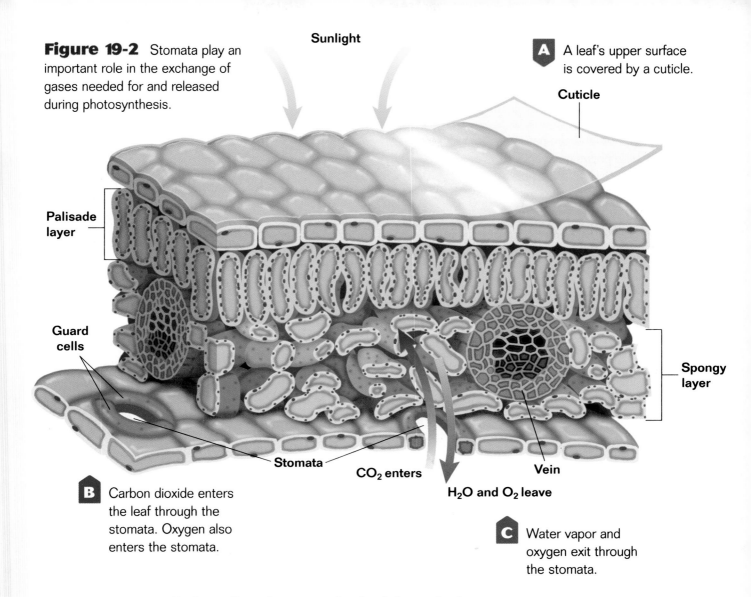

Figure 19-2 Stomata play an important role in the exchange of gases needed for and released during photosynthesis.

Sunlight

A A leaf's upper surface is covered by a cuticle.

Cuticle

Palisade layer

Guard cells

Spongy layer

Stomata

CO₂ enters

Vein

H₂O and O₂ leave

B Carbon dioxide enters the leaf through the stomata. Oxygen also enters the stomata.

C Water vapor and oxygen exit through the stomata.

creating a stoma. Carbon dioxide enters the leaf through the stoma and water vapor may escape during this process. When guard cells lose water, they deflate and change shape again. This action closes the stoma. **Figure 19-1** shows open and closed stomata.

Light, water, and carbon dioxide all affect the opening and closing of stomata. Stomata usually are open during the day and closed at night. Less carbon dioxide enters and less water vapor escapes from the leaf when stomata are closed. Because leaves usually have more stomata on the lower surface, more carbon dioxide reaches the spaces around the spongy layer, as shown in **Figure 19-2.** Water vapor also is found in the air spaces of the spongy layer.

If you did the Explore Activity for this chapter, you saw that water vapor condensed on the inside of the plastic bag. Loss of water vapor through stomata of a leaf is called **transpiration.** Far more water is lost by transpiration than is used during the food-making process of photosynthesis.

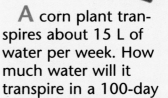

Using Math

A corn plant transpires about 15 L of water per week. How much water will it transpire in a 100-day growing season?

Figure 19-3 Light and chlorophyll are both essential parts of photosynthesis.

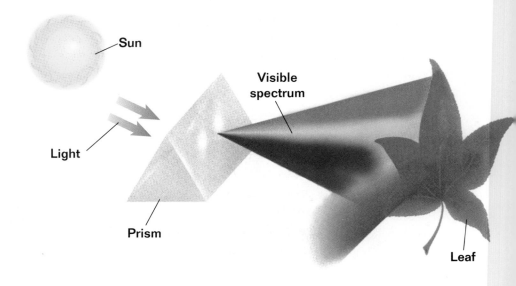

Sun

Light

Prism

Visible spectrum

Leaf

A As light from the sun passes through a prism, it separates into the colors of the visible spectrum. When light strikes a green leaf, most of the colors are absorbed. Green is reflected by the leaf and is seen by the viewer.

B Leaves of some trees, such as those on this sweet gum, change color in the autumn.

Spring

Summer

Fall

Photosynthesis

Why aren't all the leaves of the trees in **Figure 19-3B** green? If you live in a place that has changing seasons, you may see trees in the fall like in the photograph on the far right. In some places, many trees and bushes change color as the days get shorter and the weather grows colder. Leaves may change from green to red, brown, yellow, or orange. Some plants may even have leaves of different colors at the same time. These colors are the result of pigments in leaves. A pigment is a substance that reflects a particular part of the visible spectrum and absorbs the rest. In the spring and summer, there is so much green pigment chlorophyll in most leaves that it hides all other pigments. In the fall, chlorophyll breaks down and the other pigments become visible. ☑

Reading Check ☑

What happens in the fall to the chlorophyll in some leaves?

As shown in **Figure 19-3A,** light from the sun contains all colors. When you see a green leaf, orange carrot, or red rose, you are seeing the reflected color. In plant cells, pigments absorb the other colors and trap light energy.

The Food-Making Process

Chlorophyll is a pigment in plants that traps light energy. Plants use this energy to make food. **Photosynthesis,** illustrated in **Figure 19-4,** is the process in which plants use light energy to produce food.

What do plants use besides light to make food? Carbon dioxide and water are the raw materials for photosynthesis. Some of the light energy trapped in the chlorophyll is used to split water molecules. Light energy is then used to join hydrogen from the water to carbon dioxide molecules. The new molecule formed is a simple sugar called glucose. The chemical bonds of glucose contain the energy a plant uses for growth and maintenance.

Mini Lab

Observing Plant Use of Carbon Dioxide

Procedure

1. Pour 5 mL of tap water into a clean test tube.
2. Add 10 drops carbonated water and 20 drops of bromothymol blue indicator to the tap water. Place the test tube in a holder.
3. Write the color of the solution in your Science Journal.
4. Repeat steps 1 and 2. Then, add a sprig of *Elodea* to this test tube.
5. Write the color of this test tube's solution in your Science Journal.
6. Place the two test tubes in sunlight for 30 minutes. Observe the test tubes every five minutes. If using artificial lights, increase the time to one hour.

Analysis

1. In your Science Journal, describe and compare the two test tubes of solution before and after the 15 minutes.
2. What gas did you add to the solution?
3. Relate your observations to photosynthesis.

VISUALIZING Photosynthesis

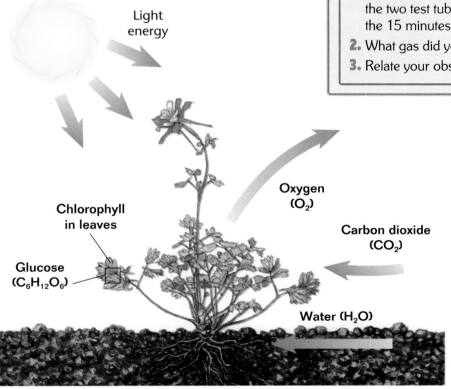

Light energy

Chlorophyll in leaves

Glucose
($C_6H_{12}O_6$)

Oxygen
(O_2)

Carbon dioxide
(CO_2)

Water (H_2O)

Figure 19-4 During photosynthesis, carbon dioxide from the air, water from the soil, and light energy react to form glucose and oxygen.

Photosynthesis is illustrated in the following equation:

$$6CO_2 + 6H_2O + \text{light energy} \longrightarrow C_6H_{12}O_6 + 6O_2$$

carbon dioxide   water   chlorophyll   glucose   oxygen

A plant needs six molecules of carbon dioxide (CO_2) and six molecules of water (H_2O) to make one molecule of glucose ($C_6H_{12}O_6$). Six molecules of oxygen gas (O_2) are also produced during photosynthesis. Light energy is used in photosynthesis, then stored in the chemical bonds that hold the glucose molecule together.

What happens to the products of photosynthesis? Most of the oxygen from photosynthesis is released through stomata. But some of it is used to break down food molecules and release the energy stored in the chemical bonds of the food molecules. This energy is used for all of the plant's life processes such as growth and reproduction. Glucose is the main form of food for plant cells. A plant usually produces more glucose than it can use. Excess glucose is stored in plants as other sugars and starches. When you eat beets, carrots, potatoes, or onions, you are eating stored food. Glucose is also the basis of a plant's structure. The cellulose in plant cell walls is made from glucose.

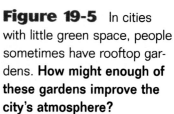

interNET CONNECTION

Besides glucose, what other sugars do plants produce? Visit the Glencoe Science Web Site at **www.glencoe. com/sec/science/fl** for more information about plant sugars.

Figure 19-5 In cities with little green space, people sometimes have rooftop gardens. **How might enough of these gardens improve the city's atmosphere?**

Importance of Photosynthesis

Why is photosynthesis important to living things? First, photosynthesis is food production. Organisms that carry on photosynthesis provide food for nearly all the other organisms on Earth. Second, photosynthetic organisms, like the plants in **Figure 19-5,** use carbon dioxide and release oxygen. This removes carbon dioxide from the atmosphere and replaces the oxygen most organisms, including humans, need to stay alive. As much as 90 percent of the oxygen entering our atmosphere today is a result of photosynthesis.

In most algae and photosynthetic bacteria, photosynthesis occurs in every cell. However, in green plants, only cells with chloroplasts carry on photosynthesis.

Respiration

Look at the photographs in **Figure 19-6.** Do these organisms have anything in common? Both of these organisms are similar in that they break down food to release energy.

EARTH SCIENCE
INTEGRATION

Photosynthesis and Earth's Air
Earth's atmosphere had no oxygen before the evolution of organisms that carry on photosynthesis. In the last 2 billion years, the relative amount of oxygen in Earth's atmosphere has increased more than 50 times. What might happen if photosynthesis suddenly stopped?

Figure 19-6 Respiration, the release of energy from food, occurs in all living cells. You may know that animals such as the cheetah respire, but so do all plants such as the oak tree.

MiniLab

Demonstrating Respiration in Yeast

Procedure 🐾 🥽 🧤 🚫

1. Pour 10 mL of bromothymol blue into a clean test tube.
2. Add 20 drops of yeast suspension and 10 drops of sugar solution.

Analysis

1. Record in your Science Journal any color change observed after five minutes, ten minutes, and 15 minutes.
2. What caused the color change you observed?
3. Compare the results of this MiniLab with those from the one earlier in the chapter.

Respiration is a series of chemical reactions by which all organisms break down food to release energy. The breakdown of food may or may not require oxygen. For organisms that are only one prokaryotic cell—a cell without a nucleus or other organelles—respiration takes place in the cytoplasm of the cell. For organisms made of one or more eukaryotic cells—cells that have a nucleus and other organelles—respiration involves organelles called mitochondria (sing., *mitochodrion*), as shown in **Figure 19-7.** Respiration that uses oxygen to chemically break down food is called aerobic respiration. The overall chemical equation for aerobic respiration is as follows.

$$C_6H_{12}O_6 \ + \ 6O_2 \longrightarrow 6CO_2 \ + \ 6H_2O \ + \ energy$$

glucose   oxygen   carbon   water
                                    dioxide

Is the equation for aerobic respiration familiar? How does it relate to the chemical equation for photosynthesis? If you look closely, you can see that aerobic respiration is the reverse of photosynthesis. Photosynthesis combines carbon dioxide and water by using light energy. The end products are glucose (food) and oxygen. During photosynthesis, energy is stored in food. Photosynthesis occurs only in cells that contain chlorophyll, such as those in the leaves of plants. Aerobic respiration

Table 19-1

Comparing Photosynthesis and Aerobic Respiration				
	Energy	**Raw materials**	**End products**	**Where**
Photosynthesis	stored	water and carbon dioxide, plus energy	glucose, oxygen	cells with chlorophyll
Aerobic respiration	released	glucose, oxygen	water and carbon dioxide, plus energy	all eukaryotic cells

combines oxygen and food to release the energy in the chemical bonds of the food. The end products of aerobic respiration are energy, carbon dioxide, and water. Aerobic respiration occurs in cells with mitochondria. It provides the energy needed by the cell and the entire organism. **Table 19-1** compares the processes of photosynthesis and aerobic respiration.

Magnification: 4000×

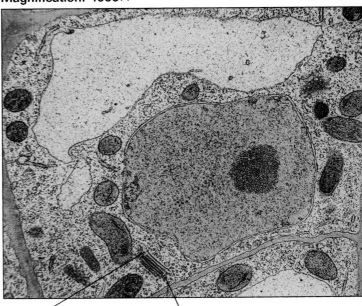

VISUALIZING
Respiration

Figure 19-7 Respiration takes place in the mitochondria of eukaryotic cells.

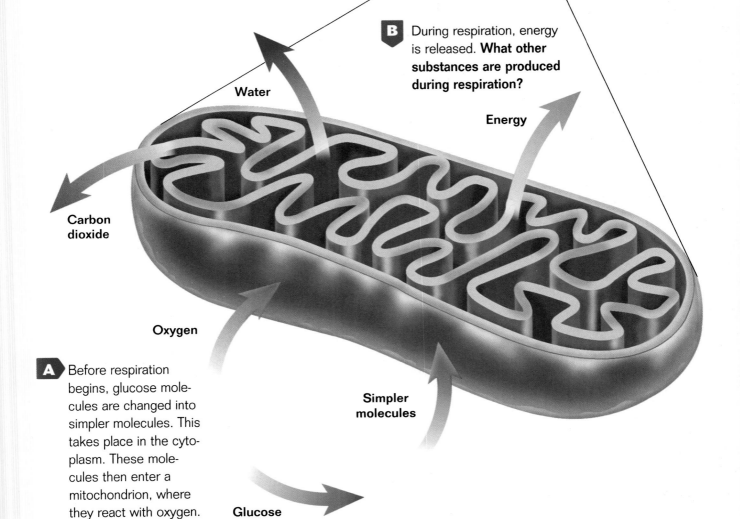

Water

B During respiration, energy is released. **What other substances are produced during respiration?**

Energy

Carbon dioxide

Oxygen

A Before respiration begins, glucose molecules are changed into simpler molecules. This takes place in the cytoplasm. These molecules then enter a mitochondrion, where they react with oxygen.

Simpler molecules

Glucose

Importance of Respiration

If food, like the items in **Figure 19-8**, contains energy, why do cells carry out the process of respiration? The energy in food molecules is in a form that cannot be used by cells. During respiration, the food energy is changed into a form all cells can use. This energy drives the life processes used by almost all organisms on Earth. Even the process of photosynthesis uses some of this energy. Aerobic respiration returns carbon dioxide to the atmosphere, where it may again be used by photosynthetic organisms.

Figure 19-8 Humans and other animals depend on the glucose produced by plants during photosynthesis. Animals use the glucose to produce energy through respiration.

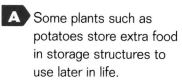 Some plants such as potatoes store extra food in storage structures to use later in life.

B Wheat and rice are important sources of food for much of the world's population.

Section Assessment

1. Explain how carbon dioxide and water vapor are exchanged by a leaf.
2. Why are photosynthesis and respiration important?
3. What must happen to food molecules before respiration begins?
4. **Think Critically:** Humidity is water vapor in the air. How do plants contribute to humidity?
5. **Skill Builder**
   Observing and Inferring To learn how observation is a good scientific tool, do the **Chapter 19 Skill Activity** on page 726.

Using Math

How many carbon dioxide molecules (CO_2) result from the aerobic respiration of one glucose molecule ($C_6H_{12}O_6$)? Refer to the equation in the section about respiration.

Stomata in Leaves

Materials

- Lettuce in dish of water
- Coverslip
- Microscope
- Microscope slide
- Salt solution
- Forceps

O ne of the interesting things about leaves is how stomata open and close to allow gases into and out of a leaf. Stomata are usually invisible without the use of a microscope. Try this activity to see some stomata for yourself.

What You'll Investigate

Where are stomata in lettuce leaves?

Goals

- **Describe** guard cells and stomata.
- **Infer** the conditions that make them open and close.

Procedure

1. Copy the Stomata Data table into your Science Journal.
2. From a head of lettuce, tear off a piece of an outer, crisp, green leaf.
3. Bend the piece of leaf in half to remove the epidermis, the transparent tissue that covers a leaf. Carefully use a pair of forceps to peel off some of the epidermis. Prepare a wet mount of this tissue.
4. Examine your wet mount slide under low and high power on the microscope. Using **Figure 19-2** as a guide, draw and label this tissue in your Science Journal.
5. Count the total number of stomata in your field of view and then count the number of open stomata. Enter these numbers in the data table.
6. Make a second slide of the lettuce leaf epidermis. This time, place a few drops of salt solution on the leaf instead of water.
7. Repeat steps 4 and 5 with the second wet mount of tissue.

8. Using the following equation, calculate the percent of open stomata.

   (number of stomata open ÷ total number of stomata) × 100 = percent open

Stomata Data		
	Wet mount	**Salt solution mount**
Total number of stomata		
Number of open stomata		
Percent open		

Conclude and Apply

1. How are guard cells different from the other cells of the leaf epidermis?
2. **Infer** why fewer stomata were open in the salt solution mount.
3. Which slide preparation had a greater percent of open stomata?
4. What can you **infer** about the function of stomata in a leaf?

Plant Responses

What are plant responses?

It's dark. You're alone in a room watching a horror film on television. Suddenly, the telephone near you rings. You jump, and your heart begins to beat faster. Did you know that you've just responded to a stimulus? A stimulus is anything in the environment that causes a change in the behavior of an organism. The organism's change in behavior is called a response. A stimulus may come from outside or inside the organism. The ringing telephone is an example of an outside stimulus. It caused you to jump, a response. Inside stimuli include chemical reactions and hormones. Hormones are substances made by cells for use somewhere else in the organism. Your beating heart is a response to inside stimuli. All living organisms, including plants, respond to stimuli. Plants respond to outside and inside stimuli. The response of a plant to an outside stimulus is a **tropism.** A tropism may be seen as movement or a change in growth. Tropisms can be positive or negative. For example, plants might grow toward or away from a stimulus.

Tropisms

Touch is one stimulus that results in a change in a plant's behavior. The pea plants in **Figure 19-9** show a response to touch. The response to touch is thigmotropism, from the Greek

Figure 19-9
The pea plant's tendrils respond to touch by coiling around things. The response to touch is called *thigmotropism.*

Figure 19-10 Plants also show phototropism. This plant is obviously growing toward the light, an example of positive phototropism. **What do you think would happen if the plant were turned halfway around?**

word *thigma*, meaning "touch." Plants also respond to the stimuli of light, gravity, temperature, and amount of water.

Did you ever see a plant leaning toward a window? Light is an important stimulus to plants. When a plant responds to sunlight, the cells on the side of the plant opposite the light get longer than those facing the light. This causes the plant to bend toward the light. The response of a plant to light is called phototropism. A plant growing toward light is called a positive phototropism, as shown in **Figure 19-10.**

The response of an organism to gravity is called gravitropism. The downward growth of plant roots is a positive gravitropism. A stem growing upward is a negative gravitropism.

Plant Hormones

When you visit a supermarket or fruit stand, have you ever noticed that oranges are all about the same size and color? In nature, orange trees flower and produce fruit over a period of time. How do growers get fruits to respond so that most of it is ripe when it reaches the market? One way that growers do this is by using plant hormones.

Auxin and Ethylene

Plant hormones are chemical substances that affect growth. An **auxin** is a type of plant hormone. One of the ways auxin affects plants is that it causes plant stems and leaves to exhibit positive phototropism. When light shines on a plant from one side, the auxin moves to the shaded side of the stem. The auxin causes cells on the shaded side of the stem to increase in length. This causes the stem to curve toward the light.

*inter***NET**
C O N N E C T I O N

Auxin and ethylene are just two of the hormones found in plants. Visit the Glencoe Science Web Site at **www.glencoe. com/sec/science/fl** for more information about other plant hormones.

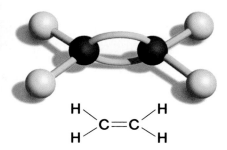

Figure 19-11 Ethylene, C_2H_4, is the plant hormone responsible for fruit ripening, such as these grapes.

Many plants produce the hormone ethylene, a chemical of carbon and hydrogen, as illustrated in **Figure 19-11.** Ethylene causes different plant responses. One response is that it causes fruit to ripen.

Today, fruit growers and shippers use this knowledge to get ripe fruit to market. Fruits such as oranges, grapes, and bananas are picked when they are still green. Green fruit is easier to handle because it does not bruise like ripe fruit does. During shipping, green fruit is exposed to ethylene gas. When the fruit arrives at the store, most of it has ripened.

Problem Solving

Predicting Plant Responses

Jason and his family returned from their two-week vacation and found that several potted plants on the patio were on their sides. After unpacking the car, Jason began to set up the potted plants. To his surprise, the plants looked like they were growing sideways. Later that day, Jason's grandmother telephoned. Jason told her about the plants. She told him not to worry because the plants would soon start to grow upright again.

Solve the Problem

1. Explain why the plants grew as they did.

2. What hormone may have played a part in this plant response?

Think Critically: Predict what Jason might find if he removed a plant's pot and looked at its roots. Explain.

Photoperiods

Sunflowers bloom in the summer, and cherry trees flower in the spring. Some plant species produce flowers at specific times during the year. **Photoperiodism** is a plant's response to the number of hours of daylight and darkness it receives daily.

Earth makes one revolution around the sun every year. As it moves in its orbit about the sun, Earth also rotates. One rotation takes 24 hours. Because Earth is tilted about 23.5° from a line perpendicular to its orbit, the hours of daylight and darkness vary with the seasons. You may have noticed that the sun sets later in summer than in winter. These changes in lengths of daylight and darkness affect plant growth.

Most plants require a specific length of darkness to begin the flowering process. Generally, plants that require less than ten to 12 hours of darkness are called **long-day plants.** You may be familiar with long-day plants such as spinach, lettuce, and beets. Those plants that need 12 or more hours of darkness are called **short-day plants.** Some short-day plants are poinsettias, strawberries, and ragweed. **Figure 19-12** shows both long-day plants and short-day plants. ✔

EARTH SCIENCE
◄ INTEGRATION

Reading Check ✔

What is needed to begin the flowering process?

Figure 19-12 Long-day plants such as zinnias (A) and short-day plants such as primroses (B) flower in response to specific periods of darkness.

Figure 19-13 Day-neutral plants, as seen in this garden, produce flowers all summer long.

Other plants like the marigolds shown in **Figure 19-13** are day-neutral. **Day-neutral plants** have no specific photoperiod, and the flowering process can begin within a range of hours of darkness.

In nature, photoperiodism is one factor that affects where flowering plants can grow and produce fruit. Even if the proper temperature and other growing conditions for a plant are in a particular environment, the plant will not flower and produce fruit without the correct photoperiod. Sometimes, the photoperiod of a plant has a narrow range. For example, some soybeans will flower with 14.5 hours of daylight but will not flower with only 14 hours of daylight. Farmers must choose the variety of soybeans with a photoperiod that matches the hours of daylight where they plant their crop.

Today, greenhouse growers can provide any length of artificial daylight or darkness. This means that all types of flowers are available year-round. You can buy short-day plants during the summer and long-day plants during the winter.

Section Assessment

1. Describe the difference between a response and a tropism.

2. Compare photoperiodism and phototropism.

3. Some red raspberries produce fruit in late spring, then again in the fall. What term describes their photoperiod?

4. **Think Critically:** What is the relationship between plant hormones and tropisms?

5. **Skill Builder**
   Comparing and Contrasting Different plant parts exhibit positive and negative tropisms. Compare and contrast the responses of roots, stems, and leaves to light. If you need help, refer to Comparing and Contrasting in the **Skill Handbook** on page 686.

For three years, a farmer in Costa Rica grew healthy strawberry plants. But, each year he was disappointed because the plants never produced any fruit. In your Science Journal, explain why this happened.

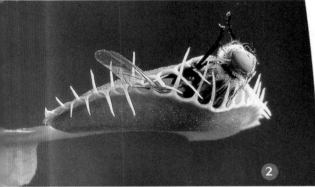

Carnivorous Plants

Carnivorous plants grow in soils that lack or are low in certain nutrients, particularly nitrogen. Over time, these plants have evolved ways to secure the nutrients they need. A Venus's-flytrap is one kind of carnivorous plant. It is currently on the list of endangered species. The ones available in stores are grown in nurseries because collecting Venus's-flytraps in the wild is illegal.

EATING HABITS OF A VENUS'S-FLYTRAP

1 The leaves form a hinged trap. Each half of the trap has three trigger hairs (see arrow) in a triangular arrangement.

2 When an insect or other small animal touches two of these hairs in quick succession, it causes a series of reactions that snap the trap shut within 0.4 s.

3 Stiff hairs along the outer edges of the leaf interlock, preventing the animal's escape.

4 Glands on the leaf secrete enzymes that help digest the prey. The glands are stimulated as the prey struggles to get free.

5 Digestion takes about ten days. During this time, the plant absorbs the digested nutrients. The leaf opens again when digestion and absorption are complete. The insect remains are then blown away.

Think Critically

1. Insects and other small animals provide carnivorous plants with nitrogen compounds. From what other sources do these plants get nutrients?

2. A pitcher plant is another carnivorous plant. Look again at the name of this plant. How do you think this plant traps its prey?

Career CONNECTION

Knowing about soils is important when growing Venus's-flytraps or any plants. Soil science is called *agronomy*. An agronomist studies the biological, chemical, and physical components and properties of soil. Research this career, and then make a list of jobs that require a degree in agronomy or knowledge of soil science.

Plant Tropisms

Possible Materials

- Petri dish
- Tape
- String
- Corn seeds
- Bean seeds
- Paper towels
- Water

Have you ever seen a Venus's-flytrap's leaves close around an insect? Its movement was a response to a stimulus. In this case, the stimulus was the movement of the insect against sensitive, hairlike structures on the leaves. Tropisms are specific plant responses to stimuli outside of the plant. They can be positive or negative. What stimuli will cause responses by plants?

Recognize the Problem

How do plants respond to stimuli?

Form a Hypothesis

Based on your knowledge of tropisms, state a hypothesis about how the plant will respond to a stimulus.

Goals

- **Design** an experiment that tests the effects of a variable.
- **Observe** and analyze a plant response to a stimulus.

Safety Precautions

Some kinds of seeds are poisonous. Do not put any seed in your mouth.

Test Your Hypothesis

Plan

1. As a group, agree upon and write out a hypothesis statement.

2. As a group, **list** the steps needed to test your hypothesis. Be specific, describing exactly what you will do at each step. **List** your materials.

3. It is important to keep the seeds moist during the experiment. **Devise a method** to keep your seeds moist.

4. **Read** over your entire experiment to make sure that all your steps are in a logical order.

5. **Identify** any constants, variables, and controls of the experiment.

6. Is it necessary to run any tests more than one time?

7. If you need a data table, design one in your Science Journal so that it is ready to use as your group collects data.

8. Will the data be summarized in a graph? If yes, what kind of graph would be most useful?

Do

1. Make sure your teacher approves your plan before you proceed.

2. Carry out the experiment as planned.

3. While you are conducting the experiment, write down any observations that you make and complete the data table in your Science Journal.

Analyze Your Data

1. **Compare** your results with those of other groups.

2. **Identify** how the plants responded to the stimulus.

Draw Conclusions

1. What name would you give to the response you observed?

2. **Classify** the responses as positive or negative.

3. **Infer** why many plant growers sprout seeds under artificial light from lamps that are placed just a short distance above the soil.

For a **preview** of this chapter, study this Reviewing Main Ideas before you read the chapter. After you have studied this chapter, you can use the Reviewing Main Ideas to **review** the chapter.

The Glencoe MindJogger, Audiocassettes, and CD-ROM provide additional opportunities for review.

Section
19-1 PHOTOSYNTHESIS AND RESPIRATION

Gases like carbon dioxide and water vapor enter and leave a plant through openings called **stomata.** Stomata are usually found in the epidermis covering a leaf. Two guard cells surround each stoma. Water diffusing into and out of the guard cells causes stomata to open and close. *What role do stomata play in transpiration?*

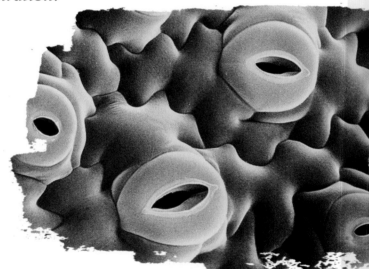

PHOTOSYNTHESIS

In plants, food is produced during the process of **photosynthesis.** Photosynthesis takes place in the chloroplasts of plant cells. Light energy is trapped by chlorophyll, the green pigment in chloroplasts. This energy is used to produce glucose and oxygen from carbon dioxide and water. The energy is stored in the chemical bonds of glucose. Photosynthesis provides the food for most organisms on Earth. *Why are plants called producers?*

RESPIRATION

All organisms use **respiration** to release the energy stored in food molecules. The process begins in the cytoplasm of cells. First, food molecules are broken down into simpler forms. In prokaryotic cells, the process continues in the cytoplasm and some energy is released. Eukaryotic cells generally use oxygen to complete respiration. The release of energy occurs in the mitochondria. Carbon dioxide and water vapor are also products of respiration in eukaryotic cells. *What are the three products of respiration for most eukaryotic cells?*

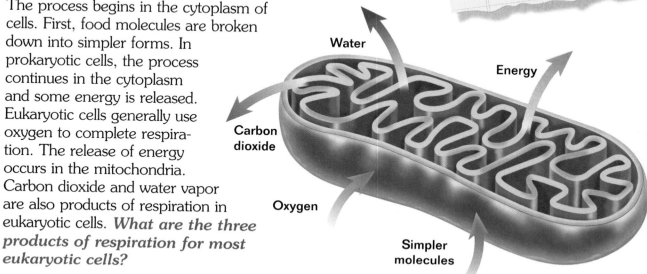

Water

Energy

Carbon dioxide

Oxygen

Simpler molecules

Glucose

Section 19-2 PLANT RESPONSES

Plants respond to stimuli. The response may be a movement, change in growth, or the beginning of some process, such as flowering. A stimulus from outside the plant is called a **tropism.** Outside stimuli include such things as light, gravity, and touch. The lengths of daylight and darkness each day may affect flowering times of plants. Hormones are stimuli from inside plants. These chemicals affect plants in many ways. **Auxin** and ethylene are two plant hormones. *What things may act as outside stimuli for plants?*

Using Vocabulary

a. auxin
b. day-neutral plant
c. long-day plant
d. photoperiodism
e. photosynthesis
f. respiration
g. short-day plant
h. stomata
i. transpiration
j. tropism

Match each phrase with the correct term from the list of Vocabulary words.

1. a plant hormone
2. using light to make glucose and oxygen
3. loss of water through stomata
4. plant that requires long nights to flower
5. releases energy from food

Checking Concepts

Choose the word or phrase that best answers the question.

6. What enters a plant when stomata open?
   A) sugar
   B) water
   C) carbon dioxide
   D) light

7. Which of these is a product of respiration?
   A) CO_2
   B) O_2
   C) C_2H_4
   D) H_2

8. Water, carbon dioxide, and energy are all products of what plant process?
   A) cell division
   B) photosynthesis
   C) growth
   D) respiration

9. What type of plant needs short nights to flower?
   A) day-neutral
   B) short-day
   C) long-day
   D) nonvascular

10. What do you call such things as light, touch, and gravity that cause plant responses?
    A) tropisms
    B) growth behaviors
    C) responses
    D) stimuli

11. What is a plant's response to gravity called?
    A) phototropism
    B) gravitropism
    C) thigmotropism
    D) hydrotropism

12. What are plant substances that affect plant growth called?
    A) tropisms
    B) glucose
    C) germination
    D) hormones

13. Leaves change colors because what substance breaks down?
    A) hormone
    B) carotenoid
    C) chlorophyll
    D) cytoplasm

14. What is a function of stomata?
    A) photosynthesis
    B) to guard the interior cells
    C) to allow sugar to escape
    D) to permit the release of oxygen

15. What are the products of photosynthesis?
    A) glucose and oxygen
    B) carbon dioxide and water
    C) chlorophyll and glucose
    D) carbon dioxide and oxygen

Thinking Critically

16. Growers of bananas pick green bananas, then treat them with ethylene during shipping. Why?

17. Identify each response as a positive or negative tropism.
    a. stem grows up
    b. roots grow down
    c. plant grows toward light
    d. a vine grows around a pole

18. Scientists who study sedimentary rocks and fossils suggest that oxygen did not occur on Earth until plantlike protists appeared. Why?

19. Explain why crab apple trees bloom in the spring but not in the summer.

20. Why do day-neutral and long-day plants grow best in countries near the equator?

Assessment

Developing Skills

If you need help, refer to the **Skill Handbook.**

21. **Hypothesizing:** Make a hypothesis about when guard cells open and close in desert plants.

22. **Designing an Experiment to Test a Hypothesis:** Design an experiment to test your hypothesis from question 21.

23. **Observing and Inferring:** Based on your knowledge of plants, infer how the number and location of stomata differ in land and water plants.

24. **Classifying:** Make a chart that classifies these plants according to their photoperiod: flower year-round—corn, dandelion, tomato; flower in the spring, fall, or winter—chrysanthemum, rice, poinsettia; flower in summer—spinach, lettuce, petunias.

25. **Comparing and Contrasting:** Compare and contrast the action of auxin and the action of ethylene on a plant.

26. **Concept Mapping:** Complete the following concept map using the terms and plants in question 24.

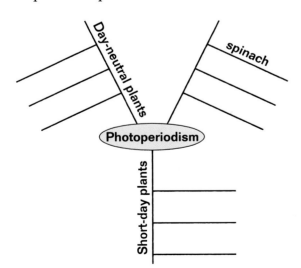

Test-Taking Tip

You Are Smarter Than You Think
Nothing on the science tests you will take this year is too difficult for you to understand. You can learn to master any of it. Be self-confident, and just keep practicing.

Test Practice

Use these questions to test your Science Proficiency.

1. What diffuses into and out of guard cells, causing them to open and close?
   A) carbon dioxide
   B) ethylene
   C) water
   D) glucose

2. What does respiration provide for every cell?
   A) energy
   B) food
   C) oxygen
   D) water

3. What is a plant's change in behavior to an outside stimulus called?
   A) hormone
   B) tropism
   C) transpiration
   D) reactant

4. What term is used for a plant's response to the number of hours of daylight and darkness it receives daily?
   A) gravitropism
   B) thigmotropism
   C) transpiration
   D) photoperiodism

Invertebrate Animals

Chapter Preview

Skills Preview

Skill Builders
• Map Concepts

Activities
• Design an Experiment

MiniLabs
• Model

Reading Check ✔

As you read, create an outline of the chapter that includes the headings and subheadings. List important points under each one.

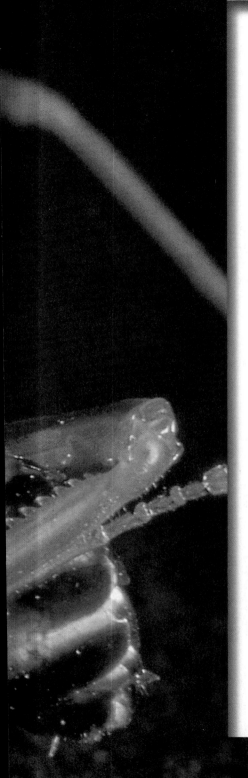

Explore Activity

What is an animal? Is the insect in the photo an animal? What characteristics does the praying mantis have that makes it an animal? More than 1.8 million different kinds of animals have been identified by scientists. How are these animals organized? In the following activity, your class will learn about organizing animals by building a bulletin board display.

Organize Animal Groups

1. Your class is going to make a bulletin board display of different groups of animals. It will look similar to the concept map in **Figure 20-2.**

2. Label large envelopes with the names of different groups.

3. Pick one animal group to study. Make information cards of animals that belong in your group. These cards should have pictures on one side and information on the other.

4. Place your finished cards inside the appropriate envelope on the bulletin board.

Science Journal

In your Science Journal, write down the group of animals you want to study. Collect information on animals that belong to your group. List similarities and differences between your animals and animals of different groups.

What is an animal?

Animal Characteristics

Think about the animals shown in **Figure 20-1.** These animals would be described differently. They have a wide variety of body parts, as well as ways to move, get food, and protect themselves. So, what do all animals have in common? What makes an animal an animal?

1. Animals cannot make their own food. Some animals eat plants to supply their energy needs. Some animals eat other animals, and some eat both plants and animals.
2. Animals digest their food. Large food substances are broken down into smaller substances that their cells can use.
3. Most animals can move from place to place. They move to find food, shelter, and mates and to escape from predators.
4. Animals are many-celled organisms that are made of many different kinds of cells. These cells digest food, get rid of wastes, and reproduce.
5. Most animal cells have a nucleus and organelles surrounded by a membrane. This type of cell is called a eukaryotic cell.

Figure 20-1 Animals come in a variety of shapes and sizes.

B The largest lion's mane jellyfish was found dead on shore. It had a bell over 2 m across with tentacles that dangled over 36 m long.

A The thorny devil lizard lives in the Australian desert. It feeds on ants and survives with little water to drink.

C The East African crowned crane is the only crane that will roost in trees. The adults perform spectacular dances when excited.

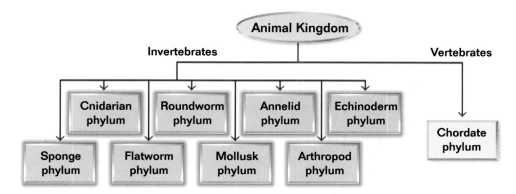

Figure 20-2 This diagram shows the relationships among different groups in the animal kingdom. Different forms of this diagram will appear at the beginning of each section in this and the following chapter. The groups that are highlighted with an orange outline are the groups that will be discussed in that particular section. For example, this section will deal with the invertebrates, which includes the sponge, cnidarian, flatworm, roundworm, mollusk, annelid, arthropod, and echinoderm phylums.

Animal Classification

Deciding whether an organism is an animal is only the first step in classifying it. Scientists place all animals into smaller, related groups. They begin by separating animals into two distinct groups—vertebrates and invertebrates. **Vertebrates** (VURT uh brayts) are animals that have a backbone. **Invertebrates** (ihn VURT uh brayts) are animals that do not have a backbone. There are far more invertebrates than vertebrates. About 97 percent of all animals are invertebrates.

Scientists classify or group the invertebrates into several different phyla (FI lah), as shown in **Figure 20-2.** The animals within each phylum share similar characteristics. These characteristics indicate that the animals within the group descended from a common ancestor. The characteristics also show a change from less complex to more complex animals as you move from phylum to phylum.

Symmetry

As you study the different groups of invertebrates, one feature becomes apparent—symmetry. **Symmetry** (SIH muh tree) refers to the arrangement of the individual parts of an object. Scientists also use body symmetry to classify animals. ☑

Most animals have either radial or bilateral symmetry. Animals with body parts arranged in a circle around a central point have radial symmetry. These animals can locate food and gather other information from all directions. Animals with radial symmetry, such as jellyfish and sea urchins, live in water.

Reading Check

What is symmetry?

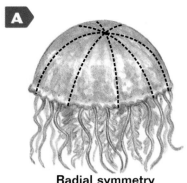

Radial symmetry

Bilateral symmetry

Asymmetry

Figure 20-3 Jellyfish (A) have radial symmetry, butterflies (B) have bilateral symmetry, and sponges (C) are asymmetrical. **What type of symmetry do humans exhibit?**

On the other hand, animals with bilateral symmetry have parts that are mirror images of each other. A line can be drawn down the center of their bodies to divide them into two matching parts. Grasshoppers and lobsters are bilaterally symmetrical.

Some animals have no definite shape. They are called asymmetrical. Their bodies cannot be divided into matching halves. Many sponges are asymmetrical (AY suh meh trih kul). As you learn more about invertebrates, see how their body symmetry is related to how they gather food. **Figure 20-3** shows the three ways an animal's body parts can be arranged.

Section Assessment

1. What are the characteristics of animals?
2. How are invertebrates different from vertebrates?
3. What are the types of symmetry? Name an animal that has bilateral symmetry.
4. **Think Critically** Radial symmetry is found among species that live in water. Why might radial symmetry be an adaptation uncommon among animals that live on land?
5. **Skill Builder**
   Concept Mapping Using the information in this section, make a concept map showing the steps a scientist might use to classify a new animal. If you need help, refer to Concept Mapping in the **Skill Handbook** on page 680.

Using Computers

Word Processing
Create a table that you will use as you complete this chapter. Label the following columns: *animal, group,* and *body symmetry.* Create ten rows to enter animal names. If you need help, refer to page 698.

Sponges, Cnidarians, Flatworms, and Roundworms

Sponges

Sponges are the simplest of animals. They bridge the gap between single-celled organisms and more complex animals. Their body structure is made of two layers of cells. Adult sponges live attached to one place. Organisms that remain attached to one place during their lifetimes are called sessile (SES ul). Because they do not move about in search of food, scientists used to classify sponges, shown in **Figure 20-4,** as plants. Once scientists found out that sponges can't make their own food, they reclassified them as animals.

What You'll Learn

▶ The structures that make up sponges and cnidarians
▶ How sponges and cnidarians get food and reproduce
▶ The body plans of flatworms and roundworms

Vocabulary

cnidarian   free-living
polyp   parasite
medusa

Why It's Important

▶ Sponges, cnidarians, flatworms, and roundworms exhibit simple cell and tissue organization.

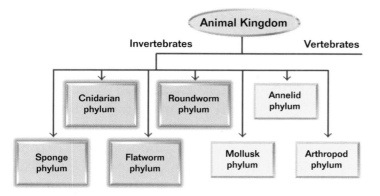

Figure 20-4 Orange finger sponges form long "fingers" from 2 cm to 20 cm in length. They are also called dead man's finger sponges.

Filter Feeders

Sponges live in water. They are called filter feeders because they filter food out of the water that flows through their bodies. Microscopic organisms and oxygen are carried with the water through pores into the central cavity of the sponge. The phylum that sponges belong to, Porifera, gets its name from these pores. The inner surface of the central cavity is lined with specialized cells called collar cells. Thin, whiplike structures, called flagella, extend from the collar cells and keep the water moving through the sponge. Other specialized cells digest the food, carry nutrients to all parts of the sponge, and remove wastes.

Body Support and Defense

At first glance, you might think that sponges have few defenses against predators. Actually, not many animals eat sponges. The soft bodies of many sponges are supported by sharp, glasslike structures called spicules. Many other sponges have a material called spongin. Spongin can be compared to foam rubber because it makes sponges both soft and elastic. Some sponges have both spicules and spongin, which protects their soft bodies.

Sponge Reproduction

Sponges are able to reproduce both sexually and asexually. Asexual reproduction occurs when a bud located on the side of the parent sponge develops into a small sponge. The small sponge breaks off, floats away, and attaches itself to a new surface. New sponges also grow when a sponge is cut or broken into pieces. The broken pieces regenerate or grow into a complete new sponge.

Most sponges that reproduce sexually produce both eggs and sperm. The sponge releases sperm into the water. Currents carry the sperm to eggs of another sponge, where fertilization occurs. The fertilized eggs grow into larvae that look different from the adult sponge. The larvae are able to swim to a different area before attaching themselves to a rock or other surface.

Observing Sponge Spicules

Procedure

1. Add a few drops of bleach to a microscope slide. **CAUTION:** *Do not inhale the bleach. Do not spill it on your hands, clothing, or on the microscope.*
2. Put a small piece of the sponge into the bleach on the slide. Add a coverslip. Observe the cells of the sponge.

Analysis

1. Are spicules made of the same materials as the rest of the sponge? Explain.
2. What is the function of spicules?

Cnidarians

Have you ever cast a fishing line into the water to catch your dinner? In a somewhat similar way, animals in the phylum Cnidaria have tentacles that are used to capture prey. Jellyfish, sea anemones, hydra, and corals belong to this phylum.

Cnidarians (NIH dar ee uns) are a phylum of hollow-bodied animals that have stinging cells. They have radial symmetry that allows them to locate food that floats by from any direction. Their bodies have two cell layers that are organized into tissues. The inner layer forms a digestive cavity where food is broken down. Their tentacles surround the mouth. Stinging cells shoot out to stun or grasp prey. The word *cnidaria* is Latin for "stinging cells." Oxygen moves into the cells from the surrounding water, and carbon dioxide waste moves out of the cells. Nerve cells work together as a nerve net throughout the whole body.

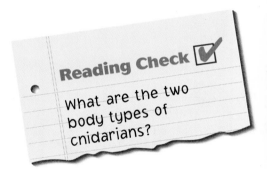

EXAMPLES OF Cnidarians

- Jellyfish
- Sea anemones
- Hydra
- Corals
- Portuguese man-of-war

Two Body Plans

Study the two cnidarians in **Figure 20-5.** They represent the two different body plans found in this animal's phylum. The vase-shaped body of the hydra is called a **polyp** (PAHL up). Although hydras are usually sessile, they can twist to capture prey. They also can somersault to a new location. Jellyfish have a free-swimming, bell-shaped body that is called a **medusa.** Jellyfish are not strong swimmers. Instead, they drift along with the ocean currents. Some cnidarians go through both the polyp and medusa stages during their life cycles. ☑

Reading Check

What are the two body types of cnidarians?

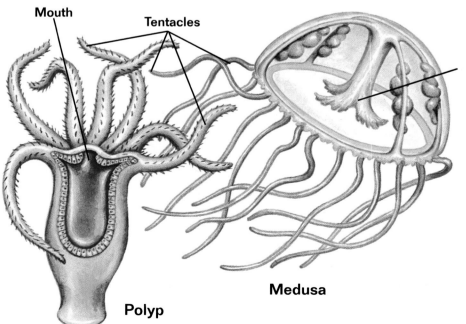

Mouth

Tentacles

Mouth

Figure 20-5 The polyp and medusa forms are the two body plans of cnidarians.

Medusa

Polyp

Cnidarian Reproduction

Cnidarians produce both asexually and sexually. Polyp forms of cnidarians, such as hydras, reproduce asexually by budding, as illustrated in **Figure 20-6.** The bud eventually falls off of the parent organism and develops into a new polyp. Some polyps also can reproduce sexually by releasing eggs or sperm into the water. The eggs are fertilized by sperm and develop into a new polyp. Medusa forms of cnidarians, such as jellyfish, have both an asexual and a sexual stage, which are illustrated in **Figure 20-7.** These stages alternate between generations. Medusa reproduce sexually to produce polyps, which in turn, reproduce asexually to form new medusa.

Figure 20-6 Polyps, like these hydra, reproduce by budding.

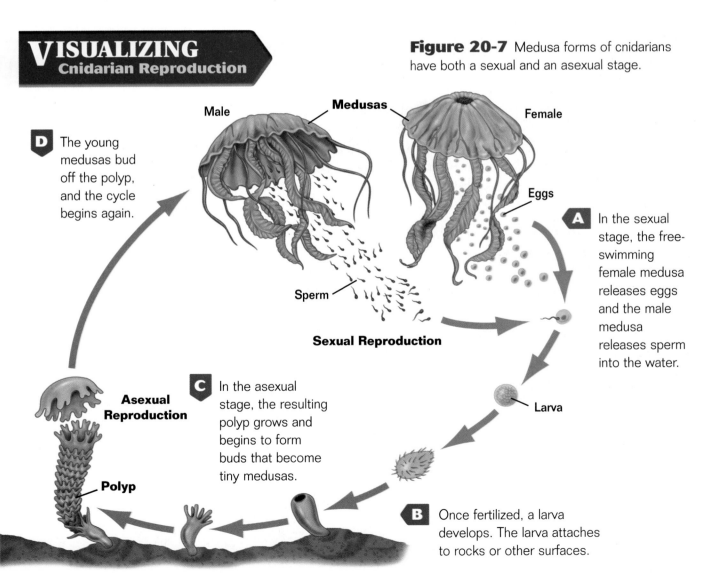

VISUALIZING
Cnidarian Reproduction

Figure 20-7 Medusa forms of cnidarians have both a sexual and an asexual stage.

Medusas

Male

Female

D The young medusas bud off the polyp, and the cycle begins again.

Sperm

Eggs

A In the sexual stage, the free-swimming female medusa releases eggs and the male medusa releases sperm into the water.

Sexual Reproduction

C In the asexual stage, the resulting polyp grows and begins to form buds that become tiny medusas.

Asexual Reproduction

Larva

Polyp

B Once fertilized, a larva develops. The larva attaches to rocks or other surfaces.

Flatworms

Unlike sponges and cnidarians that wait for food to pass their way, flatworms actively search for their food. Worms are invertebrates with soft bodies and bilateral symmetry. Flatworms are members of the phylum Platyhelminthes (plat ih hel MIHN theez). They have long, flattened bodies. They also have three distinct layers of tissue organized into organs and organ systems.

Some flatworms are free-living, such as the planarian in **Figure 20-8A. Free-living** organisms don't depend on one particular organism for food or a place to live. But, most flatworms are parasites that live in or on their hosts. A **parasite** depends on its host for food and a place to live.

Tapeworms

One parasitic flatworm that lives in humans is called the tapeworm. It lacks a digestive system. To survive, it lives in the intestines of its hosts. The tapeworm absorbs nutrients directly into its body from digested material in the host's intestines. Find the hooks and suckers on the tapeworm's head in **Figure 20-8B.** The hooks and suckers attach the tapeworm to the host's intestines.

Figure 20-8 Flatworms have members that are free-living and other members that are parasites.

Eyespot

Head

Cilia

Mouth/Anus

Digestive tract

Excretory system

B Planarians have eyespots that have been known to respond to light. They also have the power to regenerate. A planarian can be cut in two, and each piece will grow into a new worm.

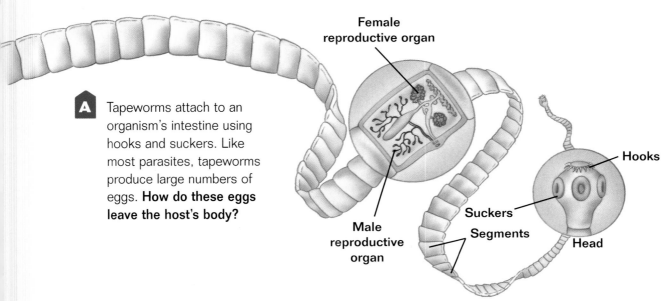

Female reproductive organ

A Tapeworms attach to an organism's intestine using hooks and suckers. Like most parasites, tapeworms produce large numbers of eggs. **How do these eggs leave the host's body?**

Male reproductive organ

Hooks

Suckers

Segments

Head

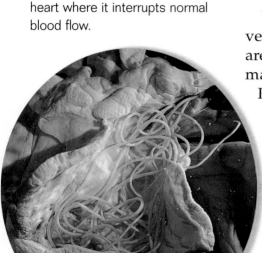

Figure 20-9 Mosquitoes are the carriers of dog heartworm. Mosquitoes bite infected dogs and, in turn, infect still other dogs by biting them. The worm larva travels through the circulatory system and lodges in the heart where it interrupts normal blood flow.

A tapeworm grows by adding sections directly behind its head. Each body segment produces both eggs and sperm from separate male and female reproductive organs. The eggs and sperm are released into the segment. Once filled with fertilized eggs, the segment breaks off and passes out of the host's body. If another host eats a fertilized egg, the egg hatches and develops into a new worm.

Roundworms

Dog owners regularly give their pets a medicine that prevents heartworm disease. Heartworms can kill a dog. They are just one kind of the many thousands of roundworms that make up the phylum Nematoda (nem uh TOH duh). Roundworms are the most widespread animal on Earth. Billions can live in a single acre of soil.

A roundworm's body is described as a tube within a tube, with fluid in between. The cavity separates the digestive tract from the body wall. Roundworms are also more complex than flatworms because their digestive tract is complete with two openings. Food enters through the mouth and wastes exit through an anus.

Roundworms are a diverse group. Some are decomposers. Some are predators. Some are parasites of animals and some are parasites of plants. **Figure 20-9** shows a parasitic heartworm that can infect dogs. What type of body symmetry does a roundworm have?

Section Assessment

1. How do sponges and cnidarians get food?
2. What are three common characteristics of worms?
3. Compare the body plans of flatworms and roundworms.
4. **Think Critically:** Sponges are sessile organisms. They remain attached to one place during their lifetimes. Explain why a sponge is still considered to be an animal.
5. **Skill Builder**
   Comparing and Contrasting Do the **Chapter 20 Skill Activity** on page 727 to compare and contrast types of symmetry found in different animals.

Using Math

A sponge is 1 cm in diameter and 10 cm tall. It can move 22.5 L of water through its body in a day. Calculate the volume of water it pumps through its body in one minute.

Mollusks and Segmented Worms

Mollusks

Imagine yourself walking along the beach at low tide. On the rocks by a small tide pool, you see small conelike shells. The blue-black shelled mussels are exposed along the shore, and one arm of a shy octopus can be seen inside the opening of its den. How could all of these different animals belong to the same phylum? What do they have in common?

Common Characteristics

The snail, slug, mussel, and octopus belong to the phylum Mollusca. **Mollusks** are soft-bodied invertebrates that usually have a shell. Characteristics shared by mollusks include a mantle and a large, muscular foot. The **mantle** is a thin layer of tissue covering the mollusk's soft body. It secretes the protective shell of those mollusks that have a shell. The foot is used for moving the animal or for attaching it to an object.

Between the soft body and the mantel is a space called the mantle cavity. Water-dwelling mollusks have gills in the mantle cavity. **Gills** are organs that exchange oxygen and carbon dioxide with the water. Land-dwelling mollusks have lungs to exchange gases with air. Mollusks have a complete digestive system with two openings. Many also have a scratchy, tonguelike organ called the radula. The **radula** (RAJ uh luh) acts like a file with rows of teeth to break up food into smaller pieces.

Figure 20-10

What You'll Learn

► The characteristics of mollusks
► The similarities and differences between an open and a closed circulatory system
► The characteristics of segmented worms
► The structures and digestive process of an earthworm

Vocabulary

mollusk
mantle
gills
radula
open circulatory system
closed circulatory system

Why It's Important

► Mollusks and segmented worms have specialized structures that allow them to live in their environments.

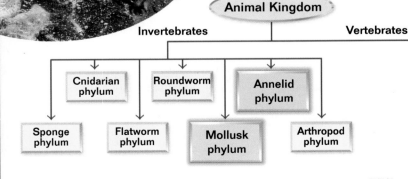

Fire Bristleworm

Octopus

```
                    Animal Kingdom
        Invertebrates            Vertebrates

    Cnidarian    Roundworm    Annelid
    phylum       phylum       phylum

  Sponge    Flatworm    Mollusk    Arthropod
  phylum    phylum      phylum     phylum
```

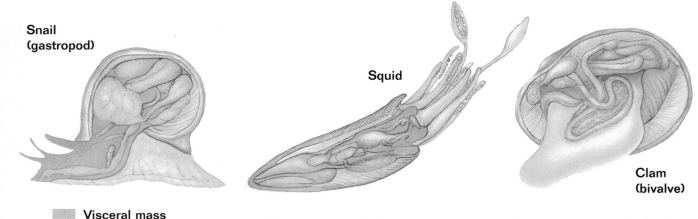

Snail (gastropod)

Squid

Clam (bivalve)

■ Visceral mass
■ Mantle
■ Shell
■ Foot

Figure 20-11 All mollusks have the same basic body plan: with a mantle, a shell, a foot, and an area called visceral mass where the body organs are located.

EXAMPLES OF
Bivalves Gastropods

Figure 20-12 Although these animals look different from one another, they are all mollusks.

A Tree snails are cone-shaped gastropods ranging in size from 1 cm to 6 cm long. They feed on tiny lichens, fungi, and algae that grow on the bark, leaves, and fruit of trees.

Some mollusks have an open circulatory system. Animals with an **open circulatory system** do not have their blood contained in vessels. Instead, the blood surrounds the organs. These organs are grouped together in a fluid-filled body cavity. **Figure 20-11** shows the basic structure of all mollusks.

Types of Mollusks

To classify mollusks, scientists first find out whether the mollusk has a shell. Then, they look at the kind of shell. They also look at the kind of foot. In this section, you will learn about three kinds of mollusks. **Figure 20-12** shows examples of two groups of mollusks—the gastropods and bivalves.

Gastropods and Bivalves

Gastropods are the largest class of mollusks. Most gastropods, such as the snails and conches, have a single shell. Slugs are also gastropods, but they don't have a shell. All move about on the large, muscular foot. A secretion of mucus allows them to glide across objects. Gastropods live in water or on land.

Bivalves are another class of mollusks. How many shells do you think bivalves have? Think of other words that start

B Scallops are marine bivalves. They swim by flapping their shells with a powerful muscle, the only part that humans eat.

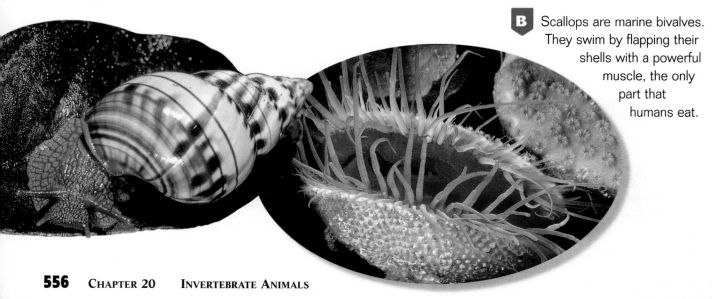

Figure 20-13 Although the chambered nautilus's shell resembles a snail's shell, the nautilus is a cephalopod. Like the octopus and the squid, it swims using jet propulsion, as shown in **Figure 20-14.**

with *bi-*. A clam is a bivalve, or an organism with two shell halves joined by a hinge. Powerful, large muscles open and close the shells. Bivalves are water animals that are also filter feeders. Food is removed from water that is brought into and filtered through the gills.

Cephalopods

Cephalopods (SEF ah loh pawdz) are the most complex type of mollusk. Squid, octopuses, and the chambered nautilus, pictured in **Figure 20-13,** are all cephalopods. Most cephalopods have no shell but they do have a well-developed head. The "foot" is divided into tentacles with strong suckers. These animals also have a **closed circulatory system** in which blood is carried through blood vessels.

Both the squid and octopus are adapted for quick movement in the ocean. The squid's mantle is a muscular envelope that surrounds its internal organs. Water enters the space between the mantle and the other body organs. When the mantle closes around the collar of the squid, the water is squeezed rapidly through a siphon, which is a funnel-like structure. The rapid expulsion of water from the siphon causes the squid to move in the opposite direction of the stream of water. **Figure 20-14** shows how this propulsion system works.

EXAMPLES OF
Cephalopods

- **Octopus**
- **Squid**
- **Chambered nautilus**

PHYSICS
◀**INTEGRATION**

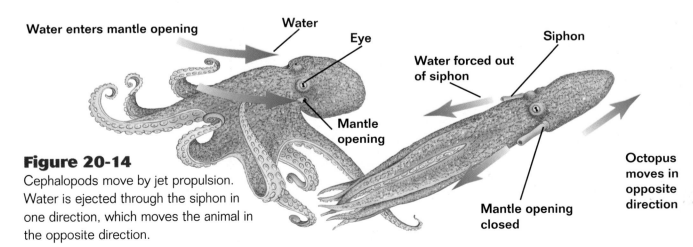

Figure 20-14
Cephalopods move by jet propulsion. Water is ejected through the siphon in one direction, which moves the animal in the opposite direction.

Water enters mantle opening

Water

Eye

Mantle opening

Siphon

Water forced out of siphon

Mantle opening closed

Octopus moves in opposite direction

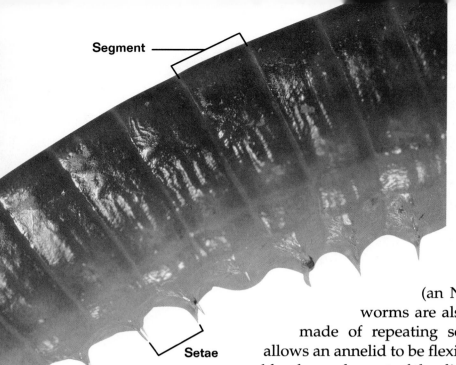

Segment

Setae

Magnification: 5×

Figure 20-15 Earthworms move using bristlelike hairs called setae. **How would the setae help the earthworms move?**

Segmented Worms

What kind of animal do you think of when you hear the word *worm?* Most likely, you think of an earthworm. Earthworms belong to a group of segmented worms in the phylum Annelida (an NEL ud uh). Leeches and marine worms are also annelids. An annelid's body is made of repeating segments or rings. Segmentation allows an annelid to be flexible. Each segment has nerve cells, blood vessels, part of the digestive tract, and the coelum (SEE lum). The coelum, or internal body cavity, separates the internal organs from the body wall. Annelids also have a closed circulatory system and a complete digestive system with two body openings.

Earthworms

Earthworms have more than 100 body segments. Setae (SEE tee), or bristlelike structures pictured in **Figure 20-15,** are found on the outside of these segments. Earthworms use the setae and two sets of muscles to move through or hold onto

**EXAMPLES OF
Segmented Worms**

- **Earthworms**
- **Leeches**
- **Marine worms**

Figure 20-16 Segmented worms have circulatory, respiratory, excretory, digestive, muscular, and reproductive systems.

Mouth

Brain

Reproductive structures

Main nerve cord

Intestine

Hearts

Waste removal tubes

Blood vessels

Crop

Gizzard

Anus

Setae

soil. Moving through soil is important for earthworms because they eat it. Earthworms get the energy they need to live from the bits of leaves and other living matter found in the soil. You can trace the path through an earthworm's digestive system in **Figure 20-16.** First, the soil moves to the crop, where it is stored. Behind the crop is a muscular structure called the gizzard. Here, the soil is ground. As the food passes to the intestine, it is broken down and absorbed by the blood. Undigested soil and wastes leave the worm through the anus. ☑️

What body structures are not present in the earthworm shown in **Figure 20-16?** Notice that you don't find gills or lungs. An earthworm lives in a thin film of water. It exchanges carbon dioxide and oxygen by diffusion through its skin.

Reading Check ☑️

What are setae?

Leeches

Leeches are parasites that have a lifestyle that is different from earthworms'. These worms have flat bodies from 5 mm to 46 cm long and have sucking disks on both ends of their bodies. Leeches attach themselves to and remove blood from the body of a host. Some leeches can store as much as ten times their own weight in blood. The blood can be stored for months and released a little at a time into the digestive system. Leeches are found in freshwater, marine waters, and on land in mild and tropical regions.

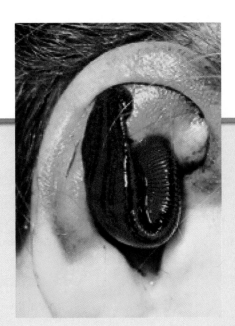

Problem Solving

Leeches to the Rescue

Since ancient times, doctors have used leeches to treat a variety of diseases. Early doctors thought leeches removed the bad blood that resulted in disease. Unfortunately, so many leeches were used sometimes that patients died from blood loss. With the rise of modern medical treatments, the use of leeches was abandoned. People thought it was useless.

Now, the leech is back! Surgeons are able to reattach severed ears or fingers, but it is difficult to keep blood flowing to the reattached body part. If blood clots appear, they stop blood circulation and the cells in the ear or finger die. Medicinal leeches are the key to success. Surgeons place a leech on the reattached ear or finger. It inflicts a painless bite from a sucking disk at each end of its body. As the leech feeds on the blood, chemicals in the saliva break up clots that have already formed and prevent new clots from forming. Eventually, normal circulation is established. The leech is removed and the reattached part survives.

Think Critically: Blood clots are major factors in strokes and some heart and blood vessel diseases. How might research about leeches play an important role in developing treatments for these conditions?

Figure 20-17 Polychaetes come in a variety of forms and colors. The Christmas tree (A) and feather duster (B) use their appendages to filter out food from their watery environments. **How are these organisms similar to cnidarians and sponges?**

Marine Worms

Look at the animals in **Figure 20-17.** You may wonder how these feathery animals can possibly be related to the earthworm and leech. These animals belong to a third group of annelids called polychaetes (PAHL ee kitz). The word *polychaete* means "many spines." There are more species of polychaetes than of any other kind of annelid. More than 6000 known species of polychaetes have been discovered.

The setae of these annelids occur in bundles along their segments. Marine worms are polychaetes that float, burrow, build structures, or walk on the ocean floor. While earthworms find nutrients in the soil and leeches are parasites, polychaetes are predators. Some use powerful jaws or tentacles to catch prey. Some of these strange-looking annelids can even produce their own light.

While annelids may not look complex, they are much more complex than sponges and cnidarians. In the next section, you will learn how they compare to the most complex invertebrates.

Section Assessment

1. Name the three classes of mollusks and identify a member from each class.
2. What are the characteristics of segmented worms?
3. Describe how an earthworm feeds and digests its food.
4. **Think Critically:** How does an annelid's segmentation help it move?
5.  **Skill Builder**
   Comparing and Contrasting Compare and contrast an open circulatory system with a closed circulatory system. If you need help, refer to Comparing and Contrasting in the **Skill Handbook** on page 686.

Science Journal
Choose a mollusk and write about it in your Science Journal. Describe its appearance, how it gets food, where it lives, and other interesting facts.

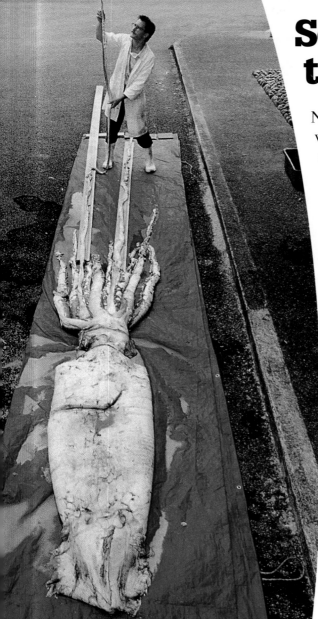

Science
JOURNAL ▶

How big is a giant squid? Find out the length of the wall in your classroom, a school bus, and an airplane. Record the lengths in your Science Journal. Compare the lengths of these objects to an 18 m giant squid. Which is longest?

Searching for the Giant Squid

No one has ever seen a giant squid in its natural habitat, which is 300 m to 1500 m below the ocean's surface. Nor has any live, healthy giant squid been kept in an aquarium or research facility to be studied by scientists. The only live specimens of giant squid available for study have been those that washed up on beaches or were brought up in deep-sea commercial fishing nets. These squids have been sick and unsuitable for study.

Rare Find

In the late 1500s, accounts were written about several large sea creatures stranded on Norwegian shores. It was not until 1854 that scientists concluded that these creatures were giant squid. In the late 1800s, a dead giant squid caught by commercial fishers in Newfoundland became the first specimen available for study. The one-metric-ton giant squid at left was netted at a depth of 425 m in the waters off New Zealand. The creature was nearly dead when pulled on board the research vessel. The three-year-old squid measured 8 m from top to tip of tentacle and might have reached a much greater length at maturity.

The Search Goes On

The Smithsonian's Clyde Roper, one of the world's leading experts on the giant squid, has spent more than 30 years studying these remarkable animals. In 1997, Roper and his crew used the *Odyssey*, a robotic under-water vehicle, and a camera to explore the cold, black depths of Kaikoura Canyon, a deep-sea ecosystem located off New Zealand's South Island. Dr. Roper and his colleagues collected valuable information on the temperature, salt content, and depth of the ocean. On a ship at the surface, they viewed many hours of videotapes of this deep-water ecosystem—but alas, no giant squids. One day, perhaps crewed submersibles in the area will be the first to catch a glimpse of the giant squid at home.

Garbage-eating Worms

Possible Materials

- Worms (red wigglers)
- Plastic containers with drainage holes (4 L) (2)
- Soil (7 L)
- Chopped food scraps including fruit and vegetable peels, pulverized eggshells, tea bags, and coffee grounds
- Shredded newspaper
- Spray bottle

You know that soil conditions can influence the growth of plants. You are trying to decide what factors might improve the soil in your backyard garden. A friend suggests that earthworms improve the quality of the soil. Does the presence of earthworms have any value in improving soil conditions?

Recognize the Problem

How does the presence of earthworms change the condition of the soil?

Form a Hypothesis

Based on your reading and observations, state a hypothesis about how earthworms might improve the conditions of soil.

Goals

- **Design an experiment** that compares the condition of soil in two environments, one with earthworms and one without.
- **Observe** the change in soil conditions for two weeks.

Safety Precautions

Be careful when working with live animals. Always keep your hands wet when handling earthworms. Dry hands will remove the mucus from the earthworms.

Test Your Hypothesis

Plan

1. As a group, agree upon the hypothesis and **decide** how you will test it. **Identify** what results will confirm the hypothesis.

2. **List** the steps you will need to take to test your hypothesis. Be specific. **Describe** exactly what you will do in each step. **List** your materials.

3. Prepare a data table in your Science Journal to **record** your observations.

4. **Read** over the entire experiment to make sure all steps are in logical order.

5. **Identify** all constants, variables, and controls of the experiment.

Do

1. Make sure your teacher approves your plan and your data table before you proceed.

2. Carry out the experiment as planned.

3. While doing the experiment, **record** your observations and complete the data table in your Science Journal.

Analyze Your Data

1. **Compare** the changes in the two sets of soil samples.

2. **Compare** your results with those of other groups.

3. What was your control in this experiment?

4. What were your variables?

Draw Conclusions

1. Did the results support your hypothesis? **Explain.**

2. **Describe** what effect you think rain would have on the soil and worms.

20•4 Arthropods and Echinoderms

What You'll Learn

▶ Features used to classify arthropods
▶ How the structure of the exoskeleton relates to its function
▶ Features of echinoderms

Vocabulary
arthropod
appendage
exoskeleton
metamorphosis

Why It's Important

▶ Arthropods and echinoderms show great diversity and are found in many different environments.

Arthropods

By far, the largest group of animals belongs in the phylum Arthropoda. More than 900 000 species of arthropods have been discovered. The term **arthropod** comes from *arthros*, meaning "jointed," and *poda*, meaning "foot." Arthropods are animals that have jointed appendages. They are similar to annelids because they have segmented bodies. Yet, in most cases, they have fewer, more specialized segments. Instead of setae, they have different kinds of appendages. **Appendages** are the structures such as claws, legs, and even antennae that grow from the body.

Every arthropod has an **exoskeleton** that protects and supports its body. The exoskeleton also protects the arthropod from drying out. This lightweight body covering is made of a carbohydrate and a protein. As the animal grows, the exoskeleton is shed in a process called molting. The weight of the outer covering increases as the size of the animal increases. Weight and hardness of the exoskeleton produce a problem for the animal. They make it more difficult to move. The jointed appendages solve part of this problem.

Figure 20-18 shows an example of the five different types of arthropods: insects, spiders, centipedes, millipedes, and crustaceans. Find the body segments on these animals. Which arthropods appear most like the annelids?

Figure 20-18 Arthropods include insects (A), spiders (B), centipedes (C), millipedes (D), and crustaceans (E).

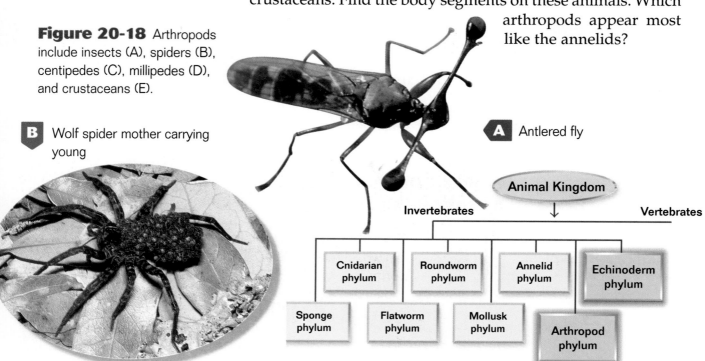

B Wolf spider mother carrying young

A Antlered fly

Animal Kingdom

Invertebrates | Vertebrates

Cnidarian phylum

Roundworm phylum

Annelid phylum

Echinoderm phylum

Sponge phylum

Flatworm phylum

Mollusk phylum

Arthropod phylum

Insects

When asked to name an insect, your answer might be some kind of flying insect, such as bee, fly, beetle, or butterfly. In fact, insects are the only invertebrates that can fly. Insects make up the largest group of invertebrates. There are more than 700 000 classified species of insects, and scientists describe more each year.

Insects have three distinct body regions, as shown in **Figure 20-18A:** the head, thorax, and abdomen. The head has well-developed sensory organs, including the eyes and antennae. The thorax has three pairs of jointed legs and, in many species, one or two pairs of wings. The wings and legs of insects are highly specialized.

The abdomen is divided into segments and has neither wings nor legs attached to it. Reproductive organs are located in this region. Insects produce many more young than can survive. For example, a single female fly can produce thousands of eggs.

Insects have an open circulatory system. Oxygen is not transported by blood in the system, but food and waste materials are. Oxygen is brought directly to tissues inside of the insect through small holes called spiracles (SPIHR ih kulz) located along the thorax and abdomen.

*inter*NET
CONNECTION

Visit the Glencoe Science Web Site at **www.glencoe.com/ sec/science/fl** for more information about butterflies.

 Sally lightfoot crab

C Centipede

D Forest floor millipede

Figure 20-19

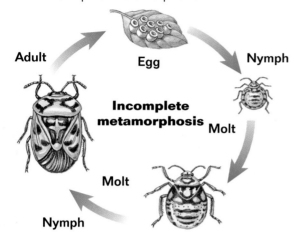

A Harlequin bugs undergo incomplete metamorphosis.

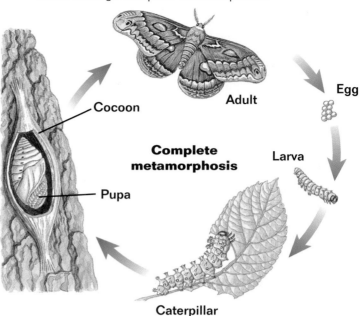

B Butterflies and moths, such as this silk moth, undergo complete metamorphosis.

Figure 20-20 A spider's web is made from a liquid silk that the arachnid produces in its abdomen. Each kind of spider weaves its own unique style of web.

EXAMPLES OF
Arachnids

- Spiders
- Mites
- Ticks
- Scorpions
- Lice

Metamorphosis

Identifying the young of some insects can be difficult. They don't look anything like the adult forms. This happens because many insects completely change their body form as they mature. This change in body form is called **metamorphosis** (met uh MOR fuh sus). There are two kinds of metamorphosis. Butterflies, ants, bees, and moths undergo complete metamorphosis. Complete metamorphosis has four stages: egg, larva, pupa (PYEW puh), and adult. You can trace the stages of this process in **Figure 20-19.** Notice how different the larva and pupa stages are from the adults.

Other insects go through incomplete metamorphosis, which is made up of only three stages: egg, nymph, and adult. Grasshopper nymphs look like a tiny version of the parents except they don't have wings. A nymph molts several times before reaching the adult stage. They replace their old exoskeletons as they grow larger. Grasshoppers get their wings and become adults after their final molt.

Arachnids

Spiders, ticks, mites, and scorpions are often confused with insects. They actually belong to a separate group of arthropods known as arachnids. Arachnids have two body regions. The first, called the cephalothorax (sef uh luh THOR aks), is made of the fused head and thorax regions. The abdomen is the second region. All arachnids have four pairs of legs attached to the cephalothorax.

Figure 20-21 Millipedes (A) may have more than 100 segments in their long abdomens. Centipedes (B) may have from 15 segments to 181 segments—always an odd number.

 Giant millipede

Spiders are predators, but they can't chew and eat prey the way insects do. Instead, a spider uses a pair of fanglike appendages in its mouth to inject venom into the prey and paralyze it. The spider releases enzymes that turn its victim into a liquid. The spider then drinks its food. In **Figure 20-20,** a spider is weaving a web that will trap prey.

 Soil centipede

Centipedes and Millipedes

Centipedes and millipedes are long, thin, segmented arthropods that look like worms. Instead of setae, these arthropods have pairs of jointed legs. Centipedes have one pair of joined legs attached to each body segment. Millipedes have two pairs. Centipedes are predators that use poisonous venom to capture their prey. Millipedes eat plants. Besides the number of legs, how else is the centipede different from the millipede in **Figure 20-21?**

Crustaceans

The exoskeleton gets larger and heavier each time an arthropod molts. The weight of the exoskeleton can limit the size of the animal. Now, think about where you can lift the most weight—on land or in water? Water is more buoyant than air, and it provides a greater upward force on an object. Because of this buoyant property, a large, heavy exoskeleton is less limiting for arthropods that live in water. These arthropods belong to a class known as crustaceans.

Most crustaceans live in water. Examples include crabs, crayfish, lobsters, shrimp, barnacles, and water fleas. They have five pairs of jointed legs. The first pair is usually larger and thicker and is used as claws to hold food, as illustrated in **Figure 20-22.** The other four pairs are walking legs. The five pairs of appendages on the abdomen are swimmerets. These are used to help move the animals through water and for reproduction. The swimmerets also force water over the feathery gills. If a crustacean loses an appendage, it can regenerate the lost part.

EXAMPLES OF
Crustaceans

- Crabs
- Crayfish
- Lobsters
- Shrimp
- Barnacles

Figure 20-22 This rock crab, found in the Atlantic Ocean, is using its claws to hold the scallop it eats.

B Sand dollar

Figure 20-23 Echinoderms include sea stars (A), sand dollars (B), and basket stars (C). **What do these organisms have in common?**

A Fireback sea star

C Basket star

Reading Check ✓
What does the word *echinoderm* mean?

EXAMPLES OF
Echinoderms

- Sea stars
- Sea urchins
- Sand dollars
- Basket star
- Sea cucumber

Echinoderms

Unless you live near the ocean, you may not have seen an echinoderm (ih KI nuh durm), but most people know what a sea star is. Echinoderms have radial symmetry and are represented by sea stars, brittle stars, sea urchins, sand dollars, and sea cucumbers. They also don't have heads, brains, or advanced nervous systems.

The name *echinoderm* means "spiny skin." You can see from those shown in **Figure 20-23** that echinoderms have spines of various lengths that cover the outside of their bodies. Most echinoderms, such as sea stars, are supported and protected by an internal skeleton made up of calcium carbonate plates. These plates are covered by thin, spiny skin. ✓

Water-Vascular System

Sea stars have a unique characteristic shared by all echinoderms—a water-vascular system. The water-vascular system is a network of water-filled canals. Thousands of tube feet are connected to this system. As water moves into and out of the water-vascular system, the tube feet act as suction cups and help the sea star move and eat. **Figure 20-24** shows these tube feet and how they are used to pry open a dead rock crab.

Sea stars also have a unique way of eating. Think about how you eat. You bring food to your mouth and swallow. The food then travels down to your stomach. The sea star actually pushes its stomach out of its mouth and into the opened shell of the oyster. It then digests the oyster's body while it is still inside the shell.

Like some other invertebrates, sea stars can regenerate damaged parts. Early settlers of the Chesapeake Bay area found the bay teeming with oysters. Eventually, more people moved into the area and deposited their wastes into the bay. Because some sea stars do well in polluted water, their population grew. People who harvested oysters found that the oyster population was decreasing. They decided to kill the sea stars by cutting them into pieces and

Figure 20-24 Sea bat sea stars use their tube feet to feed on a dead rock crab.

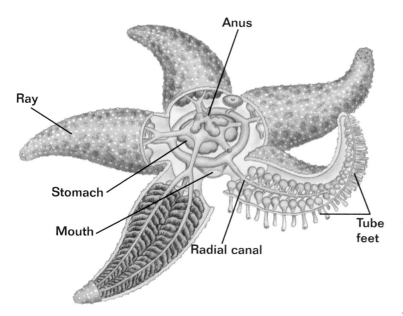

Speckled sea cucumbers can grow up to 25 cm in length. The black sea cucumber can grow up to 30 cm. The sea worm sea cucumber can reach 1 m in length. Calculate the average length of these three types of sea cucumbers.

throwing them back into the bay. Within a short time, the sea star population was five times larger than before due to regeneration. The entire oyster bed was destroyed!

Sea Cucumbers

The sea cucumber in **Figure 20-25** looks nothing like the other members of the echinoderm class. They have soft bodies with a leathery covering. They have few calcium carbonate plates. Sea cucumbers have tentacles around their mouths that are used to capture food. Although they have five rows of tube feet on the sides of their bodies, they appear to be more bilaterally symmetrical than the other echinoderms. When threatened, sea cucumbers may expel their internal organs. These organs regenerate in a few weeks.

Scientists continue to study echinoderms to learn more about the process of regeneration. These animals are also important in keeping saltwater environments free of pollution. They feed on dead organisms and help recycle materials within the environment.

Figure 20-25 A sea cucumber moves along the ocean water using tube feet.

Section Assessment

1. What are three characteristics of all arthropods?

2. What are the advantages and disadvantages of an exoskeleton?

3. What characteristics set echinoderms apart from other invertebrates?

4. **Think Critically:** What might happen to the sea star population after the oyster beds are destroyed? Explain your answer.

5. **Skill Builder**
   Observing and Inferring Observe the echinoderms pictured in **Figure 20–23**. Infer why they are slow moving. If you need help, refer to Observing and Inferring in the **Skill Handbook** on page 686.

Using Math

A flea measuring 4 mm in length can jump 25 cm from a resting position. If a flea were as tall as you are, how far could it jump?

Observing Complete Metamorphosis

Many insects go through the four stages of complete metamorphosis during their life cycles. Chemicals that are secreted by the body of the animal control the changes. How different do the body forms look between the stages of metamorphosis?

Materials
- Large-mouth jar or old fish bowl
- Bran or oatmeal
- Dried bread or cookie crumbs mixed with flour
- Slice of apple or carrot
- Paper towel
- Cheesecloth
- Mealworms
- Rubber band

What You'll Investigate
What do the stages of metamorphosis look like for a mealworm?

Goals
- **Observe** the stages of metamorphosis of mealworms to adult darkling beetles.
- **Compare** the physical appearance of mealworms as they go through two stages of metamorphosis.

Procedure 🥽 🧤 🐭

1. **Set up** a habitat for the mealworms by placing a 1-cm layer of bran or oatmeal on the bottom of the jar. Add a 1-cm layer of dried bread or cookie crumbs mixed with flour. Then, add another layer of bran or oatmeal.

2. **Add** a slice of apple or carrot as a source of moisture. Replace the apple or carrot daily.

3. **Place** 20 to 30 mealworms in the jar. Add a piece of crumpled paper towel.

4. **Cover** the jar with a piece of cheesecloth. Use the rubber band to secure the cloth to the jar.

5. **Observe** the mealworms daily for two to three weeks. **Record** daily observations in your Science Journal.

Conclude and Apply

1. In your Science Journal, **draw** and **describe** the mealworms' metamorphosis to adults.

2. **Identify** the stages of metamorphosis that mealworms go through to become adult darkling beetles.

3. Which of these stages did you not see during this investigation?

4. What are some of the advantages of an insect's young being different from the adult form?

5. Based on the food you placed in the habitat, **infer** where you might find mealworms or the adult darkling beetles in your house.

6. Why do you think pet stores would stock and sell mealworms?

For a **preview** of this chapter, study this Reviewing Main Ideas before you read the chapter. After you have studied this chapter, you can use the Reviewing Main Ideas to **review** the chapter.

The Glencoe MindJogger, Audiocassettes, and CD-ROM provide additional opportunities for review.

Section

20-1 WHAT IS AN ANIMAL?

Animals are many-celled organisms that must find and digest their own food. **Invertebrates** are animals without backbones. **Vertebrates** have backbones. Animals that have body parts arranged the same way on both sides of their bodies have bilateral **symmetry.** Animals with body parts arranged in a circle around a central point have radial symmetry. Asymmetrical animals have no definite shape. *What are five characteristics of animals?*

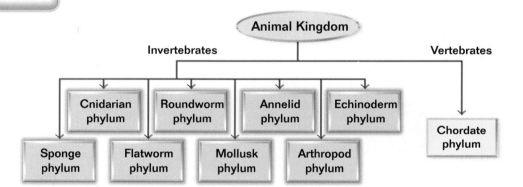

Animal Kingdom

Invertebrates — Cnidarian phylum | Roundworm phylum | Annelid phylum | Echinoderm phylum

Sponge phylum | Flatworm phylum | Mollusk phylum | Arthropod phylum

Vertebrates — Chordate phylum

Section

20-2 SPONGES, CNIDARIANS, FLATWORMS, AND ROUNDWORMS

Sponges and cnidarians are only two layers thick. Sponge cells do not form tissues, organs, or organ systems. Sponges are sessile and obtain food and oxygen by filtering water through pores. **Cnidarian** bodies have tissues and are radially symmetrical. Most have tentacles with stinging cells that get food. Regeneration allows an organism to replace lost or damaged parts or to reproduce sexually. Flatworms and roundworms have bilateral symmetry. They have both parasitic and **free-living** members. *Why are sponges considered the least complex of all animals?*

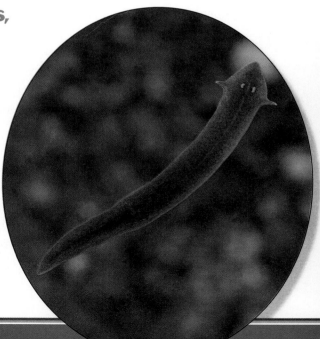

Reading Check ✓

Choose a group of unlike objects, such as the items in your book bag or your locker. Classify these objects into groups and subgroups.

^{Section}
20-3 MOLLUSKS AND SEGMENTED WORMS

Mollusks with one shell are gastropods. Bivalve mollusks have two shells. Cephalopods have a foot divided into tentacles and no outside shell. Except for cephalopods, mollusks have an **open circulatory system** in which the blood surrounds the organs directly. Cephalopods have a **closed circulatory system** with the blood contained in vessels. Annelids have a body cavity that separates the internal organs from the body wall. Setae help annelids move.

How are cephalopods adapted for swimming?

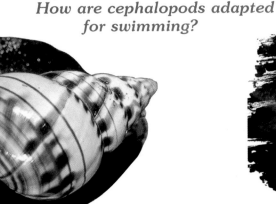

^{Section}
20-4 ARTHROPODS AND ECHINODERMS

Arthropods are classified by the number of body segments and **appendages.** Their **exoskeletons** cover, protect, and support their bodies. Arthropods develop either by complete or incomplete **metamorphosis.** Echinoderms are spiny-skinned invertebrates most closely related to vertebrates. They move by means of a water-vascular system. *What are some common characteristics for all arthropods?*

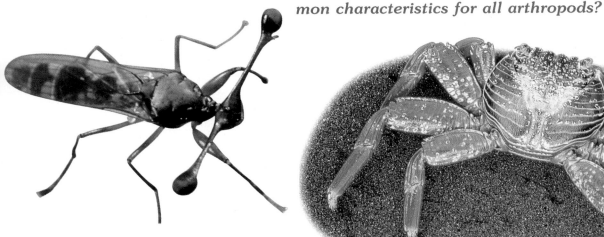

Chapter 20 Assessment

Using Vocabulary

a. appendage
b. arthropod
c. closed circulatory system
d. cnidarian
e. exoskeleton
f. free-living
g. gills
h. invertebrate
i. mantle
j. medusa
k. metamorphosis
l. mollusk
m. open circulatory system
n. parasite
o. polyp
p. radula
q. symmetry
r. vertebrate

Explain the differences between the terms in each of the following sets.

1. medusa, polyp
2. closed circulatory system, open circulatory system
3. vertebrate, invertebrate
4. arthropod, mollusk
5. exoskeleton, mantle

Checking Concepts

Choose the word or phrase that best answers the question.

6. Which of the following refers to animals that can be divided in half along a single line?
   A) asymmetrical
   B) bilaterally symmetrical
   C) radially symmetrical
   D) anterior

7. Which of the following do **NOT** belong to the same group?
   A) fish   C) jellyfish
   B) hydras   D) sea anemones

8. Which of the following phylums do sponges belong to?
   A) Cnidaria   C) Porifera
   B) Nematoda   D) Platyhelminthes

9. The body plans of cnidarians are polyp and which of the following?
   A) larva   C) ventral
   B) medusa   D) bud

10. Which of the following is an example of a parasite?
    A) sponge   C) tapeworm
    B) planarian   D) jellyfish

11. Which of the following covers the organs of mollusks?
    A) radula   C) gill
    B) mantle   D) foot

12. Which organism has a closed circulatory system?
    A) octopus   C) oyster
    B) snail   D) sponge

13. Which organism has two body regions?
    A) insect   C) arachnid
    B) mollusk   D) annelid

14. Which phylum has many organisms with radial symmetry?
    A) annelids   C) echinoderms
    B) mollusks   D) arthropods

15. Which of the following are sharp and cause predators to avoid eating sponges?
    A) thorax   C) collar cells
    B) spicules   D) tentacles

Thinking Critically

16. What aspect of sponge reproduction would be evidence that they are more like animals than plants?

17. What is the advantage for simple organisms to have more than one means of reproduction?

18. What are the differences between the tentacles of cnidarians and cephalopods?

19. What is the difference between budding and regeneration?

20. Centipedes and millipedes have segments. Why are they **NOT** classified as worms?

Developing Skills

If you need help, refer to the Skill Handbook.

21. **Comparing and Contrasting:** Compare and contrast the feeding habits of sponges and cnidarians.

22. **Using Variables, Constants, and Controls:** Design an experiment to test the sense of touch in planarians.

23. **Observing and Inferring:** Why are gastropods sometimes called univalves? Use examples in your answer.

24. **Classifying:** Classify the following animals into arthropod classes: *spider, grasshopper, ladybug, beetle, crab, scorpion, lobster, butterfly, tick,* and *shrimp.*

25. **Concept Mapping:** Complete the concept map of classification in the cnidarian phylum.

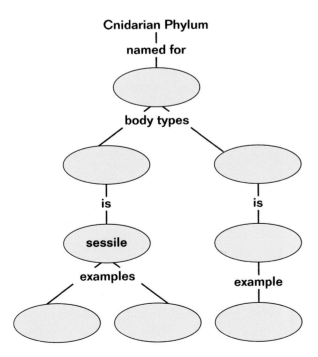

THE PRINCETON REVIEW

Test-Taking Tip

Words Are Easy to Learn Make a huge stack of vocabulary flash cards and study them. Use your new words in daily conversation. The great thing about learning new words is the ability to express yourself more specifically.

Test Practice

Use these questions to test your Science Proficiency.

1. Symmetry refers to the arrangement of the individual parts of an object. Which of the following organisms have radial symmetry?
   A) cnidarians
   B) sponges
   C) tapeworms
   D) mollusks

2. Echinoderms have a unique way of eating. Which of the following structures are used by echinoderms to move about and open a mollusk's shell?
   A) spicules
   B) arms
   C) spines
   D) tube feet

3. A water-vascular system is a network of water-filled canals. Which of the following phylums of invertebrates possess a water-vascular system?
   A) echinoderms
   B) arthropods
   C) mollusks
   D) cnidarians

Vertebrate Animals

Chapter Preview

Skills Preview

Skill Builders
- Map Concepts
- Classify

Activities
- Design an Experiment
- Observe and Infer

MiniLabs
- Make a Model
- Compare and Contrast

Reading Check ☑

As you read, create two lists: vocabulary terms that apply to humans (such as *endo-skeleton*) and terms that apply to other vertebrates, but not humans (such as *ectotherm*).

Explore Activity

You have something in common with the whale remains on the opposite page. This common feature protects some of the organs inside your body. It supports and gives your body shape. It also works with your muscles to help move your body. This common feature is your skeleton. Most internal skeletons are made of bone. Bones are many shapes and sizes. They must be strong enough to carry your weight yet light enough for you to move. To learn more about the structure of bones, complete the following Explore Activity.

Model Bones

1. Think about the different shapes of your bones. What shape is your shoulder blade? Your hip bone? Your neck? Your ribs?

2. Use five index cards to make bone models. Fold and bend the cards into different shapes. Use tape to hold the shapes if necessary.

3. Stack books on top of each card to find out which shape supports the most weight.

In your Science Journal, draw a picture of each bone model. Infer which shape would make the strongest bone. Write a paragraph comparing the strengths of each bone model.

21•1 Fish

What You'll Learn

► The major characteristics of chordates
► The difference between ectotherms and endotherms
► The characteristics of the three classes of fish

Vocabulary

chordate   fish
endoskeleton   fin
ectotherm   cartilage
endotherm

Why It's Important

► Fish have many adaptations for living in water.

Figure 21-1 This concept map showing the different groups of animals will appear at the beginning of each section. The groups that are highlighted with a red outline are the groups to be discussed. This diagram shows that the Chordate phylum is made up of three groups: the tunicates, the lancelets, and the vertebrates.

What is a vertebrate?

Suppose you took a survey in which you asked your classmates to list their pets. Probably dogs, cats, birds, snakes, and fish appear on the list. A large percentage of the animals listed, along with yourself, would belong to a group called vertebrates. Vertebrates are animals with backbones. They are the most complex of three animal groups that belong to the Chordate phylum, as illustrated in **Figure 21-1.** All **chordates** have a notochord, which is a rod of stiffened tissue. Chordates also have a hollow nerve cord in their backs and gill slits. In most vertebrates, a backbone made of vertebra replaces the notochord as the animal develops.

Whereas most invertebrates have exoskeletons, vertebrates have an internal system of bones called an **endoskeleton.** *Endo-* means "within." The vertebrae, skull, and other bones of the endoskeleton support and protect the animal's internal organs. The skeleton also provides a place where muscles are attached.

Vertebrates have two different ways of dealing with internal body temperature. Most vertebrates are ectotherms. **Ectotherms** are vertebrates whose body temperature changes with the temperature of their surroundings. **Endotherms** are animals with a constant body temperature. The body temperature of an endotherm usually remains the same no matter what the temperature of its surrounding environment.

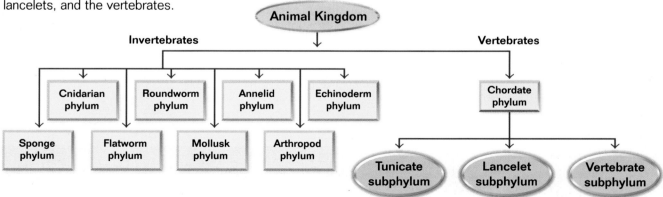

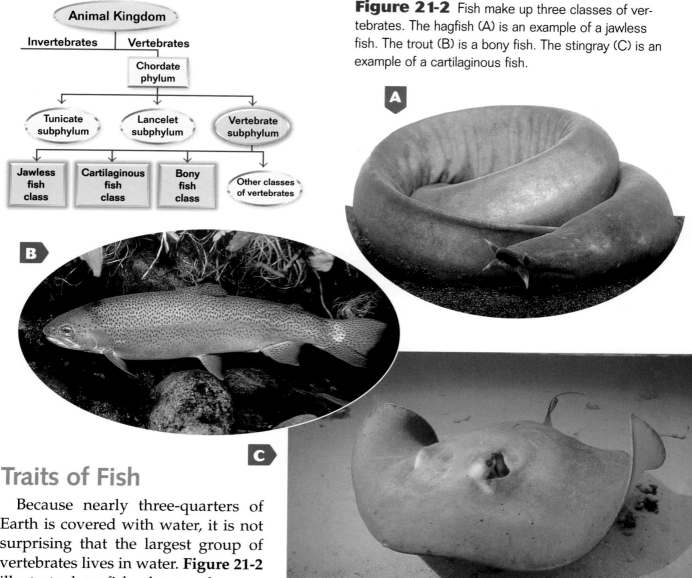

Figure 21-2 Fish make up three classes of vertebrates. The hagfish (A) is an example of a jawless fish. The trout (B) is a bony fish. The stingray (C) is an example of a cartilaginous fish.

Traits of Fish

Because nearly three-quarters of Earth is covered with water, it is not surprising that the largest group of vertebrates lives in water. **Figure 21-2** illustrates how fish relate to other vertebrates. Fish can be found in warm desert pools and the subfreezing Arctic ocean. They swim in shallow streams and far down in the ocean depths.

Fish are ectotherms that live in water and use gills to get oxygen. Gills are fleshy filaments that are filled with tiny blood vessels. The heart of the fish pumps blood to the gills. As blood passes through the gills, it picks up oxygen from water that is passing over the gills. Carbon dioxide is released from the blood into the water.

Most fish have fins. **Fins** are fanlike structures used for steering, balancing, and moving. Usually, they are paired. Those on the top and bottom stabilize the fish. Those on the side steer and move the fish. Scales are another common characteristic of fish although not all fish have scales. Scales are hard, thin, overlapping plates that cover the skin. These protective plates are made of a bony material.

Using Math

Make a circle graph of the number of fish species currently classified. There are 70 species of jawless fish, 820 species of cartilaginous fish, and 23 500 species of bony fish. What percent of this graph is accounted for by cartilaginous fish?

Types of Fish

Scientists group fish into three distinct classes. They are bony fish, jawless fish, and cartilaginous fish. Bony fish have skeletons made of bone, while cartilaginous fish and jawless fish both have endoskeletons made of cartilage. **Cartilage** (KART uh lihj) is a tough, flexible tissue that is similar to bone but is not as hard. Your ears and the tip of your nose are made of cartilage.

Bony Fish

About 95 percent of all fish belong to the class known as bony fish. The body structure of a typical bony fish, a tuna, is shown in **Figure 21-3.** These fish have skeletons made of bone. Their scales are covered with slimy mucus that allows the water to easily flow over the fishes' bodies as they swim in water. The majority of bony fish use external fertilization to reproduce. Females release large numbers of eggs into the water. Males release sperm as they swim over the eggs.

An important adaptation in most bony fish is the swim bladder. This air sac helps control the depth at which the fish swim. Transfer of gases between the swim bladder and the blood, mostly oxygen in deep-water fish and nitrogen in shallow-water fish, changes the inflation of the swim bladder. As the swim bladder fills with gases, the fish becomes more buoyant and rises in the water. When the bladder deflates, the fish becomes less buoyant and sinks lower in the water.

EXAMPLES OF
Bony Fish

- Trout
- Cod
- Salmon
- Catfish
- Tuna
- Sea horse

PHYSICS
INTEGRATION

Regulating Buoyancy
Unlike fish that regulate the gas content of their fish bladders, submarines pump water into and out of special chambers to regulate the vertical forces that cause the submarine to sink or rise.

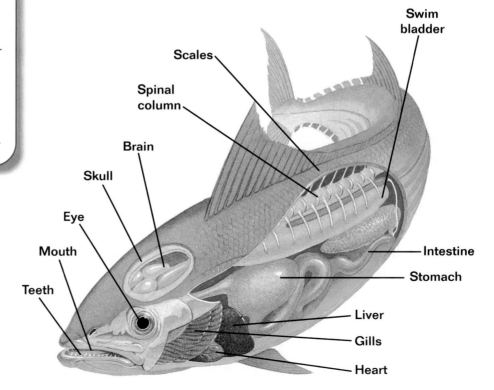

Figure 21-3 Although there are many different kinds of bony fish, they all share basic structures. **What are two unique fish structures?**

Figure 21-4 This sea lamprey (A) with its sucker disk mouth belongs to the class of jawless fish. Sharks (B) belong to the cartilaginous class and are efficient at finding and killing food.

Jawless and Cartilaginous Fish

Few fish belong to the class known as jawless fish. Jawless fish have long, scaleless, tubelike bodies and an endoskeleton made of cartilage. They have round mouths but no jaws, as seen in **Figure 21-4A.** Their mouths act like suckers with sharp toothlike parts. Once a lamprey attaches itself to another larger fish, it uses the toothlike parts to scrape through the host's skin. It then feeds on the blood of the larger fish.

Sharks, skates, and rays are cartilaginous fish. Cartilaginous fish have skeletons made of cartilage just like the jawless fish. However, cartilaginous fish, such as the shark in **Figure 21-4B,** have movable jaws and scales. Their scales feel rough like sandpaper. Most cartilaginous fish are predators.

Section Assessment

1. What are three characteristics of chordates?
2. Name the three classes of fish. What materials make up their skeletons?
3. Compare and contrast ectotherms and endotherms.
4. **Think Critically:** Female fish lay thousands of eggs. Why aren't lakes overcrowded with fish?
5. **Skill Builder**
   Observing and Inferring Fish without swim bladders, such as sharks, must move constantly, or they sink. They need more energy to maintain this constant movement. What can you infer about the amount of food sharks must eat when compared to another fish of similar size that have swim bladders? If you need help, refer to Observing and Inferring in the **Skill Handbook** on page 686.

Using Math

There are 353 known species of sharks. Of that number, only about 30 species have been known to attack humans. What percentage of shark species is known to attack humans?

21•2 Amphibians and Reptiles

What You'll Learn

▶ How amphibians have adapted to live in water and on land
▶ What happens during frog metamorphosis
▶ The adaptations that allow reptiles to live on land

Vocabulary

amphibian   estivation
hibernation   reptile

Why It's Important

▶ Amphibians are adapted to living in both water and on land while reptiles live only on land.

Amphibians

Have you ever heard of a person leading a double life? Amphibians are animals that lead double lives. In fact, the term *amphibian* comes from the Greek word *amphibios*, which means "double life." **Amphibians** are vertebrates that spend part of their lives in water and part on land. They are also ectotherms, which means that their internal body temperatures changes with their environment. Frogs, toads, and salamanders such as the barred tiger salamander pictured in **Figure 21-5** are the most common kinds of amphibians.

Amphibian Adaptations

Living on land is different from living in water. Air temperature changes more quickly and more often than water temperature. Also, air doesn't support body weight as well as water. Certain adaptations help amphibians survive both in water and on land.

Amphibians have behavioral adaptations that allow them to cope with swings in the air temperature of their particular environment. During cold winter months, they are inactive. They bury themselves in mud or leaves until the temperature warms up. In winter, this period of inactivity and lower metabolic needs

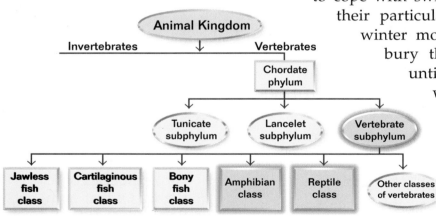

Figure 21-5 This barred tiger salamander has legs that extend straight out from the body.

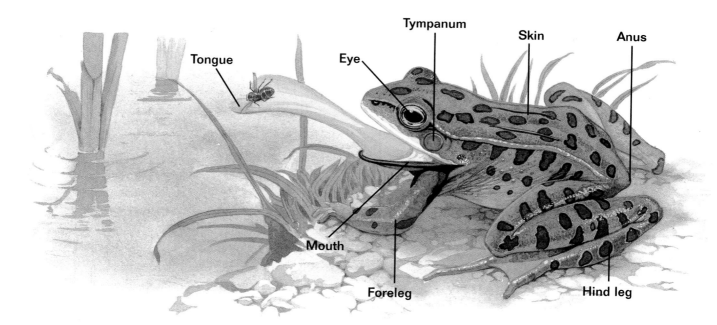

Tongue
Eye
Tympanum
Skin
Anus
Mouth
Foreleg
Hind leg

Figure 21-6 A frog's body is adapted for life in the water and on land. **What adaptations can you see in this illustration?**

is called **hibernation.** Metabolic needs refer to the chemical activities in an organism that enable it to live, grow, and reproduce. Amphibians that live in hot, drier environments are inactive and hide in the ground where it is likely to be cooler and more humid. This kind of inactivity during hot, dry summer months is called **estivation.** ✓

Amphibians have a strong endoskeleton made of bones. The skeleton helps to support the bodies of amphibians while on land. Adult frogs and toads have short, broad bodies, with four legs and no neck or tail. The strong hind legs are used for swimming and jumping.

Another adaptation increases amphibians' chances of survival on land. Instead of using gills to obtain oxygen from water, lungs become the primary method of obtaining oxygen from air. To increase the oxygen supply, amphibians exchange oxygen and carbon dioxide through their moist, scaleless skin or the lining of their mouths.

Moving to land provides an increased food supply for adult amphibians. Land habitats offer a variety of insects as food for these organisms. **Figure 21-6** shows some adaptations used to catch prey. The tympanic membranes, or eardrums, vibrate in response to sound and are used for hearing. Large eyes provide excellent vision. The long sticky tongue extends quickly to capture the insect and bring it into the waiting mouth.

Reading Check ✓

What is the difference between hibernation and estivation?

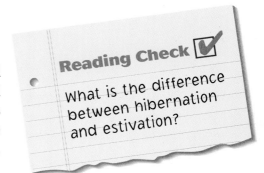

Visit the Glencoe Science Web Site at **www.glencoe.com/ sec/science/fl** for more information about amphibians.

Amphibian Metamorphosis

Although young animals such as kittens and calves are almost miniature duplicates of their parents, young amphibians look nothing like their parents. Metamorphosis is a series of body changes that occur during the life cycle of an amphibian. Most amphibians go through a two-stage metamorphosis as illustrated in **Figure 21-7.** The larval stage lives in water, and the adult lives on land.

Most amphibians mate in water. Here, the eggs hatch, and the young larval forms live. The larvae have no legs and breathe through gills. You can see that as the larval form of frogs, called tadpoles, go through metamorphosis, they change form. The young tadpoles develop body structures needed for life on land, including legs and lungs. The rate at which metamorphosis occurs depends on the species, the water temperature, and the amount of available food. The less available food is and the cooler the water temperatures are, the longer it takes for metamorphosis to occur.

VISUALIZING
Frog Metamorphosis

Figure 21-7 Frogs undergo a two-stage metamorphosis from the larval stage that lives in water to the adult stage that lives on land.

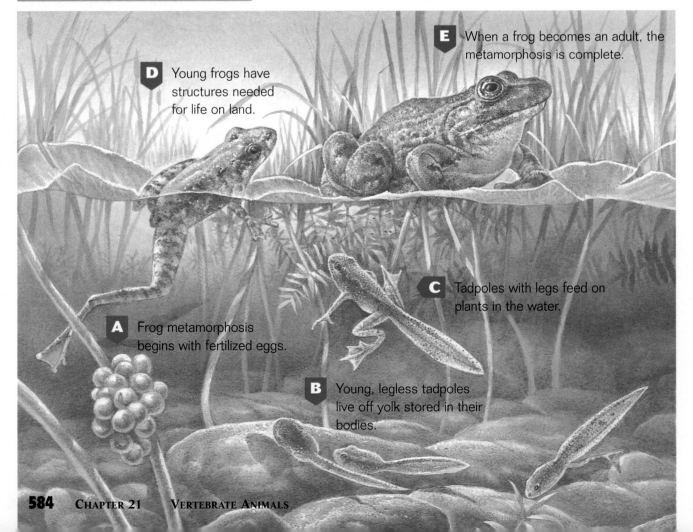

E When a frog becomes an adult, the metamorphosis is complete.

D Young frogs have structures needed for life on land.

C Tadpoles with legs feed on plants in the water.

A Frog metamorphosis begins with fertilized eggs.

B Young, legless tadpoles live off yolk stored in their bodies.

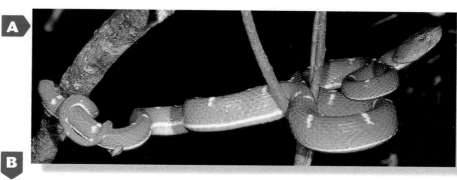

Figure 21-8 The green tree viper snake (A), the collared lizard (B), the spotted turtle (C), and the American alligator (D) are all reptiles.

Reptiles

The snake, lizard, turtle, and crocodile in **Figure 21-8** are all reptiles. A **reptile** is an ectothermic vertebrate with dry, scaly skin. Reptiles are vertebrates that do not depend on water for reproduction. Several adaptations allow reptiles to live on land.

Types of Reptiles

Reptiles vary greatly in size, shape, and color. Turtles are covered with a hard shell. They withdraw into the shell for protection. They eat insects, worms, fish, and plants. Alligators and crocodiles are feared predators that live in and near water. These large reptiles live in tropical climates.

Lizards and snakes are the largest group of reptiles. Lizards have movable eyelids, external ears, and legs with clawed toes. Snakes don't have eyelids, ears, or legs. Instead of hearing sounds, they feel vibrations in the ground. Snakes are also sensitive to chemicals in the air. They use their tongue to "smell" these chemicals.

Reptile Adaptations

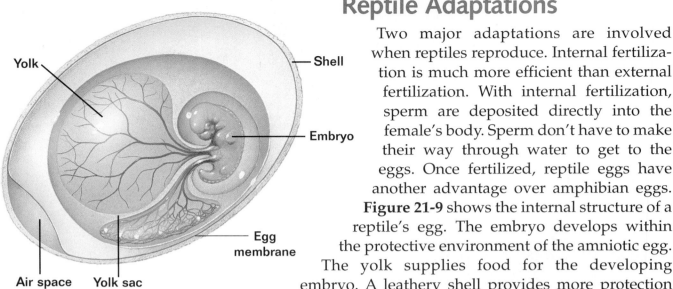

Yolk

Shell

Embryo

Egg membrane

Air space   Yolk sac

Figure 21-9 The amniotic egg is one of the adaptations reptiles have for living on land. Young reptiles hatch from their eggs fully developed.

Two major adaptations are involved when reptiles reproduce. Internal fertilization is much more efficient than external fertilization. With internal fertilization, sperm are deposited directly into the female's body. Sperm don't have to make their way through water to get to the eggs. Once fertilized, reptile eggs have another advantage over amphibian eggs. **Figure 21-9** shows the internal structure of a reptile's egg. The embryo develops within the protective environment of the amniotic egg. The yolk supplies food for the developing embryo. A leathery shell provides more protection than the jelly-covered frog's egg. When hatched, the young reptiles are fully developed. With some snakes, the young even develop and mature within the female's body. Then, the young snakes are born alive.

Another adaptation for life on land includes a thick, dry, waterproof skin. This skin is covered with scales and prevents dehydration and injury. All reptiles breathe with lungs. Even sea snakes and sea turtles must come to the surface to breathe.

Section Assessment

1. List the adaptations amphibians have for living in water and on land.
2. Sequence the steps of frog metamorphosis.
3. List the adaptations reptiles have for living on land.
4. **Think Critically:** Some harmless snakes have the same red, yellow, and black colors as the poisonous coral snake. How is this coloring an advantage for a nonpoisonous snake?
5.  **Skill Builder**
   Comparing and Contrasting Compare and contrast the types of eggs amphibians and reptiles have. If you need help, refer to Comparing and Contrasting in the **Skill Handbook** on page 686.

Science Journal In your Science Journal, explain why it is important for amphibians to live in moist or wet environments.

Activity 21•1

Frog Metamorphosis

Frogs and other amphibians use external fertilization to reproduce. Female frogs lay hundreds of jellylike eggs in water. Male frogs then fertilize these eggs. Once larvae hatch, the process of metamorphosis begins. Over a period of time, young tadpoles develop into adult frogs.

Materials
- Aquarium or jar (4 L)
- Frog egg mass
- Lake or pond water
- Stereoscopic microscope
- Watch glass
- Small fishnet
- Aquatic plants
- Washed gravel
- Lettuce (previously boiled)
- Large rock

What You'll Investigate

What changes occur as a tadpole goes through metamorphosis?

Goals

- **Observe** how body structures change as a tadpole develops into an adult frog.
- **Determine** how long metamorphosis takes to be completed.

Procedure 🐀 🐄 🥽

1. **Copy** the data table in your Science Journal.
2. As a class, use the aquarium, pond water, gravel, rock, and plants to prepare a water habitat for the frog eggs.
3. **Place** the egg mass in the water of the aquarium. Use the fishnet to separate a few eggs from the mass. **Place** these eggs in the watch glass. The eggs should have the dark side up. **CAUTION:** *Handle the eggs with care.*
4. **Observe** the eggs. **Record** your observations in the data table.

5. **Observe** the eggs twice a week. **Record** any changes that occur.
6. Continue observing the tadpoles twice a week after they hatch. **Identify** the mouth, eyes, gill cover, gills, nostrils, fin on the back, hind legs, and front legs. **Observe** how tadpoles eat boiled lettuce that has been cooled.

Conclude and Apply

1. How long does it take for the eggs to hatch and the tadpoles to develop legs?
2. Which pair of legs appears first?
3. **Explain** why the jellylike coating around the eggs is important.
4. **Compare** the eyes of young tadpoles with the eyes of older tadpoles.
5. **Calculate** how long it takes for a tadpole to change into a frog.

Frog Metamorphosis	
Date	**Observations**

Birds

Characteristics of Birds

Have you ever heard the term *pecking order?* Originally, it meant the ranking order of all the birds within a flock. High-ranking birds peck at lower-ranking birds to keep them away from food. This action is an example of a behavioral characteristic. Now, let's look at some physical characteristics of birds.

Despite the wide variety of birds, they all share some common characteristics. **Birds** are vertebrates with two legs, two wings, and bills, or beaks. They lay hard-shelled eggs, have feathers, and are endotherms. Recall that endothermic vertebrates keep a constant body temperature no matter what the temperature of the environment. Birds are the only animals that have feathers. The hard-shelled eggs protect the developing birds. Birds often sit on these eggs to keep them warm until they hatch. You learned that endotherms maintain a constant body temperature. A bird's body temperature is about 40°C. Your body temperature is about 37°C. Bird watchers can tell where a bird lives and what it eats by looking at the type of wing, beak, and feet it has. **Figure 21-10** illustrates some of the more than 8600 species of birds.

What You'll Learn
▶ The characteristics of birds
▶ How birds have adapted in order to fly

Vocabulary
bird
contour feather
down feather

Why It's Important
▶ Many birds demonstrate structural and behavioral adaptations for flight.

Figure 21-10 Birds are classified into orders based on the characteristic beaks, feet, feathers, and other physical features.

A Flightless land birds, such as ostriches, have their wings reduced in size and strong feet with fused toes for running.

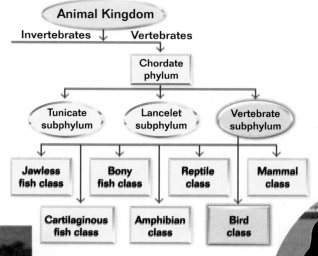

B King penguins use their wings as paddles to propel themselves through water.

C The more than 200 species of ducks, such as this Mandarin duck, have webbed feet and short tails, as do geese and swans.

D Eagles and other birds of prey have sharp, hooked beaks for tearing flesh and large talons for grasping prey.

E Chickens, grouse, quail, turkeys, and this ringneck pheasant are ground-dwelling birds capable of short bursts of flight.

F Long-legged herons, storks, and these flamingos feed on fish and other aquatic organisms. Many of these species form nesting colonies in trees.

G Hummingbirds have specialized beaks for feeding on the nectar of flowers.

H Hairy woodpeckers have long, thin beaks adapted for digging insects out of wood and four toes—two toes in front and two toes in back. Such feet enable them to climb trees effectively.

I Mockingbirds and other perching birds, including crows and jays, have three toes facing forward and one backward. Their feet are adapted for perching on twigs.

J With two toes facing forward and two facing backward, roadrunners are adapted for running.

Using Math

Count the number of different birds you observe outside during a certain time each day for three days. Graph your data.

PHYSICS
INTEGRATION ▶

Adaptations for Flight

Most body adaptations for birds are designed to enable them to fly. Their bodies are streamlined. Their skeletons are light, yet strong. If you could look inside the bone of a bird, you would see that it is hollow. Flying requires that they have a rigid body. Fused vertebrae provide the needed rigidity, strength, and stability. Birds need a good supply of oxygen to fly. Efficient hearts and lungs aid in respiration. The lungs are connected to air sacs that can be found throughout the body. Air sacs make a bird lighter for flight and help bring more oxygen to the blood. Large, powerful flight muscles in the wings are attached to the breastbone or sternum. Birds beat their wings to attain both thrust and lift. Slow motion pictures show that birds beat their wings both up and down as well as forward and back.

A bird's wing provides lift without constant beating. Like the airplane wing in **Figure 21-11,** a bird's wing is curved on top. It is flat or slightly curved on the bottom. A wing with this shape is important. As air moves across the wings, it has a greater distance to move across the top of the wing than along the bottom. The longer path taken by the air moving over the upper surface reduces the air pressure there. As a result, greater pressure is felt on the lower surface of the wing. The difference in air pressure results in lift.

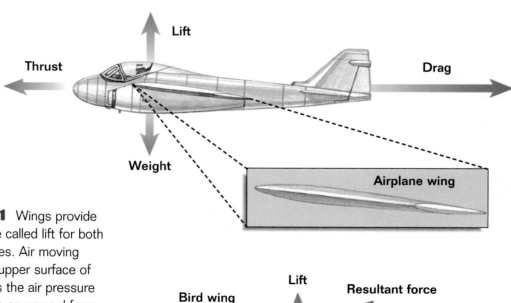

Figure 21-11 Wings provide the upward force called lift for both birds and airplanes. Air moving over the curved upper surface of the wing reduces the air pressure there, resulting in an upward force. The amount of lift depends on wing area, the speed of air across the wing, and the shape and angle of the wing.

Figure 21-12 Adult birds such as this great gray owl have an insulating layer of down feathers under their contour feathers. The owlets, like other young birds, are completely covered with down.

The Function of Feathers

Every body part of a bird is designed with flight in mind. Each feather is designed for flight. A bird's body is covered with two types of feathers, contour feathers and down feathers. Strong, lightweight **contour feathers** give birds their coloring and streamlined shape. Surface contour feathers overlap each other. This means that the bird can move more easily through the air or water. Feather colors and pattern are important because they identify a bird's species and sex. They also serve as protection that helps blend some birds into their surroundings. Contour feathers are also used to fly. It is these long feathers on the wings and tail that help the bird to steer and keep from spinning out of control.

Have you ever noticed that the hair on your arm stands up on a cold day? This response is your body's way to trap and keep warm air next to your skin. Birds have a similar response. This response helps birds maintain a constant body temperature. The birds in **Figure 21-12** have down feathers that trap and keep warm air next to their bodies. Soft, fluffy **down feathers** provide an insulating layer next to the skin of adult birds and cover the bodies of young birds. ✔

Mini Lab

Observing Bird Feathers

Procedure

1. Use a hand lens to examine a contour feather.
2. Hold the shaft end while carefully bending the opposite end. Observe what happens when you release the bent end.
3. Examine a down feather with a hand lens.
4. Hold each feather separately. Blow on them. Note any differences in the way each reacts to the stream of air.

Analysis

1. What happens when you release the bent end of the contour feather?
2. Which of the two feathers would you find on a bird's wing?
3. Which type of feather would you find in a pillow? Why?

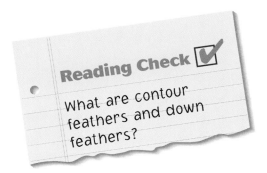

Reading Check ✔

What are contour feathers and down feathers?

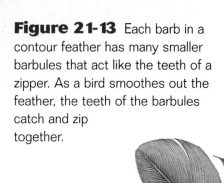

Figure 21-13 Each barb in a contour feather has many smaller barbules that act like the teeth of a zipper. As a bird smoothes out the feather, the teeth of the barbules catch and zip together.

Contour feather

Vane

Barbule

Barb

Shaft

Care of Feathers

Feathers may be strong but they need to be kept in good condition. Only then can they keep birds warm, dry, and able to fly. Birds preen their feathers to take care of them. When they preen, they run their beaks through the feathers, much like people run their hands through their hair. Preening reorganizes the feathers and repairs the breaks, or gaps, in them. A close look at the contour feather in **Figure 21-13** shows the parallel strands, called barbs, that branch off the main shaft.

In addition to repairing and reorganizing feathers, preening makes feathers water-repellent. The bird rubs its beak against an oil gland found at the base of the tail. It then rubs off the oil from its beak and onto its feathers. Making sure that the feathers stay water-repellent is important. Watersoaked birds can't fly or maintain their body temperature.

Section Assessment

1. List four characteristics shared by all birds.
2. Explain how a bird's skeleton is adapted for flight.
3. **Think Critically:** Explain why birds can reproduce in the arctic but reptiles cannot.
4. **Skill Builder**
   Concept Mapping Make a network tree concept map that details the characteristics of birds. Use the following terms in your map: *birds, adaptations for flight, air sacs, beaks, eggs, feathers, hollow bones,* and *wing.* If you need help, refer to Concept Mapping in the **Skill Handbook** on page 680.

Using Computers

Spreadsheet Every 10 s a crow beats its wings 20 times, a robin 23 times, a chickadee 270 times, and a hummingbird 700 times. Using a spreadsheet, find out how many times the wings of each bird beat during a five-minute flight? If you need help, see page 704.

Flight Through the Ages

For thousands of years, people watched birds soar through the sky and yearned to experience the freedom of flight. The Maori people of what is now New Zealand made kites shaped like birds. The ancient Chinese loved kites, too (inset), and made them in all shapes and sizes.

In the early sixteenth century, artist and inventor Leonardo da Vinci made notes and diagrams about birds and flying machines. He reasoned that a bird's wings must work according to certain laws of physics and math and that therefore people should be able to build a device that could imitate the action of a bird in flight.

Da Vinci's drawings of flying machines inspired the invention of the ornithopter, or flapping-wing machine. People continued to experiment with these odd-looking devices—made out of willow, silk, and feathers—but never managed to get more than a few feet off the ground.

In the early 1800s, English scientist Sir George Cayley carried out his own studies of birds and bird flight. He concluded that it was impossible for people to fly using artificial flapping wings. Eventually, Cayley designed the first successful fixed-wing glider that could carry a person—a milestone that inspired Wilbur and Orville Wright.

Only after the Wright brothers solved a number of problems with gliding aircraft and built several gliders themselves did they focus on building an engine-powered aircraft. The Wright brothers identified the successful features of other aircraft and then added their own ideas about lift, the action of air currents, and the shape of wings. On December 17, 1903, Orville and Wilbur Wright made the world's first powered, sustained, and controlled flights in an airplane, the longest of which was 260 m. That momentous day set the stage for the evolution of many different kinds of engine-powered craft, from biplanes to supersonic jets and space shuttles.

Science JOURNAL

Think of how a bird flies. In your Science Journal, record the similarities and differences between airplane flight and the flight of birds.

Characteristics of Mammals

How many different kinds of mammals can you name? Cats, dogs, bats, dolphins, horses, and people are all mammals. They live on land and in water, in cold and in hot climates. They burrow through the ground or fly through the air. Mammals have many characteristics that they share with other vertebrates. For example, they all have an internal skeleton with a backbone. But what characteristics make mammals unique?

Mammals are endotherms that have hair and produce milk to nourish their young. Being endothermic is not unique. Birds also are endotherms. However, mammals are unique because their skin is covered with hair or fur. Hair is mostly made of a protein called keratin. Some mammals, such as bears, are covered with thick fur. Others, like humans, have patches of hair. Still others, like the whale pictured in **Figure 21-14,** are almost hairless. Hair insulates the mammal's body from both cold and heat. It also protects the animal from wind and rain. Wool, spines, quills, and certain horns are made of keratin. What function do you think quills and spines serve?

Mammary Glands

Mammals put a great deal of time and energy into the care of their young. This begins at birth. Female mammals have mammary glands that form in the skin. During pregnancy, they increase in size. After birth, milk is produced and released in these glands. For the first weeks or months, the milk provides all of the nutrition that the young mammal needs.

Figure 21-14 Unlike other mammals, whales, such as this humpback whale, are practically hairless with the exception of a few sensory whiskers on their snouts.

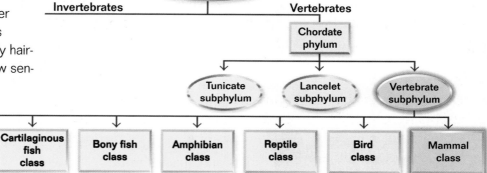

Animal Kingdom

Invertebrates   Vertebrates

Chordate phylum

Tunicate subphylum   Lancelet subphylum   Vertebrate subphylum

| Jawless fish class | Cartilaginous fish class | Bony fish class | Amphibian class | Reptile class | Bird class | Mammal class |

Body Systems

Think of all the different activities that mammals do. They run, swim, climb, hop, fly, and so on. They live active lives. Their body systems must be able to support all of these activities. Well-developed lungs made of millions of microscopic sacs called alveoli allow the exchanges of carbon dioxide and oxygen.

Mammals also have a more complex nervous system than other animals. The brain, spinal cord, and nerves allow these animals to utilize their senses and to gather information from their surrounding environment. They quickly sense and react to changes in their environment. Mammals are able to learn and remember more than other animals. The large brain plays an important part in this ability. In fact, the brain of a mammal is usually larger than the brain of other animals of the same size. Another factor in a mammal's ability to learn is the time spent by its parents to care for and teach it as it matures.

All mammals reproduce sexually and have internal fertilization. Most mammals give birth to live young after a period of development inside an organ called a uterus. While some mammals are nearly helpless when born, others must be able to stand and move quickly after birth. Why do you think a young deer must be able to run soon after it is born?

Mammal Classification

Once an egg is fertilized, the developing mammal is called an embryo. Mammals can be divided into three groups based on how their embryos develop.

Monotremes

Look at the animal in **Figure 21-15.** The duck-billed platypus looks like someone took parts from several different animals and put them together as a practical joke.

Observing Hair

Procedure

1. Brush or comb your hair to remove a few loose hairs.
2. Take two hairs from your brush that look like they still have the root attached.
3. Make a wet mount slide of the two hairs, being sure to include the root.
4. Focus on the hairs with the low-power objective. Draw what you see.
5. Switch to the high-power objective and focus on the hairs. Draw what you see.

Analysis

1. Describe the characteristics of hair and root.
2. Infer how hair keeps an organism warm.

Figure 21-15 A duck-billed platypus is a mammal, yet it lays eggs. **Why is it classified as a mammal?**

Figure 21-16 Marsupials carry their developing young in a pouch on the outside of their bodies. Opossums are the only marsupials found in North America.

But, in fact, the duck-billed platypus belongs to the smallest group of mammals called monotremes. **Monotremes** lay eggs with tough leathery shells. The female incubates the eggs for about ten days. Mammary glands that produce the milk of monotremes lack nipples. When the young hatch, they nurse by licking up the milk that seeps through the skin surrounding the glands. The duck-billed platypus and two species of spiny anteaters are the only surviving members of this group.

Marsupials

Can you think of an animal that carries its young in a pouch? Mammals that do this are called marsupials. **Marsupials** are pouched mammals that give birth to immature offspring. Their embryos develop for only a few weeks within the uterus. When the young are born, they are naked, blind, and not fully formed. Using their sense of smell, the young crawl into the pouch and attach themselves to a nipple. Here they complete their development. Most marsupials live in Australia, Tasmania, and New Guinea. Kangaroos, koalas, Tasmanian devils, and wallabies are marsupials. The opossum in **Figure 21-16** is a marsupial that lives in North America.

Problem Solving

Predicting Bat Behavior

Bats are acrobats of the night. They can fly around obstacles and can find insects to eat in complete darkness. Have you ever wondered how they do this? Some bats emit, or send out, extremely high-pitched sounds through the mouth and nose when hunting for food. These sounds are usually too high pitched for humans to hear. Bats also make noises that people hear, from whining sounds to loud twitters and squeaks. Bats can catch fast-flying insects or darting fish and at the same time avoid branches, wires, and other obstacles in a process called echolocation. The sound waves they send out travel in front of them, and this helps them locate objects.

The diagram illustrates what happens when a sound wave emitted by a bat comes in contact with an object.

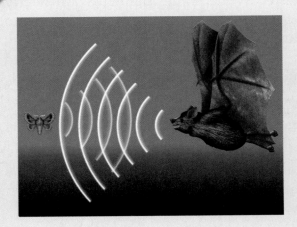

Think Critically: How does a bat locate an object in the dark? Explain what might happen to bats if they were allowed to search for food in a sound-proof room, where walls absorb most of the sound. Infer what would happen if a bat's mouth and nose are covered.

Placental Mammals

By far, the largest number of mammals belongs to the third group known as placental mammals. The most important characteristic of **placental mammals** is that their embryos develop in the uterus of the female. This time of development, from fertilization to birth, is the gestation period. Gestation periods vary greatly among placental mammals. Imagine waiting almost two years for the young elephant in **Figure 21-17** to be born! Placental mammals are named for the placenta, a saclike organ developed by the growing embryo that is attached to the uterus. The placenta absorbs oxygen and food from the mother's blood. An umbilical cord, **Figure 21-18,** attaches the embryo to the placenta. Several blood vessels in the umbilical cord act as a transportation system. Food and oxygen are transported from the placenta to the embryo. Waste products are taken away.

Figure 21-17 Gestation periods vary among mammals. While an elephant carries its young for 624 days, a golden hamster's gestation period is about 16 days.

*inter*NET
CONNECTION

Visit the Glencoe Science Web Site at **www.glencoe.com/ sec/science/fl** for more information about small mammals.

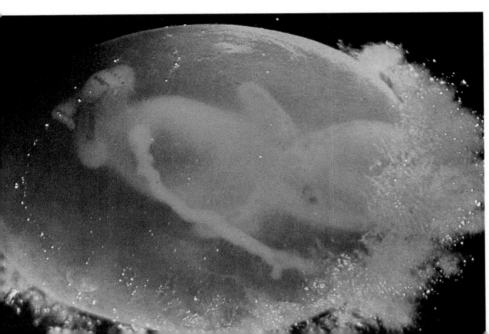

Figure 21-18 A placental mammal's embryo, such as this human embryo, develops in the uterus of a female. The umbilical cord allows the embryo to receive food and oxygen from the mother.

Figure 21-19 In addition to monotremes (A) and marsupials (B), many of the major orders of placental mammals are shown here.

You have learned the basic characteristics that distinguish mammals—vertebrae, hair or fur, mammary glands that produce milk, type of teeth, and the ability of young to learn. In addition, each kind of animal has certain adaptations that enable it to live successfully within its environment. Some of the 4000 species of mammals are shown in **Figure 21-19.**

A **Monotremata** (mahn uh tru MAH tah): Monotremes, such as this duck-billed platypus, are the only egg-laying mammals.

B **Marsupiala** (mar sew pee AH luh): Pouched mammals include kangaroos, shown here, and opossums.

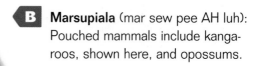

C **Insectivora** (ihn sek tih VOR ah): Burrowing woodland moles have poor eyesight but an excellent sense of touch to catch insects.

D **Edentata** (ee duhn TAH tuh): Armadillos, shown here, anteaters, and tree sloths are toothless or have few teeth with which to eat insects.

E **Chiroptera** (cher OP ter uh): Bats are the only true flying mammals. Their front limbs are designed for flight. They use echolocation, a process that uses sound and echoes, to navigate while flying.

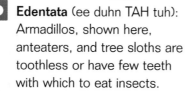

F **Carnivora** (kar NIH vor uh): The household cat and dog are meat-eaters that have canine teeth used to capture prey. This red fox is also a carnivore.

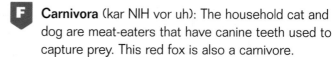

G **Cetacea** (sih TAY shuh): Marine mammals, including dolphins, spend their entire lives in the ocean.

H **Proboscidea** (proh boh SIH dee uh): Elephants are the largest land mammals. They have an elongated nose that forms a trunk.

I **Perissodactyla** (per ih soh DAHK tih luh): Herbivorous hoofed mammals with an odd number of toes. Horses, zebras, tapirs (shown here), and rhinoceroses belong to this group.

J **Artiodactyla** (ar tee oh DAHK tih luh): Herbivorous, hoofed mammals have an even number of toes. They also have large, flat molars and complex stomachs. Cows, camels, deer, giraffes, and the moose (shown here) belong to this group.

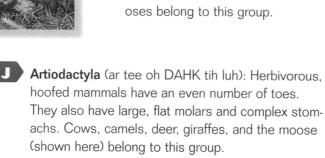

K **Rodentia** (roh DEN cha): The largest order, these gnawing mammals have two pairs of chisel-shaped teeth that never stop growing. These teeth wear down through use. This golden mouse, along with squirrels, beavers, porcupines, and gophers are in this group.

L **Lagomorpha** (lah gah MOR fuh): Lagomorphs include herbivorous rabbits, hares, and pikas. This Eastern cottontail rabbit has long hind legs that are adapted for jumping and running. It also has two pairs of upper incisors.

M **Primates** (PRI maytz): Humans, apes, monkeys, and this orangutan are representative of this group. They have long arms with grasping hands and feet, and opposable thumbs. They are omnivores and the most intelligent of mammals.

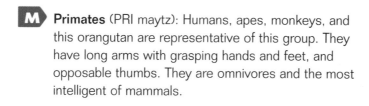

Figure 21-20 Mammals have teeth specialized for the food they eat. **How would you classify a horse (A), a hyena (B), and a human (C)? Herbivore? Carnivore? Omnivore?**

Reading Check ✓

What are herbivores, carnivores, and omnivores?

Different Teeth

Mammals have teeth that are specialized for the type of food they eat. There are four types of teeth: incisors, canines, premolars, and molars. Incisors are the sharp, chisel-shaped front teeth used to bite and cut off food. Grazing mammals, which eat plants, are called **herbivores.** They have sharp incisors to grab and cut grass. Horses, buffalo, and rabbits are some mammals that eat plants. Some mammals, such as lions and tigers, are predators and eat flesh. Flesh-eating mammals are called **carnivores.** They use long and pointed canine teeth to stab, grip, and tear flesh. They also have sharp-edged premolars that cut and shred food. Large premolars and molars shred, crush, and grind food. Horses have large, flat molars that grind both grains and grasses.

Some mammals eat both plants and animals. These mammals are called **omnivores.** Humans are capable of being omnivores. They have all four types of teeth. You usually can tell whether a mammal eats plants, other animals, or both from the kind of teeth it has. Look at **Figure 21-20.** ✓

Mammals Today

Mammals are important in maintaining a balance in the environment. Large carnivores, such as lions, help control populations of grazing animals. Bats help pollinate flowers, and some pick up plant seeds in their fur and distribute them. But mammals are in trouble today. As millions of acres of wildlife habitat are developed for housing and recreational areas, many mammals are left without food, shelter, and space to survive. The Bengal tiger pictured in **Figure 21-21** lives in India and is considered an endangered species.

Figure 21-21 Illegal poaching and decreasing habitat help account for the extreme decline in the Bengal tiger population in nature. In the early 1900s, there were around 100 000 tigers, but that has declined by roughly 95 percent this century.

Section Assessment

1. Describe five characteristics of all mammals and explain how these characteristics allow mammals to survive in different environments.

2. Compare and contrast herbivores with omnivores.

3. **Think Critically:** Compare reproduction in placental mammals with that of monotremes and marsupials.

4. 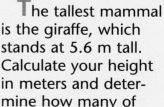 **Skill Builder**
   Observing and Inferring Mammals have many adaptations to their environments. Do the **Chapter 21 Skill Activity** on page 728 to observe tracks to infer how mammals' feet are adapted.

Using Math

The tallest mammal is the giraffe, which stands at 5.6 m tall. Calculate your height in meters and determine how many of you it would take to be as tall as a giraffe.

Bird Counts

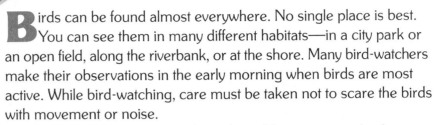

Birds can be found almost everywhere. No single place is best. You can see them in many different habitats—in a city park or an open field, along the riverbank, or at the shore. Many bird-watchers make their observations in the early morning when birds are most active. While bird-watching, care must be taken not to scare the birds with movement or noise.

It's simple to get started bird-watching. You can attract birds to your yard at home or at school by filling a bird feeder with seeds that birds like most. Then, sit back and observe the birds while they enjoy your hospitality.

Recognize the Problem

What type of bird is present in your neighborhood in the largest number?

Form a Hypothesis

Think about the types of birds that you observe around your neighborhood. What types of food do they eat? Do all birds come to a bird feeder? Make a hypothesis about the type of bird that you think you will see most often at your bird feeder.

Goals

- **Observe** the types of birds in your neighborhood.
- **Research** how to attract birds to a bird feeder.
- **Build** a bird feeder.
- **Identify** the types of birds observed.
- **Graph** your results in order to communicate them with other students.

Data Source

Go to the Glencoe Science Web Site at **www.glencoe.com/ sec/science/fl** for more information about how to build a bird feeder, hints on bird watching, and data from other students.

Test Your Hypothesis

Plan

1. **Research** general information about how to attract and identify birds. Determine where you will make your observations.

2. **Search** reference materials to find out how to build a bird feeder. Do all birds eat the same types of seeds?

3. What variables can you control in this activity? How long will you make your observations? Does the season or the weather conditions affect your observations?

4. What will you do to **identify** the birds that you do not recognize?

Do

1. Make sure your teacher approves your plan before you start.

2. **Record** your data in your Science Journal each time you **observe** your bird feeder.

Analyze Your Data

1. **Describe** the location where you made your observations and the time of year.

2. **Calculate** the total number of each type of bird by adding the numbers you recorded each day.

3. **Graph** your data. Will your results be best displayed in a line, circle, or bar graph?

4. **Post** your data on the Glencoe Science Web Site.

Draw Conclusions

1. What type of bird was present in your neighborhood in the largest number?

2. Did all of your classmates' data agree with yours? Why or why not?

3. **Compare and contrast** your observations with the observations posted by other students on the Glencoe Science Web Site. **Map** the data you collect from the Web site to **recognize** patterns in bird populations.

4. Many birds include an enormous number of insects in their diet. **Infer** the need for humans to maintain a healthy environment for birds.

For a **preview** of this chapter, study this Reviewing Main Ideas before you read the chapter. After you have studied this chapter, you can use the Reviewing Main Ideas to **review** the chapter.

GLENCOE TECHNOLOGY The Glencoe MindJogger, Audiocassettes, and CD-ROM provide additional opportunities for review.

Section
21-1 VERTEBRATES AND FISH

All animals in the Chordate Phylum have a notochord, dorsal hollow nerve cord, and gill slits. The body temperature of an **ectotherm** changes with its environment. **Endothermic** animals maintain body temperature. **Fish** are ectotherms that have scales and **fins.** Classes of fish include jawless fish, cartilaginous fish, and bony fish. *Why can't jawless fish be predators?*

White sh

Section
21-2 AMPHIBIANS AND REPTILES

Amphibians are vertebrates that spend part of their lives in water and part on land. Most frogs, toads, and salamanders are amphibians that go through metamorphosis from a water-living larva to a land-living adult. **Reptiles** are ectothermic land animals that have dry, scaly skin. Turtles, crocodiles, alligators, snakes, and lizards are reptiles. Reptiles lay eggs with a leathery skin. *Why does the reptile's egg provide better protection for the embryo than a frog's egg?*

Collared lizard

Barred tiger salamander

Reading Check ✓

Explain the major differences among the five groups of vertebrates described in this chapter in a way that a child could understand. (You might create a chart).

Hummingbird

Section 21-3 BIRDS

Birds are endotherms that are covered with feathers and lay eggs. Their front legs are modified into wings. Adaptations birds have for flight include wings, feathers, and a light, strong skeleton. Birds lay eggs enclosed in hard shells. Most birds keep their eggs warm until they hatch. *How do down feathers keep a bird warm?*

Mandarin duck

Flamingo

Bat

Section 21-4 MAMMALS

Mammals are endotherms with hair. Female mammals have mammary glands that produce milk. There are three groups of mammals. **Monotremes** are mammals that lay eggs. **Marsupials** are mammals that have pouches for the development of their embryos. **Placental mammals** have offspring that develop within the female's uterus. *What are some adaptations of mammals that allow them to be endothermic?*

Red fox

Chapter 21 Assessment

Using Vocabulary

a. amphibian
b. bird
c. carnivore
d. cartilage
e. chordate
f. contour feather
g. down feather
h. ectotherm
i. endoskeleton
j. endotherm
k. estivation
l. fin
m. fish
n. herbivore
o. hibernation
p. mammal
q. marsupial
r. monotreme
s. omnivore
t. placental mammal
u. reptile

Define the following Vocabulary terms and give two examples of each.

1. fish
2. amphibian
3. reptile
4. bird
5. mammal

Checking Concepts

Choose the word or phrase that best answers the question.

6. Which of the following animals have fins, scales, and gills?
   A) amphibians   C) reptiles
   B) crocodiles   D) fish

7. Which of the following stuctures is used for steering and balancing?
   A) cartilage   C) bone
   B) endoskeleton   D) fin

8. Which of the following is **NOT** an example of a bony fish?
   A) trout   C) shark
   B) bass   D) goldfish

9. Which of the following has a swim bladder?
   A) shark   C) trout
   B) lamprey   D) skate

10. Which of the following is **NOT** an adaptation that helps a bird fly?
    A) hollow bones   C) hard-shelled eggs
    B) fused vertebrae   D) feathers

11. Which of the following does **NOT** have scales?
    A) birds   C) frogs
    B) snakes   D) fish

12. Which of the following are vertebrates with lungs and moist skin?
    A) amphibians   C) reptiles
    B) fish   D) lizards

13. Which of the following are mammals that lay eggs?
    A) carnivores   C) monotremes
    B) marsupials   D) placental mammals

14. Which of the following have mammary glands but no nipples?
    A) marsupials   C) monotremes
    B) placental mammals   D) omnivores

15. Which of the following animals eat only plant materials?
    A) carnivores   C) omnivores
    B) herbivores   D) endotherms

Thinking Critically

16. Why do you think there are fewer species of amphibians on Earth than any other type of vertebrate?

17. What important adaptation allows a reptile to live on land while an amphibian must return to water to live out part of its life cycle?

18. Give two reasons why whales have little hair.

19. You observe a mammal catching and eating a rabbit. What kind of teeth does this animal probably have? Tell how it uses its teeth.

20. Explain how the development of the amniotic egg led to the early success of reptiles.

Developing Skills

If you need help, refer to the **Skill Handbook.**

21. **Comparing and Contrasting:** Compare and contrast the eggs of fish, reptiles, birds, and mammals. How well does each egg type protect the developing embryo?

22. **Concept Mapping:** Complete the concept map describing groups of mammals.

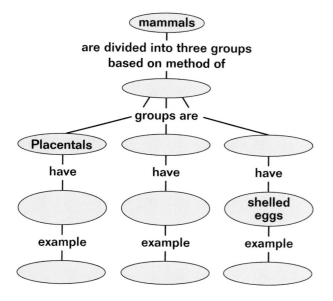

23. **Designing an Experiment:** Design an experiment to find out the effect of water temperature on frog egg development.

24. **Observing and Inferring:** How could you use the feet of a bird to identify it?

25. **Comparing and Contrasting:** Compare and contrast the teeth of herbivores, carnivores, and omnivores. How is each tooth type adapted to the animal's diet?

THE PRINCETON REVIEW

Test-Taking Tip

Let Bygones Be Bygones Once you have read a question, consider the answers and choose one. Then, put that question behind you. Don't try to keep the question in the back of your mind, thinking that maybe a better answer will come to you as the test continues.

Test Practice

Use these questions to test your Science Proficiency.

1. Vertebrates make up a large percentage of animals. Which of the following statements is true of all vertebrates?
   A) Vertebrates are animals without backbones.
   B) All vertebrates have a notochord.
   C) Only fish have gill slits.
   D) Dorsal hollow nerve cords always develop into a spinal cord with a brain at the front end.

2. Placental mammals, along with monotremes and marsupials, are the orders that make up mammals. Which of the following animals is an example of a placental mammal?
   A) elephant
   B) koala
   C) duck-billed platypus
   D) turtle

3. Which of the following terms describes inactivity during the summer?
   A) estivation
   B) hibernation
   C) metamorphosis
   D) preening

CHAPTER

22 Animal Behavior

Chapter Preview

Section 22-1
Types of Behavior

Section 22-2
Behavioral Adaptations

Skills Preview

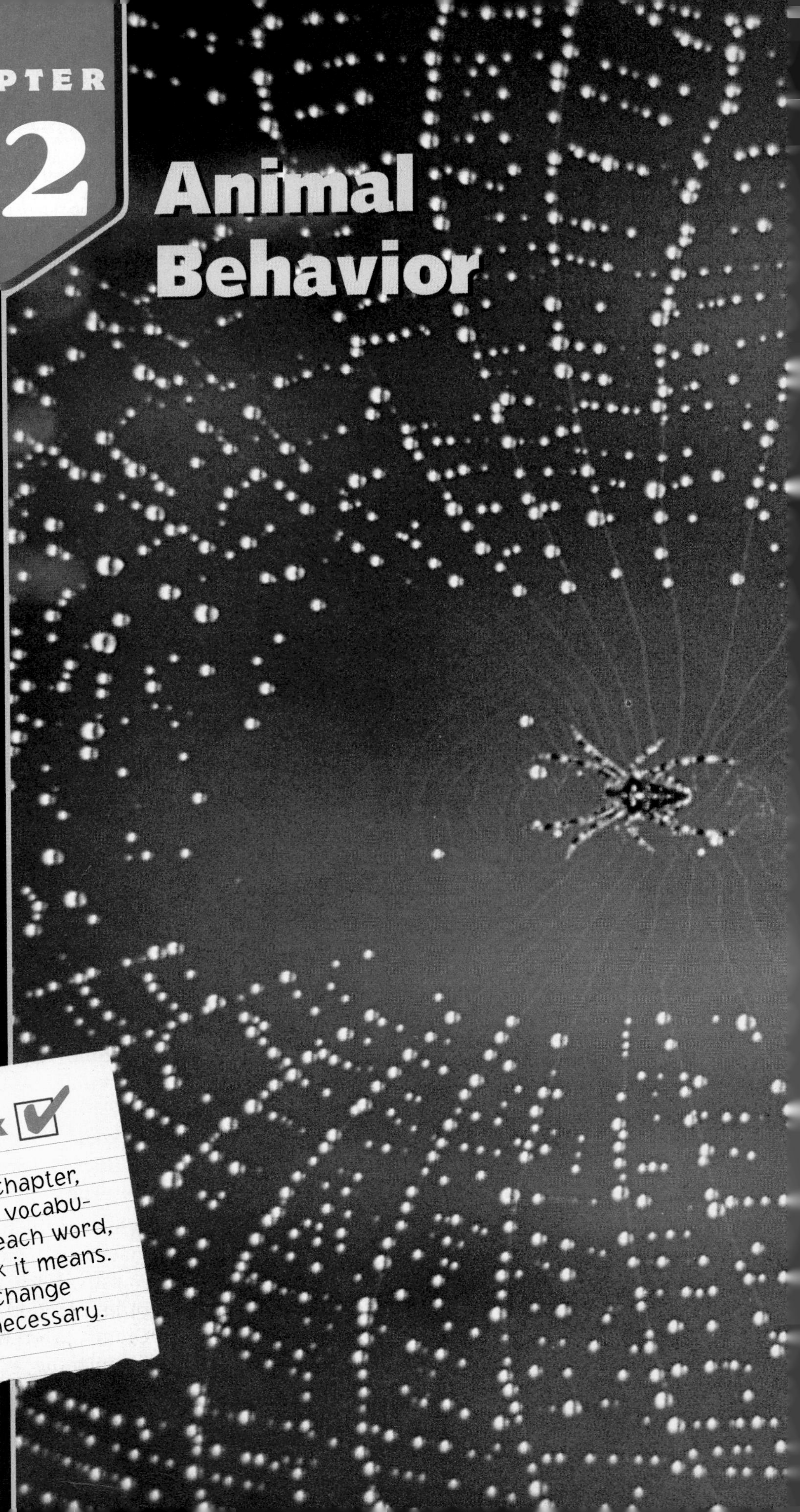

Skill Builders
- Observe
- Infer

Activities
- Observe
- Record Data

MiniLabs
- Hypothesize
- Experiment

Reading Check ✓

Before you read the chapter, make a list of all the vocabulary words. Next to each word, write what you think it means. Then, as you read, change your definitions if necessary.

Explore Activity

A spider spins a web to catch its food. A bird makes a nest. Human infants cry when they are born and begin to focus on faces and smile when they are four weeks old. Do organisms learn these actions or do they occur automatically? In the activity, find out about things you do. Then in the chapter that follows, learn more about animal behavior.

Investigate a Response

1. Obtain a clear piece of plastic and a wadded-up sheet of paper from your teacher.

2. Have a partner hold the plastic a few centimeters from his or her face.

3. Stand about one meter away and gently toss the paper ball toward your partner's face.

4. Tell your partner not to blink and toss the paper ball again.

In your Science Journal, describe how the tossed paper affected your partner's eyes. Describe this behavior. Is this behavior learned or does it occur without learning?

22•1 Types of Behavior

Innate Behavior

What You'll Learn

► The difference between innate and learned behavior
► How reflexes and instincts help organisms survive
► Examples of imprinting and conditioning

Vocabulary
behavior
innate behavior
reflex
instinct
imprinting
conditioning

Why It's Important

► Behavior helps you survive on your own.

When you come home from school, does your dog run to meet you, barking and wagging its tail? After you play with it a while, does it sit at your feet and watch every move you make? Why does it do these things? Dogs are pack animals that generally follow a leader. They have been living with people for about 20 000 years. Dogs treat people as part of their own pack.

Behavior is the way an organism acts toward its environment. Anything in the environment that causes a reaction is called a stimulus. You are the stimulus that causes your dog to bark and wag its tail. Your dog's reaction to you is a response. But how does your dog know when to wag and when to growl? Was this behavior learned or did your dog behave this way on its own?

Innate Behavior Is Inherited

Dogs and cats are quite different from one another in their behavior. They were born with certain behaviors, and they have learned others. A behavior that an organism is born with is an **innate behavior.** Such behaviors are inherited and they do not have to be learned.

Innate behavior patterns are usually correct the first time an animal responds to a stimulus. Kittiwakes are seabirds that nest on narrow ledges, as you can see in **Figure 22-1**. The chicks stand still as soon as they hatch. The chicks of a related bird, the

Figure 22-1
Kittiwakes, shown here, have an innate behavior for nesting on narrow ledges. **Why is this adaptation necessary for their survival?**

Figure 22-2 Baby sea turtles move toward the ocean as soon as they hatch. **What stimulus do you think baby sea turtles are responding to when they move toward the ocean?**

herring gull, which nests on the ground, move around as soon as they can stand. Kittiwake chicks can't do this because one step could mean instant death. They hatch already knowing they must not move around.

Animals that have short life spans often have patterns of innate behavior. The lives of most insects, for example, are too short for the young to learn from the parents. In many cases, the parents have died by the time the young hatch. And yet, every insect reacts automatically to its environment. A moth will fly toward a light, and a cockroach will run away from it. They do not have to spend time learning what to do. Innate behavior allows animals to respond quickly to a stimulus in their environment without taking the time to choose a proper response.

Reading Check

What is a reflex?

Reflexes

The simplest innate behaviors are reflex actions. A **reflex** is an automatic response that does not involve the brain. Sneezing, shivering, yawning, jerking your hand away from a hot surface, and blinking your eyes when something is thrown toward you are all reflex actions. All animals have reflexes.

During a reflex, a message passes from a sense organ along the nerve to the spinal cord and back to the muscles. The message does not go to the brain. You are aware of the reaction only after it has happened. When you respond reflexively, you do not think about how you will respond. Your body reacts on its own, without your thought processes. A reflex is not the result of conscious thinking.

Instincts

An **instinct** is a complex pattern of innate behavior. Have you ever watched a spider spin a web? Spinning a web is complicated, and yet spiders spin webs correctly on the first try. **Figure 22-2** shows how sea turtles instinctively head for the sea as soon as they hatch. Unlike reflexes, instinctive behaviors may have several parts and take weeks

Figure 22-3 Salmon instinctively return to the same stream or river where they were born to spawn.

to complete. Instinctive behavior begins when the animal recognizes a stimulus and continues until all parts of the behavior have been performed.

Learned Behavior

All animals have both innate and learned behaviors. Learned behavior develops during an animal's lifetime. Learning is the result of experience or practice. You aren't born knowing how to play the piano; you must learn this behavior through practice. In animals, the more complex their brains, the more their behavior is the result of learning. Instinct almost completely determines the behavior of insects, spiders, and other arthropods. But fish, reptiles, amphibians, birds, and mammals all can learn.

Why is learning important for animals? Learning allows animals to respond to new situations. In changing environments, animals that have the ability to learn new behavior are more likely to survive. This is especially important in animals with long life spans because the longer an animal lives, the more likely it is that the environment in which it lives will change. Learning can modify instincts. For example, grouse and quail chicks leave their nests the day they hatch. They can run and find food, but they can't fly. When something moves above them, they crouch down and keep perfectly still until the danger is past, as you can see in **Figure 22-4.** They will crouch without moving even if the falling object is only a leaf. Older birds have learned that leaves will not harm them, but they, too, freeze when a hawk moves overhead.

Figure 22-4 These quail chicks must learn how to react when a predator gets too close.

Imprinting

Learned behavior includes imprinting, trial and error, conditioning, and insight. Have you ever seen young ducks following their mother? This is an important behavior because the adult bird has had more experience in finding food, escaping predators, and getting along in the world. **Imprinting** is a type of learning in which an animal forms a social attachment to another organism within a specific time period after birth or hatching.

Figure 22-5 shows Konrad Lorenz, an Austrian naturalist. Lorenz developed the concept of imprinting. Working with geese, he discovered that a gosling follows the first moving object it sees after hatching. It recognizes the moving object as

Using Math

As many as two million spiders may live in one hectare of undisturbed meadow and catch as many as 500 insects per web in a single day. What is the total number of insects trapped in the webs of the spiders in one hectare per day?

its parent. It later recognizes similar objects as members of its own species. This behavior works well when the first moving object a young goose sees is an adult female goose. But goslings hatched in an incubator may see a human first and may imprint on him or her. Animals that become imprinted toward animals of another species never learn to recognize members of their own species.

Trial and Error

Can you remember when you learned to ride a bicycle? You probably fell many times before you learned to balance on the bicycle. But after a while you could ride without having to think about it. You have many skills that you have learned through trial and error. Skating and riding a bicycle are just a few.

Behavior that is modified by experience is called trial and error learning. Both invertebrates and vertebrates learn by trial and error. When baby chicks first learn to feed themselves, they peck at many spots before they get any food. As a result of trial and error, they learn to peck only at grain.

A particular stimulus may cause a different response in the same animal at different times. When your cat sees food, it will eat it if it's hungry, but if it has just eaten, it will ignore the food. For a hungry rat, shown in **Figure 22-6,** the motive to learn basketball may be the food received after a successful basket. Motivation is something inside an animal that causes the animal to act. It is necessary for learning to take place.

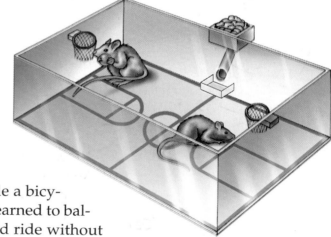

Figure 22-6 Some rats can be trained to play basketball. When the rat places the ball in the basket, it is rewarded with a treat. **Why does a rat learn how to get food by putting a ball in the basket?**

Mini Lab

Observing Insight

Procedure

1. Obtain 15 safety pins in a chain.
2. Make a hypothesis as to the fewest number of times you can open and close pins to break the chain into the following: 5 pins attached; 4 pins attached; 3 pins attached; 2 pins attached; and 1 alone. All pins must be closed at the end.
3. Test your hypothesis and compare it with those of your classmates.

Analysis

1. How was insight used in solving the problem?
2. What can you conclude about insight learning?

Conditioning

Animals often learn new behaviors by conditioning. In **conditioning,** behavior is modified so that a response previously associated with one stimulus becomes associated with another. Russian scientist Ivan P. Pavlov was the first person to study conditioning. He knew that the sight and smell of food made hungry dogs secrete saliva. Pavlov added another stimulus. He rang a bell when he gave the dogs food. The dogs began to connect the sound of the bell with food. Then Pavlov rang the bell without giving the dogs food. The dogs secreted saliva when the bell was rung even though he did not show them food. The dogs were conditioned to respond to the bell, shown in **Figure 22-7.**

American psychologist John B. Watson demonstrated that responses of humans can also be conditioned. In one experiment, he struck a metal object each time an infant touched a furry animal. The loud noise frightened the child. In time, the child became frightened by the furry animal when no sound was made.

Figure 22-7 Pavlov demonstrated conditioning in dogs in the late 1800s.

A Pavlov noted that when dogs smell food, they salivate, a reflex.

B Ringing a bell each time he presented food to a dog established a connection between the bell and the food. The dog salivated when it smelled food and a bell was rung.

C Eventually the dog would salivate just at the sound of the bell. It had become conditioned to respond to the bell as if it were food.

Insight

But how does behavior learned in the past help an animal when it is confronted by a new situation? Suppose you are given a new math problem to solve. Do you use what you have previously learned in math to solve the problem? If you have, then you have used a kind of learned behavior called insight. Insight is a form of reasoning that allows animals to use past experiences to solve new problems. In Wolfgang Kohler's experiments with chimpanzees, a bunch of bananas was placed too high for the chimpanzees to reach. Chimpanzees piled up boxes found in the room, climbed up on them, and reached the bananas, as you can see in **Figure 22-8**. Much of adult human learning also is based on insight.

Figure 22-8
Chimpanzees use insight to solve problems.

Section Assessment

1. Compare innate behavior with learned behavior.
2. Compare a reflex with an instinct.
3. Describe the four types of learned behavior.
4. **Think Critically:** Use what you know about conditioning to explain how the term mouthwatering food came about.

5. **Skill Builder**
   Classifying Organizing objects or events will help you learn more about science. Do the **Chapter 22 Skill Activity** on page 729 to learn how to classify your daily activities.

Using Computers

Spreadsheet Make a spreadsheet of the behaviors in this section. Sort the behaviors according to whether they are innate or learned behaviors. Then identify the type of innate or learned behavior. If you need help, refer to page 704.

Design Your Own Experiment

Fish Conditioning

How do fish locate and obtain their food? Can you predict how behaviors in fish can be modified?

Possible Materials

- Aquarium
- Glass cover for aquarium
- Thermometer
- Water heater for aquarium
- Washed coarse sand
- Tap water aged three days
- Metric ruler
- Dish
- Food for guppies
- Fish net
- Guppies
- Snails
- Water plants

Recognize the Problem

How can fish be conditioned to respond to a stimulus involving food?

Form a Hypothesis

Based on your observations, state a hypothesis about how fish can be conditioned to respond to a stimulus involving food.

Goals

- **Observe** the behavior of fish in response to food.
- **Design** and **carry out** an experiment to demonstrate conditioning in fish.

Safety Precautions

Protect clothing and eyes and be careful when handling live animals.

Test Your Hypothesis

Plan

1. As a group, agree upon and write out the hypothesis statement.

2. As a group, list the steps that you need to take to test your hypothesis. Be specific; describe exactly what you will do at each step. List your materials.

3. Identify how you will condition the fish. Will you feed them at the same time each day, or at the same place? What other stimulus will you condition the fish to respond to?

4. How will you determine that conditioning has taken place?

5. Prepare a data table in your Science Journal.

6. Read over your entire experiment to make sure that all steps are in logical order.

7. Identify any constants, variables, and controls of the experiment.

8. How long will you conduct the conditioning experiment? How often will you feed the fish during that time?

9. Record the behavior of the fish in your data table.

Do

1. Make sure your teacher approves your plan before you proceed.

2. Carry out the experiment as planned.

3. While the experiment is going on, write down any observations that you make and complete the data table in your Science Journal.

Analyze Your Data

1. Compare your results with those of other groups.

2. Describe the stimulus you used to condition the fish.

3. Explain how long it took the fish to become conditioned.

4. How did you know the fish were conditioned?

Draw Conclusions

1. Why was it important to follow the same routine every day?

2. Based on your observations, can all animals be conditioned over time?

22•2 Behavioral Adaptations

Instinctive Behavior Patterns

Many types of animal behavior are the result of complex patterns of innate behavior. Courtship and mating behavior within most animal groups is an example of an instinctive ritual that helps animals of one species recognize one another as possible mates. Animals also protect themselves and their sources of food by defending their territories. Instinctive behavior patterns such as these are the result of natural selection. Individual animals that did not show these behaviors died or failed to reproduce. Instinctive behavior, just like hair color, is inherited from an animal's parents.

Territorial Behavior

Many animals set up territories for feeding, mating, and raising young. A **territory** is an area that an animal defends from other members of the same species. Ownership of a territory is set up in different ways. Songbirds sing to set up territories. Sea lions bellow and squirrels chatter. Other animals leave scent marks. Some patrol the area to warn intruders. Why do animals defend their territories? Territories are areas that contain food, shelter, and potential mates. Animals need these things in order to survive. Defending territories is an instinctive behavior that improves the chances of survival for the offspring of an animal. **Figure 22-9** illustrates one way in which animals defend their territories.

Figure 22-9 Male tigers will attack other males that attempt to enter their territories. **What other animals defend their territories?**

Aggression

Have you ever watched a dog approach another dog eating a bone? What happens to the appearance of the dog with the bone? The hair stands up on its back, the lips curl, and the dog makes growling noises. This behavior is aggression. **Aggression** is a forceful act used to dominate or control another animal. Fighting and threatening are aggressive behaviors animals use to defend their territories, protect their young, or to get food.

Aggressive behaviors seen in birds include letting the wings droop below the tail feathers, taking another's perch, and thrusting the head forward in a pecking motion. These behaviors are intended to avoid physical contact. Fighting wastes valuable energy, and a missing feather or two can greatly reduce a bird's ability to fly.

Animals seldom fight to the death. They rarely use their teeth, beaks, claws, or horns to fight members of their own species. These structures are used for killing prey or for defense against members of another species. To avoid being killed, a defeated animal shows submission by crouching down or retreating, as shown in **Figure 22-10.**

Figure 22-10 Wolf puppies show their submission to adult males by making themselves as small as possible. **How does a pet dog respond when its owner reprimands it for poor behavior? Do you see any similarities in these two responses?**

Courtship Behavior

You have probably seen a male turkey, like the one shown in **Figure 22-11,** spread its feathers and strut. A male frigate bird has a bright red pouch on his throat that takes about 25 minutes to blow up. A male sage grouse fans his tail, fluffs his feathers, and blows up his two air sacs. These are examples of a behavior that animals perform before mating. This type of behavior is called **courtship behavior.** Courtship behaviors allow male and female members of a species to recognize each other. They also allow males and females to be ready to mate at the same time. This helps ensure reproductive success.

CHEMISTRY
INTEGRATION

Firefly Courtship
There are many kinds of courtship behavior in nature. Find out what causes the flashes of light produced by male fireflies. How does this behavior help fireflies survive?

Figure 22-11 Male turkeys strut to attract females.

Figure 22-12 Emperor penguins huddle together for warmth and protection.

In most species, the males perform courtship displays to attract a mate. Some courtship behaviors allow males and females to find each other across distances. Male fireflies produce different patterns in their flashes of light. A female of the same species recognizes the pattern and flashes back.

Social Behavior

Animals live together in groups for several reasons. One reason is that there is safety in large numbers. A wolf pack is less likely to attack a herd of musk oxen than an individual musk ox. In some groups, large numbers of animals help keep each other warm. Migrating animals in large groups are less likely to get lost than if they traveled alone. **Figure 22-12** shows social behavior among penguins.

Interactions among organisms of the same species are examples of **social behavior.** Social behaviors include courtship and mating, caring for the young, claiming territories, protecting each other, and getting food. These behaviors provide advantages for survival of the species.

Insects such as ants, bees, and termites live together in societies. A **society** is a group of animals of the same species living and working together in an organized way. Each member has a certain job. Usually, there is a female that lays eggs, a male that fertilizes the eggs, and workers that do all the other jobs in the society.

Some societies are organized by dominance. Wolves usually live together in packs. In a wolf pack, there is a dominant female. The top female controls the mating of the other females. If there is plenty of food, she mates and allows the others to do so. If food is scarce, she allows less mating, and usually she is the only one to mate.

Communication

In all social behavior, communication is important. Communication is an exchange of information. How do you communicate with the people around you? Animals in a group communicate with sounds and actions. Alarm calls, chemicals, speech, courtship behavior, and aggression are all forms of communication.

Reading Check

name 4 types of social behavior.

interNET
CONNECTION

Visit the Glencoe Science Web Site at www. glencoe.com/sec/ science/fl to learn more about wolf-pack behavior.

Chemical Communication

Ants can sometimes be seen, as in **Figure 22-13,** moving single file toward a piece of food. Male dogs stop frequently to urinate on bushes when you take them for walks. Both behaviors are based on chemical communication. The ants have laid down chemical trails that the others can follow, and the dog is letting other dogs know he has been there. In these behaviors, the animals are using pheromones to communicate. A **pheromone** (FER uh mohn) is a chemical that is produced by one animal that influences the behavior of another animal of the same species. Animals that secrete pheromones range from one-celled organisms to mammals.

Both males and females use pheromones to establish territories, warn of danger, and attract mates. Certain ants, mice, and snails release alarm pheromones when injured or threatened. The odor warns other members of the species to leave the area.

Pheromones are powerful chemicals needed only in small amounts. They remain in the environment so the sender and the receiver do not have to be at a certain place in order to communicate. Because they linger in the environment, they may advertise the presence of an animal to predators as well as to the intended receiver of the message.

CHEMISTRY
◄ **INTEGRATION**

Sound Communication

Many insects communicate through sound. Male crickets rub a scraper on one forewing against a vein on the other forewing to produce chirping sounds. They use the sound to attract females and warn other males away from their territories. Each cricket species produces several calls that are different from those of other cricket species. The calls are often used to identify species. Male mosquitoes that are ready to mate use tiny hairs on their antennae to sense the buzzing sounds produced by females. The tiny hairs vibrate only to the frequency emitted by a female of the same species.

Figure 22-14 Prairie dogs bark warnings to other members of their group that predators may be near.

Vertebrates use a number of different forms of sound communication. Fish produce sounds by manipulating their air bladder. Rabbits thump the ground, gorillas pound their chests, and prairie dogs, like the one in **Figure 22-14,** bark. Sound communication is useless in noisy environments. Seabirds that live on shorelines with pounding waves must rely on vision for communication.

Cyclic Behavior

What determines when a bear hibernates in the winter and wakes up in the spring? Animals, like the owl in **Figure 22-15,** show regularly repeated behaviors such as feeding in the day and sleeping at night or the opposite.

Cyclic behaviors are innate behaviors that occur in a repeating pattern. They are often repeated in response to changes in the environment. Behavior that is based on a 24-hour cycle is called a circadian rhythm. Animals that are active during the day are diurnal (dy UR nul). Animals that are active at night are nocturnal.

Figure 22-15 Owls usually feed at night and rest during the day. **What type of behavior does this demonstrate?**

Hibernation

Cyclic behaviors also occur over long periods of time. **Hibernation** is a cyclic response to cold temperatures and limited food supplies. During hibernation, an animal's body temperature drops to near that of its surroundings, and its breathing rate is greatly reduced. An animal in hibernation survives on stored body fat. The animal remains inactive until the weather becomes warm in the spring. Some mammals and many amphibians and reptiles, like the snakes in **Figure 22-16,** hibernate.

Migration

Many birds and mammals move to new locations when the seasons change instead of hibernating. This instinctive seasonal movement of animals is called **migration.** Why do animals migrate? Most migrate in order to find food or reproduce in a better environment. Many species of birds fly

Figure 22-16 These garter snakes den together during the cold months and emerge when the weather gets warm. **Why do cold blooded animals hibernate together in large numbers?**

Problem Solving

Abilities of Homing Pigeons

If a homing pigeon is placed into a dark box and transported to a strange, distant location, then released, there is a good chance it will soon show up in its home loft. Pigeons fitted with frosted lenses placed over their eyes to prevent them from seeing landmarks will still return to the area of their loft. Experiments have shown that pigeons can detect magnetic fields and sense changes in altitude as small as four millimeters. They use the magnetic fields as a compass to direct them home. Pigeons also see ultraviolet light and hear extremely low sounds that come from wind blowing over ocean surf and mountain ranges thousands of kilometers away. What kind of behaviors do homing pigeons use to find their way back to their lofts?

Think Critically

1. Are there learned behaviors that may help homing pigeons?

2. How would a pigeon that lost its vision find its way home?

3. In 1998, a group of homing pigeons became lost while trying to find their way home along the East coast. What may have caused the pigeons to get lost?

hours or days without stopping. The blackpoll warbler flies nonstop a distance of more than 4000 km from North America to its winter home in South America. The trip takes nearly 90 hours. Arctic terns fly about 17 700 km from their breeding grounds in the Arctic to their winter home in the Antarctic. They return a few months later, traveling a distance of more than 35 000 km in less than a year. Gray whales swim from the cold Arctic waters to the waters off the coast of northern Mexico. After the young are born, they make the return trip. **Figure 22-17** shows other animals that migrate.

VISUALIZING Migration

Figure 22-17 Organisms migrate for different reasons.

A Elephants migrate to find water and food.

B Ruby-throated hummingbirds migrate to warmer climates during the winter.

C Gray whales migrate to warmer water to have their young.

Figure 22-18 Some animals like these wildebeest migrate in large numbers. They migrate to find food.

Animals have many different behaviors. Some behaviors are innate and some are learned. Many are a combination of innate and learned behaviors. Appropriate behaviors help animals survive, reproduce, and maintain the species.

Section Assessment

1. What are some examples of courtship behavior?
2. How are cyclic behaviors a response to stimuli in the environment?
3. Name 2 reasons why animals migrate.
4. What is the difference between hibernation and migration?
5. **Think Critically:** How does migration help a species survive and reproduce?
6. 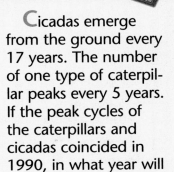 **Skill Builder**
   Designing an Experiment to Test a Hypothesis Design an experiment to show that ants leave chemical trails to show other ants where food can be found. If you need help, refer to Designing an Experiment to Test a Hypothesis in the **Skill Handbook** on page 689.

Using Math

Cicadas emerge from the ground every 17 years. The number of one type of caterpillar peaks every 5 years. If the peak cycles of the caterpillars and cicadas coincided in 1990, in what year will they coincide again?

Observing Ants

Materials

- Ants (20)
- Large jar with screen wire cover
- Soil
- Black paper
- Small moist sponge
- Water
- Food—honey, sugar, bread crumbs
- Small can with lid
- Spoon or trowel
- Hand lens

Ants live and work together in an organized way. Each member of an ant society has a certain job. In this activity you will observe ways in which ants are adapted to their environment and how they work together to survive.

What You'll Investigate

How do ants live and work together to survive?

Goals

- **Observe** social behavior.

Procedure

1. **Pour** moistened, loose soil into a jar until it is ¾ full. Place the damp sponge on top of the soil.

2. Find an anthill. **Use** the spoon or trowel to place loose soil from the nest into the small can. **Look** for ants, small white eggs, cocoons, and larvae. Try to find a queen. The queen will be larger than the other ants. Cover. Place the ants in the refrigerator for a few minutes to slow their movements.

3. Gently **place** the ants in the jar. Add a small amount of each food in different areas. **Place** the screen wire cover on the jar.

4. Tape the black paper around the jar. Leave about 2 cm at the top uncovered.

5. Take the paper off for a short period of time each day and observe the ants at work. Use a hand lens to observe individual ants.

6. Keep the sponge moistened and add food each day. Record your observations each day.

Ant Behavior		
Date	Number of Visible Ants	Other Observations

Conclude and Apply

1. What is a society?

2. What evidence do you have that ants are social insects?

3. What kinds of foods do ants prefer?

Hatchet
by Gary Paulsen

Brian opened his eyes and screamed.

For seconds he did not know where he was, only that the crash was still happening and he was going to die, and he screamed until his breath was gone.

Then silence, filled with sobs as he pulled in air, half crying. How could it be so quiet? Moments ago there was nothing but noise, crashing and tearing, screaming, now quiet.

Some birds were singing.

How could birds be singing?

In the book *Hatchet*, Brian Robeson, age 13, is stranded alone in the North Woods of Canada after a plane crash. With a hatchet as his only tool, how will he survive? As he struggles to find food and shelter, Brian gradually forms a strategy for survival. "First food," he thinks, "then thought, then action."

Brian applies what he knows from school and from his parents and friends to make sense of what he finds around him. After he carries out a plan of action, he evaluates it. What should he change in order to get a better result? Brian makes a guess about what kind of wood he needs to make a bow and how it should be shaped. The first result? Failure! When Brian pulls back on the shoelace he's used for a bow-string, the bow snaps in half. He thinks carefully about the failure and makes a new guess, a new plan, and this time, it works. Brian has to think like a scientist—not to do an assignment or to make a dramatic discovery, but to survive.

Science JOURNAL ▶

Think of an experience when you used scientific skills and methods outside of school. Then, in your Science Journal, write a short story about your experiences.

Section

22-1 INNATE BEHAVIOR

Behavior that an animal is born with is **innate behavior.** Other animal behaviors are learned through experience. Innate behavior includes reflexes and instincts. **Reflexes** are automatic responses that do not involve the brain. Shivering is an example of a reflex. An **instinct** is a complex pattern of innate behavior. A spider instinctively knows how to spin a web. *How do instincts help less complex animals survive?*

LEARNED BEHAVIOR

Learned behavior includes imprinting, trial and error, conditioning, and insight. **Imprinting** occurs when an animal forms a social attachment soon after birth. Behavior modified by experience is learning by trial and error. A **conditioned** behavior occurs when a response associated with one stimulus becomes associated with another. Insight uses past experiences to solve new problems. *What is the difference between insight and trial and error behavior?*

Reading Check ✓

Reread the information on conditioning. Write numbered steps to Pavlov's experiment.

Section
22-2 BEHAVIORAL ADAPTATIONS

Behavioral adaptations such as defense of **territory,** courtship, and **social behavior** help species of animals survive and reproduce. **Courtship behavior** allows males and females to recognize each other. **Cyclic behaviors** like **migration** and **hibernation** occur in repeating patterns. Generally, cyclic behaviors happen due to changes in the environment. For example, bears hibernate during the winter when food is hard to find and it is cold. *How are defense of territory and courtship behavior related?*

Career
CONNECTION

Alfred Gonzalez, Salmon Habitat Researcher

Natural disasters and human activity can often be harmful to animal habitats. Alfred Gonzalez is a researcher interested in salmon habitat restoration. His techniques for restoring salmon habitats include placing objects, such as logs, in a stream. These objects serve as places for the salmon to hide, and increase the amount of gravelly material in the streambed that salmon prefer to use for their nests in which they lay their eggs. *How can understanding animals' behavior help protect their natural habitats?*

Using Vocabulary

a. aggression
b. behavior
c. conditioning
d. courtship behavior
e. cyclic behavior
f. hibernation
g. imprinting
h. innate behavior
i. instinct
j. migration
k. pheromone
l. reflex
m. social behavior
n. society
o. territory

Match each phrase with the correct term from the list of Vocabulary words.

1. an inherited, not learned behavior
2. forming a social bond to another organism after birth
3. the way an organism behaves toward its environment
4. a chemical produced by an animal to influence the behavior of another animal
5. instinctive seasonal movement

Checking Concepts

Choose the word or phrase that best answers the question.

6. What is an example of a reflex?
   A) writing
   B) talking
   C) sneezing
   D) riding a bicycle

7. What is an instinct an example of?
   A) innate behavior
   B) learned behavior
   C) imprinting
   D) conditioning

8. What is nest building an example of?
   A) conditioning
   B) imprinting
   C) learned behavior
   D) an instinct

9. Which animals depend least on instinct and most on learning?
   A) birds
   B) fish
   C) mammals
   D) amphibians

10. What are behaviors that occur in repeated patterns?
    A) cyclic
    B) imprinting
    C) reflex
    D) society

11. What is an area that an animal defends from other members of the same species called?
    A) society
    B) territory
    C) migration
    D) aggression

12. What is a forceful act used to dominate or control?
    A) courtship
    B) reflex
    C) aggression
    D) hibernation

13. Which of the following is **NOT** an example of courtship behavior?
    A) fluffing feathers
    B) taking over a perch
    C) singing songs
    D) releasing pheromones

14. What is an organized group of animals working specific jobs?
    A) community
    B) territory
    C) society
    D) circadian rhythm

15. What is the response of inactivity and slowed metabolism that occurs during cold conditions?
    A) hibernation
    B) imprinting
    C) migration
    D) circadian rhythm

Thinking Critically

16. Explain the type of behavior involved when the bell rings at the end of class.
17. Discuss the advantages and disadvantages of migration as a means of survival.
18. Explain how a habit, such as tying your shoes, is different from a reflex.
19. Use one example to explain how behavior increases an animal's chance for survival.
20. Hens lay more eggs in the spring when day length increases. How can farmers use this knowledge of behavior to their advantage?

Developing Skills

If you need help, refer to the **Skill Handbook.**

21. **Concept Mapping:** Complete the concept map below outlining the types of behavior.

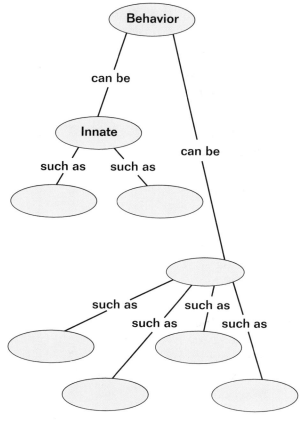

22. **Hypothesizing:** Make a hypothesis about how frogs communicate with each other. How could you test your hypothesis?

23. **Observing and Inferring:** Make observations of a dog, cat, or bird for a week. Record what you see. How did the animal communicate with other animals and with you?

24. **Designing an Experiment to Test a Hypothesis:** Design an experiment to get a specific response to a stimulus from an animal.

THE PRINCETON REVIEW

Test-Taking Tip

Become an Expert on What You Fear the Most If you just can't remember all of that information, don't run away. Instead, consider it a challenge, meet the problem head on, and you'll be surprised at how easy it is to conquer even the toughest concepts.

Test Practice

Use these questions to test your Science Proficiency.

1. What is a reflex behavior?
   A) a complex pattern of innate behavior
   B) the way mates can find each other
   C) a simple innate behavior
   D) learning from past experiences

2. Some animals have been known to imprint on humans. What could result from this type of behavior?
   A) The animal may never recognize members of its own species.
   B) The animal will die.
   C) The animal will miss its mother.
   D) The animal will not be affected.

3. Why do males perform courtship behavior?
   A) to defend their territory
   B) to attract a mate
   C) to scare a predator
   D) to communicate that it is time to migrate

Exploring Space

What's Happening Here?

Much of the light you see twinkling in the night sk
bears witness to a distant past. How so? If yc
peered at one of those stars through a powerf
telescope, you would discover not how the st₂
appears today but how it appeared millions c
years ago. Likewise, if people on a distant plan
were to aim a telescope at you, they would se
Earth as it existed in the age of the dinosaur
Outer space is so vast that light traveling ₂
300 000 kilometers a second takes millions c
years to span the distance from a distant star t
Earth. To grasp the subject of astronomy, yo
must expand your notion of distance to th
unfathomable. In this unit, you will learn ho
the lure of this vastness has triggered a new ag
of exploration. En route into deep space, th
Voyager probes launched in 1977 photographe
Jupiter's Great Red Spot (left), a massiv
storm in the planet's outer gases. I
1996, this astronaut (inset) teste
a minirocket backpack by flyin
solo above the space shuttl
Discovery.

inter**NET** CONNECTION

Explore the Glencoe Scienc
Web Site at **www.gler
coe.com/sec/science/fl** t
find out more about topi
found in this unit.

Skills Preview

Skill Builders
Infer
Develop a Multimedia Presentation

Activities
Infer
Classify

MiniLabs
Observe
Model

Reading Check ✓

As you read about the phases of the moon and other topics in this chapter, write down unfamiliar words. Define them as you read.

spacelab

esa

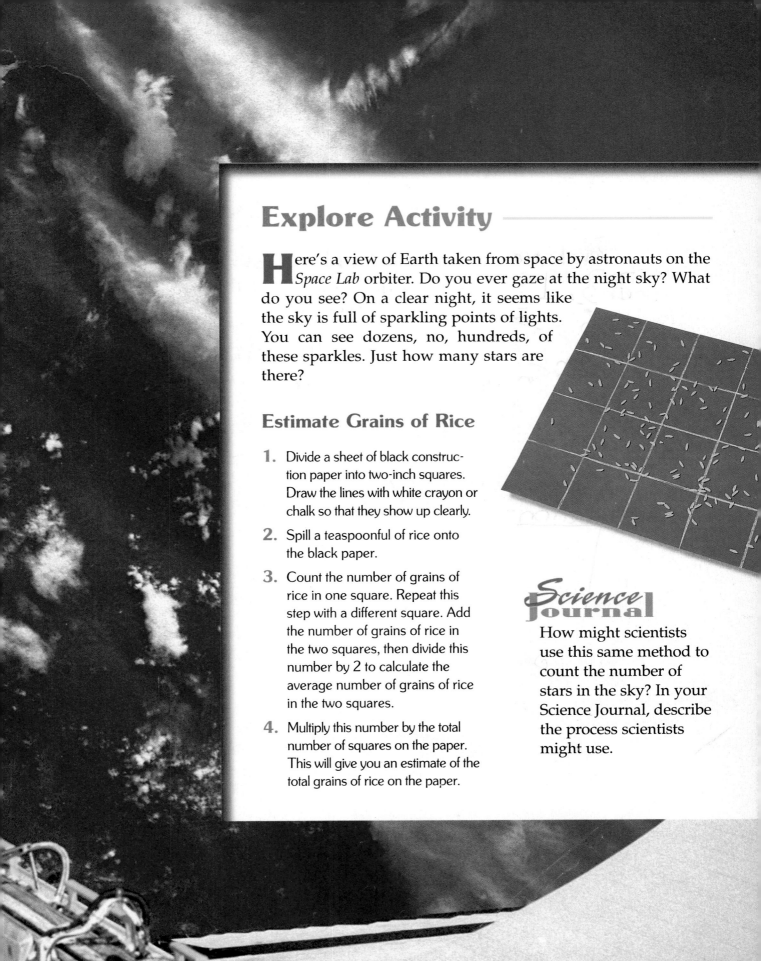

Explore Activity

Here's a view of Earth taken from space by astronauts on the *Space Lab* orbiter. Do you ever gaze at the night sky? What do you see? On a clear night, it seems like the sky is full of sparkling points of lights. You can see dozens, no, hundreds, of these sparkles. Just how many stars are there?

Estimate Grains of Rice

1. Divide a sheet of black construction paper into two-inch squares. Draw the lines with white crayon or chalk so that they show up clearly.

2. Spill a teaspoonful of rice onto the black paper.

3. Count the number of grains of rice in one square. Repeat this step with a different square. Add the number of grains of rice in the two squares, then divide this number by 2 to calculate the average number of grains of rice in the two squares.

4. Multiply this number by the total number of squares on the paper. This will give you an estimate of the total grains of rice on the paper.

Science Journal

How might scientists use this same method to count the number of stars in the sky? In your Science Journal, describe the process scientists might use.

23•1 Earth's Place in Space

What You'll Learn

► How seasons are caused by the tilt of Earth's axis
► What causes the phases of the moon

Vocabulary
rotation
revolution
eclipse

Why It's Important

► The movement of Earth causes night and day.

Earth Moves

You wake up, stretch and yawn, then glance out your window to see the first rays of dawn peeking over the houses. By lunch, the sun is high in the sky. As you sit down to dinner that evening, the sun appears to sink below the horizon. It might seem like the sun moves across the sky. But, it is Earth that is really moving.

Earth's Rotation

Earth spins in space like a dog chasing its tail—but not as fast! Our planet spins around an imaginary line called an axis. **Figure 23-1** shows this imaginary axis.

The spinning of Earth on its axis is called Earth's **rotation** (roh TAY shun). Earth rotates once every 24 hours. In the morning, as Earth rotates, the sun comes into view. In the afternoon, Earth continues to rotate, and the sun appears to move across the sky. In the evening, the sun seems to go down because the place where you are on Earth has rotated away from the sun.

You can see how this works by standing and facing the chalkboard. Pretend you are Earth and the chalkboard is the sun. Now, turn around slowly in a counterclockwise direction. The chalkboard moves across your vision, then disappears. You rotate until finally you see the chalkboard again. The chalkboard didn't move—you did. When you rotated, you were like Earth, spinning in space so that different parts of the planet face the sun at different times. This movement of Earth, not the movement of the sun, causes night and day.

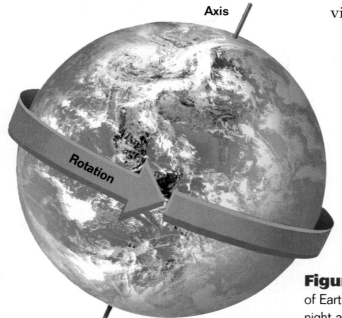

Axis

Rotation

Figure 23-1 The rotation of Earth on its axis causes night and day.

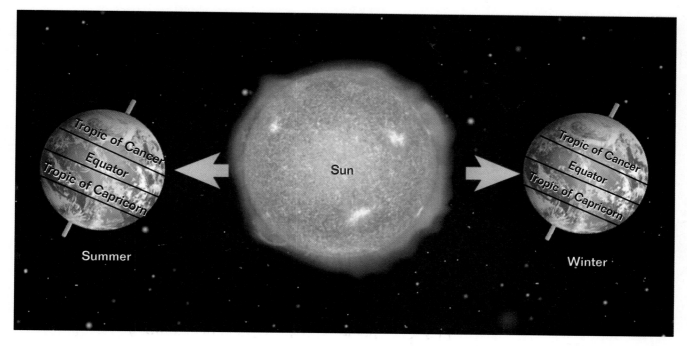

Figure 23-2 In the northern hemisphere on June 21 or 22, the sun's rays directly strike the tropic of Cancer. On December 21 or 22, the sun's direct rays strike the tropic of Capricorn. **When it's summer in the northern hemisphere, what season is it in the southern hemisphere?**

Earth's Revolution

You know that Earth rotates in space. It also moves in other ways. Like an athlete running around a track, Earth moves around the sun in a regular, curved path. This path is called an orbit. The movement of Earth around the sun is known as Earth's **revolution** (rev uh LEW shun). A year on Earth is the time it takes for Earth to revolve around the sun once. How many revolutions old are you?

Seasons

Who doesn't love summer? The days are long and warm. It's a great time to go swimming, ride a bike, or read a book just for fun. Why can't we have summer all year round? Blame it on Earth's axis. The axis, that imaginary line that our planet spins around, is not straight up and down. It is tilted at an angle. It's because of this tilt that there are seasons in many areas on Earth. Why?

Look at **Figure 23-2.** The part of Earth that is tilted toward the sun receives more direct sunlight and more energy from the sun than the part of Earth that is tilted away from the sun. When the part of Earth that you live on is tilted away from the sun, you have winter. When the part of Earth that you live on is tilted toward the sun, you have summer. ✔

Reading Check ✔

What causes seasons?

First quarter

Waxing crescent

New moon

Waxing gibbous

Movements of the Moon

Imagine a dog running in circles around an athlete who is jogging on a track. That's how you can picture the moon moving around Earth. As Earth revolves around the sun, the moon revolves around Earth. The moon revolves around Earth once every 27.3 days. But, as you have probably noticed, the moon does not always look the same from Earth. Sometimes, it looks like a big, glowing disk. Other times, it's a thin sliver.

Moon Phases

How many different moon shapes have you seen? Round shapes? Half-circle shapes? The moon looks different at different times of the month, but it doesn't really change. What does change is the way the moon appears from Earth. We call these changes moon phases. **Figure 23-3** shows the different phases of the moon.

Full moon

Light from the Sun

The moon phase you see on any given night depends on the positions of the moon, the sun, and Earth in space. Wait a minute. How can we see the different phases of the moon? Is someone shining a giant flashlight up there? No, the moon receives light from the sun, just as Earth does. And, just as half of Earth experiences day while the other half experiences night, one half of the moon is lit by the sun while the other half is dark. As the moon revolves around Earth, we see different parts of the side of the moon that is facing the sun. This makes the moon appear to change shape.

Waning gibbous

Figure 23-3 The moon is said to be waxing when it seems to be getting larger night by night. It is said to be waning when it seems to be getting smaller.

Third quarter

Waning crescent

Eclipses

Have you ever tried to watch TV with someone standing between you and the screen? You can't see a thing! The light from the screen can't reach your eyes because someone is blocking it. Sometimes, the moon is like that person standing in front of the TV. It moves between the sun and Earth in a position that blocks sunlight from reaching Earth. The moon's shadow travels across parts of Earth. This event, shown in **Figure 23-4,** is called an **eclipse** (ih KLIHPS). Because it is an eclipse of the sun, it is known as a solar eclipse. The moon is much smaller than the sun, so not everywhere on Earth is in the moon's shadow. Sunlight is completely blocked only in the small area of Earth where the moon's shadow falls. In that area, the eclipse is said to be a total solar eclipse.

Lunar Eclipse

Sometimes, Earth can be like a person standing in front of the TV. It gets between the sun and the moon, blocking sunlight from reaching the moon. When Earth's shadow falls on the moon, we have an eclipse of the moon, which is called a lunar eclipse. **Figure 23-5** shows a lunar eclipse.

Mini Lab

Observing Distance and Size

Procedure

1. Place a basketball on a table at the front of the classroom. Then, stand at the back of the room.
2. Extend your arm, close one eye, and try to block the ball from sight with your thumb.
3. Slowly move your thumb closer to you until it completely blocks the ball.
4. Repeat the experiment using a golf ball.

Analysis

1. In your Science Journal, describe what you observed. When did your thumb block your view of the basketball? When did your thumb block your view of the golf ball?
2. A small object can sometimes block a larger object from view. Explain how this relates to the moon, the sun, and Earth during a solar eclipse.

Figure 23-4 The photo below shows a solar eclipse. Only a small area of Earth ever experiences a total solar eclipse. **Why?**

Sun

Area of partial eclipse

Moon

Area of total eclipse

Earth

Sun

Moon

Earth

Figure 23-5 During a lunar eclipse, Earth moves between the sun and the moon.

Our Neighbors in Space

In this section, you've learned about what causes day and night and the seasons. You've also learned about the moon, Earth's nearest neighbor in space. Next, you'll look at our other neighbors in space—the planets that make up our solar system.

Section Assessment

1. Explain the difference between Earth's revolution and its rotation.

2. Draw a picture showing the positions of the sun, the moon, and Earth during a solar eclipse.

3. **Think Critically:** Seasons are caused by the tilt of Earth's axis. What do you think seasons would be like if Earth's axis were not tilted?

4. **Skill Builder**

   Inferring The surfaces of Earth's moon and other objects in space are covered with impact craters. Do the **Chapter 23 Skill Activity** on page 730 to infer the ages of impact craters.

Using Math

Light travels 300 000 km per second. There are 60 s in a minute. If it takes eight minutes for the sun's light to reach us, how far is the sun from Earth?

Moon Phases

The moon is our nearest neighbor in space. But, the sun, which is much farther away, affects how we see the moon from Earth. In this activity, you'll observe how the positions of the sun, the moon, and Earth cause the different phases of the moon.

Materials

- Drawing paper (several sheets)
- Softball
- Flashlight
- Scissors

What You'll Investigate

How do the positions of the sun, the moon, and Earth affect the phases of the moon?

Goals

- **Observe** moon phases.
- **Record** and **label** phases of the moon.
- **Infer** how the positions of the sun, the moon, and Earth affect phases of the moon.

Procedure

1. **Turn on** the flashlight and darken other lights in the room. **Select** a member of your group to hold the flashlight. This person will be the "sun." **Select** another member of your group to hold up the softball so that the light shines directly on the ball. The softball will be the "moon" in your experiment.

2. The remaining members of your group should sit between the sun and the moon.

3. **Observe** how light shines on the moon. **Draw** the moon, being careful to **shade** in its dark portion.

4. The student who is holding the "moon" should begin to **walk** in a slow circle around the group, stopping at least seven times at different spots. Each time the "moon" stops, **observe** the moon, **draw** the moon, and **shade** in its dark portion.

Conclude and Apply

1. **Compare** and **contrast** your drawings with those of other students. **Discuss** similarities and differences in the drawings.

2. In your own words, **explain** how the positions of the sun, the moon, and Earth affect the phase of the moon we see on Earth.

3. **Compare** your drawings with **Figure 23-3**. Which phase is the moon in for each drawing? **Label** each drawing with the correct moon phase.

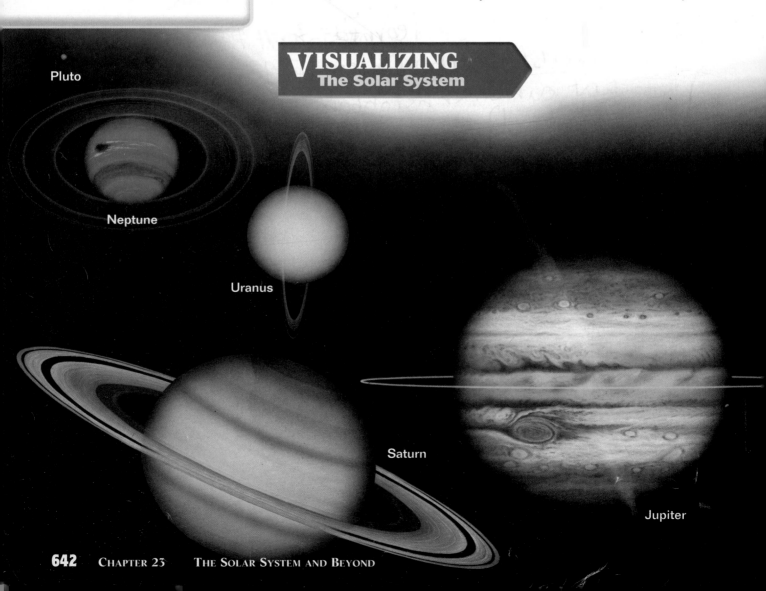

23•2 The Solar System

Distances in Space

Imagine that you are an astronaut living far in the future, doing research on a space station near the edge of our solar system. You've been working hard for a long time. You need a vacation. Where will you go? How about a tour of the solar system? The **solar system,** shown in **Figure 23-6,** is made up of the nine planets and numerous other objects that orbit the sun. How long do you think it would take you to cross the solar system?

Measuring Space

Distances in space are hard to imagine because space is so vast. Let's get back down to Earth for a minute. Suppose you had to measure your pencil, the hallway outside your classroom, and the distance from your home to school. Would you

What **You'll Learn**

► About distances in space
► About the objects in our solar system

Vocabulary
solar system
astronomical unit

Why **It's Important**

► You'll learn more about how the planets, including Earth, were formed.

VISUALIZING
The Solar System

Pluto

Neptune

Uranus

Saturn

Jupiter

use the same units for each measurement? Probably not. You'd probably measure your pencil in centimeters. You'd probably use something bigger to measure the length of the hallway, such as meters. You might measure the trip from your home to school in kilometers. We use larger units to measure longer distances. Imagine trying to measure the trip from your home to school in centimeters. If you didn't lose count, you'd end up with a very large number!

Astronomical Unit

Kilometers are fine for measuring long distances on Earth. But, we need even bigger units to measure vast distances in space. One such measure is the **astronomical** (as truh NAHM ih kul) **unit.** An astronomical unit equals 150 million km, which is the average distance from Earth to the sun. It is abbreviated *AU.* If something is 3 AU away from Earth, it means that the object is three times as far away as Earth is from the sun.

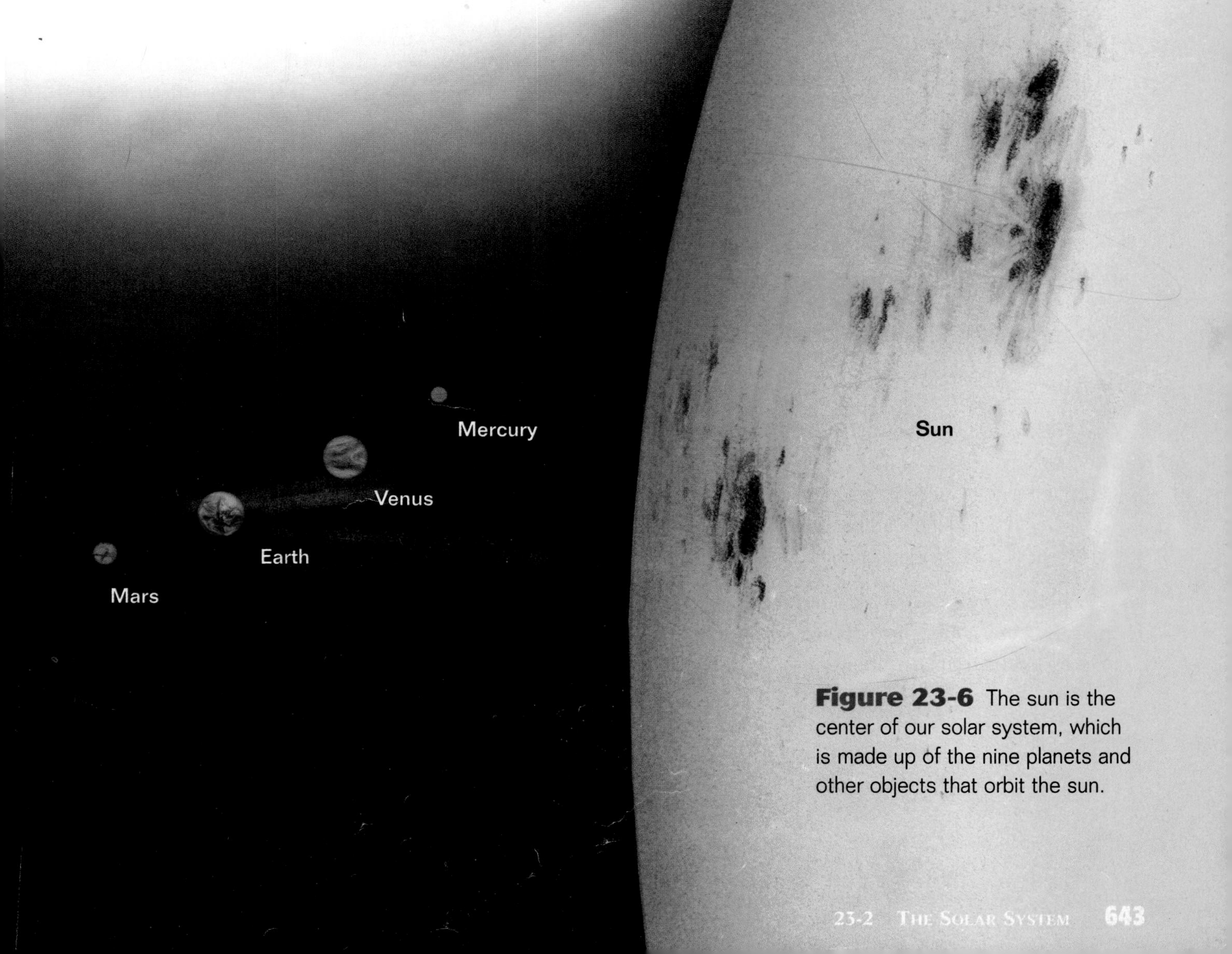

Mercury

Venus

Earth

Mars

Sun

Figure 23-6 The sun is the center of our solar system, which is made up of the nine planets and other objects that orbit the sun.

Figure 23-7 The tails of comets point away from the sun, pushed by solar wind. Solar wind is a stream of charged particles from the sun.

A Tour of the Solar System

Now you know how far you have to travel to tour the solar system, starting from your space station on the outer edge of the solar system. Strap yourself into your spacecraft. It's time to begin your journey. What will you see first as you enter the solar system?

Comets

What's this in **Figure 23-7?** A giant, dirty snowball? No, it's a comet—the first thing you see on your trip. Comets are made up of dust and frozen gases such as ice. From time to time, they swing close to the sun. When they do, the sun's radiation vaporizes some of the material. Gas and dust spurt from the comet, forming bright tails.

*inter***NET**
CONNECTION

Visit the Glencoe Science Web Site at **www. glencoe.com/sec/ science/fl** for more information about comets.

Problem Solving

Determining Distances in Space

The following table shows the distances in AU between the planets in our solar system and the sun. Notice that the inner planets are fairly close together, while the outer planets are far apart. Study the distances carefully, then answer the questions below.

Think Critically: Which planets do you think scientists know the most about? Explain your answer. Based on the distances shown in the table, how would you go about making a scale model of the solar system? What unit of measurement would you use to show the distances between the planets? What scale would you use to show size?

Solar System Data	
Planet	**Average Distance from Sun**
Mercury	0.39 AU
Venus	0.72 AU
Earth	1 AU
Mars	1.5 AU
Jupiter	5.2 AU
Saturn	9.5 AU
Uranus	19 AU
Neptune	30 AU
Pluto	40 AU

Outer Planets

Moving past the comets, you come to the outer planets. The outer planets are Pluto, Neptune, Uranus, Saturn, and Jupiter. Let's hope you aren't looking for places to stop and rest. Trying to stand on most of these planets would be like trying to stand on a cloud. That's because all of the outer planets except Pluto are huge balls of gas. Each may have a solid core, but none of them has a solid surface. The gas giants have lots of moons, which orbit the planets just like our own moon orbits Earth. They have outer rings made of dust and ice. In fact, the only outer planet that doesn't have rings is Pluto. Pluto isn't a gas giant. What does it look like? You'll soon find out.

Pluto

The first planet that you come to on your tour is Pluto, a small, rocky planet with a frozen crust. Pluto, the last planet discovered by scientists, is normally farthest from the sun. It is the smallest planet in the solar system and the one we know the least about. Pluto, shown in **Figure 23-8A,** has no ring system. Its one moon, Charon, is more than half the size of the planet itself.

Neptune

Neptune is the next stop in your space travel. Neptune, shown in **Figure 23-8B,** is the eighth planet from the sun most of the time. Sometimes, Pluto's orbit crosses inside Neptune's orbit during part of its voyage around the sun. When that happens, Neptune is the ninth planet from the sun. Neptune is the first of the big, gas planets with rings around it. Neptune's atmosphere includes a gas called methane. Methane gives the planet a blue-green color.

Uranus

After Neptune, you come to the seventh planet from the sun, Uranus. Uranus needs a careful look because of the interesting way it spins on its axis.

The axis of most planets, including Earth, is tilted just a little, somewhat like the hands of a clock when they are at 1 and 7. Uranus is shown in **Figure 23-8C.**

Figure 23-8 The outer planets include Pluto, Neptune, and Uranus. Pluto is so small and far away that this is the best image current technology can produce.

A Pluto

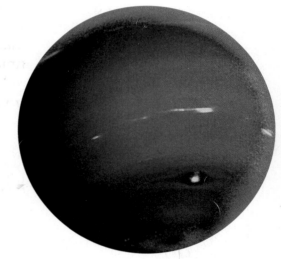

B Neptune

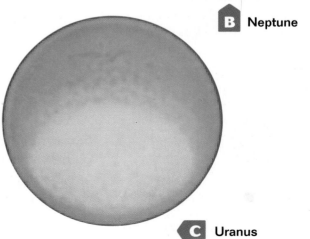

C Uranus

Figure 23-9 Saturn and Jupiter are gas giants. **In your Science Journal, list one unique characteristic of each of these planets.**

A Saturn

B
Jupiter

Reading Check ✓

What are asteroids?

Uranus has an axis that is tilted almost even with the plane of its orbit, as if the hands of the clock were at 3 and 9.

Saturn

You might think that Uranus was unusual. Wait until you see Saturn, the sixth planet from the sun! You'll be dazzled by its rings, shown in **Figure 23-9A.** Saturn's several broad rings are made up of thousands of smaller rings, which are made up of pieces of ice and rock. Some of these pieces are like specks of dust. Others are many meters across.

Jupiter

If you're looking for excitement, you'll find it on Jupiter, the largest planet in the solar system and the fifth from the sun. Watch out for a huge, red whirlwind rotating slowly around the middle of the planet. That's the Great Red Spot, a giant storm in Jupiter's atmosphere. Jupiter, shown in **Figure 23-9B,** has 16 moons. Some are larger than Pluto! One of Jupiter's moons, Io, is more volcanically active than anyplace else in the solar system.

Asteroid Belt

Look out for asteroids! On the next part of your trip, you must make your way through the asteroid belt that lies between Jupiter and the next planet, Mars. Asteroids are pieces of rock made of minerals similar to those that formed the planets. In fact, asteroids might have become planets if it weren't for that big giant, Jupiter. Jupiter's huge gravitational force probably kept any planets from forming in the area of the asteroid belt. ✓

Inner Planets

After traveling dozens of astronomical units, you finally reach the inner planets. These planets are solid and rocky. How do we know that? As with all the planets, much of what we know about planets comes from spacecraft that send data back to Earth to help us learn more about space. Look at **Figure 23-10A.** This photograph was taken by a spacecraft.

Mars

Hey! Has someone else been here? You see signs of earlier visits to Mars, the first of the inner planets. Tiny robot explorers have been left behind. But, it wasn't a person who left them here. The roving robots were left by spacecraft sent from Earth to explore Mars's surface. If you stay long enough and look around, you may notice that Mars, shown in **Figure 23-10A,** has seasons and polar ice caps. There are signs that the planet once had liquid water. You'll also notice that the planet looks red. That's because the rocks on its surface contain iron oxide, which is what makes rust look red.

Earth

Home sweet home! You've finally reached Earth, the third planet from the sun. You didn't realize how unusual your home planet was until you saw the other planets. Earth's surface temperatures allow water to exist as a solid, a liquid, and a gas. Also, Earth's atmosphere works like a screen to keep ultraviolet (ul truh VI uh lut) rays from reaching the planet's surface. Ultraviolet rays are harmful rays from the sun. Because of Earth's atmosphere, life can thrive on the planet. You would like to linger on Earth, shown in **Figure 23-10B,** but you have two more planets to explore.

Venus

Maybe you should have stayed on Earth. You won't be able to see much at your next stop, shown in **Figure 23-10C.** Venus, the second-closest planet to the sun, is hard to see because its surface is surrounded by thick clouds. Venus's clouds trap the energy that reaches the planet's surface from the sun. That energy causes surface temperatures on the planet to hover around 470°C. That's hot enough to melt lead, and far too hot for you. You're on to your next stop.

Figure 23-10 Mars, Earth, and Venus are inner planets.

A Mars

B Earth

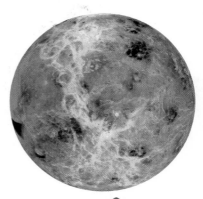

C Venus

Figure 23-11
Mercury is the closest planet to the sun. Like our moon, its surface is scarred by meteorites.

Mercury

The last planet that you visit, the one that is closest to the sun, is Mercury. Mercury, shown in **Figure 23-11,** is the second-smallest planet. Its surface is heavily scarred by craters made by meteorites. Meteorites are chunks of rock that fall from the sky when asteroids break up. Because of Mercury's small size and low gravitational pull, most gases that could form an atmosphere escape into space. The thin atmosphere and the closeness of this planet to the sun cause Mercury to have great extremes in temperature. Its surface temperature can reach 450°C during the day and drop to −170°C at night.

Section Assessment

1. List the nine planets in order from the sun, beginning with the planet closest to the sun.

2. In general, how are the outer planets different from the inner planets? How are they alike?

3. **Think Critically:** We use larger units of measure for increasingly larger distances. How do you think scientists handle increasingly smaller distances, such as the distances between molecules?

4. **Skill Builder**
Developing Multimedia Presentations Use your knowledge of the solar system to develop a multimedia presentation of the solar system. You may want to begin by drawing a poster that includes the sun, the planets, the asteroid belt, and comets. If you need help, refer to Developing Multimedia Presentations in the **Technology Skill Handbook** on page 776.

Using Computers

Spreadsheet Using the table in the Problem Solving on page 644, make a spreadsheet showing the distances of the planets from the sun. Calculate the distances using a scale of 10 cm = 1 AU. If you need help, refer to page 778.

Barbary
by Vonda N. McIntyre

…But the stars were fantastic. Barbary thought she must be able to see a hundred times as many as on earth, even in the country where sky-glow and smog did not hide them. They spanned the universe, all colors, shining with a steady, cold, remote light. She wanted to write down what they looked like, but every phrase she could think of sounded silly and inadequate.

Barbary is hoping to find a home for herself—and her mysterious stowaway—on the space station *Einstein.* (See NASA's concept of a possible space station at left.) On the way, Barbary learns from Jeanne Velory, the astronaut who is taking command of the station, that an alien ship is moving into the solar system. Some people think it may be abandoned. Others aren't so sure.

The alien vessel is approaching on a path above the plane of the solar system. *Einstein,* circling Earth in a long orbit, is the ideal spot from which to observe, and hopefully contact, the mysterious ship.

Barbary explores the research station with her new sister, Heather. She learns how to "sly," or move gracefully in zero gravity, how to pilot a space raft, and how to do her homework with a helpful computer. Along the way, she also learns to trust others and her own abilities.

Then, without warning, Barbary finds herself using all her newfound skills to save her friends and discover the truth about the alien vessel and its inhabitants.

The construction of the International Space Station is paving the way for cooperation in space exploration. Sixteen nations, including the United States, are working together in this effort. Construction in Earth's orbit began in 1998, and the space station is scheduled for completion in 2004. The space station will provide a laboratory for researching and developing new technologies in industrial materials, communications, medicine, and much more.

Science JOURNAL ▶

In your Science Journal, describe what you think life would be like at a remote outpost in space. What life-support systems would you need? How would you deal with weightlessness? What would you miss most about Earth?

Space Colony

Possible Materials

- Drawing paper
- Markers
- Books about the planets

Have you ever seen a movie or read a book about astronauts from Earth living in space colonies on other planets? Some of these make-believe space colonies look awfully strange! So far, we haven't built a space colony on another planet. But, if we did, what do you think it would look like?

Recognize the Problem

How would conditions on a planet affect the type of space colony that might be built there?

Form a Hypothesis

Research a planet. Review conditions on the surface of the planet. Make a hypothesis about the things that would have to be included in a space colony to allow humans to survive on the planet.

Goals

- **Infer** what a space colony might look like on another planet.
- **Classify** planetary surface conditions.
- **Draw** a space colony for a planet.

Test Your Hypothesis

Plan

1. **Select** a planet and **study** its surface conditions.

2. **Classify** the surface conditions in the following ways.

   a. solid or gas

   b. hot, cold, or changing temperatures

   c. heavy atmosphere or no atmosphere

   d. bright or dim sunlight

   e. special conditions unlike other planets

3. **List** the things that humans need to survive. For example, humans need air to breathe. Does your planet have air that humans can breathe, or would your space colony have to provide the air?

4. **Make a table** for the planet showing its surface conditions and the features the space colony would have to have so that humans could survive on the planet.

5. **Discuss** your decisions as a group to make sure they make sense.

Do

1. Make sure your teacher approves your plan and your data table before you proceed.

2. **Draw** a picture of the space colony. **Draw** another picture showing the inside of the space colony. **Label** the parts of the space colony and explain how they help humans to survive.

3. Present your drawing to the class. **Explain** the reasoning behind it.

Analyze Your Data

1. **Compare and contrast** your space colony with those of other students who researched the same planet you did. How are they alike? How are they different?

2. Would you change your space colony after seeing other groups' drawings? If so, what changes would you make?

Draw Conclusions

1. What was the most interesting thing you learned about the planet you studied?

2. Was your planet a good choice for a space colony? **Explain** your answer.

23·3 Stars and Galaxies

Stars

What You'll Learn

- ► How a star is born
- ► About the galaxies that make up our universe

Vocabulary
constellation
galaxy
light-year

Why It's Important

- ► Understanding the vastness of the universe helps us understand Earth's place in space.

Stars

Every night, a whole new world opens to us. The stars come out. The fact is, stars are always in the sky. We just can't see them during the day because the sun's light is brighter than starlight. The sun is a star, too. It is the closest star to Earth. We can't see it at night because as Earth rotates, our part of Earth is facing away from it.

Constellations

Ursa Major, Orion, Taurus. Do these names sound familiar? They are **constellations** (kahn stuh LAY shunz), or groups of stars that form patterns in the sky. **Figure 23-12** shows some constellations.

Constellations are named after animals, objects, and people—real or imaginary. We still use many names that early Greek astronomers gave the constellations. But, throughout history, different groups of people have seen different things in the constellations. In early England, people thought the Big Dipper, found in the constellation Ursa Major, looked like a plow. Native Americans saw it as a giant bear. To the Chinese, it looked like a governmental official and his helpers moving on a cloud. What does the Big Dipper look like to you?

Figure 23-12 Find the Big Dipper in the constellation Ursa Major. **Why do you think people call it the Big Dipper?**

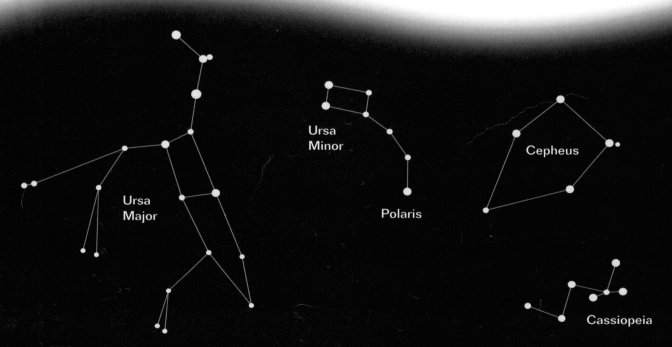

Ursa Minor

Polaris

Cepheus

Ursa Major

Cassiopeia

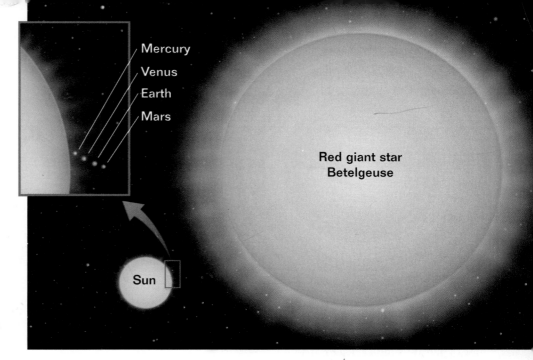

Figure 23-13 Although our sun is large compared to the inner planets, it looks small next to the giant star Betelgeuse.

Mercury
Venus
Earth
Mars

Red giant star
Betelgeuse

Sun

Starry Colors

When you glance at the sky on a clear night, the stars look like tiny pinpoints of light. It's hard to tell one from another, but stars come in different sizes and colors.

The larger a star is, the cooler it tends to be. How do you measure a star's temperature? You can't go there with a big thermometer. But, you can use a star's color as a clue to its temperature. Red stars are the coolest. Yellow stars are of medium temperature. Bluish-white stars are the hottest. Our sun is a yellow, medium-sized star. The giant red star called Betelgeuse (BEE tul joos) is much bigger than the sun. Look at **Figure 23-13**. If this huge star were in the same place as our sun, it would swallow Mercury, Venus, Earth, and Mars.

The Lives of Stars

You've grown up and changed a lot since you were born. You've gone through several stages in your life, and you'll go through many more. Stars go through stages in their lives, just as people do.

Scientists theorize that stars begin their lives as huge clouds of gas and dust. The force of gravity causes the dust and gases to move closer together. When this happens, temperatures within the cloud begin to rise. A star is formed when this cloud gets so dense and hot that it starts producing energy.

Try at Home

Mini Lab

Modeling Constellations

1. Draw a dot pattern of a constellation on a piece of black construction paper. Choose a constellation from **Figure 23-12** or make your own pattern of stars.

2. With an adult's help, cut off the end of a round, empty box. You now have a cylinder with both ends open.

3. Place the box over the constellation. Trace around the rim of the box. Cut the paper along the traced circle.

4. Tape the paper to the end of the box. Using a pencil, carefully poke holes through the dots on the paper.

5. Place a flashlight inside the open end of the box. Darken the room and observe your constellation on the ceiling.

Analysis

1. Turn on the overhead light and view your constellation again. Can you still see it? Why or why not?

2. The stars are always in the sky, even during the day. Knowing this, explain how the overhead light is similar to our sun.

Figure 23-14 The life of a star depends greatly on its mass. **What happens to supergiants when their cores collapse?**

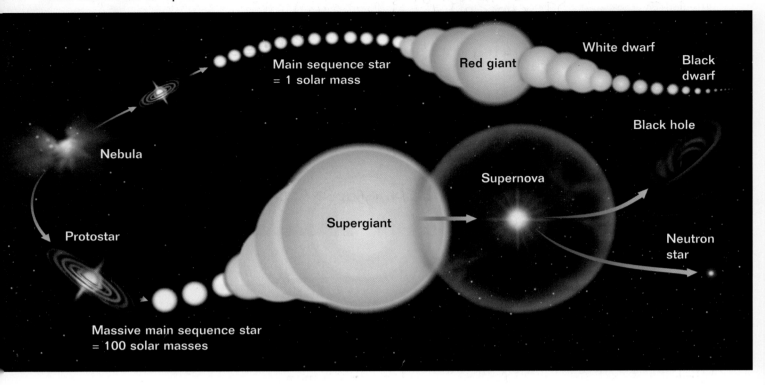

The stages a star goes through in its life depend on the star's size. When a medium-sized star like our sun uses up some of the gases in its center, it expands to become a giant. Our sun will become a giant in about 5 billion years. When the remaining gases are used up, our sun will contract to become a black dwarf. **Figure 23-14** illustrates the lives of stars.

Supergiants

When a huge star begins to use up the gases in its core, it becomes a supergiant. Over time, the core of a supergiant collapses. Then, the outer part of the star explodes and gets very bright. This event, shown in **Figure 23-15,** is called a supernova. For a few brief days, the supernova might shine more brightly than a whole galaxy. The dust and gases released by this explosion may eventually form other stars.

Meanwhile, the core of the supergiant is still around. It is now called a neutron star. If the core is massive enough, it may rapidly become a black hole. Black holes are so dense that light shone into them would disappear.

Figure 23-15 This photo shows the remains of the Vela supernova, located trillions of kilometers from Earth.

Galaxies

What do you see when you look at the night sky? If you live in a city, you may not see much. The glare from city lights makes it hard to see the stars. If you go to a dark place, far from the lights of towns and cities, you can see much more. In a dark area, with a powerful telescope, you might see dim clusters of stars grouped together. These clusters are galaxies (GAL uk seez). A **galaxy** is a group of stars, gas, and dust held together by gravity. **Figure 23-16** shows two differently shaped galaxies.

*inter*NET
CONNECTION

Explore the Glencoe Science Web Site at **www.glencoe.com/ sec/science/fl** for more information about telescopes.

Figure 23-16 Elliptical galaxies are shaped like footballs or spheres. Irregular galaxies have irregular shapes. **Which of the galaxies shown here is an irregular galaxy?**

Types of Galaxies

You know planets and stars differ from one another. Galaxies come in different shapes and sizes, too. The three major types of galaxies are elliptical, spiral, and irregular. Elliptical galaxies may be the most common. They're shaped like huge footballs or spheres. Spiral galaxies have arms radiating outward from their center. Irregular galaxies are just that—irregular. They come in all sorts of different shapes and can't be classified easily. Irregular galaxies are usually smaller and less common than other galaxies.

The Milky Way Galaxy

Which type of galaxy do you live in? Look at Figure 23-17. We live in the Milky Way Galaxy, a spiral galaxy. There are about 200 billion stars in the Milky Way Galaxy, including our sun. Just as Earth revolves around the sun, stars revolve around the centers of galaxies. Our sun revolves around the center of the Milky Way Galaxy about once every 240 million years.

A View from Within

We can see part of the Milky Way Galaxy as a band of light across the sky. But, we can't see the whole Milky Way Galaxy. Why not? Think about it. When you're sitting in your classroom, can you see the whole school? No, you are inside the school and can see only parts of it. Our view of the Milky Way Galaxy from Earth is like the view of your school from a classroom. We can see only parts of our galaxy because we are inside it.

PHYSICS
INTEGRATION

Galaxies in Motion
The Milky Way belongs to a cluster of galaxies called the Local Group. Scientists have determined that galaxies outside of the Local Group are moving away from us. Based on this, what can you infer about the size of the universe?

Reading Check

Why can't we see the whole Milky Way?

Figure 23-17 The Milky Way Galaxy has spiral arms made up of dust and gas. Its inner region is an area of densely packed stars.

Light-Years

Do you remember what you learned earlier about astronomical units, or AU? Distances between the planets are measured in AU. But, to measure distances between galaxies, we need an even bigger unit of measure. Scientists use light-years to measure distances between galaxies. A **light-year** is the distance light travels in a year—about 9.5 trillion km. Light travels so fast it could go around Earth seven times in one second.

Have you ever wished that you could travel back in time? In a way, that's what you're doing when you look at a galaxy. The galaxy might be millions of light-years away. So, the light that you see started on its journey long ago. You are seeing the galaxy as it was millions of years ago.

The Universe

Each galaxy probably has as many stars as the Milky Way Galaxy. Some may have more. And, there may be as many as 100 billion galaxies. All these galaxies, with all their countless stars, make up the universe. Look at **Figure 23-18.** In this great vastness of revolving solar systems, exploding supernovas, and star-filled galaxies is one small planet called Earth. If you think about how huge the universe is, Earth seems like a speck of dust. Yet, as far as we know, it's the only place where life exists.

Figure 23-18 Stars are forming in the Orion Nebula.

Section Assessment

1. What is a constellation? Name three constellations.
2. Describe the life of a medium-sized star such as the sun.
3. **Think Critically:** Some stars may no longer be in existence, but we still see them in the night sky. Why?
4. **Skill Builder**
   Making Models The Milky Way Galaxy is 100 000 light-years in diameter. How would you build a model of the Milky Way Galaxy? If you need help, refer to Making Models in the **Skill Handbook** on page 767.

Science Journal
Observe the stars in the night sky. In your Science Journal, draw the stars you observed. Now draw your own constellation based on those stars. Give your constellation a name. Why did you choose that name?

For a **preview** of this chapter, study this Reviewing Main Ideas before you read the chapter. After you have studied this chapter, you can use the Reviewing Main Ideas to **review** the chapter.

The Glencoe MindJogger, Audiocassettes, and CD-ROM provide additional opportunities for review.

Section

23-1 EARTH'S PLACE IN SPACE

The spinning of Earth on its axis is called **rotation.** This movement causes night and day. Earth also orbits around the sun in a regular, curved path. This movement is known as Earth's **revolution.** The moon moves, too, as it orbits Earth. The different positions of Earth, the sun, and the moon in space cause moon phases and **eclipses.** *Explain the difference between a lunar eclipse and a solar eclipse.*

Section

23-2 THE SOLAR SYSTEM

The solar system is made up of the nine planets and numerous other objects that orbit the sun. Planets are classified according to their distances from the sun. The inner planets—Mercury, Venus, Earth, and Mars—are closest to the sun. The outer planets—Jupiter, Saturn, Uranus, Neptune, and Pluto—are much farther away. Most of the outer planets are large, gas giants with rings and moons. *How is Pluto different from the other outer planets?*

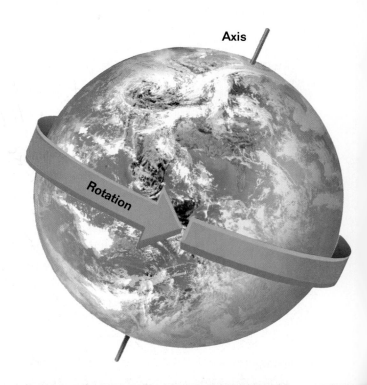

Axis

Rotation

Reading Check ✓

Use these words in sentences that do not relate to the sun, Earth, and moon: *rotation, revolution, waxing, waning, eclipse.*

Section

23-3 STARS

Constellations are groups of stars that form patterns in the sky. They are named after animals, objects, or people—real or imaginary. Although stars may look the same from Earth, they differ greatly in temperature, size, and color. Our sun, for instance, is a medium-sized, yellow star. *What color are the hottest stars? The coolest?*

GALAXIES

Galaxies are groups of stars, gas, and dust held together by gravity. The three main types of galaxies are elliptical, spiral, and irregular. We live in the Milky Way, a spiral galaxy. Distances between galaxies are measured in light-years. A **light-year** is the distance light travels in a year—about 9.5 trillion km. *Why do we need special units of measurement for studying distances in space?*

Chapter 23 Assessment

Using Vocabulary

a. astronomical unit   e. light-year
b. constellation   f. revolution
c. eclipse   g. rotation
d. galaxy   h. solar system

Each phrase below describes a science term from the list. Write the term that matches the phrase describing it.

1. the shadow produced by the moon or Earth passing in front of the sun
2. the motion of Earth that produces day and night
3. a group of stars, gas, and dust held together by gravity
4. a group of stars that forms a pattern in the sky
5. the movement of Earth around the sun

Checking Concepts

Choose the word or phrase that best answers the question.

6. What causes seasons?
   A) equator   C) moon
   B) oceans   D) tilt of Earth's axis

7. When the moon is waning, it appears to be what?
   A) growing larger   C) a full moon
   B) growing smaller   D) a new moon

8. An astronomical unit measures the distance from Earth to what?
   A) the moon
   B) the sun
   C) Mercury
   D) Pluto

9. Earth is which planet from the sun?
   A) first   C) third
   B) second   D) fourth

10. How many galaxies may be in the universe?
    A) 1 billion   C) 50 billion
    B) 10 billion   D) 100 billion

11. What does the spinning of Earth on its axis cause?
    A) night and day
    B) summer and winter
    C) moon phases
    D) solar eclipses

12. A light-year is used to measure distances between what?
    A) cities
    B) Earth and other planets
    C) galaxies
    D) oceans

13. How many planets are in the solar system?
    A) six
    B) seven
    C) eight
    D) nine

14. During a solar eclipse, the shadow of what object travels across part of Earth?
    A) the moon
    B) the sun
    C) Mars
    D) a comet

15. If the core of a neutron star is massive enough, what does it become?
    A) a galaxy
    B) a black hole
    C) a black dwarf
    D) a superstar

Thinking Critically

16. What conditions on Earth allow life to thrive?

17. Which of the planets in our solar system seems most like Earth? Which seems most different? Explain your answers, using facts about the planets.

18. How might a scientist predict the day and time of a solar eclipse?

19. Throughout history, different groups of people have viewed the constellations in different ways. Infer why this is true.

20. Which of the moon's motions are real? Which are apparent? Explain why each occurs.

Developing Skills

If you need help, refer to the **Skill Handbook**.

21. Making and Using Tables: Research the size, period of rotation, and period of revolution for each planet. Show this information in a table. How do tables help us to better understand information?

22. Comparing and Contrasting: Compare the inner planets with the outer planets. How are they alike? How are they different?

23. Making a Model: Based on what you have learned about the sun, the moon, and Earth, make a model of a lunar or a solar eclipse.

24. Sequencing: Sequence the following terms in order of smallest object to largest group: galaxy, inner planets, solar system, universe, Earth.

Solar System Information

Planet	Diameter (km)	Period of rotation	Period of revolution
Mercury	4878	59 d	87.97 d
Venus	12 104	243 d	224.70 d
Earth	12 756	24 h	365.26 d
Mars	6794	24.5 h	686.98 d
Jupiter	142 796	10 h	11.86 y
Saturn	120 660	10.4 h	29.46 y
Uranus	51 810	16.8 h	84.04 y
Neptune	49 528	16 h	164.79 y
Pluto	2290	7 d	248.53 y

THE PRINCETON REVIEW

Test-Taking Tip

Get to the Root of Things If you don't know a word's meaning, you can still get an idea of its meaning if you focus on its roots, prefixes, and suffixes. For instance, words that start with *non-*, *un-*, *dis-*, and *in-* generally reverse what the rest of the word means.

Test Practice

Use these questions to test your Science Proficiency.

1. As the moon revolves around Earth, it appears to change shape. What determines the moon shape you see on any given night?
A) the speed of Earth's rotation
B) the positions of the sun, the moon, and Earth in space
C) the distance between the moon and the sun
D) the tilt of Earth's axis

2. Stars begin their lives as huge clouds of gas and dust. Which statement **BEST** describes our sun?
A) Our sun will become a supernova in 2 billion years.
B) Our sun is cooler than the red giant star, Betelgeuse.
C) Our sun is a medium-sized, yellow star.
D) Our sun was formed when dust and gas came together and froze.

Appendices

Appendix A

Safety in the Science Classroom

1. Always obtain your teacher's permission to begin an investigation.

2. Study the procedure. If you have questions, ask your teacher. Be sure you understand any safety symbols shown on the page.

3. Use the safety equipment provided for you. Goggles and a safety apron should be worn during an investigation.

4. Always slant test tubes away from yourself and others when heating them.

5. Never eat or drink in the lab, and never use lab glassware as food or drink containers. Never inhale chemicals. Do not taste any substances or draw any material into a tube with your mouth.

6. If you spill any chemical, wash it off immediately with water. Report the spill immediately to your teacher.

7. Know the location and proper use of the fire extinguisher, safety shower, fire blanket, first aid kit, and fire alarm.

8. Keep all materials away from open flames. Tie back long hair and loose clothing.

9. If a fire should break out in the classroom, or if your clothing should catch fire, smother it with the fire blanket or a coat, or get under a safety shower. NEVER RUN.

10. Report any accident or injury, no matter how small, to your teacher.

Follow these procedures as you clean up your work area.

1. Turn off the water and gas. Disconnect electrical devices.

2. Return all materials to their proper places.

3. Dispose of chemicals and other materials as directed by your teacher. Place broken glass and solid substances in the proper containers. Never discard materials in the sink.

4. Clean your work area.

5. Wash your hands thoroughly after working in the laboratory.

Table A-1

First Aid	
Injury	**Safe Response**
Burns	Apply cold water. Call your teacher immediately.
Cuts and bruises	Stop any bleeding by applying direct pressure. Cover cuts with a clean dressing. Apply cold compresses to bruises. Call your teacher immediately.
Fainting	Leave the person lying down. Loosen any tight clothing and keep crowds away. Call your teacher immediately.
Foreign matter in eye	Flush with plenty of water. Use eyewash bottle or fountain.
Poisoning	Note the suspected poisoning agent and call your teacher immediately.
Any spills on skin	Flush with large amounts of water or use safety shower. Call your teacher immediately.

Appendix
B

SI/Metric to English Conversions

	When you want to convert:	To:	Multiply by:
Length	inches	centimeters	2.54
	centimeters	inches	0.39
	feet	meters	0.30
	meters	feet	3.28
	yards	meters	0.91
	meters	yards	1.09
	miles	kilometers	1.61
	kilometers	miles	0.62
Mass and Weight*	ounces	grams	28.35
	grams	ounces	0.04
	pounds	kilograms	0.45
	kilograms	pounds	2.2
	tons (short)	tonnes (metric tons)	0.91
	tonnes (metric tons)	tons (short)	1.10
	pounds	newtons	4.45
	newtons	pounds	0.23
Volume	cubic inches	cubic centimeters	16.39
	cubic centimeters	cubic inches	0.06
	cubic feet	cubic meters	0.03
	cubic meters	cubic feet	35.30
	liters	quarts	1.06
	liters	gallons	0.26
	gallons	liters	3.78
Area	square inches	square centimeters	6.45
	square centimeters	square inches	0.16
	square feet	square meters	0.09
	square meters	square feet	10.76
	square miles	square kilometers	2.59
	square kilometers	square miles	0.39
	hectares	acres	2.47
	acres	hectares	0.40
Temperature	Fahrenheit	$5/9 \, (°F - 32)$ =	Celsius
	Celsius	$9/5 \, (°C) + 32$ =	Fahrenheit

*Weight as measured in standard Earth gravity

Appendix
C

SI Units of Measurement

Table C-1

SI Base Units					
Measurement	**Unit**	**Symbol**	**Measurement**	**Unit**	**Symbol**
length	meter	m	temperature	kelvin	K
mass	kilogram	kg	amount of substance	mole	mol
time	second	s			

Table C-2

Units Derived from SI Base Units		
Measurement	**Unit**	**Symbol**
energy	joule	J
force	newton	N
frequency	hertz	Hz
potential difference	volt	V
power	watt	W
pressure	pascal	Pa

Table C-3

Common SI Prefixes					
Prefix	**Symbol**	**Multiplier**	**Prefix**	**Symbol**	**Multiplier**
Greater than 1			Less than 1		
mega-	M	1 000 000	*deci-*	d	0.1
kilo-	k	1 000	*centi-*	c	0.01
hecto-	h	100	*milli-*	m	0.001
deca-	da	10	*micro-*	μ	0.000 001

Care and Use of a Microscope

Eyepiece Contains a magnifying lens you look through

Arm Supports the body tube

Low-power objective Contains the lens with low-power magnification

Stage clips Hold the microscope slide in place

Coarse adjustment Focuses the image under low power

Fine adjustment Sharpens the image under high and low magnification

Body tube Connects the eyepiece to the revolving nosepiece

Revolving nosepiece Holds and turns the objectives into viewing position

High-power objective Contains the lens with the highest magnification

Stage Supports the microscope slide

Light source Allows light to reflect upward through the diaphragm, the specimen, and the lenses

Base Provides support for the microscope

Care of a Microscope

1. Always carry the microscope holding the arm with one hand and supporting the base with the other hand.

2. Don't touch the lenses with your fingers.

3. Never lower the coarse adjustment knob when looking through the eyepiece lens.

4. Always focus first with the low-power objective.

5. Don't use the coarse adjustment knob when the high-power objective is in place.

6. Store the microscope covered.

Using a Microscope

1. Place the microscope on a flat surface that is clear of objects. The arm should be toward you.

2. Look through the eyepiece. Adjust the diaphragm so that light comes through the opening in the stage.

3. Place a slide on the stage so that the specimen is in the field of view. Hold it firmly in place by using the stage clips.

4. Always focus first with the coarse adjustment and the low-power objective lens. Once the object is in focus on low power, turn the nosepiece until the high-power objective is in place. Use ONLY the fine adjustment to focus with the high-power objective lens.

Making a Wet-Mount Slide

1. Carefully place the item you want to look at in the center of a clean, glass slide. Make sure the sample is thin enough for light to pass through.

2. Use a dropper to place one or two drops of water on the sample.

3. Hold a clean coverslip by the edges and place it at one edge of the drop of water. Slowly lower the coverslip onto the drop of water until it lies flat.

4. If you have too much water or a lot of air bubbles, touch the edge of a paper towel to the edge of the coverslip to draw off extra water and force out air.

Appendix E

Diversity of Life: Classification of Living Organisms

Scientists use a six-kingdom system of classification of organisms. In this system, there are two kingdoms of organisms, Kingdoms Archaebacteria and Eubacteria, which contain organisms that do not have a nucleus and lack membrane-bound structures in the cytoplasm of their cells. The members of the other four kingdoms have cells which contain a nucleus and structures in the cytoplasm that are surrounded by membranes. These kingdoms are Kingdom Protista, Kingdom Fungi, the Kingdom Plantae, and the Kingdom Animalia.

Kingdom Archaebacteria

One-celled prokaryotes; absorb food from surroundings or make their own food by chemosynthesis; found in extremely harsh environments including salt ponds, hot springs, swamps, and deep-sea hydrothermal vents.

Kingdom Eubacteria

Cyanobacteria one-celled prokaryotes; make their own food; contain chlorophyll; some species form colonies; most are blue-green

Bacteria one-celled prokaryotes; most absorb food from their surroundings; some are photosynthetic; many are parasites; round, spiral, or rod-shaped

Kingdom Protista

Phylum Euglenophyta one-celled; can photosynthesize or take in food; most have one flagellum; euglenoids

Phylum Bacillariophyta one-celled; make their own food through photosynthesis; have unique double shells made of silica; diatoms

Phylum Dinoflagellata one-celled; make their own food through photosynthesis; contain red pigments; have two flagella; dinoflagellates

Phylum Chlorophyta one-celled, many-celled, or colonies; contain chlorophyll; make their own food; live on land, in fresh water, or salt water; green algae

Phylum Rhodophyta most are many-celled; photosynthetic; contain red pigments; most live in deep saltwater environments; red algae

Phylum Phaeophyta most are many-celled; photosynthetic; contain brown pigments; most live in saltwater environments; brown algae

Phylum Foraminifera many-celled; take in food; primarily marine; shells constructed of calcium carbonate, or made from grains of sand; forams

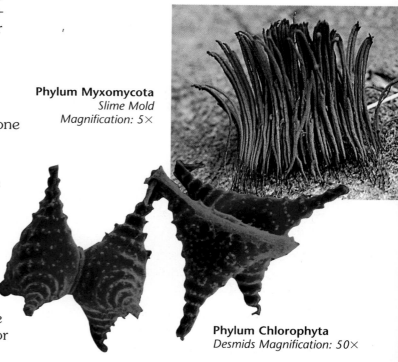

Phylum Myxomycota
Slime Mold
Magnification: 5×

Phylum Chlorophyta
Desmids Magnification: 50×

Phylum Rhizopoda one-celled; take in food; move by means of pseudopods; free-living or parasitic; amoebas

Phylum Zoomastigina one-celled; take in food; have one or more flagella; free-living or parasitic; zoomastigotes

Phylum Ciliophora one-celled; take in food; have large numbers of cilia; ciliates

Phylum Sporozoa one-celled; take in food; no means of movement; parasites in animals; sporozoans

Phylum Myxomycota and Acrasiomycota: one- or many-celled; absorb food; change form during life cycle; cellular and plasmodial slime molds

Phylum Oomycota many-celled; live in fresh or salt water; are either parasites or decomposers; water molds, rusts and downy mildews

Kingdom Fungi

Phylum Zygomycota many-celled; absorb food; spores are produced in sporangia; zygote fungi; bread mold

Phylum Ascomycota one- and many-celled; absorb food; spores produced in asci; sac fungi; yeast

Phylum Basidiomycota many-celled; absorb food; spores produced in basidia; club fungi; mushrooms

Phylum Deuteromycota: members with unknown reproductive structures; imperfect fungi; penicillin

Lichens organisms formed by symbiotic relationship between an ascomycote or a basidiomycote and green alga or cyanobacterium

Kingdom Plantae
Non-seed Plants

Division Bryophyta nonvascular plants; reproduce by spores produced in capsules; many-celled; green; grow in moist land environments; mosses and liverworts

Division Lycophyta many-celled vascular plants; spores produced in conelike structures; live on land; are photosynthetic; club mosses

Division Sphenophyta vascular plants; ribbed and jointed stems; scalelike leaves; spores produced in conelike structures; horsetails

Division Pterophyta vascular plants; leaves called fronds; spores produced in clusters of sporangia called sori; live on land or in water; ferns

Division Bryophyta
Liverwort

Lichens
British soldier lichen Magnification: 3×

Appendix E

Seed Plants

Division Ginkgophyta: deciduous gymnosperms; only one living species; fan-shaped leaves with branching veins; reproduces with seeds; ginkgos

Division Cycadophyta: palmlike gymnosperms; large featherlike leaves; produce seeds in cones; cycads

Division Coniferophyta: deciduous or evergreen gymnosperms; trees or shrubs; needlelike or scalelike leaves; seeds produced in cones; conifers

Division Gnetophyta: shrubs or woody vines; seeds produced in cones; division contains only three genera; gnetum

Division Anthophyta: dominant group of plants; ovules protected in an ovary; sperm carried to ovules by pollen tube; produce flowers and seeds in fruits; flowering plants

Kingdom Animalia

Phylum Porifera: aquatic organisms that lack true tissues and organs; they are asymmetrical and sessile; sponges

Phylum Cnidaria: radially symmetrical organisms; have a digestive cavity with one opening; most have tentacles armed with stinging cells; live in aquatic environments singly or in colonies; includes jellyfish, corals, hydra, and sea anemones

Phylum Platyhelminthes: bilaterally symmetrical worms; have flattened bodies; digestive system has one opening; parasitic and free-living species; flatworms

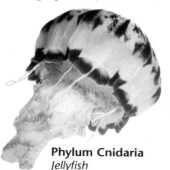

Phylum Cnidaria
Jellyfish

Phylum Arthropoda
Orb Weaver Spider

Phylum Arthropoda
Hermit Crab

Division Coniferophyta
Pine cone

Division Anthophyta
Strawberry Blossoms

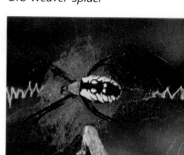

Phylum Mollusca
Florida Fighting Conch

Division Anthophyta
Strawberries

Phylum Annelida
*Sabellid Worms
Feather Duster*

Phylum Nematoda: round, bilaterally symmetrical body; digestive system with two openings; many parasitic forms but mostly free-living; roundworms

Phylum Mollusca: soft-bodied animals, many with a hard shell; a mantle covers the soft body; aquatic and terrestrial species; includes clams, snails, squid, and octopuses

Phylum Annelida: bilaterally symmetrical worms; have round, segmented bodies; terrestrial and aquatic species; includes earthworms, leeches, and marine polychaetes

Phylum Arthropoda: largest phylum of organisms; have segmented bodies; pairs of jointed appendages; have hard exoskeletons; terrestrial and aquatic species; includes insects, crustaceans, spiders, and horseshoe crabs

Phylum Echinodermata: marine organisms; have spiny or leathery skin; water-vascular system with tube feet; radial symmetry; includes sea stars, sand dollars, and sea urchins

Phylum Chordata: organisms with internal skeletons; specialized body systems; paired appendages; all at some time have a notochord, dorsal nerve cord, gill slits, and a tail; include fish, amphibians, reptiles, birds, and mammals

Phylum Arthropoda
Giant Swallowtail Butterfly

Phylum Echinodermata
Blood Sea Star and Red Sea Urchin

Phylum Chordata
Eastern Box Turtle

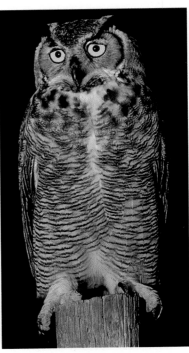

Phylum Chordata
Lemon Butterfly fish

Phylum Chordata
Great Horned Owl

Appendix F

Minerals

Mineral (formula)	Color	Streak	Hardness	Breakage pattern	Uses and other properties
graphite (C)	black to gray	black to gray	1–1.5	basal cleavage (scales)	pencil lead, lubricants for locks, rods to control some small nuclear reactions, battery poles
galena (PbS)	gray	gray to black	2.5	cubic cleavage perfect	source of lead, used in pipes, shields for X rays, fishing equipment sinkers
hematite (Fe_2O_3)	black or reddish brown	reddish brown	5.5–6.5	irregular fracture	source of iron; converted to "pig" iron, made into steel
magnetite (Fe_3O_4)	black	black	6	conchoidal fracture	source of iron, naturally magnetic, called lodestone
pyrite (FeS_2)	light, brassy, yellow	greenish black	6–6.5	uneven fracture	source of iron, "fool's gold"
talc ($Mg_3Si_4O_{10}(OH)_2$)	white greenish	white	1	cleavage in one direction	used for talcum powder, sculptures, paper, and tabletops
gypsum ($CaSO_4 \cdot 2H_2O$)	colorless, gray, white brown	white	2	basal cleavage	used in plaster of paris and dry wall for building construction
sphalerite (ZnS)	brown, reddish brown, greenish	light to dark brown	3.5–4	cleavage in six directions	main ore of zinc; used in paints, dyes and medicine
muscovite ($KAl_3Si_3O_{10}(OH)_2$)	white, light gray, yellow, rose, green	colorless	2–2.5	basal cleavage	occurs in large flexible plates; used as an insulator in electrical equipment, lubricant
biotite ($K(Mg, Fe)_3(AlSi_3O_{10})(OH)_2$)	black to dark brown	colorless	2.5–3	basal cleavage	occurs in large flexible plates
halite (NaCl)	colorless, red, white, blue	colorless	2.5	cubic cleavage	salt; soluble in water; a preservative

Appendix F

Minerals

Mineral (formula)	Color	Streak	Hardness	Breakage pattern	Uses and other properties
calcite ($CaCO_3$)	colorless, white, pale blue	colorless, white	3	cleavage in three directions	fizzes when HCl is added; used in cements and other building materials
dolomite ($CaMg(CO_3)_2$)	colorless, white, pink green, gray black	white	3.5–4	cleavage in three directions	concrete and cement; used as an ornamental building stone
fluorite (CaF_2)	colorless, white, blue green, red yellow, purple	colorless	4	cleavage in four directions	used in the manufacture of optical equipment; glows under ultraviolet light
hornblende ($(CaNa)_{2-3}(Mg, Al,Fe)_5(Al,Si)_2 Si_6O_{22}(OH)_2$	green to black	gray to white	5–6	cleavage in two directions	will transmit light on thin edges; 6-sided cross section
feldspar ($KAlSi_3O_8$) ($NaAlSi_3O_8$) ($CaAl_2Si_2O_8$)	colorless, white to gray, green	colorless	6	two cleavage planes meet at ~90° angle	used in the manufacture of ceramics
augite ($(Ca, Na) (Mg, Fe, Al) (Al, Si)_2O_6)$	black	colorless	6	cleavage in two directions	square or 8-sided cross section
olivine ($(Mg, Fe)_2 SiO_4)$	olive, green	none	6.5–7	conchoidal fracture	gemstones, refractory sand
quartz (SiO_2)	colorless, various colors	none	7	conchoidal fracture	used in glass manufacture, electronic equipment, radios, computers, watches, gemstones

Appendix

G

Rocks

Rock Type	Rock Name	Characteristics
Igneous (intrusive)	Granite	Large mineral grains of quartz, feldspar, hornblende, and mica. Usually light in color.
	Diorite	Large mineral grains of feldspar, hornblende, mica. Less quartz than granite. Intermediate in color.
	Gabbro	Large mineral grains of feldspar, hornblende, augite, olivine, and mica. No quartz. Dark in color.
Igneous (extrusive)	Rhyolite	Small mineral grains of quartz, feldspar, hornblende, and mica or no visible grains. Light in color.
	Andesite	Small mineral grains of feldspar, hornblende, mica or no visible grains. Less quartz than rhyolite. Intermediate in color.
	Basalt	Small mineral grains of feldspar, hornblende, augite, olivine, mica or no visible grains. No quartz. Dark in color.
	Obsidian	Glassy texture. No visible grains. Volcanic glass. Fracture looks like broken glass.
	Pumice	Frothy texture. Floats. Usually light in color.
Sedimentary (detrital)	Conglomerate	Coarse-grained. Gravel or pebble-sized grains.
	Sandstone	Sand-sized grains 1/16 to 2 mm in size.
	Siltstone	Grains are smaller than sand but larger than clay.
	Shale	Smallest grains. Usually dark in color.
Sedimentary (chemical or biochemical)	Limestone	Major mineral is calcite. Usually forms in oceans, lakes, rivers, and caves. Often contains fossils.
	Coal	Occurs in swampy, low-lying areas. Compacted layers of organic material, mainly plant remains.
Sedimentary (chemical)	Rock Salt	Commonly forms by the evaporation of seawater.
Metamorphic (foliated)	Gneiss	Well-developed banding because of alternating layers of different minerals, usually of different colors. Common parent rock is granite.
	Schist	Well-defined parallel arrangement of flat, sheet-like minerals, mainly micas. Common parent rocks are shale, phyllite.
	Phyllite	Shiny or silky appearance. May look wrinkled. Common parent rocks are shale, slate.
	Slate	Harder, denser, and shinier than shale. Common parent rock is shale.
Metamorphic (non-foliated)	Marble	Interlocking calcite or dolomite crystals. Common parent rock is limestone.
	Soapstone	Composed mainly of the mineral talc. Soft with a greasy feel.
	Quartzite	Hard and well cemented with interlocking quartz crystals. Common parent rock is sandstone.

Topographic Map Symbols

Primary highway, hard surface

Secondary highway, hard surface

Light-duty road, hard or
Improved surface

Unimproved road

Railroad: single track and
multiple track

Railroads in juxtaposition

Buildings

Schools, church, and cemetery

Buildings (barn, warehouse, etc)

Wells other than water
(labeled as to type)

Tanks: oil, water, etc.
(labeled only if water)

Located or landmark object;
windmill

Open pit, mine, or quarry;
prospect

Marsh (swamp)

Wooded marsh

Woods or brushwood

Vineyard
Land subject to controlled
inundation

Submerged marsh

Mangrove

Orchard

Scrub

Urban area

Spot elevation   ×7369

Water elevation   670

Index contour

Supplementary contour

Intermediate contour

Depression contours

Boundaries: National

    State

    County, parish, municipal

    Civil township, precinct,
    town, barrio

    Incorporated city, village,
    town, hamlet

    Reservation, National or State

    Small park, cemetery,
    airport, etc.

    Land grant

Township or range line,
United States land survey

Township or range line,
approximate location

Perennial streams

Elevated aqueduct

Water well and spring

Small rapids

Large rapids

Intermittent lake

Intermittent streams

Aqueduct tunnel

Glacier

Small falls

Large falls

Dry lake bed

Appendix
I

Weather Map Symbols

Sample Plotted Report at Each Station

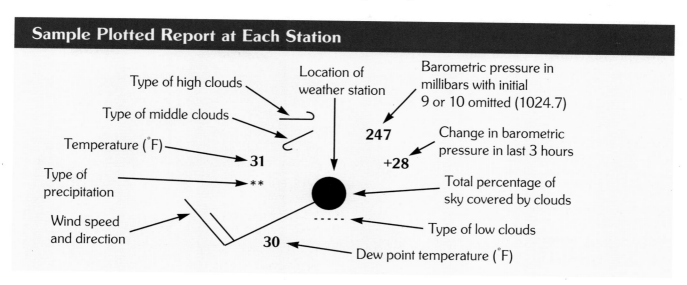

- Type of high clouds
- Location of weather station
- Barometric pressure in millibars with initial 9 or 10 omitted (1024.7) — **247**
- Type of middle clouds
- Change in barometric pressure in last 3 hours — **+28**
- Temperature (°F) — **31**
- Type of precipitation — ******
- Total percentage of sky covered by clouds
- Wind speed and direction
- Type of low clouds
- Dew point temperature (°F) — **30**

Sample Plotted Report at Each Station

Precipitation		Wind speed and direction		Sky coverage		Some types of high clouds	
≡	Fog	◯	0 knots; calm	◯	No cover		Scattered cirrus
★	Snow		1–2 knots	◐	1/10 or less		Dense cirrus in patches
●	Rain		3–7 knots	◔	2/10 to 3/10		Veil of cirrus covering entire sky
⊺κ	Thunder-storm		8–12 knots	◑	4/10		Cirrus not covering entire sky
,	Drizzle		13–17 knots	◐	1/2		
			18–22 knots	◕	6/10		
▽	Showers		23–27 knots	◕	7/10		
			48–52 knots	◑	Overcast with openings		
		1 knot = 1.852 km/h		●	Complete overcast		

Some types of middle clouds		Some types of low clouds		Fronts and pressure systems	
/	Thin altostratus layer	⌒	Cumulus of fair weather	(H) or High	Center of high-or
∥	Thick altostratus layer	⌣	Stratocumulus	(L) or Low	low-pressure system
/	Thin altostratus in patches	-----	Fractocumulus of bad weather	▲▲▲▲	Cold front
/	Thin altostratus in bands	—	Stratus of fair weather	●●●●	Warm Front
				▲●▲●	Occluded front
				●▲●▲	Stationary front

Appendix J

Star Charts

Shown here are star charts for viewing stars in the northern hemisphere during the four different seasons. These charts are drawn from the night sky at about 35° north latitude, but they can be used for most locations in the northern hemisphere. The lines on the charts outline major constellations. The dense band of stars is the Milky Way. To use, hold the chart vertically, with the direction you are facing at the bottom of the map.

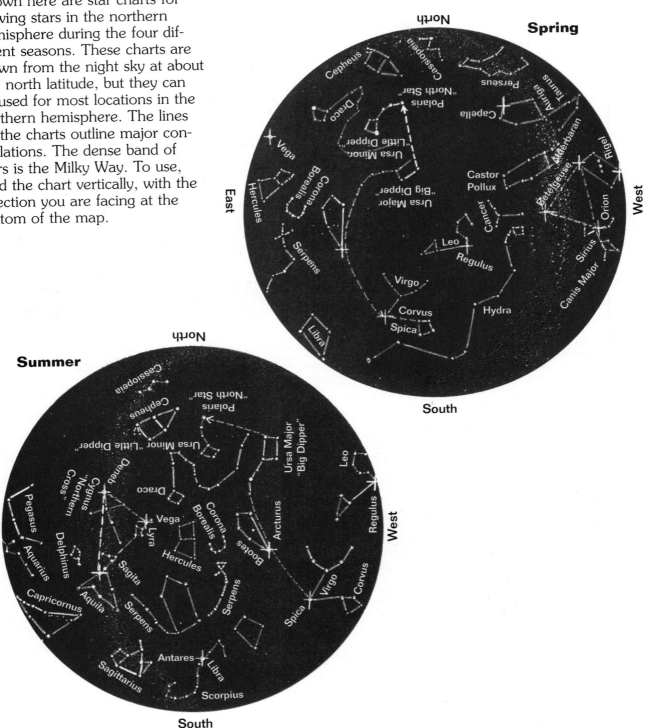

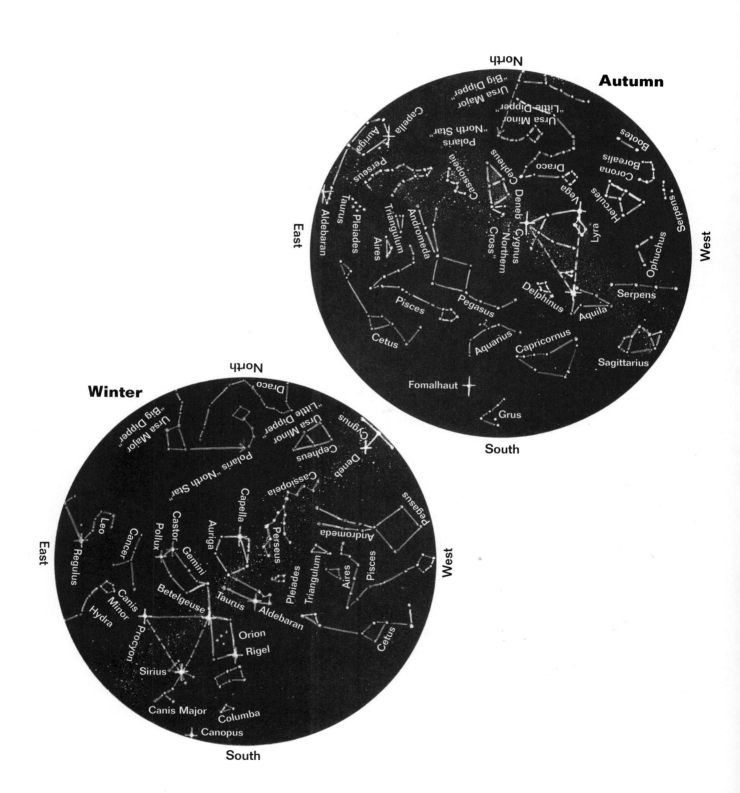

Skill Handbook

Table of Contents

Organizing Information

Communicating

The communication of ideas is an important part of our everyday lives. Whether reading a book, writing a letter, or watching a television program, people everywhere are expressing opinions and sharing information with one another. Writing in your Science Journal allows you to express your opinions and demonstrate your knowledge of the information presented on a subject. When writing, keep in mind the purpose of the assignment and the audience with which you are communicating.

Examples Science Journal assignments vary greatly. They may ask you to take a viewpoint other than your own; perhaps you will be a scientist, a TV reporter, or a committee member of a local environmental group. Maybe you will be expressing your opinions to a member of Congress, a doctor, or to the editor of your local newspaper, as shown in **Figure 1.** Sometimes, Science Journal writing may allow you to summarize information in the form of an outline, a letter, or in a paragraph.

Figure 1 A Science Journal entry

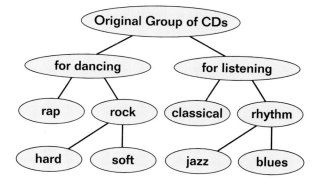

Figure 2 Classifying CDs

Classifying

You may not realize it, but you make things orderly in the world around you. If you hang your shirts together in the closet or if your favorite CDs are stacked together, you have used the skill of classifying.

Classifying is the process of sorting objects or events into groups based on common features. When classifying, first observe the objects or events to be classified. Then, select one feature that is shared by some members in the group, but not by all. Place those members that share that feature into a subgroup. You can classify members into smaller and smaller subgroups based on characteristics.

Remember, when you classify, you are grouping objects or events for a purpose. Keep your purpose in mind as you select the features to form groups and subgroups.

Example How would you classify a collection of CDs? As shown in **Figure 2,** you might classify those you like to dance to in one subgroup and CDs you like to listen to in the next subgroup. The CDs you like to dance to could be subdivided into a rap subgroup and a rock subgroup. Note that for each feature selected, each CD fits into only one subgroup. You would keep selecting features until all the CDs are classified. **Figure 2** shows one possible classification.

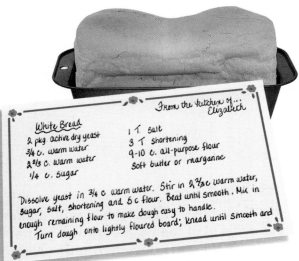

Figure 3 A recipe for bread contains sequenced instructions

Sequencing

A sequence is an arrangement of things or events in a particular order. When you are asked to sequence objects or events within a group, figure out what comes first, then think about what should come second. Continue to choose objects or events until all of the objects you started out with are in order. Then, go back over the sequence to make sure each thing or event in your sequence logically leads to the next.

Example A sequence with which you are most familiar is the use of alphabetical order. Another example of sequence would be the steps in a recipe, as shown in **Figure 3.** Think about baking bread. Steps in the recipe have to be followed in order for the bread to turn out right.

Concept Mapping

If you were taking an automobile trip, you would probably take along a road map. The road map shows your location, your destination, and other places along the way. By looking at the map and finding where you are, you can begin to understand where you are in relation to other locations on the map.

A concept map is similar to a road map. But, a concept map shows relationships among ideas (or concepts) rather than places. A concept map is a diagram that visually shows how concepts are related. Because the concept map shows relationships among ideas, it can make the meanings of ideas and terms clear, and help you understand better what you are studying.

There is usually not one correct way to create a concept map. As you construct one type of map, you may discover other ways to construct the map that show the

Figure 4 Network tree describing U.S. currency

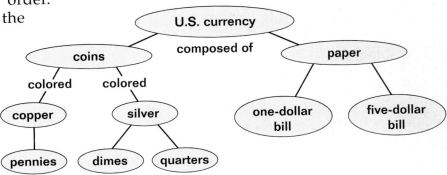

relationships between concepts in a better way. If you do discover what you think is a better way to create a concept map, go ahead and use the new one. Overall, concept maps are useful for breaking a big concept down into smaller parts, making learning easier.

Examples

Network Tree Look at the concept map about U.S. currency in **Figure 4.** This is called a network tree. Notice how some words are in ovals while others are written across connecting lines. The words inside the ovals are science concepts. The lines in the map show related concepts. The words written on the lines describe the relationships between concepts.

When you are asked to construct a network tree, write down the topic and list the major concepts related to that topic on a piece of paper. Then look at your list and begin to put them in order from general to specific. Branch the related concepts from the major concept and describe the relationships on the lines. Continue to write the more specific concepts. Write the relationships between the concepts on the lines until all concepts are mapped. Examine the concept map for relationships that cross branches, and add them to the concept map.

Events Chain An events chain is another type of concept map. An events chain map, such as the one describing a typical morning routine in **Figure 5,** is used to describe ideas in order. In science, an events chain can be used to describe a sequence of events, the steps in a procedure, or the stages of a process.

When making an events chain, first find the one event that starts the chain. This

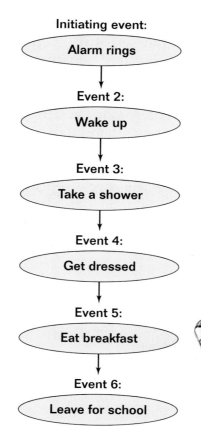

Initiating event:

Alarm rings

Event 2:

Wake up

Event 3:

Take a shower

Event 4:

Get dressed

Event 5:

Eat breakfast

Event 6:

Leave for school

Figure 5 Events chain of a typical morning routine

event is called the initiating event. Then, find the next event in the chain and continue until you reach an outcome. Suppose you are asked to describe what happens when your alarm rings. An events chain map describing the steps might look like **Figure 5.** Notice that connecting words are not necessary in an events chain.

Science Skill Handbook

Cycle Map A cycle concept map is a special type of events chain map. In a cycle concept map, the series of events does not produce a final outcome. Instead, the last event in the chain relates back to the initiating event.

As in the events chain map, you first decide on an initiating event and then list each event in order. Because there is no outcome and the last event relates back to the initiating event, the cycle repeats itself. Look at the cycle map describing the relationship between day and night in **Figure 6.**

Figure 7 Spider map about homework.

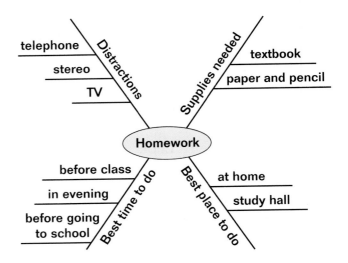

Figure 6 Cycle map of day and night.

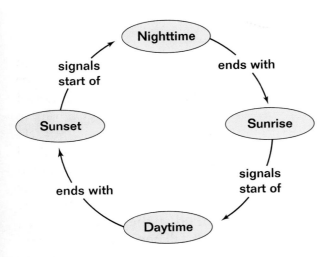

Spider Map A fourth type of concept map is the spider map. This is a map that you can use for brainstorming. Once you have a central idea, you may find you have a jumble of ideas that relate to it, but are not necessarily clearly related to each other. As illustrated by the homework spider map in **Figure 7,** by writing these ideas outside the main concept, you may begin to separate and group unrelated terms so that they become more useful.

Making and Using Tables

Browse through your textbook and you will notice tables in the text and in the activities. In a table, data or information are arranged in a way that makes it easier for you to understand. Activity tables help organize the data you collect during an activity so that results can be interpreted.

Example Most tables have a title. At a glance, the title tells you what the table is about. A table is divided into columns and rows. The first column lists the items to be compared. In **Figure 8,** the collection of recyclable materials is being compared in a table. The row across the top lists the specific characteristics being compared. Within the grid of the table, the collected data are recorded.

What is the title of the table in **Figure 8?** The title is "Recycled Materials." What is being compared? The different materials being recycled and on which days they are recycled.

Making Tables To make a table, list the items to be compared down in columns and the characteristics to be compared across in rows. The table in

Science Skill Handbook

Figure 8 Table of recycled materials

Recycled Materials			
Day of Week	Paper (kg)	Aluminum (kg)	Plastic (kg)
Mon.	4.0	2.0	0.5
Wed.	3.5	1.5	0.5
Fri.	3.0	1.0	1.5

Figure 8 compares the mass of recycled materials collected by a class. On Monday, students turned in 4.0 kg of paper, 2.0 kg of aluminum, and 0.5 kg of plastic. On Wednesday, they turned in 3.5 kg of paper, 1.5 kg of aluminum, and 0.5 kg of plastic. On Friday, the totals were 3.0 kg of paper, 1.0 kg of aluminum, and 1.5 kg of plastic.

Using Tables How much plastic, in kilograms, is being recycled on Wednesday? Locate the column labeled "Plastic (kg)" and the row "Wed." The data in the box where the column and row intersect is the answer. Did you answer "0.5"? How much aluminum, in kilograms, is being recycled on Friday? If you answered "1.0," you understand how to use the parts of the table.

Making and Using Graphs

After scientists organize data in tables, they may display the data in a graph. A graph is a diagram that shows the relationship of one variable to another. A graph makes interpretation and analysis of data easier. There are three basic types of graphs used in science—the line graph, the bar graph, and the circle graph.

Examples

Line Graphs A line graph is used to show the relationship between two variables. The variables being compared go on two axes of the graph. The independent variable always goes on the horizontal axis, called the x-axis. The dependent variable always goes on the vertical axis, called the y-axis.

Suppose your class started to record the amount of materials they collected in one week for their school to recycle. The collected information is shown in **Figure 9.**

You could make a graph of the materials collected over the three days of the school week. The three weekdays are the independent variables and are placed on the x-axis of your graph. The amount of materials collected is the dependent variable and would go on the y-axis.

After drawing your axes, label each with a scale. The x-axis lists the three weekdays. To make a scale of the amount of materials collected on the y-axis, look at the data values. Because the lowest amount collected was 1.0 and the highest was 5.0, you will have to start numbering at least at 1.0 and go through 5.0. You decide to start numbering at 0 and number by ones through 6.0, as shown in **Figure 10.**

Next, plot the data points for collected paper. The first pair of data you want to plot is Monday and 5.0 kg of paper.

Figure 9 Amount of recyclable materials collected during one week

Materials Collected During Week		
Day of Week	Paper (kg)	Aluminum (kg)
Mon.	5.0	4.0
Wed.	4.0	1.0
Fri.	2.5	2.0

Science Skill Handbook

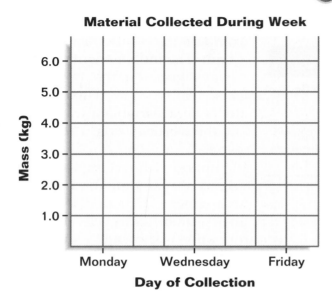

Material Collected During Week

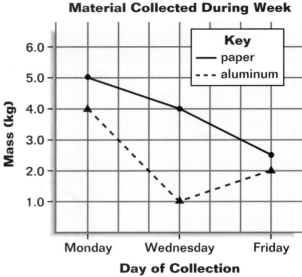

Material Collected During Week

Figure 10 Graph outline for material collected during week

Figure 11 Line graph of materials collected during week

Locate "Monday" on the *x*-axis and locate "5.0" on the *y*-axis. Where an imaginary vertical line from the *x*-axis and an imaginary horizontal line from the *y*-axis would meet, place the first data point. Place the other data points the same way. After all the points are plotted, connect them with the best smooth curve. Repeat this procedure for the data points for aluminum. Use continuous and dashed lines to distinguish the two line graphs. The resulting graph should look like **Figure 11.**

Bar Graphs Bar graphs are similar to line graphs. They compare data that do not continuously change. In a bar graph, vertical bars show the relationships among data.

To make a bar graph, set up the *x*-axis and *y*-axis as you did for the line graph. The data is plotted by drawing vertical bars from the *x*-axis up to a point where the *y*-axis would meet the bar if it were extended.

Look at the bar graph in **Figure 12** comparing the mass of aluminum collected

over three weekdays. The *x*-axis is the days on which the aluminum was collected. The *y*-axis is the mass of aluminum collected, in kilograms.

Circle Graphs A circle graph uses a circle divided into sections to display data. Each section represents part of the whole. All the sections together equal 100 percent.

Suppose you wanted to make a circle graph to show the number of seeds that germinated in a package. You would count the total number of seeds. You find that there are 143 seeds in the package. This represents 100 percent, the whole circle.

You plant the seeds, and 129 seeds germinate. The seeds that germinated will make up one section of the circle graph, and the seeds that did not germinate will make up the remaining section.

To find out how much of the circle each section should take, divide the number of seeds in each section by the total number of seeds. Then, multiply your answer by 360, the number of degrees in a circle, and round to the nearest whole number. The

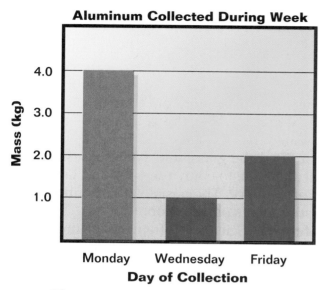

Aluminum Collected During Week

Mass (kg): 4.0, 3.0, 2.0, 1.0

Monday Wednesday Friday

Day of Collection

Figure 12 Bar graph of aluminum collected during week

section of the circle graph in degrees that represents the seeds germinated is figured below.

$$\frac{129}{143} \times 360 = 324.75 \text{ or } 325 \text{ degrees (or } 325°)$$

Plot this group on the circle graph using a compass and a protractor. Use the compass to draw a circle. It will be easier to

measure the part of the circle representing the non-germinating seeds, so subtract 325° from 360° to get 35°. Draw a straight line from the center to the edge of the circle. Place your protractor on this line and use it to mark a point at 325°. Use this point to draw a straight line from the center of the circle to the edge. This is the section for the group of seeds that did not germinate. The other section represents the group of 129 seeds that did germinate. Label the sections of your graph and title the graph as shown in **Figure 13.**

Figure 13 Circle graph of germinated seeds

Seeds Germinated

Not germinating (35°)

Germinating (325°)

Science Skill Handbook

Thinking Critically

Observing and Inferring

Observing Scientists try to make careful and accurate observations. When possible, they use instruments such as microscopes, thermometers, and balances to make observations. Measurements with a balance or thermometer provide numerical data that can be checked and repeated.

When you make observations in science, you'll find it helpful to examine the entire object or situation first. Then, look carefully for details. Write down everything you observe.

Example Imagine that you have just finished a volleyball game. At home, you open the refrigerator and see a jug of orange juice on the back of the top shelf. The jug, shown in **Figure 14,** feels cold as you grasp it. Then, you drink the juice, smell the oranges, and enjoy the tart taste in your mouth.

Figure 14 Why is this jug of orange juice cold?

As you imagined yourself in the story, you used your senses to make observations. You used your sense of sight to find the jug in the refrigerator, your sense of touch when you felt the coldness of the jug, your sense of hearing to listen as the liquid filled the glass, and your senses of smell and taste to enjoy the odor and tartness of the juice. The basis of all scientific investigation is observation.

Inferring Scientists often make inferences based on their observations. An inference is an attempt to explain or interpret observations or to say what caused what you observed.

When making an inference, be certain to use accurate data and observations. Analyze all of the data that you've collected. Then, based on everything you know, explain or interpret what you've observed.

Example When you drank a glass of orange juice after the volleyball game, you observed that the orange juice was cold as well as refreshing. You might infer that the juice was cold because it had been made much earlier in the day and had been kept in the refrigerator, or you might infer that it had just been made, using both cold water and ice. The only way to be sure which inference is correct is to investigate further.

Comparing and Contrasting

Observations can be analyzed by noting the similarities and differences between two or more objects or events that you observe. When you look at objects or events to see how they are similar, you are comparing them. Contrasting is looking for differences in similar objects or events.

Figure 15 Table comparing the nutritional value of *Cereal A* and *Cereal B*

Nutritional Value		
	Cereal A	**Cereal B**
Serving size	103 g	105 g
Calories	220	160
Total Fat	10 g	10 g
Protein	2.5 g	2.6 g
Total Carbohydrate	30 g	15 g

Example Suppose you were asked to compare and contrast the nutritional value of two kinds of cereal, *Cereal A* and *Cereal B.* You would start by looking at what is known about these cereals. Arrange this information in a table, like the one in **Figure 15.**

Similarities you might point out are that both cereals have similar serving sizes, amounts of total fat, and protein. Differences include *Cereal A* having a higher calorie value and containing more total carbohydrates than *Cereal B.*

Recognizing Cause and Effect

Have you ever watched something happen and then made suggestions about why it happened? If so, you have observed an effect and inferred a cause. The event is an effect, and the reason for the event is the cause.

Example Suppose that every time your teacher fed the fish in a classroom aquarium, she or he tapped the food container on the edge of the aquarium. Then, one day your teacher just happened to tap the edge of the aquarium with a pencil while making a point. You observed the fish swim to the surface of the aquarium to feed, as shown in **Figure 16.** What is the effect, and what would you infer to be the cause? The effect is the fish swimming to the surface of the aquarium. You might infer the cause to be the teacher tapping on the edge of the aquarium. In determining cause and effect, you have made a logical inference based on your observations.

Perhaps the fish swam to the surface because they reacted to the teacher's waving hand or for some other reason. When scientists are unsure of the cause of a certain event, they design controlled experiments to determine what causes the event. Although you have made a logical conclusion about the behavior of the fish, you would have to perform an experiment to be certain that it was the tapping that caused the effect you observed.

Figure 16 What cause-and-effect situations are occurring in this aquarium?

Science Skill Handbook

Practicing Scientific Processes

You might say that the work of a scientist is to solve problems. But when you decide how to dress on a particular day, you are doing problem solving, too. You may observe what the weather looks like through a window. You may go outside and see whether what you are wearing is heavy or light enough.

Scientists use an orderly approach to learn new information and to solve problems. The methods scientists may use include observing to form a hypothesis, designing an experiment to test a hypothesis, separating and controlling variables, and interpreting data.

Forming Operational Definitions

Operational definitions define an object by showing how it functions, works, or behaves. Such definitions are written in terms of how an object works or how it can be used; that is, what is its job or purpose?

Figure 17 What observations can be made about this dog?

Example Some operational definitions explain how an object can be used.
- A ruler is a tool that measures the size of an object.
- An automobile can move things from one place to another.

Or such a definition may explain how an object works.
- A ruler contains a series of marks that can be used as a standard when measuring.
- An automobile is a vehicle that can move from place to place.

Forming a Hypothesis

Observations You observe all the time. Scientists try to observe as much as possible about the things and events they study so they know that what they say about their observations is reliable.

Some observations describe something using only words. These observations are called qualitative observations. Other observations describe how much of something there is. These are quantitative observations and use numbers, as well as words, in the description. Tools or equipment are used to measure the characteristic being described.

Example If you were making qualitative observations of the dog in **Figure 17,** you might use words such as *furry, yellow,* and *short-haired.* Quantitative observations of this dog might include a mass of 14 kg, a height of 46 cm, ear length of 10 cm, and an age of 150 days.

Hypotheses Hypotheses are tested to help explain observations that have been made. They are often stated as *if* and *then* statements.

Examples Suppose you want to make a perfect score on a spelling test. Begin by thinking of several ways to accomplish this. Base these possibilities on past observations. If you put each of these possibilities into sentence form, using the words *if* and *then*, you can form a hypothesis. All of the following are hypotheses you might consider to explain how you could score 100 percent on your test:

If the test is easy, then I will get a perfect score.

If I am intelligent, then I will get a perfect score.

If I study hard, then I will get a perfect score.

Perhaps a scientist has observed that plants that receive fertilizer grow taller than plants that do not. A scientist may form a hypothesis that says: If plants are fertilized, then their growth will increase.

Designing an Experiment to Test a Hypothesis

In order to test a hypothesis, it's best to write out a procedure. A procedure is the plan that you follow in your experiment. A procedure tells you what materials to use and how to use them. After following the procedure, data are generated. From this generated data, you can then draw a conclusion and make a statement about your results.

If the conclusion you draw from the data supports your hypothesis, then you can say that your hypothesis is reliable. *Reliable* means that you can trust your conclusion. If it did not support your hypothesis, then you would have to make new observations and state a new hypothesis—just make sure that it is one that you can test.

Example Super premium gasoline costs more than regular gasoline. Does super premium gasoline increase the efficiency or fuel mileage of your family car? Let's figure out how to conduct an experiment to test the hypothesis, "*if* premium gas is more efficient, *then* it should increase the fuel mileage of our family car." Then a procedure similar to **Figure 18** must be written to generate data presented in **Figure 19** on the next page.

These data show that premium gasoline is less efficient than regular gasoline. It took more gasoline to travel one mile (0.064) using premium gasoline than it does to travel one mile using regular gasoline (0.059). This conclusion does not support the original hypothesis made.

Figure 18 Possible procedural steps

PROCEDURE

1. Use regular gasoline for two weeks.

2. Record the number of miles between fill-ups and the amount of gasoline used.

3. Switch to premium gasoline for two weeks.

4. Record the number of miles between fill-ups and the amount of gasoline used.

Figure 19 Data generated from procedure steps

Gasoline Data

	Miles traveled	Gallons used	Gallons per mile
Regular gasoline	762	45.34	0.059
Premium gasoline	661	42.30	0.064

Separating and Controlling Variables

In any experiment, it is important to keep everything the same except for the item you are testing. The one factor that you change is called the *independent variable*. The factor that changes as a result of the independent variable is called the *dependent variable*. Always make sure that there is only one independent variable. If you allow more than one, you will not know what causes the changes you observe in the independent variable. Many experiments have *controls*—a treatment or an experiment that you can compare with the results of your test groups.

Example In the experiment with the gasoline, you made everything the same except the type of gasoline being used. The driver, the type of automobile, and the weather conditions should remain the same throughout. The gasoline should also be purchased from the same service station. By doing so, you made sure that at the end of the experiment, any differences were the result of the type of fuel being used—regular or premium. The type of gasoline was the *independent factor* and the gas mileage achieved was the *dependent factor*. The use of regular gasoline was the *control*.

Interpreting Data

The word *interpret* means "to explain the meaning of something." Look at the problem originally being explored in the gasoline experiment and find out what the data show. Identify the control group and the test group so you can see whether or not the variable has had an effect. Then, you need to check differences between the control and test groups.

Figure 20 Which gasoline type is most efficient?

These differences may be qualitative or quantitative. A qualitative difference would be a difference that you could observe and describe, while a quantitative difference would be a difference you can measure using numbers. If there are differences, the variable being tested may have had an effect. If there is no difference between the control and the test groups, the variable being tested apparently has had no effect.

Example Perhaps you are looking at a table from an experiment designed to test the hypothesis: If premium gas is more efficient, then it should increase the fuel mileage of our family car. Look back at **Figure 19** showing the results of this experiment. In this example, the use of regular gasoline in the family car was the control, while the car being fueled by premium gasoline was the test group.

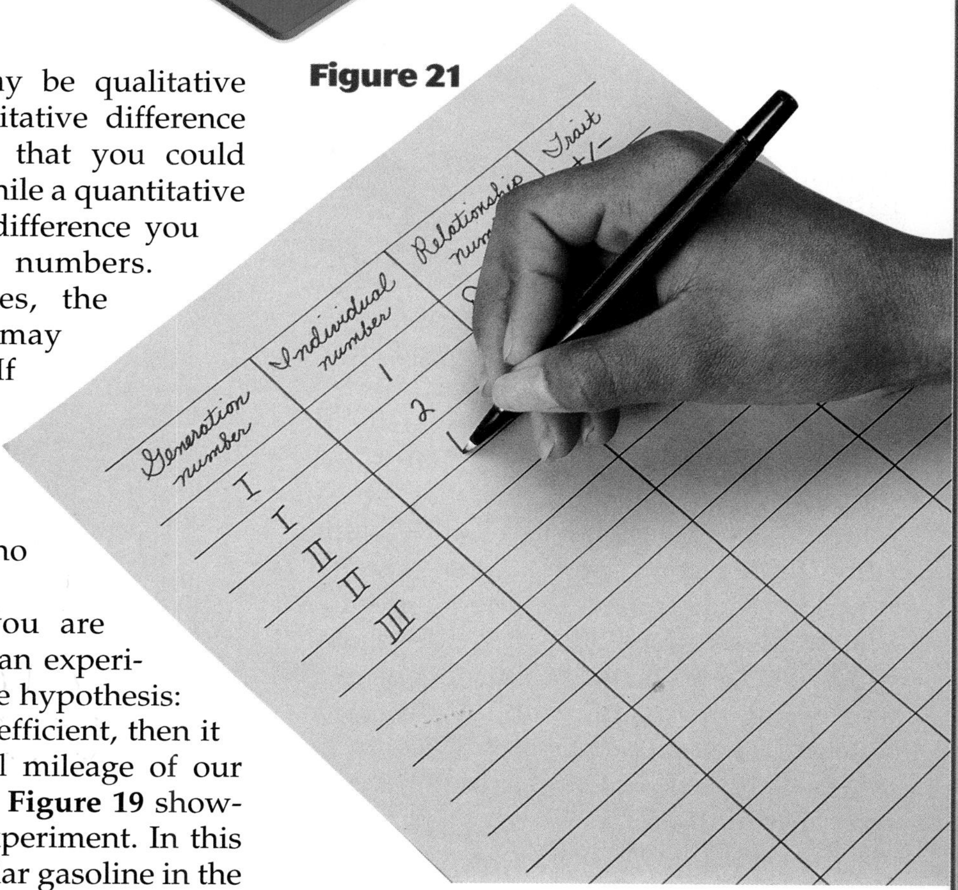

Data showed a quantitative difference in efficiency for gasoline consumption. It took 0.059 gallons of regular gasoline to travel one mile, while it took 0.064 gallons of the premium gasoline to travel the same distance. The regular gasoline was more efficient; it increased the fuel mileage of the family car.

What are data? In the experiment described on these pages, measurements were taken so that at the end of the experiment, you had something concrete to interpret. You had numbers to work with. Not every experiment that you do will give you data in the form of numbers. Sometimes, data will be in the form of a description. At the end of a chemistry experiment, you might have noted that

Figure 21

one solution turned yellow when treated with a particular chemical, and another remained colorless, as water, when treated with the same chemical. Data, therefore, are stated in different forms for different types of scientific experiments.

Are all experiments alike? Keep in mind as you perform experiments in science that not every experiment makes use of all of the parts that have been described on these pages. For some, it may be difficult to design an experiment that will always have a control. Other experiments are complex enough that it may be hard to have only one dependent variable. Real scientists encounter many variations in the methods that they use when they perform experiments. The skills in this handbook are here for you to use and practice. In real situations, their uses will vary.

Science Skill Handbook

Representing and Applying Data

Interpreting Scientific Illustrations

As you read a science textbook, you will see many drawings, diagrams, and photographs. Illustrations help you to understand what you read. Some illustrations are included to help you understand an idea that you can't see easily by yourself. For instance, we can't see atoms, but we can look at a diagram of an atom and that helps us to understand some things about atoms. Seeing something often helps you remember more easily. Illustrations also provide examples that clarify difficult concepts or give additional information about the topic you are studying. Maps, for example, help you to locate places that may be described in the text.

Examples

Captions and Labels Most illustrations have captions. A caption is a comment that identifies or explains the illustration. Diagrams, such as **Figure 22,** often have

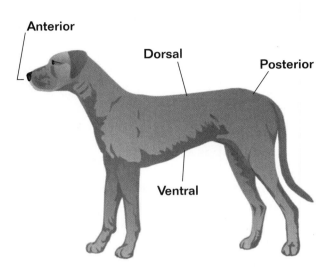

Figure 23 The orientation of a dog is shown here.

labels that identify parts of the organism or the order of steps in a process.

Learning with Illustrations An illustration of an organism shows that organism from a particular view or orientation. In order to understand the illustration, you may need to identify the front (anterior) end, tail (posterior) end, the underside (ventral), and the back (dorsal) side, as shown in **Figure 23.**

You might also check for symmetry. A shark in **Figure 24** has bilateral symmetry. This means that drawing an imaginary line through the center of the animal from the anterior to posterior end forms two mirror images.

Radial symmetry is the arrangement of similar parts around a central point. An object or organism, such as a hydra, can be divided anywhere through the center into similar parts.

Some organisms and objects cannot be divided into two similar parts. If an

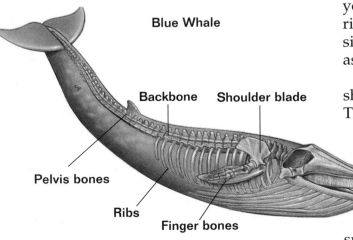

Figure 22 A labeled diagram of a blue whale

Figure 24 A shark (A) illustrating bilateral symmetry and a pear (B) illustrating a longitudinal section and a cross section

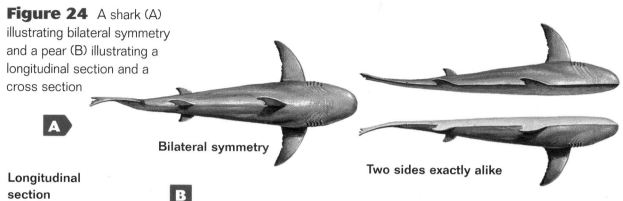

A

Bilateral symmetry

Two sides exactly alike

Longitudinal section

B

Cross section

organism or object cannot be divided, it is asymmetrical. Regardless of how you try to divide a natural sponge, you cannot divide it into two parts that look alike.

Some illustrations enable you to see the inside of an organism or object. These illustrations are called sections. **Figure 24** also illustrates some common sections.

Look at all illustrations carefully. Read captions and labels so that you understand exactly what the illustration is showing you.

Making Models

Have you ever worked on a model car, plane, or rocket? These models look, and sometimes work, much like the real thing, but they are often on a different scale than the real thing. In science, models are used to help simplify large or small processes or structures that otherwise would be dif-

ficult to see and understand. Your understanding of a structure or process is enhanced when you work with materials to make a model that shows the basic features of the structure or process.

Example In order to make a model, you first have to get a basic idea about the structure or process involved. You decide to make a model to show the differences in size of arteries, veins, and capillaries. First, read about these structures. All three are hollow tubes. Arteries are round and thick. Veins are flat and have thinner walls than arteries. Capillaries are small.

Now, decide what you can use for your model. Common materials are often most useful and cheapest to work with when making models. As illustrated in **Figure 25** on the next page, different kinds and sizes of pasta might work for these models. Different sizes of rubber tubing might do just as well. Cut and glue the different noodles or tubing onto thick paper so the openings can be seen. Then label each. Now you have a simple, easy-to-understand model showing the differences in size of arteries, veins, and capillaries.

What other scientific ideas might a model help you to understand? A model of a molecule can be made from balls of modeling clay (using different colors for the different elements present) and toothpicks (to show different chemical bonds).

from larger units to smaller, multiply by 10. For example, to convert millimeters to centimeters, divide the millimeters by 10. To convert 30 millimeters to centimeters, divide 30 by 10 (30 millimeters equal 3 centimeters).

Prefixes are used to name units. Look at **Figure 26** for some common metric prefixes and their meanings. Do you see how the prefix *kilo-* attached to the unit *gram* is *kilogram*, or 1000 grams? The prefix *deci-* attached to the unit *meter* is *decimeter*, or one-tenth (0.1) of a meter.

Examples

Length You have probably measured lengths or distances many times. The meter is the SI unit used to measure length. A baseball bat is about one meter long. When measuring smaller lengths, the meter is divided into smaller units called centimeters and millimeters. A centimeter is one-hundredth (0.01) of a meter, which is about the size of the width of the fingernail on your ring finger. A millimeter is one-thousandth of a meter (0.001), about the thickness of a dime.

Most metric rulers have lines indicating centimeters and millimeters, as shown in

Figure 25 Different types of pasta may be used to model blood vessels

A working model of a volcano can be made from clay, a small amount of baking soda, vinegar, and a bottle cap. Other models can be devised on a computer. Some models are mathematical and are represented by equations.

Measuring in SI

The metric system is a system of measurement developed by a group of scientists in 1795. It helps scientists avoid problems by providing standard measurements that all scientists around the world can understand. A modern form of the metric system, called the International System, or SI, was adopted for worldwide use in 1960.

The metric system is convenient because unit sizes vary by multiples of 10. When changing from smaller units to larger units, divide by 10. When changing

Figure 26 Common metric prefixes

Metric Prefixes			
Prefix	**Symbol**	**Meaning**	
kilo-	k	1000	thousand
hecto-	h	200	hundred
deca-	da	10	ten
deci-	d	0.1	tenth
centi-	c	0.01	hundredth
milli-	m	0.001	thousandth

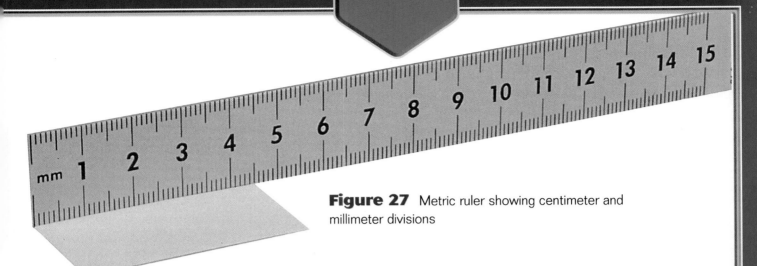

Figure 27 Metric ruler showing centimeter and millimeter divisions

Figure 27. The centimeter lines are the longer, numbered lines; the shorter lines are millimeter lines. When using a metric ruler, line up the 0-centimeter mark with the end of the object being measured, and read the number of the unit where the object ends, in this instance 4.5 cm.

Surface Area   Units of length are also used to measure surface area. The standard unit of area is the square meter (m²). A square that's one meter long on each side has a surface area of one square meter. Similarly, a square centimeter, (cm²), shown in **Figure 28,** is one centimeter long on each side. The surface area of an object is determined by multiplying the length times the width.

Volume   The volume of a rectangular solid is also calculated using units of length. The cubic meter (m³) is the standard SI unit of volume. A cubic meter is a cube one meter on each side. You can determine the volume of rectangular solids by multiplying length times width times height.

Liquid Volume   During science activities, you will measure liquids using beakers and graduated cylinders marked in milliliters, as illustrated in **Figure 29.** A graduated cylinder is a cylindrical container marked with lines from bottom to top.

Liquid volume is measured using a unit called a liter. A liter has the volume of 1000 cubic centimeters. Because the prefix *milli-* means thousandth (0.001), a milliliter equals one cubic centimeter. One milliliter of liquid would completely fill a cube measuring one centimeter on each side.

Figure 29 A volume of 79 mL is measured by reading at the lowest point of the curve.

Figure 28 A square centimeter

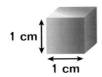

1 cm
1 cm

Mass Scientists use balances to find the mass of objects in grams. You might use a beam balance similar to **Figure 30.** Notice that on one side of the balance is a pan and on the other side is a set of beams. Each beam has an object of a known mass called a *rider* that slides on the beam.

Before you find the mass of an object, set the balance to zero by sliding all the riders back to the zero point. Check the pointer on the right to make sure it swings an equal distance above and below the zero point on the scale. If the swing is unequal, find and turn the adjusting screw until you have an equal swing.

Place an object on the pan. Slide the rider with the largest mass along its beam until the pointer drops below zero. Then move it back one notch. Repeat the process on each beam until the pointer swings an equal distance above and below the zero point. Add the masses on each beam to find the mass of the object.

You should never place a hot object or pour chemicals directly onto the pan. Instead, find the mass of a clean beaker or a glass jar. Place the dry or liquid chemicals in the container. Then find the combined mass of the container and the chemicals. Calculate the mass of the chemicals by subtracting the mass of the empty container from the combined mass.

Predicting

When you apply a hypothesis, or general explanation, to a specific situation, you predict something about that situation. First, you must identify which hypothesis fits the situation you are considering.

Examples People use prediction to make everyday decisions. Based on previous observations and experiences, you may form a hypothesis that if it is wintertime, then temperatures will be lower. From past experience in your area, temperatures are lowest in February. You may then use this hypothesis to predict specific temperatures and weather for the month of February in advance. Someone could use these predictions to plan to set aside more money for heating bills during that month.

Figure 30 A beam balance is used to measure mass.

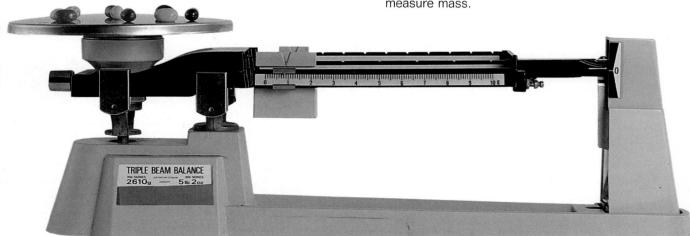

Using Numbers

When working with large populations of organisms, scientists usually cannot observe or study every organism in the population. Instead, they use a sample or a portion of the population. To sample is to take a small representative portion of organisms of a population for research. By making careful observations or manipulating variables within a portion of a group, information is discovered and conclusions are drawn that might then be applied to the whole population.

Scientific work also involves estimating. To estimate is to make a judgment about the size of something or the number of something without actually measuring or counting every member of a population.

Examples Suppose you are trying to determine the effect of a specific nutrient on the growth of black-eyed Susans. It would be impossible to test the entire population of black-eyed Susans, so you would select part of the population for your experiment. Through careful experimentation and observation on a sample of the population, you could generalize the effect of the chemical on the entire population.

Here is a more familiar example. Have you ever tried to guess how many beans were in a sealed jar? If you did, you were estimating. What if you knew the jar of beans held one liter (1000 mL)? If you knew that 30 beans would fit in a 100-milliliter jar, how many beans would you estimate to be in the one-liter jar? If you said about 300 beans, your estimate would be close to the actual number of beans. Can you estimate how many jelly beans are on the cookie sheet in **Figure 31?**

Scientists use a similar process to estimate populations of organisms from bacteria to buffalo. Scientists count the actual number of organisms in a small sample and then estimate the number of organisms in a larger area. For example, if a scientist wanted to count the number of bacterial colonies in a petri dish, a microscope could be used to count the number of organisms in a one-square-centimeter sample. To determine the total population of the culture, the number of organisms in the square-centimeter sample is multiplied by the total number of square centimeters in the culture.

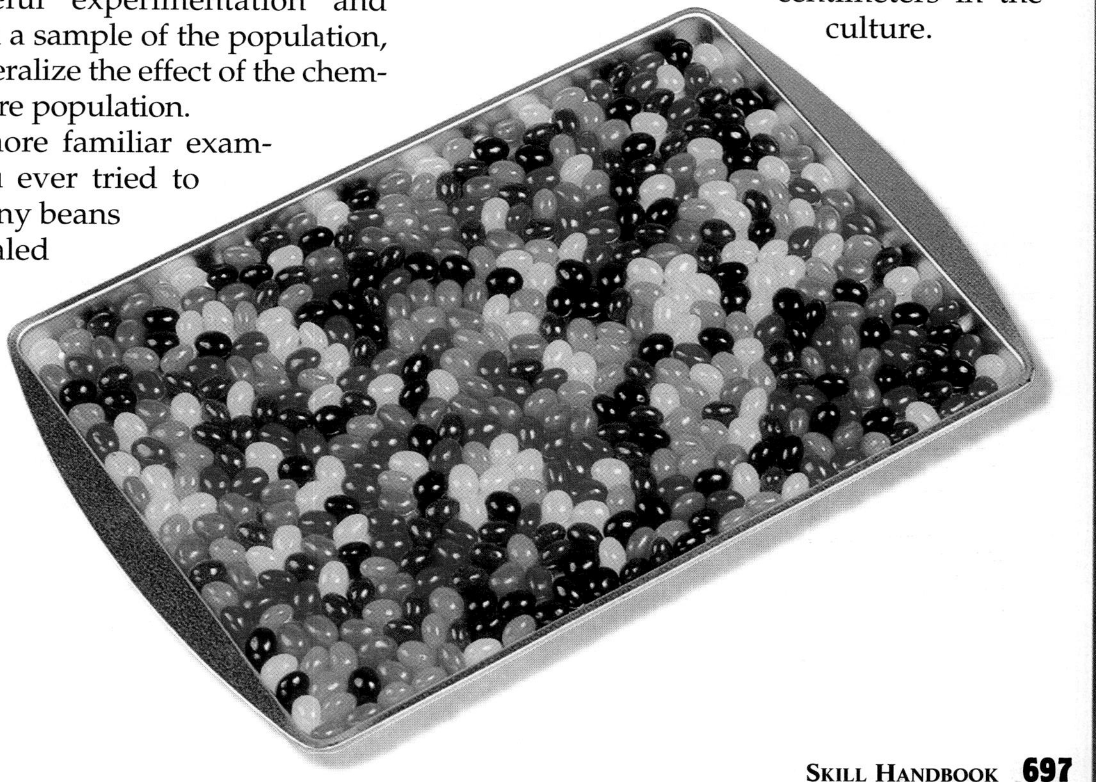

Figure 31

Sampling a group of jelly beans allows for an estimation of the total number of jelly beans in the group.

Technology Skill Handbook

Using a Word Processor

Suppose your teacher has assigned you to write a report. After you've done your research and decided how you want to write the information, you need to put all that information on paper. The easiest way to do this is with a word processor.

A word processor is a computer program in which you can write your information, change it as many times as you need to, and then print it out so that it looks neat and clean. You can also use a word processor to create tables and columns, add bullets or cartoon art, include page numbers, and even check your spelling.

Example Last week in Science class, your teacher assigned a report on the history of the atom. It has to be double spaced and include at least one table. You've collected all the facts, and you're ready to write your report. Sitting down at your computer, you decide you want to begin by explaining early scientific ideas about the atom and then talk about what scientists think about the atom now.

After you've written the two parts of your report, you decide to put a heading or subtitle above each part and add a title to the paper. To make each of these look different from the rest of your report, you can use a word processor to make the words bigger and bolder. The word processor also can double space your entire report, so that you don't have to add an extra space between each line.

You decide to include a table that lists each scientist that contributed to the theory of the atom along with his or her contribution. Using your word processor, you can create a table with as many rows and columns as you need. And, if you forget to include a scientist in the middle, you can go back and insert a row in the middle of your table without redoing the entire table.

When you've finished with your report, you can tell the word processor to check your spelling. If it finds misspelled words, it often will suggest a word you can use to replace the misspelled word. But, remember that the word processor may not know how to spell all the words in your report. Scan your report and double check your spelling with a dictionary if you're not sure if a word is spelled correctly.

After you've made sure that your report looks just the way you want it on the screen, the word processor will print your report on a printer. With a word processor, your report can look like it was written by a real scientist.

Helpful Hints

- If you aren't sure how to do something using your word processor, look under the help menu. You can look up how to do something, and the word processor will tell you how to do it. Just follow the instructions that the word processor puts on your screen.

- Just because you've spelled checked your report doesn't mean that the spelling is perfect. The spell check can't catch misspelled words that look like other words. So, if you've accidentally typed *mind* instead of *mine,* the spell checker won't know the difference. Always reread your report to make sure you didn't miss any mistakes.

Technology Skill Handbook

Using a Database

Imagine you're in the middle of research project. You are busily gathering facts and information. But, soon you realize that its becoming harder and harder to organize and keep track of all the information. The tool to solve "information overload" is a database. A database is exactly what it sounds like—a base on which to organize data. Similar to how a file cabinet organizes records, a database also organizes records. However, a database is more powerful than a simple file cabinet because at the click of a mouse, the entire contents can be reshuffled and reorganized. At computer-quick speeds, databases can sort information by any characteristic and filter data into multiple categories. Once you use a database, you will be amazed at how quickly all those facts and bits of information become manageable.

Example For the past few weeks, you have been gathering information on living and extinct primates. A database would be ideal to organize your information. An entry for gorillas might contain fields (categories) for fossil locations, brain size, average height, earliest fossil, and so on. Later on, if you wanted to know which primates have been found in Asia, you could quickly filter all entries using Asia in the field that listed locations. The database will scan all the entries and select the entries containing Asia. If you wanted to rank all the primates by arm length, you would sort all the entries by arm length. By using different combinations of sorting and filtering, you can discover relationships between the data that otherwise might remain hidden.

Helpful Hints

- Before setting up your own database, it's easier to learn the features of your database software by practicing with an established database.
- Entering the data into a database can be time consuming. Learn shortcuts such as tabbing between entry fields and automatic formatting of data that your software may provide.
- Get in the habit of periodically saving your database as you are entering data. That way, if something happens and your computer locks up or the power goes out, you won't lose all of your work.

Most databases have specific words you can use to narrow your search.

- AND: If you place an AND between two words in your search, the database will look for any entries that have both the words. For example, "blood AND cell" would give you information about both blood and cells.
- OR: If you place an OR between two words, the database will show entries that have at least one of the words. For example, "bird OR fish" would show you information on either birds or fish.
- NOT: If you place a NOT between two words, the database will look for entries that have the first word but do not have the second word. For example, "reproduction NOT plant" would show you information about reproduction but not about plant reproduction.

Technology Skill Handbook

Using Graphics Software

Having trouble finding that exact piece of art you're looking for? Do you have a picture in your mind of what you want but can't seem to find the right graphic to represent your ideas? To solve these problems, you can use graphics software. Graphics software allows you to change and create images and diagrams in almost unlimited ways. Typical uses for graphics software include arranging clip-art, changing scanned images, and constructing pictures from scratch. Most graphics-software applications work in similar ways. They use the same basic tools and functions. Once you master one graphics application, you can use any other graphics application relatively easily.

Example For your report on bird adaptations, you want to make a poster displaying a variety of beak and foot types. You have acquired many photos of birds, scanned from magazines and downloaded off the Internet. Using graphics software, you separate the beaks and feet from the birds and enlarge them. Then, you use arrows and text to diagram the particular features that you want to highlight. You also highlight the key features in color, keeping the rest of the graphic in black and white. With graphics software, the possibilities are endless. For the final layout, you place the picture of the bird next to enlarged graphics of the feet and beak. Graphics software allows you to integrate text into your diagrams, which makes your bird poster look clean and professional.

Helpful Hints

- As with any method of drawing, the more you practice using the graphic software, the better your results.
- Start by using the software to manipulate existing drawings. Once you master this, making your own illustrations will be easier.
- Clip art is available on CD-ROMs, and on the Internet. With these resources, finding a piece of clip art to suit your purposes is simple.
- As you work on a drawing, save it often.
- Often you can learn a lot from studying other people's art. Look at other computer illustrations and try to figure out how the artist created it.

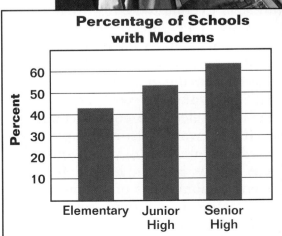

Percentage of Schools with Modems

Technology Skill Handbook

Using a Computerized Card Catalog

When you have a report or paper to research, you go to the library. To find the information, skill is needed in using a computerized card catalog. You use the computerized card catalog by typing in a subject, the title of a book, or an author's name. The computer will list on the screen all the holdings the library has on the subject, title, or author requested.

A library's holdings include books, magazines, databases, videos, and audio materials. When you have chosen something from this list, the computer will show whether an item is available and where in the library to find it.

Example You have a report due on dinosaurs, and you need to find three books on the subject. In the library, follow the instructions on the computer screen to select the "Subject" heading. You could start by typing in the word *dinosaurs*. This will give you a list of books on that subject. Now you need to narrow your search to the kind of dinosaur you are interested in, for example, *Tyrannosaurus rex*. You can type in *Tyrannosaurus rex* or just look through the list to find titles that you think would have information you need. Once you have selected a short list of books, click on each selection to find out if the library has the books. Then, check on where they are located in the library.

Helpful Hints
- Remember that you can use the computer to search by subject, author, or

title. If you know a book's author, but not the title, you can search for all the books the library has by that author.
- When searching by subject, it's often most helpful to narrow your search by using specific search terms. If you don't find enough, you can then broaden your search.
- Pay attention to the type of materials found in your search. If you need a book, you can eliminate any videos or other resources that come up in your search.
- Knowing how your library is arranged can save a lot of time. The librarian will show you where certain types of material are kept and how to find something.

Technology Skill Handbook

Developing Multimedia Presentations

It's your turn—you have to present your science report to the entire class. How do you do it? You can use many different sources of information to get the class excited about your presentation. Posters, videos, photographs, sound, computers, and the Internet can help show our ideas. First, decide the most important points you want your presentation to make. Then, sketch out what materials and types of media would be best to illustrate those points. Maybe you could start with an outline on an overhead projector, then show a video, followed by something from the Internet or a slide show accompanied by music or recorded voices. Make sure you don't make the presentation too complicated, or you will confuse yourself and the class. Practice your presentation a few times for your parents or brothers and sisters before you present it to the class.

Example Your assignment is to give a presentation on bird-watching. You could have a poster that shows what features you use to identify birds, with a sketch of your favorite bird. A tape of the calls of your favorite bird or a video of birds in your area would work well with the poster. If possible, include an Internet site with illustrations of birds that the class can look at.

Helpful Hints

- Carefully consider what media will best communicate the point you are trying to make.
- Keep your topic and your presentation simple.
- Make sure you learn how to use any equipment you will be using in your presentation.
- Practice the presentation several times.
- If possible, set up all of the equipment ahead of time. Make sure everything is working correctly.

Using E-mail

It's science fair time and you want to ask a scientist a question about your project, but he or she lives far away. You could write a letter or make a phone call. But you can also use the computer to communicate. You can do this using electronic mail (E-mail). You will need a computer that is connected to an E-mail network. The computer is usually hooked up to the network by a device called a *modem*. A modem works through the telephone lines. Finally, you need an address for the person you want to talk with. The E-mail address works just like a street address to send mail to that person.

Example There are just a few steps needed to send a message to a friend on an E-mail network. First, select Message from the E-mail software menu. Then, enter the E-mail address of your friend. Next, type your message. Make sure you check it for spelling and other errors. Finally, click the Send button to mail your message and off it goes! You will get a reply back in your electronic mailbox. To read your reply, just click on the message and the reply will appear on the screen.

Helpful Hints
- Make sure that you have entered the correct address of the person you're sending the message to.
- Reread your message to make sure it says what you want to say, and check for spelling and grammar.
- If you receive an E-mail message, respond to it as soon as possible.
- If you receive frequent E-mail messages, keep them organized by either deleting them or saving them in folders according to the subject or sender.

Technology Skill Handbook

Using an Electronic Spreadsheet

Your science fair experiment has produced lots of numbers. How do you keep track of all the data, and how can you easily work out all the calculations needed? You can use a computer program called a *spreadsheet* to keep track of data that involve numbers. A spreadsheet is an electronic worksheet. Type in your data in rows and columns, just as in a data table on a sheet of paper. A spreadsheet uses some simple math to do calculations on the data. For example, you could add, subtract, divide, or multiply any of the values in the spreadsheet by another number. Or you can set up a series of math steps you want to apply to the data. If you want to add 12 to all the numbers and then multiply all the numbers by 10, the computer does all the calculations for you in the spreadsheet. Below is an example of a spreadsheet that is a schedule.

Example Let's say that to complete your project, you need to calculate the speed of the model cars in your experiment. Enter the distance traveled by each car in the rows of the spreadsheet. Then enter the time you recorded for each car to travel the measured distance in the column across from each car. To make the formula, just type in the equation you want the computer to calculate; in this case, *speed = distance ÷ time.* You must make sure the computer knows what data are in the rows and what data are in the columns so the calculation will be correct. Once all the distance and time data and the formula have been entered into the spreadsheet program, the computer will calculate the speed for all the trials you ran. You can even make graphs of the results.

Helpful Hints

- Before you set up the spreadsheet, sketch out how you want to organize the data. Include any formulas you will need to use.
- Make sure you have entered the correct data into the correct rows and columns.
- As you experiment with your particular spreadsheet program you will learn more of its features.
- You can also display your results in a graph. Pick the style of graph that best represents the data you are working with.

Test Runs	Time	Distance	Speed
Car 1	5 mins.	5 miles	60 mph
Car 2	10 mins.	4 miles	24 mph
Car 3	6 mins.	3 miles	30 mph

Technology Skill Handbook

Using a CD-ROM

What's your favorite music? You probably listen to your favorite music on compact discs (CDs). But, there is another use for compact discs, called CD-ROM. CD-ROM means Compact Disc-Read Only Memory. CD-ROMs hold information. Whole encyclopedias and dictionaries can be stored on CD-ROM discs. This kind of CD-ROM and others are used to research information for reports and papers. The information is accessed by putting the disc in your computer's CD-ROM drive and following the computer's installation instructions. The CD-ROM will have words, pictures, photographs, and maybe even sound and video on a range of topics.

Example Load the CD-ROM into the computer. Find the topic you are interested in by clicking on the Search button. If there is no Search button, try the Help button. Most CD-ROMs are easy to use, but refer to the Help instructions if you have problems. Use the arrow keys to move down through the list of titles on your topic. When you double-click on a title, the article will appear on the screen. You can print the article by clicking on the Print button. Each CD-ROM is different. Click the Help menu to see how to find what you want.

Helpful Hints

- Always open and close the CD-ROM drive on your computer by pushing the button next to the drive. Pushing on the tray to close it will stress the opening mechanism over time.
- Place the disc in the tray so the side with no printing is facing down.
- Read through the installation instructions that come with the CD-ROM.
- Remember to remove the CD-ROM before you shut your computer down.

Using Probeware

Data collecting in an experiment sometimes requires that you take the same measurement over and over again. With probeware, you can hook a probe directly to a computer and have the computer collect the data about temperature, pressure, motion, or pH. Probeware is a combination sensor and software that makes the process of collecting data easier. With probes hooked to computers, you can make many measurements quickly, and you can collect data over a long period of time without needing to be present. Not only will the software record the data, most software will graph the data.

Example Suppose you want to monitor the health of an enclosed ecosystem. You might use an oxygen and a carbon dioxide sensor to monitor the gas concentrations or humidity or temperature. If the gas concentrations remain stable, you could predict that the ecosystem is healthy. After all the data is collected, you can use the software to graph the data and analyze it. With probeware, experimenting is made efficient and precise.

Helpful Hints

- Find out how to properly use each probe before using it.
- Make sure all cables are solidly connected. A loose cable can interrupt the data collection and give you inaccurate results.
- Because probeware makes data collection so easy, do as many trials as possible to strengthen your data.

Technology Skill Handbook

Using a Graphing Calculator

Science can be thought of as a means to predict the future and explain the past. In other language, if x happens, can we predict y? Can we explain the reason y happened? Simply, is there a relationship between x and y? In nature, a relationship between two events or two quantities, x and y, often occurs. However, the relationship is often complicated and can only be readily seen by making a graph. To analyze a graph, there is no quicker tool than a graphing calculator. The graphing calculator shows the mathematical relationship between two quantities.

Example If you have collected data on the position and time for a migrating whale, you can use the calculator to graph the data. Using the linear regression function on the calculator, you can determine the average migration speed of the whale. The more you use the graphing calculator to solve problems, the more you will discover its power and efficiency.

Graphing calculators have some keys that other calculators do not have. The keys on the bottom half of the calculator are those found on all scientific calculators. The keys located just below the screen are the graphing keys. You will also notice the up, down, left, and right arrow keys. These allow you to move the cursor around on the screen, to "trace" graphs that have been plotted, and to choose items from the menus. The other keys located on the top of the calculator access the special features such as statistical computations and programming features.

A few of the keystrokes that can save you time when using the graphing calculator are listed below.

- The commands above the calculator keys are accessed with the [2nd] or [ALPHA] key. The [2nd] key and its commands are yellow and the [ALPHA] and its commands are green.
- [2nd] [ENTRY] copies the previous calculation so you can edit and use it again.
- Pressing [ON] while the calculator is graphing stops the calculator from completing the graph.
- [2nd] [QUIT] will return you to the home (or text) screen.
- [2nd] [A-LOCK] locks the [ALPHA] key, which is like pressing "shift lock" or "caps lock" on a typewriter or computer. The result is that all letters will be typed and you do not have to repeatedly press the [ALPHA] key. (This is handy for programming.) Stop typing letters by pressing [ALPHA] again.
- [2nd] [OFF] turns the calculator off.

Helpful Hints

- Mastering the graphing calculator takes practice. Don't expect to learn it all in an afternoon.
- Programming a graphing calculator takes a plan. Write out all of the steps before entering them.
- It's easiest to learn how to program the calculator by first using programs that have already been written. As you enter them, figure out what each step is telling the calculator to do.

Skill Activities

Table of Contents

Separating and Controlling Variables

Background

Scientists often will conduct experiments to answer questions, test hypotheses, or solve problems. In any experiment, it is important to keep all factors the same except for the one you are testing. The factor you change is called the independent variable. If you change more than one variable in an experiment, you will not know which factor caused the effects you observe in the experiment.

Identify the independent variable in the following experiment.

Suppose a scientist has the job of studying the factors that affect the growth rate of marigolds. She sets up four plants to test her experiment. Descriptions of the plants are listed below.

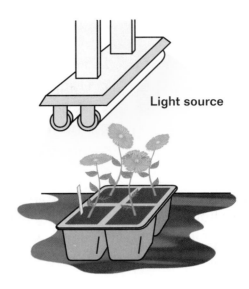

Light source

Procedure

Study the experiment descriptions and identify the independent variable. You may wish to make a table to organize the information.

Plant 1—soil mix A, 12 hours of light per day, no fertilizer, 22°C, water every other day.

Plant 2—soil mix A, 12 hours of light per day, no fertilizer, 22°C, water once a week.

Plant 3—soil mix A, 12 hours of light per day, no fertilizer, 22°C, water every day.

Plant 4—soil mix A, 12 hours of light per day, no fertilizer, 22°C, no water.

Practicing the SKILL

1. What variable is being tested in this experiment?
2. Name three other variables in this experiment.
3. Plant 2 grew taller than Plant 3. Infer what caused this effect.
4. Write a hypothesis that would be appropriate for this experimental design.
5. How might the experiment change if the scientist wanted to study the effect of sunlight on the growth rate of marigolds? Write a hypothesis for this experiment.

For more skill practice, do the

GLENCOE TECHNOLOGY

Chapter 1 Interactive Exploration on the **Science Voyages Level Red CD-ROM.**

Using Numbers

Background

Data can be reported in a variety of ways. Sometimes, data presented as percentages are more useful than data presented as a list of numbers. For example, if you learned that your city experienced 91 days that had a high temperature of over 20°C last year, you might think that the weather was quite warm for most of the year. But, what if you learned that the temperature rose above 20°C only 25 percent of the year? Would you interpret those results differently than the first results? The data presented as a percentage can provide a meaningful description.

However, you need to make sure you know exactly what the percentage represents. Sometimes, data results can be misleading. If 70 percent of the people polled before an election said they planned to vote for candidate A and 30 percent said they planned to vote for candidate B, would you think that candidate A would be the winner? Before you make a decision based on data, you should find out if the research method is biased, or slanted toward one particular view.

Percentages provide a useful means of summarizing and reporting data. How would you go about presenting information as a percentage?

Procedure

(1) Results of a class survey show the different types of transportation that 35 students use to get to school every day. Look at the data in the table.

(2) To calculate the percentage of the class that walks to school, use the following formula:

$$\frac{\text{number of students who walk}}{\text{total number of students surveyed}} \times 100$$

$$\frac{10}{35} \times 100 = 29\%$$

About 29 percent of the class walks to school.

Transportation to School	
Method of Transportation	**Number of Students**
Walk	10
Ride a bus	14
Ride a bike	4
Ride in a car	7

Practicing the SKILL

(1) Use the data in the table to calculate the percentage of students who use each method of transportation.

(2) There are 30 students in a class. If 65 percent of the class reports that cheese pizza is their favorite lunch, how many students is that?

For more skill practice, do the Chapter 2 Interactive Exploration on the **Science Voyages Level Red CD-ROM.**

Observing and Inferring

Background

Suppose you smell a cinnamon-like scent. You might suspect someone nearby is baking cinnamon rolls. However, you might be wrong. The scent might be from candy or a kind of air freshener. You cannot be sure unless you actually see the source of the scent. Whenever you use your senses, you are making *observations* about the world around you. When you make a conclusion based on what you observe, you are making an *inference*. When you smell a scent and conclude that the scent is from a cinnamon roll, you are *inferring*.

Scientists use their senses to make observations. Based on what they observe, they make inferences. The inferences help them solve problems and predict future events. You can make observations and inferences about almost anything. Try improving your observing skills by looking carefully at an object. A visual observation should be made in an orderly way. First, look at the entire object. Then, look at its parts.

Procedure

1. Observe **Figure A** carefully. Write down your observations on a separate paper.

2. Did you notice (1) the color of the candle, (2) the blackened wick, (3) the melted wax on the candle and in the holder, and (4) the color of the holder?

3. Now, try making inferences based on what you observed in **Figure A.** You can base your observations on your own experience with candles. You might infer (1) how long the candle was lit (based on the amount of melted wax), (2) how much of the candle has melted, or

(3) why the candle is not burning now. Inferences are based on incomplete information. Therefore, they may be incorrect. The flame may have been lit for only a short time, for example.

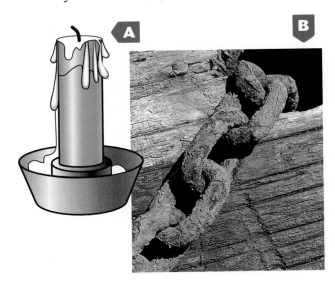

Practicing the SKILL

1. Look carefully at **Figure B.** On a separate sheet of paper, write down what you observe.

2. Write down what you can infer from your observations. Explain how you made each inference and, if possible, how it may be incorrect.

For more skill practice, do the Chapter 3 Interactive Exploration on the **Science Voyages Level Red CD-ROM.**

GLENCOE TECHNOLOGY

Communicating

Background

Sharing ideas is an important part of science. It allows you to learn more about the scientific process and give feedback. It also allows other people to give you feedback about your own ideas.

Communication in the science classroom can be done by group discussion, written reports, reading books, student presentations, or watching science programs on television. In this skill activity, you will practice communicating to try to solve a problem.

Procedure

(1) Divide the class into four groups. Each group will choose a reporter who will take notes during the discussion.

(2) Look at the photograph below.

(3) Discuss with your group what you think has happened.

(4) Think of some ways the problem could have been prevented. Then, think of some ways to solve the current problem.

(5) Choose a student from your group to share the group's ideas with the class.

(6) As a class, decide which solution is best. You may want to solve the problem before it happens or choose to fix the problem after it happens.

Practicing the SKILL

Acid rain slowly damages stone buildings and statues. Think of ways you could prevent this from occurring. Write a report about your ideas and share it with the class.

For more skill practice, do the Chapter 4 Interactive Exploration on the **Science Voyages Level Red CD-ROM.**

Interpreting Scientific Illustrations

Background

You may have heard the saying "A picture is worth a thousand words." A good scientific diagram often can explain an idea better than several paragraphs of words. In order to get the most from diagrams, do the following.

- Study the entire diagram. Review the part of the text that the diagram illustrates.

- If there is a caption, read it carefully.

- Read all the labels and identify the parts.

- Visualize the dimensions. Arrows often indicate distances and direction. Distances often are indicated between arrows. The heads of the arrows show where the measurements start and end.

Use these guidelines to interpret the diagram at right.

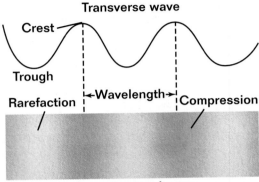

Procedure

1. What is the purpose of this diagram?

2. Identify the text in Chapter 5 to which the diagram relates. Locate the discussions about types of waves.

3. What does the crest of a transverse wave correspond to on a compressional wave?

4. What does the trough of a transverse wave correspond to on a compressional wave?

5. What is another way you can diagram the wavelength of a transverse wave?

Practicing the SKILL

1. What do the darker areas of the compressional wave represent?

2. What are the white areas?

3. How would you measure one wavelength of a compressional wave?

For more skill practice, do the Chapter 5 Interactive Exploration on the **Science Voyages Level Red CD-ROM.**

Using Numbers

Background

The ability to analyze a problem and to reason through a solution is an important skill in science. It often involves forming a mental picture of the problem. Making a quick sketch or drawing of the problem also can help you get a better sense of the problem. Your ability to "see" the problem will strengthen as you practice solving word problems.

Read the strategy below that provides a logical plan for attacking word problems. Pay attention to how each step is used in solving sample problems.

Problem Solving Strategy

1. Read the problem carefully. Be sure you understand all the terms used. Restate the problem in your own words.

2. Identify the quantities that are given in the problem.

3. Identify the quantity that is unknown.

4. Examine the problem carefully to find a relationship between what is given and what you are asked to find. Identify the equation that contains these quantities.

5. If necessary, solve the equation for the unknown quantity.

6. Substitute the given values into the equation, along with their proper units.

7. Check to see if the answer will be in the proper units.

8. Solve the equation.

9. Check your answer to see if it is reasonable.

Now, use the problem solving strategy to solve the following problem.

Procedure

1. Carefully read and understand the problem.

   > A hiker walked for 2.0 h at a speed of 6.5 km/h. How far did the hiker walk?

2. **Given:** time, $t = 2.0$ h
   speed, $v = 6.5$ km/h

3. **Unknown:** distance, d

4. **Basic Equation:** $v = d/t$

5. **Solution:** $d = vt$

6. $\quad d = (6.5 \text{ km/h})(2.0 \text{ h})$

7. $\quad d = (\text{km/h})(\text{h}) = \text{km}$

8. $\quad d = (6.5 \text{ km/h})(2.0 \text{ h}) = 13 \text{ km}$

9. It is reasonable for a hiker to cover 13 km in 2 hours.

Practicing the SKILL

1. An ant moves 30 mm in 72 s. How fast is it moving?

2. A car goes 25 km in 0.60 h and then travels 39 km in the next 1.5 h. What is the average speed for the entire trip?

For more skill practice, do the Chapter 6 Interactive Exploration on the **Science Voyages Level Red CD-ROM.**

GLENCOE TECHNOLOGY

Comparing and Contrasting

Background

Are you an educated consumer? You are when you learn about a product before you buy it. Suppose you want to buy a compact disc player. How do you choose which one to buy? You read all the available information on the various models. Then, you find properties that each CD player has in common. That is, you compare the models. However, you also consider the options available. Each model has its own options. They make each model different. When you consider differences between the CD players, you are contrasting.

Comparing and contrasting are important tools for scientists also. For example, in determining the possible health benefits, a researcher might compare and contrast the nutritional value of foods that contain artificial sweeteners with foods that do not contain artificial sweeteners. How would you go about comparing and contrasting a lever and wheel and axle shown at the right?

Procedure

1. Look at the physical characteristics of each simple machine. How do they increase force? Are they used for the same or different types of jobs?

2. Prepare a table to organize your observations.

3. Fill in your table by writing as many similarities you can think of when comparing a lever to a wheel and axle.

4. Complete your table by listing the differences between a lever and a wheel and axle.

Practicing the SKILL

Compare and contrast the following:

1. a single pulley and a pulley system having four pulleys

2. an inclined plane and a screw

For more skill practice, do the Chapter 7 Interactive Exploration on the **Science Voyages Level Red CD-ROM.**

GLENCOE TECHNOLOGY

Making Models

Background

Architects, builders, and designers often use detailed drawings as they plan their work. These are known as floorplans and represent a type of scale drawing. A scale drawing is a 2-dimensional model where an object's size and location are kept in the same proportions as in the actual object. For example, suppose a floorplan has a scale of 1 cm = 1 m. A room shown on this plan measures 10 cm × 15 cm. The actual room is 10 m × 15 m. A 1 m × 2 m desk in that room would be drawn as a rectangle 1 cm × 2 cm. The procedure below will help you make a scale drawing of your classroom.

Procedure

1. Measure the length and width of your classroom and decide on a scale to use that will allow your plan to cover most of your piece of paper. For example, if your paper is 25 cm × 36 cm and your room is 12 m × 15 m you could use a scale of 1 cm = 0.5 m. This would create a drawing of the classroom that measures 24 cm × 30 cm, which would fit on the paper.

2. Convert the dimensions of the room to your floorplan scale. Use a pencil and ruler to neatly draw the outline of the room on your paper.

3. Measure the width of the doorway and where it is located. Convert these measurements to your floorplan scale and draw the doorway on your plan.

4. Measure your teacher's desk and how far it is located from the walls. Use these measurements to accurately draw the desk in its proper position on your floorplan.

5. Repeat the procedure for any windows and other furniture in the classroom.

6. Title your classroom map and be sure to include your scale in the map key.

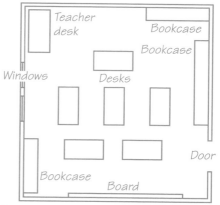

Classroom floor plan (scale: 1 cm = 2 m)

Practicing the SKILL

Imagine that your teacher has received two new computer workstations. Each station has a desk that measures 1 m × 2 m. Use your scale drawing to determine where these workstations might fit in the classroom. You may need to "move" some furniture on your map. Draw the workstations on your classroom floorplan.

For more skill practice, do the Chapter 8 Interactive Exploration on the **Science Voyages Level Red CD-ROM.**

GLENCOE TECHNOLOGY

Using Numbers

Background

Wind farms and photovoltaics use renewable energy sources. In a wind farm, wind energy is produced using large wind turbines that turn generators and create electricity. Most wind farms have hundreds or thousands of wind turbines. A typical wind turbine has rotors 43 m in diameter and produces 600 kW (kilowatt). Each turbine is generally placed 5 rotor diameters apart.

Photovoltaics (PVs) are flat panels that are able to convert sunlight into electricity. A typical PV panel produces 125 W (watts) per m^2.

Both PVs and wind farms use nonpolluting, renewable energy sources—sunlight and wind. PVs have no moving parts—this is an advantage over wind turbines. However, PVs work only when the sun is shining, while wind turbines work day and night if the wind is blowing. One drawback to both of these systems is that they require large amounts of land to be able to produce electricity for many homes and businesses.

WIND FARM INFORMATION
THIS WIND FARM OF 300 ELECTRIC WIND TURBINES IS BEING CONSTRUCTED ON THE JESS RANCH, ALTAMONT PASS, CALIFORNIA. ELECTRICITY GENERATED BY THE WIND TURBINES WILL BE PURCHASED AND DISTRIBUTED BY PACIFIC GAS AND ELECTRIC COMPANY. THE PROJECT WILL CONSERVE APPROXIMATELY 50,000 TO 60,000 BARRELS OF OIL EACH YEAR BY CONVERTING WIND POWER TO ELECTRICITY.

Procedure

1. Study the information above about wind turbines, photovoltaic panels, and electricity consumption.

2. Average domestic power demand is 0.7 kW per person. Therefore, on average, 500 000 people would require:

$$\frac{0.7\ kW}{person} \times 500\ 000\ people$$

$$=\ 350\ 000\ kW.$$

Practicing the SKILL

1. How many wind turbines would it take to meet the electrical needs of a city of 500 000 people?

2. How many square meters of PV panels would it take to produce the electricity required by a city of 500 000 people?

3. Evaluate wind power and PVs. Which do you think is a better alternative energy source? Explain your answer.

For more skill practice, do the Chapter 9 Interactive Exploration on the **Science Voyages Level Red CD-ROM.**

GLENCOE TECHNOLOGY

Predicting

Background

In the early 1600s Galileo began to observe the sun with a telescope and noticed dark spots on the surface of the sun. Scientists now know that sunspots are cooler regions on the sun's surface. The lower temperature causes these areas to appear as dark spots against the hotter, lighter colored background. Astronomers noticed that sunspots were temporary features lasting a few days or months. They began to keep track of the numbers of sunspots.

When does the sun display large numbers of sunspots? Solar maximums are times when there are large numbers of sunspots. Conversely, solar minimums are times of relatively few sunspots. It can be important to predict solar maximums because solar flares are associated with sunspots. The intense radiation from solar flares affects Earth's atmosphere and can disrupt radio, telephone, and television signals. In addition, this radiation can disable satellites and pose a hazard to astronauts in orbit.

Procedure

The sunspot table lists the average number of sunspots per month each year from 1954–1997. Use these data to construct a line graph of sunspot activity for these years.

Practicing the SKILL

1. Describe the pattern you observe in sunspot activity over the last 44 years.

2. Predict when the next solar maximum will occur.

3. Predict the average number of sunspots per month during the next solar maximum.

For more skill practice, do the Chapter 10 Interactive Exploration on the **Science Voyages Level Red CD-ROM.**

 GLENCOE TECHNOLOGY

Sunspots

Year	Avg. # sunspots/mo.	Year	Avg. # sunspots/mo.	Year	Avg. # sunspots/mo.	Year	Avg. # sunspots/mo.
1954	5	1965	15	1976	12	1987	29
1955	38	1966	46	1977	27	1988	99
1956	141	1967	93	1978	93	1989	157
1957	189	1968	105	1979	155	1990	142
1958	194	1969	105	1980	154	1991	145
1959	158	1970	104	1981	140	1992	94
1960	112	1971	66	1982	116	1993	55
1961	54	1972	68	1983	66	1994	30
1962	38	1973	38	1984	45	1995	17
1963	28	1974	34	1985	18	1996	9
1964	10	1975	15	1986	13	1997	21

Interpreting Scientific Illustrations

Background

Weather changes are caused by the movements of air masses. Meteorologists keep track of where air masses are moving in order to predict or forecast future weather. The area where two air masses come together is called a front. One type of front, a cold front, is formed when cold air pushes up warm air, causing a narrow band of violent storms. Tornados, hail, heavy rain, and strong winds can all occur along cold fronts. Strong cold fronts that move south from Canada are carefully monitored so that severe weather warnings can be issued to people living in the path of the storms. In this activity, you will predict the movement of a cold front.

Procedure

1. Examine the map below. It is a weather map showing the location of a cold front moving from Canada. This front is moving south at an average speed of 30 km/h.

   How many kilometers will the front travel in 24 hours? Use the formula:

   distance = rate × time ($d = rt$)

2. You can also calculate how much time it will take for the front to reach a specific city by using this formula:

   time = distance ÷ rate ($t = d/r$)

   How long will it take for the front to reach the cities of Bismarck, North Dakota; Lincoln, Nebraska; and Des Moines, Iowa?

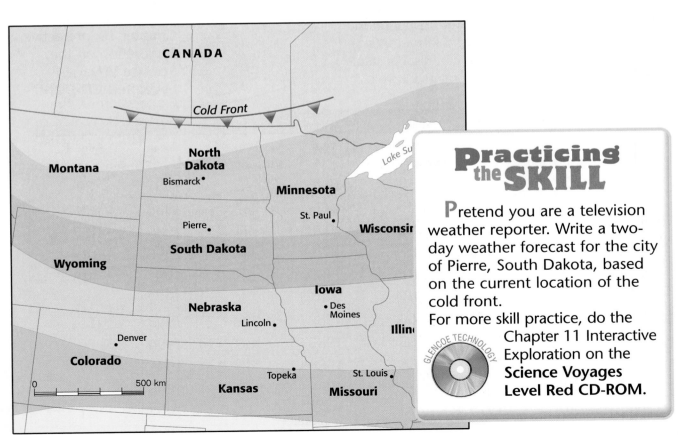

Practicing the SKILL

Pretend you are a television weather reporter. Write a two-day weather forecast for the city of Pierre, South Dakota, based on the current location of the cold front.

For more skill practice, do the Chapter 11 Interactive Exploration on the **Science Voyages Level Red CD-ROM.**

Interpreting Data

Background

Scientists use air bubbles trapped in glacial ice to study Earth's past climate. They drill a sample of ice out of the glacier. Air bubbles trapped in this ice contain atmospheric gases. The composition of these gases can be analyzed to give an indication of past average global temperatures.

How have average global temperatures changed over the past 160 000 years? The figure below is a graph of Vostok Ice core data so named because it was drilled in east Antarctica at the Soviet Research Station Vostok. The values plotted are the difference between past global temperatures and the present. For example, –2°C means that the average temperature was 2°C colder than presently. Scientists have determined that an ice age occurs when the average temperature is only 5°C colder than today.

Procedure

Study the figure below. Use this graph to infer past climate conditions on Earth.

Practicing the SKILL

1. How long ago did the last ice age end?

2. What percent of the last 160 000 years was spent in ice ages?

3. How often in the last 160 000 years has the average temperature been about the same or warmer than the present average temperature?

4. If Earth was currently experiencing an ice age, what climatic conditions do you think would exist at your location? How would they differ from present conditions?

For more skill practice, do the Chapter 12 Interactive Exploration on the **Science Voyages Level Red CD-ROM.**

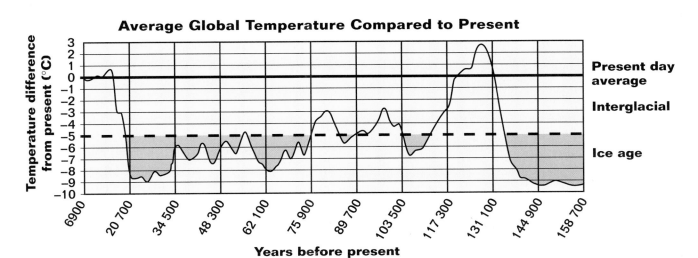

Average Global Temperature Compared to Present

Temperature difference from present (°C)

Present day average

Interglacial

Ice age

Years before present

Observing and Inferring

Background

Living things survive in their environments because they have behavioral and physical adaptations that allow them to live. For example, a jackrabbit will run when it sees a coyote. This is a behavioral adaptation. The jackrabbit also has strong legs. This is a physical adaptation. Both adaptations, working together, give the jackrabbit an advantage in escaping predators. In this activity, you will observe adaptations that help living things near your classroom survive.

Procedure

1. Read Section 2, Land Environments. Pay special attention to the Adaptations of Desert Plants and Animals.

2. In a table like the one shown below, record the names of five living things you find near your classroom.

3. Briefly describe two behavioral adaptations and two physical adaptations for each. Record these in your table.

4. Write how you think each of the adaptations might give each organism an advantage that allows it to survive in the wild.

Practicing the SKILL

1. Many birds, insects, and bats are able to fly. What are the advantages of this adaptation?

2. Many mammals in both hot and cold climates have thick fur. What might the advantages of this adaptation be?

For more skill practice, do the Chapter 13 Interactive Exploration on the **Science Voyages Level Red CD-ROM.**

 GLENCOE TECHNOLOGY

Organism Behavior			
Organism	Physical adaptations	Behavioral adaptations	Advantages in the wild

Interpreting Scientific Illustrations

Background

Every cell carries on the complex chemical processes required to survive as an organism or as part of an organism. Some chemical processes are the same for plant and animal cells. Because of this, plant and animal cells have similar parts, but there are differences.

How does a scientific illustration help you understand what you read?

Use the illustrations to determine the similarities and differences between plant and animal cells.

Procedure

1. Observe the illustrations.

2. Carefully read the labels and follow the line(s) from each label to the cell part(s).

3. Record the location of each cell part as animal, plant, or both in a table like the one below.

Animal Cell

Endoplasmic reticulum
Chromosomes
Nuclear membrane
Nucleus
Mitochondria
Cell membrane
Golgi bodies
Cytoplasm

Plant Cell

Chromosomes
Endoplasmic reticulum
Cell wall
Chloroplasts
Vacuole

Cell Data	
Cell Part	**Location**
cell membrane	
nucleus	
cytoplasm	
cell wall	
endoplasmic reticulum	
Golgi bodies	
mitochondria	
chloroplasts	
chromosomes	
vacuole	

Practicing the SKILL

1. Identify the cell parts found in both cells.

2. Identify the cell parts found only in an animal cell and those found only in a plant cell.

For more skill practice, do the Chapter 14 Interactive Exploration on the **Science Voyages Level Red CD-ROM.**

GLENCOE TECHNOLOGY

Observing and Inferring

Background

Scientists classify organisms because they are related in some way or several ways. One group of related animals is Phylum Arthropoda. It has one of the largest groups of animals, Class Insecta.

How can insects be classified?

Class Insecta is divided into orders that are smaller groups with similar features. Below are the Latin names and wing descriptions for five of the orders of insects.

- *Hymenoptera* means "membrane wing" and both pair of wings are thin and transparent.

- *Coleoptera* means "sheath wing," and the front wings are hard coverings that protect a pair of membranous wings and the insect's abdomen.

- *Hemiptera* means "half wing." One half of the front wing is thick and leathery, and the other half is membranous.

- *Lepidoptera* means "scale wing," which describes the powdery scales on the wings.

- *Orthoptera* means "straight wing," and some members of this group have long straight wings.

Procedure

1. Copy the Insect Observations table in your Science Journal.

2. Examine the eight insects shown on this page.

3. From their appearance, decide which insects belong in which order and write their names in your Insect Observations table.

Insect Observations	
Order	**Insects**
Hymenoptera	
Coleoptera	
Hemiptera	
Lepidoptera	
Orthoptera	

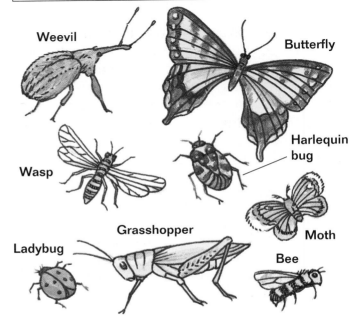

Weevil
Butterfly
Wasp
Harlequin bug
Ladybug
Grasshopper
Moth
Bee

Practicing the SKILL

1. How might this sort of classification be useful to people who study insects?

2. Using the same eight insects, make another classification of them.

For more skill practice, do the Chapter 15 Interactive Exploration on the **Science Voyages Level Red CD-ROM.**

GLENCOE TECHNOLOGY

Interpreting Data

Background

Bacteriologists are people who study microorganisms, grow bacteria in dishes, and perform experiments on them. Although individual bacteria are too small to see with the naked eye, colonies that contain large numbers of bacteria are visible.

Scientists often use tables to organize data from experiments. Having data laid out in a logical way makes it easier to interpret. To interpret means to explain why something is the way it is. Interpreting data is determining why you got the results you did. Reading the following procedure and studying the data table will help you learn to interpret data.

Procedure

1. Imagine you are a bacteriologist trying to determine which household item is most effective in preventing the growth of bacteria. You design an experiment in which you have three sterile petri dishes that contain nutrient agar. You rub your finger over the entire surface of the agar in dishes 1 and 2 to introduce bacteria. You do nothing with dish 3.

2. Next, you cut four small squares of filter paper, soaking them each in one of the following substances: hydrogen peroxide, mouthwash, alcohol, and disinfectant. They are labeled and placed in dish 1, without touching or overlapping. All three petri dishes are covered and placed in a warm, dark place for two days.

3. At the end of two days, you take out each dish to observe any growth. The Bacterial Growth table is a record of your observations.

Bacterial Growth

Dish	Square	Observations
1	hydrogen peroxide	a few colonies are observed
	mouthwash	many colonies are observed
	alcohol	very little growth under square or in surrounding area
	disinfectant	no growth under square or in surrounding area
2	none	hundreds of colonies are present
3	none	no colonies are observed

Practicing the SKILL

1. According to the data above, which substance was most effective in preventing bacterial growth? Which was least effective?

2. In dish 2, bacteria were added but no substance was placed in the dish. What was the purpose of this?

3. Dish 3 contained neither bacteria nor a substance. What purpose did this dish serve?

For more skill practice, do the Chapter 16 Interactive Exploration on the **Science Voyages Level Red CD-ROM.**

GLENCOE TECHNOLOGY

Making and Using Tables

Background

Tables are used to record information so that it can be understood easily. Tables help you find information quickly by summarizing information given in the text. A table is similar to a system of classification. Information is grouped in vertical columns so that similarities and differences can be recognized easily. A table has three main parts: a title, vertical columns, and column headings. Sometimes, horizontal lines are used to group the information further.

Procedure

1. Study **Table 17-1** in the Protists and Fungi chapter. Examine the title. Look down the four columns to see if the information is related to the title and to each of the column headings.

2. Examine the information in **Table 17-1.** Notice how all four columns contain information on plantlike protists.

3. Using **Table 17-1,** answer the questions under Practicing the Skill.

4. Make a table of your own, similar to **Table 17-1,** in which you compare the different types of fungi discussed in Section 17-2.

Practicing the SKILL

1. What is the purpose of **Table 17-1?**

2. Which plantlike protist is used to give food a creamy texture?

3. What two plantlike protists have flagella?

4. Which plantlike protist has an eye-spot?

5. What groups of protists contain one-celled organisms, and which contain many-celled organisms?

6. Which plantlike protist can cause red tide?

7. Which has cell walls that contain silica?

8. Which protist is an important food source?

9. Why are tables used?

For more skill practice, do the Chapter 17 Interactive Exploration on the **Science Voyages Level Red CD-ROM.**

GLENCOE TECHNOLOGY

Classifying

Background

Keys are used to identify things that are already classified.

In this Skill Activity, you will learn about some trees and how they have been classified. For this activity you need to know that needlelike leaves are shaped like needles and scalelike leaves are like the scales on a fish or a lizard. You also need to collect a variety of gymnosperm leaves.

Procedure

(1) Look at illustrations or actual examples of gymnosperm leaves.

(2) Make a data table and record the number of each sample in the first column.

(3) Use the key below to identify the leaves. There may be differences among the leaves. Choose the statement that describes most of the leaves on the branch. By following the key, the numbered steps will lead you to the name of the plant.

Key to Classifying Leaves

1. All leaves are needlelike.
   a. yes, go to 2
   b. no, go to 8

2. Needles are in clusters.
   a. yes, go to 3
   b. no, go to 4

3. Clusters contain 2, 3, or 5 needles.
   a. yes, pine
   b. no, cedar

4. Needles grow on all sides of the stem.
   a. yes, go to 5
   b. no, go to 7

5. Needles grow from a woody peg.
   a. yes, spruce
   b. no, go to 6

6. Needles appear to grow from the branch.
   a. yes, Douglas fir
   b. no, hemlock

7. Most of the needles grow upward.
   a. yes, fir
   b. no, redwood

8. All needles are scalelike but not prickly.
   a. yes, arborvitae
   b. no, juniper

Practicing the SKILL

(1) What trait was used to separate the gymnosperm leaves into two groups?

(2) What are two traits of a hemlock?

(3) What gymnosperms have scalelike leaves?

(4) Describe a spruce leaf.

(5) How are pine and cedar leaves alike?

For more skill practice, do the Chapter 18 Interactive Exploration on the **Science Voyages Level Red CD-ROM.**

GLENCOE TECHNOLOGY

Observing and Inferring

Background

One of the best tools for learning science is having good observation skills. You can learn by simply watching things happen. This was the main tool that Aristotle used when he made many of his discoveries. He kept detailed records of his observations. Over time, he collected much information about the living things in his surroundings. He made many inferences from his observations. Some have been proven to be true, but others have been shown not to be true. Other scientists used many of his recorded observations for further study.

Procedure

1. Your teacher will tape to your back a card with the name of a plant, flower, fruit, or vegetable written on it.

2. For thirty minutes, move around the classroom and have other students act out clues to the name on your card. No one should speak during the observation time.

3. Keep a list of the clues then make an inference about the name written on your card.

Practicing the SKILL

1. Were you able to infer the correct name on your card?

2. How many clues did you observe before you knew the name on your card?

3. How many of your classmates correctly inferred the names on their cards?

For more skill practice, do the Chapter 19 Interactive Exploration on the **Science Voyages Level Red CD-ROM.**

GLENCOE TECHNOLOGY

Comparing and Contrasting

Background

Determining the type of symmetry an animal has will help you describe the animal, as well as to determine what other animals it might be related to. In this Skill Activity, you will make some decisions about the type of symmetry of several animals.

Procedure

1. Review the discussion of symmetry in Section 20-1 of your textbook. Observe the animals pictured on this page.

2. Decide if the animal has radial symmetry, bilateral symmetry, or no symmetry.

3. Make a copy of the table below and record your answers in this table. If you need additional help, read about the animal's structure in reference books.

4. Explain how you decided what type of symmetry the animal has. Write your explanation in the table column labeled "Reason."

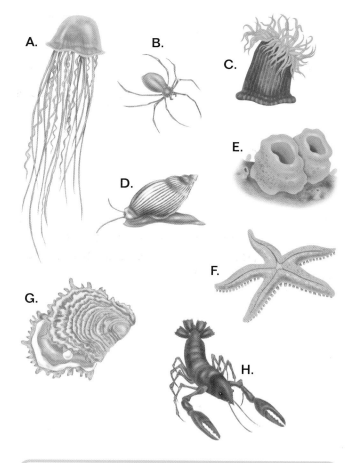

A.   B.   C.   E.   D.   F.   G.   H.

Animal Symmetry		
Animal	**Symmetry**	**Reason**
jellyfish		
crayfish		
sponge		
spider		
sea star		
oyster		
snail		
sea anemone		

Practicing the SKILL

1. Which animals have radial symmetry? Bilateral symmetry? No symmetry?

2. What kind of symmetry do you think most animals have?

3. If an animal has a front and hind end, what kind of symmetry does it have?

For more skill practice, do the Chapter 20 Interactive Exploration on the **Science Voyages Level Red CD-ROM.**

GLENCOE TECHNOLOGY

Chapter 21

Skill Activity

Observing and Inferring

Background

Have you ever seen an animal track in the snow or mud? If you have, you probably tried to identify what animal left it there. You probably inferred what type of animal left it there based on observations you made about the area you were in.

Scientists also draw conclusions based on observations of the environment. In this activity, you will identify animal tracks and determine which animal made the tracks.

Procedure

1. Look at the figure below.

2. Decide which track belongs to which type of animal.

3. Copy the table in your Science Journal and record your answers.

4. In the table, describe how each animal's foot is adapted for its environment.

Identifying Animal Tracks		
Animal	Track	Adaptation
Bear		
Beaver		
Cheetah		
Deer		
Horse		
Moose		
Raccoon		

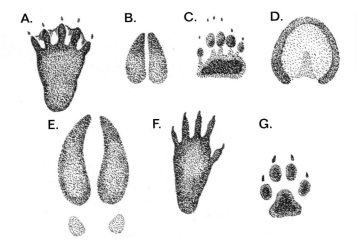

A.   B.   C.   D.

E.   F.   G.

Practicing the SKILL

1. Could you expect to find a raccoon track in the same area you found a cheetah track? Explain.

2. What are the differences between track **b** and **e**? How does that help you identify the track?

For more skill practice, do the Chapter 21 Interactive Exploration on the **Science Voyages Level Red CD-ROM.**

GLENCOE TECHNOLOGY

Classifying

Background

Classifying is the process of sorting objects or events into groups based on their common features. You may not think you use this skill, but if you stack the books in your locker in a certain order, you are classifying them. When you classify, you are grouping objects together for a specific reason.

The activities that you do every day can also be classified. Some activities are learned, and must develop through practice and experience. Other activities don't need to be learned, you are born with them. They are innate behaviors. In this activity, you will classify your daily activities as learned or innate.

Procedure

(1) Below is a list of 20 activities that you do every day.

(2) Make a copy of the Classifying Behaviors table shown and classify each activity as learned or innate.

(3) Put an X in the box that best describes the type of activity.

Classifying Behaviors

Activity	Learned	Innate

Types of Birds

Rhea flightless bird	Bald Eagle bird of prey
Great Blue Heron wading bird	Pelican water bird
Cardinal seed-eating bird	Kiwi flightless bird
Emu flightless bird	Downy Woodpecker insect-eating bird
Gold finch seed-eating bird	Blue Jay seed-eating bird
Wood duck water bird	Owl bird of prey
Nuthatch insect-eating bird	Robin insect-eating bird
Osprey bird of prey	Ostrich flightless bird

Daily Activities

blink	yawn
walk	get dressed
sneeze	read
breathe	write
talk	brush your teeth
take a shower	comb your hair
your heart beats	smile
cough	sleep
digest food	swallow
tie your shoes	eat

Practicing the SKILL

(1) Look at the Types of Birds table above.

(2) Describe ways you could classify the birds.

For more skill practice, do the Chapter 22 Interactive Exploration on the **Science Voyages Level Red CD-ROM.**

GLENCOE TECHNOLOGY

Inferring

Background

The surfaces of Earth's moon, Mercury, and other planetary bodies are often covered with craters. Scientists usually are unable to determine the exact age of the craters because they do not have actual rock samples. However, photographs taken by satellites help scientists determine the rough ages of the craters. For example, if two craters overlap, the crater that appears to be underneath is the older of the two.

Procedure

The figure below is a diagram showing an area containing several craters. Each crater is labeled by a letter in its center. Study the relationships between the craters and determine their relative ages.

Practicing the SKILL

1. Which crater appeared first, crater A or crater C?

2. Can the approximate age of crater J be determined? Why or why not?

3. What is the approximate diameter of crater D?

4. List craters A through I in order of increasing age (youngest crater first).

For more skill practice, do the Chapter 23 Interactive Exploration on the **Science Voyages Level Red CD-ROM.**

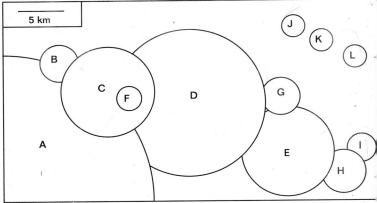

English Glossary

This glossary defines each key term that appears in bold type in the text. It also shows the chapter and page number where you can find the word used.

Pronunciation Key

a...b**a**ck (bak)	oh...g**o** (goh)	sh...**sh**elf (shelf)
ay...d**ay** (day)	aw...s**o**ft (sawft)	ch...na**t**ure (nay chur)
ah...f**a**ther (fahth ur)	or...**or**bit (or but)	g...**g**ift (gihft)
ow...fl**ow**er (flow ur)	oy...c**oi**n (coyn)	j...**g**em (jem)
ar...**car** (car)	oo...f**oo**t (foot)	ing...s**ing** (sing)
e...l**e**ss (les)	ew...f**oo**d (fewd)	zh...vi**si**on (vihzh un)
ee...l**ea**f (leef)	yoo...p**u**re (pyoor)	k...ca**k**e (kayk)
ih...tr**i**p (trihp)	yew...f**ew** (fyew)	s...**s**eed, **c**ent (seed, sent)
i (i + con + e)...**i**dea	uh...comm**a** (cahm uh)	z...**z**one, rai**s**e (zohn, rayz)
(i dee uh), l**i**fe (life)	u (+ con)...flow**er** (flo ur)	

A

acceleration: rate at which speed or direction changes; can be found by dividing the change in speed by the given time. (ch. 6, p. 143)

acid rain: acidic rain or snow produced when gases released by burning oil and coal mix with water in the air; causes damage and can kill plants and trees. (ch. 9, p. 234)

adaptation: any structure or behavior that helps an organism survive in its environment; develops in a population over a long period of time. (ch. 12, p. 335)

aerobes: organisms that require oxygen to survive—for example, humans require oxygen to live. (ch. 16, p. 448)

aggression: forceful act, such as fighting and threatening, that is used to dominate or control another animal. (ch. 22, p. 619)

air mass: large body of air that has the same properties as the Earth's surface over which it formed. (ch. 11, p. 304)

algae (AL gee): one- or many-celled plant-like protists, all of which contain chlorophyll and can make their own food; organized into six main phyla based on their structure, their pigments, and the way they store food. (ch. 17, p. 465)

amphibian: ectothermic vertebrate that spends part of its life in water and part on land. (ch. 21, p. 582)

amplitude: measure of the energy a wave carries; one-half the distance between a crest and a trough of a transverse wave. (ch. 5, p. 121)

anaerobes: organisms that are able to live without oxygen—for example, methanogens and thermophiles. (ch. 16, p. 448)

angiosperms (AN jee uh spurmz): vascular plants that flower, have their seeds contained in a fruit, and are the most common form of plant life on Earth. (ch. 18, p. 511)

antibiotic: substance, such as penicillin, produced by one organism that inhibits or kills another organism. (ch. 16, p. 452)

appendages: jointed structures, such as legs, claws, and antennae, that grow from a body. (ch. 20, p. 564)

arthropod: animals that have jointed appendages, such as an insect or a crustacean, that is classified by the number of body segments and appendages, and that has a protective exoskeleton. (ch. 20, p. 564)

astronomical (as truh NAHM uh kul) unit: average distance from Earth to the sun (150 million km), which is used to measure vast distances in space. (ch. 23, p. 643)

atom: small particle that makes up most types of matter and is made up of smaller parts called protons, neutrons, and electrons. (ch. 3, p. 61)

atomic mass: number that tells how heavy an element's atoms are compared with atoms of other elements. (ch. 3, p. 70)

atomic number: whole number that tells how many protons are in the nucleus of each atom of an element. (ch. 3, p. 70)

auxin: type of plant hormone that can cause plants to show positive phototropism. (ch. 19, p. 533)

average speed: distance traveled divided by the time it takes to travel this distance. (ch. 6, p. 142)

B

balanced forces: describes forces acting on an object that cancel each other. (ch. 6, p. 150)

bar graph: tool that uses bars to show the relationships between variables; can be horizontal or vertical and can display any numerical data. (ch. 2, p. 46)

behavior: way an organism acts toward its environment; can be innate or learned. (ch. 22, p. 610)

binomial nomenclature (bi NOH mee ul NOH mun klay chur): Linnaeus's system of classification, which gives a two-word name to every organism—the first word of the name is the genus and the second word is the specific name. (ch. 15, p. 420)

biomes (BI ohmz): large geographic areas with similar climates and ecosystems; the six most common are tundra, taiga, temperate forest, tropical rain forest, grassland, and desert. (ch. 13, p. 363)

bird: endothermic vertebrate with feathers, two legs, two wings, and bills, or beaks, and that lays hard-shelled eggs. (ch. 21, p. 588)

budding: form of asexual reproduction in which a new organism grows off the side of the parent. (ch. 17, p. 478)

C

cambium (KAM bee um): vascular plant tissue that produces new xylem and phloem cells. (ch. 18, p. 507)

carnivore: flesh-eating animals. (ch. 21, p. 600)

cartilage: tough, flexible tissue that is similar to bone but is not as hard. (ch. 21, p. 580)

cell membrane: structure that allows only certain things to pass into and out of the cell and forms the outer boundary of the cell. (ch. 14, p. 398)

cell theory: major theory based on observations and conclusions by many scientists; states that the cell is the basic unit of life, organisms are composed of one or more cells, and all cells come from other cells. (ch. 14, p. 392)

cell wall: rigid structure that supports and protects the plant cell and is made mostly of bundles of cellulose fibers. (ch. 14, p. 403)

cellulose (SEL yuh lohs): organic compound made of long chains of glucose molecules; forms the rigid cell walls of plants. (ch. 18, p. 494)

chemical change: any change where one or more of the original materials changes into other materials. (ch. 4, p. 104)

chemical property: characteristic of a substance, such as the ability to react with oxygen, that allows it to change to a new substance. (ch. 4, p. 93)

chlorofluorocarbons (CFCs): group of chemical compounds used in refrigerators, aerosol sprays, and foam packaging that destroy ozone molecules. (ch. 10, p. 273)

chloroplast: green, chlorophyll-containing organelle in the cytoplasm of many plant cells, where plants make their own food. (ch. 14, p. 403)

chordate: animal with a notochord, a dorsal hollow nerve cord, and gill slits. (ch. 21, p. 578)

chromatin: long strands of hereditary material within the cell nucleus that are made up of proteins and DNA. (ch. 14, p. 399)

cilia (SIHL ee uh): short, threadlike structures that extend from the cell membrane of ciliates and are used for movement. (ch. 17, p. 471)

circle graph: tool used to show the parts of a whole. (ch. 2, p. 46)

class: taxonomic group that is larger than an order but smaller than a phylum or division. (ch. 15, p. 424)

classify: to group information, objects, or ideas based on their similarities. (ch. 15, p. 418)

climate: pattern of weather that occurs in a particular area over many years. (ch. 12, p. 328)

climax community: community that has reached the final stage of ecological succession. (ch. 13, p. 357)

closed circulatory system: type of blood-circulation system in which blood is carried through blood vessels. (ch. 20, p. 557)

cnidarians (NIH dar ee uns): phylum of hollow-bodied, water-dwelling animals with stinging cells, radial symmetry, a body two layers thick, and both sexual and asexual reproduction. (ch. 20, p. 551)

compound: pure substance produced when elements combine, and whose properties are different from those of the elements from which it is formed. (ch. 3, p. 75)

compound light microscope: magnifies by allowing light to pass through an object and then through two or more lenses. (ch. 14, p. 389)

compound machine: combination of two or more simple machines. (ch. 7, p. 178)

compressional wave: wave in which matter in the medium moves forward and backward in the same direction the wave travels. (ch. 5, p. 119)

conditioning: process in which behavior is modified so that a response associated with one stimulus becomes associated with another stimulus. (ch. 22, p. 614)

conduction: transfer of energy that occurs when molecules bump into each other. (ch. 10, p. 279)

conic projection: map projection that is accurate for small areas of Earth and is made by projecting points and lines from a globe onto a cone. (ch. 8, p. 215)

conservation: careful use of resources with the goal of reducing damage to the environment. (ch. 9, p. 253)

constant: factor in an experiment that does not change. (ch. 1, p. 19)

constellation (kahn stuh LAY shun): group of stars that forms a pattern in the sky and is named after a real or imaginary animal, person, or object. (ch. 23, p. 652)

contour feathers: strong, lightweight feathers that give birds their coloring and streamlined shape and that are used to fly and to steer. (ch. 21, p. 591)

contour interval: difference in elevation between two side-by-side contour lines. (ch. 8, p. 217)

contour line: line on a map that connects points of equal elevation. (ch. 8, p. 217)

control: standard used for comparison in an experiment. (ch. 1, p. 19)

convection: occurs in gases and liquids. (ch. 10, p. 279)

Coriolis effect: changes the direction of all free-moving objects to the right north of the equator and to the left to the south of the equator; creates wind patterns across the world and results from the rotation of Earth. (ch. 10, p. 285)

courtship behavior: behavior that animals perform before mating; allows male and female members of a species to recognize each other and to be ready to mate at the same time. (ch. 22, p. 619)

cuticle (KYEWT ih kul): waxy, protective layer covering the stems, leaves, and flowers of some land plants; is secreted by the plant's cell walls and slows the evaporation of water. (ch. 18, p. 495)

cyclic behaviors: innate behaviors, such as migration and hibernation, that occur in a repeated pattern, often in response to changes in the environment. (ch. 22, p. 622)

cytoplasm: constantly moving, gelatin-like mixture inside the cell membrane; contains structures that carry out life processes of the cell. (ch. 14, p. 400)

D

day-neutral plant: plant that does not have a specific photoperiod and whose flowering process can begin over a wide range of hours of darkness. (ch. 19, p. 536)

deforestation: destruction or cutting down of trees. (ch. 12, p. 344)

density (DEN si tee): physical property that relates the mass of something to how much space it takes up; calculated by dividing mass by volume. (ch. 4, p. 91)

dependent variable: factor being measured in an experiment. (ch. 1, p. 19)

desert: driest biome on Earth; receives less than 25 cm of rain each year and supports little plant life. (ch. 13, p. 368)

dew point: temperature at which air is saturated and condensation forms; changes with the amount of moisture in the air. (ch. 11, p. 298)

dichotomous (di KAH toh mus) key: detailed list of characteristics used to identify organisms and that includes scientific names. (ch. 15, p. 431)

dicot: class of angiosperm that has two seed leaves inside its seeds, vascular bundles that occur in rings, and flower parts in multiples of four or five. (ch. 18, p. 512)

diffraction: bending of waves around a barrier. (ch. 5, p. 128)

division: in the taxonomy of plants, the group smaller than a kingdom but larger than a class. (ch. 15, p. 424)

Doppler radar: specialized radar system that sends out repeated radio waves, monitors the reflected waves from distant storms, and can tell the direction a storm is moving. (ch. 11, p. 309)

down feathers: soft, fluffy feathers that provide an insulating layer next to the skin of adult birds and that cover the bodies of young birds. (ch. 21, p. 591)

E

eclipse (ee KLIHPS): event that happens when the moon passes between the sun and Earth (a solar eclipse) or Earth passes between the sun and the moon (lunar eclipse). (ch. 23, p. 639)

ecological succession: process of gradual change from one community of organisms to another. (ch. 13, p. 354)

ectotherm: vertebrate whose body temperature changes with the temperature of its surroundings. (ch. 21, p. 578)

efficiency: ability of a machine to convert work input to work output; always less than 100 percent in real machines due to some loss to friction or heat. (ch. 7, p. 186)

effort force (Fe): force applied to a machine. (ch. 7, p. 179)

electromagnetic waves: waves that do not need matter to carry energy; can travel through air, through solid walls, and through space and have wavelengths and frequencies that vary greatly. (ch. 5, p. 118)

electron: negatively charged particle found in a cloudlike formation surrounding an atom's nucleus. (ch. 3, p. 64)

electron microscope: bends beams of electrons in a magnetic field and can magnify images up to one million times or more. (ch. 14, p. 390)

element: naturally occurring or synthetic material that cannot be broken down to simpler materials by ordinary means, has a unique set of properties, and that is generally classified as a metal, a metalloid, or a nonmetal. (ch. 3, p. 68)

El Niño: a climatic event that starts in the tropical Pacific Ocean and sets off changes in the atmosphere. (ch. 12, p. 339)

endoplasmic reticulum (ER): complex series of folded membranes in the cell cytoplasm that is involved in moving cellular products. (ch. 14, p. 400)

endoskeleton: internal system of bones that protects and supports an animal's internal organs and also provides a place for muscle attachment. (ch. 21, p. 578)

endospores: heat-resistant, thick-walled structures many bacteria can produce around themselves when conditions are unfavorable. (ch. 16, p. 453)

endotherm: vertebrate that maintains a constant body temperature. (ch. 21, p. 578)

equator: imaginary line at 0° latitude that circles Earth halfway between the north and south poles and divides Earth into two equal halves. (ch. 8, p. 210)

estimation: method of making a rough measurement. (ch. 2, p. 31)

estivation: behavioral adaptation for survival during hot, dry summer months, during which an animal becomes inactive; in amphibians, involves hiding in cooler, more humid ground. (ch. 21, p. 583)

estuary: area where a river meets the ocean that contains a mixture of freshwater and salt water and serves as nursery for many species of ocean fish. (ch. 13, p. 374)

exoskeleton: lightweight body covering that protects and supports an arthropod's body, prevents it from drying out, and is shed by molting. (ch. 20, p. 564)

F

family: taxonomic group that is smaller than an order but larger than a genus. (ch. 15, p. 424)

fault-block mountains: sharp, jagged mountains that are made of huge, tilted blocks of rocks that are separated from surrounding rock by faults. (ch. 8, p. 208)

fins: fanlike structures of most fish that are used for balancing, steering, and moving, and usually are paired. (ch. 21, p. 579)

fish: ectotherm that lives in water and uses gills to get oxygen; usually has fins and scales. (ch. 21, p. 579)

fission: simplest form of asexual reproduction in which two cells are produced with genetic material identical to that of the parent cell; the method by which bacteria reproduce. (ch. 16, p. 448)

flagella: whiplike tails that help many types of bacteria move around in moist environments. (ch. 16, p. 445)

fog: stratus cloud that forms when air is cooled to its dew point and condenses near the ground. (ch. 11, p. 300)

folded mountains: mountains that are created when rock layers are squeezed from opposite sides and the layers buckle and fold. (ch. 8, p. 206)

force: a push or a pull; can be measured by the amount of acceleration it can give a mass. (ch. 6, p. 149)

fossil fuel: nonrenewable energy resource that began to form millions of years ago from remains of once-living plants and animals; provides energy and includes coal, oil, and natural gas. (ch. 9, p. 232)

free-living: organism, such as a planarian, that doesn't depend on one particular organism for food or a place to live. (ch. 20, p. 553)

frequency: number of waves that pass a given point in one second; measured in waves per second, or hertz (Hz). (ch. 5, p. 123)

friction: force that resists motion between two objects in contact and that always acts opposite to the direction of motion. (ch. 6, p. 155)

front: boundary between warm and cold air masses. (ch. 11, p. 305)

fulcrum: point about which a lever pivots. (ch. 7, p. 182)

G

galaxy (GAL uk see): group of stars, gas, and dust held together by gravity. (ch. 23, p. 655)

genus (JEE nus): taxonomic group of different organisms with similar characteristics; can have one or more species. (ch. 15, p. 420)

geothermal energy: heat energy from Earth, which can be used to generate electricity. (ch. 9, p. 241)

gills: organs that exchange oxygen and carbon dioxide with water. (ch. 20, p. 555)

global warming: rise in global temperatures because of the increase of greenhouse gases in the atmosphere. (ch. 12, p. 343)

Golgi bodies: stacks of membrane-covered sacs that package materials and move them to the outside of the cell. (ch. 14, p. 401)

graph: diagram that shows the relationship; tool used to collect, organize, and summarize data in a visual way so that it is easy to use and understand. (ch. 2, p. 45)

grasslands: temperate and tropical regions that receive between 25 cm and 75 cm of precipitation each year and are dominated by climax communities of grasses. (ch. 13, p. 368)

gravity: attraction between all matter; a force that pulls on all objects that have mass. (ch. 6, p. 149)

greenhouse effect: natural heating process caused when gases in the atmosphere trap heat; prevents Earth from being too cold to support life. (ch. 12, p. 342)

groundwater: water that soaks into the ground and collects in the small spaces between bits of rock and soil. (ch. 9, p. 245)

guard cells: in a plant leaf, the cells that surround the stomata and that open and close them. (ch. 18, p. 509)

gymnosperms (JIHM nuh spurmz): vascular plants that produce seeds on the surface of the female reproductive structures, do not have flowers, and generally have needlelike or scalelike leaves. (ch. 18, p. 510)

H

herbivore: grazing animal that eats only plants. (ch. 21, p. 600)

hibernation: behavioral adaptation for survival during cold, winter months, where an animal becomes inactive and its metabolic needs are lowered; in amphibians, involves burying themselves in mud or leaves until temperatures become warmer. (ch. 12, p. 336; ch. 21, p. 583; ch. 22, p. 623)

host cell: cell in which a virus reproduces. (ch. 14, p. 408)

humidity: amount of water vapor held in the air. (ch. 11, p. 297)

hurricane: large, swirling, low-pressure system that forms over tropical oceans and has winds of at least 120 km per hour. (ch. 11, p. 310)

hydroelectric power: production of electricity by water. (ch. 9, p. 240)

hydrosphere: all the water that is found at Earth's surface, of which 97 percent is salt water and only three percent is fresh water. (ch. 10, p. 280)

hyphae (HI fee): mass of many-celled, threadlike tubes that usually make up the body of a fungus. (ch. 17, p. 476)

hypothesis: statement that can be tested; based on observations, research, and prior knowledge of a problem. (ch. 1, p. 18)

I

imprinting: type of learning in which an animal forms a social attachment to another organism soon after birth or hatching. (ch. 22, p. 612)

inclined plane: simple machine that is a sloped surface, or ramp; allows heavy loads to be lifted by using less force over a greater distance. (ch. 7, p. 180)

independent variable: the one factor changed by the person doing the experiment. (ch. 1, p. 19)

inertia (ih NUR shah): measure of an object's ability to remain at rest or to keep moving. (ch. 6, p. 151)

inference: conclusion based on an observation. (ch. 1, p. 18)

innate behavior: behavior that an animal is born with and does not have to learn. (ch. 22, p. 610)

instinct: complex pattern of innate behavior. (ch. 22, p. 611)

interference: ability of two or more waves to combine and form a new wave when they overlap; can be constructive, forming a larger wave, or destructive, forming a smaller wave. (ch. 5, p. 130)

International Date Line: transition line for calendar days, located at the 180° meridian. (ch. 8, p. 212)

intertidal zone: portion of the shoreline that is covered with water at high tide and exposed to the air at low tide. (ch. 13, p. 374)

invertebrates (ihn VURT uh brayts): animals lacking a backbone; about 97 percent of animals are invertebrates. (ch. 20, p. 547)

ionosphere: layer of electrically charged particles in the thermosphere. (ch. 10, p. 269)

isobar: line drawn on a weather map that connects points of equal atmospheric pressure. (ch. 11, p. 314)

isotherm (I suh thurm): line drawn on a weather map that connects points of equal temperature. (ch. 11, p. 314)

isotopes (I suh tohps): two or more atoms of the same element that have different numbers of neutrons. (ch. 3, p. 70)

J

jet stream: narrow belt of strong winds that blows near the top of the troposphere. (ch. 10, p. 287)

K

Kelvin: scale that measures temperature in SI; begins at zero kelvin, which is the coldest temperature possible in nature. (ch. 2, p. 41)

kilogram (kg): SI unit for mass. (ch. 2, p. 40)

kingdom: the first taxonomic category and the group that has the most members. (ch. 15, p. 419)

L

land breezes: nightly movements of air created when cold air over the land forces up the warmer air above the sea. (ch. 10, p. 288)

latitude: distance in degrees either north or south of the equator. (ch. 8, p. 210)

law of conservation of matter: states that matter is neither created nor destroyed, only changed in form. (ch. 3, p. 62)

law of definite proportions: states that a given compound is always made of the same elements in the same proportion by mass. (ch. 3, p. 76)

lever: simple machine made from a rod or plank that pivots about a point. (ch. 7, p. 182)

lichen: organism made up of a fungus and a green alga. (ch. 17, p. 479)

light-year: distance light travels in a year (about 9.5 trillion km), which is used to measure distances between galaxies. (ch. 23, p. 657)

line graph: tool used to show the relationship between two variables. (ch. 2, p. 45)

long-day plant: plant that needs less than ten to twelve hours of darkness to begin the flowering process. (ch. 19, p. 535)

longitude: distance in degrees east or west of the prime meridian. (ch. 8, p. 211)

lysosome: eukaryotic cell organelle that contains digestive chemicals that break down food molecules, cell wastes, and worn-out cell parts. (ch. 14, p. 402)

M

mammal: endothermic vertebrate that has hair and produces milk to feed its young. (ch. 21, p. 594)

mantle: thin tissue layer covering a mollusk's soft body; secretes the protective shell of those mollusks having a shell. (ch. 20, p. 555)

map legend: explains the meanings of symbols that are used on topographic maps and most other maps. (ch. 8, p. 218)

map scale: relationship between the distances on the map and the actual distances on Earth's surface; can be represented as a ratio or a small bar graph divided into units. (ch. 8, p. 218)

marsupial: mammal that gives birth to immature offspring and that has a pouch in which its young complete their development. (ch. 21, p. 596)

mass: amount of matter in an object. (ch. 2, p. 40; ch. 6, p. 151)

mass number: sum of an atom's protons and neutrons. (ch. 3, p. 70)

matter: anything that has mass and occupies space. (ch. 3, p. 60)

measurement: way to describe the world with numbers; can describe objects and events with length, volume, mass, temperature, and rates. (ch. 2, p. 30)

mechanical advantage (M.A.): comparison of the effort force to the resistance force for a machine. (ch. 7, p. 180)

mechanical waves: waves that can travel only through matter; can be either transverse or compressional waves. (ch. 5, p. 117)

medusa: free-swimming, bell-shaped body plan of a cnidarian, such as a jellyfish, that allows it to drift with the ocean currents. (ch. 20, p. 551)

Mercator projection: map projection that has correct shapes of continents, but their areas are distorted; has lines of longitude drawn parallel to each other. (ch. 8, p. 215)

metalloids: elements that have characteristics of both metals and nonmetals, generally are brittle and dull, and are poor conductors of heat and electricity. (ch. 3, p. 72)

metals: elements that are malleable, ductile, generally have a shiny or metallic luster, and are not as good conductors of heat and electricity. (ch. 3, p. 71)

metamorphosis (met uh MOR fuh sus): process in which insects change their body form as they mature; can be complete (egg, larva, pupa, and adult) or incomplete (egg, nymph, and adult). (ch. 20, p. 566)

meteorologist (meet ee uh RAHL uh just): person who studies weather, takes measurements of temperature, air pressure, winds, humidity, and precipitation, and uses information provided by weather instruments to make weather maps and forecasts. (ch. 11, p. 313)

meter (m): SI unit of length. (ch. 2, p. 38)

migration: instinctive seasonal movement of animals, usually to find food or to reproduce in a better environment. (ch. 22, p. 623)

mitochondria: eukaryotic cell organelles where food molecules are broken down and energy is released. (ch. 14, p. 402)

mixtures: combinations of two or more substances that have not combined to form new, pure substances; can be uniform, where the individual parts cannot be seen, or nonuniform, where you can see individual parts. (ch. 3, p. 77)

mollusk: soft-bodied invertebrate that has a mantle, a large muscular foot, a complete digestive system with two openings, and usually has a protective shell. (ch. 20, p. 555)

monocot: class of angiosperm that has one seed leaf inside its seeds, vascular tissues arranged as bundles scattered throughout the stem, and flower parts in multiples of three. (ch. 18, p. 512)

monotreme: mammal that lays eggs with tough, leathery shells; the duckbilled platypus and two species of spiny anteaters. (ch. 21, p. 596)

N

neutron: uncharged particle in an atom's nucleus. (ch. 3, p. 66)

Newton's laws of motion: three rules describing how things move—an object will move with constant motion if no net force is acting on it; an object that has an unbalanced force acting on it will accelerate in the direction of the force; forces occur in equal but opposite pairs. (ch. 6, p. 154)

nitrogen-fixing bacteria: bacteria that live in the root nodules of certain kinds of plants and change nitrogen from the air into forms useful for animals and plants. (ch. 16, p. 452)

nonmetals: elements that are usually dull and are poor conductors of heat and electricity. (ch. 3, p. 72)

nonpoint source: pollution that comes from many different sources, such as industries, homes, and farms. (ch. 9, p. 247)

nonrenewable: resources, such as fossil fuels, that cannot be replaced by natural processes in less than 100 years. (ch. 9, p. 236)

nonvascular plant: plant lacking vascular tissue and that absorbs water and other dissolved substances directly through its cell walls. (ch. 18, p. 496)

normal force: upward force of the ground, perpendicular to the surface. (ch. 6, p. 150)

nuclear energy: energy produced by splitting the nuclei of certain elements. (ch. 9, p. 242)

nucleus: positively charged, central part of an atom. (ch. 3, p. 66); eukaryotic organelle that directs all the activities of the cell and is surrounded by a double membrane. (ch. 14, p. 399)

O

observations: bits of information that can be gathered through your eyes, ears, and senses of touch, taste, and smell. (ch. 1, p. 18)

omnivore: animals that eat both plants and animals. (ch. 21, p. 600)

open circulatory system: type of blood-circulation system in which the blood is not contained in vessels but instead surrounds the organs. (ch. 20, p. 556)

order: taxonomic group that is larger than a family but smaller than a class. (ch. 15, p. 424)

ore: mineral resource that can be mined at a profit. (ch. 9, p. 254)

organ: structure made up of different types of tissues that work together to do a certain job. (ch. 14, p. 404)

organelle: structure within the cytoplasm of a eukaryotic cell having a specific function or functions. (ch. 14, p. 400)

ozone layer: stratospheric layer with a high concentration of ozone; protects Earth by absorbing harmful ultraviolet radiation. (ch. 10, p. 272)

P

parasite: organism, such as a tapeworm, that depends on its host for food and a place to live. (ch. 20, p. 553)

pathogen: any organism that produces disease. (ch. 16, p. 452)

pheromone: powerful chemical produced by an animal to influence the behavior of another animal of the same species. (ch. 22, p. 621)

phloem (FLOH em): vascular plant tissue made up of tubular cells that transport food from where it is made to other parts of the plant where it is used or stored. (ch. 18, p. 507)

photoperiodism: response of a plant to the number of hours of daylight and darkness it receives each day. (ch. 19, p. 535)

photosynthesis: food-making process that takes place in the chloroplasts of plant cells, where carbon dioxide from the air, water in the soil, and light energy react to form glucose and oxygen. (ch. 19, p. 525)

phylogeny (fi LAH jon nee): evolutionary history of an organism. (ch. 15, p. 423)

phylum (FI lum): taxonomic group that is smaller than a kingdom but larger than a class. (ch. 15, p. 424)

physical change: any change in the size, shape, or form of matter in which the makeup of the matter remains the same and only the physical properties change. (ch. 4, p. 101)

physical properties: properties, or characteristics, such as color, texture, and shape, that can be observed without changing the makeup of a material. (ch. 4, p. 88)

pioneer community: first community of organisms to move into a new environment. (ch. 13, p. 355)

pioneer species: first plants to grow in new or disturbed environments and that change environmental conditions so that other plant species can grow there. (ch. 18, p. 499)

placental mammal: mammal whose embryo develops in the uterus of the female. (ch. 21, p. 597)

plain: landform that is a large, flat area; interior and coastal plains make up 50 percent of all land areas in the United States. (ch. 8, p. 202)

plankton: microscopic algae, plants, and other organisms that float in warm, sunlit waters near the surface of freshwater lakes and ponds. (ch. 13, p. 373)

plateau (pla TOH): landform that is a flat, raised area made of nearly horizontal rocks that have been uplifted by forces within Earth. (ch. 8, p. 204)

point source: single, identifiable pollution source. (ch. 9, p. 247)

polar zones: regions extending from 66.5° north and south latitudes to the poles that receive solar energy at a low angle or not at all and may be covered with ice year-round. (ch. 12, p. 328)

pollution: introduction of harmful waste products, chemicals, and substances into the environment. (ch. 9, p. 234)

polyp (PAHL up): vase-shaped body plan of a cnidarian, such as a hydra, that allows it to twist to capture prey and to somersault to a new location. (ch. 20, p. 551)

power: measures the rate at which work is done in a certain period of time; unit is the watt (W). (ch. 7, p. 175)

precipitation: water falling from clouds, including rain, snow, sleet, and hail. (ch. 11, p. 301)

primary succession: ecological succession that begins in a place that does not have soil. (ch. 13, p. 355)

prime meridian: imaginary line representing 0° longitude; runs from the north pole through Greenwich, England, to the south pole. (ch. 8, p. 211)

protist: single- or many-celled eukaryotic organism that lives in a moist or wet environment; can be plantlike, animal-like, or funguslike. (ch. 17, p. 464)

proton: particle in the nucleus of an atom that carries a positive charge. (ch. 3, p. 66)

protozoans: complex, one-celled, animal-like protists that contain special vacuoles for digesting food and eliminating excess water; classified by their method of movement. (ch. 17, p. 469)

pseudopods (SEWD uh pahdz): temporary, footlike extensions of cytoplasm used by rhizopods for movement and for trapping food. (ch. 17, p. 470)

pulley: surface, such as a wheel, that redirects force using a rope; a simple machine that allows you to pull down to lift a weight. (ch. 7, p. 185)

R

radiation: transfer of energy by electromagnetic waves. (ch. 10, p. 277)

radula (RAJ uh luh): scratchy, tongue-like organ in many mollusks that acts like a file with rows of teeth to break up food into smaller pieces. (ch. 20, p. 555)

rate: ratio of two measurements with different units—for example, speed, measured in kilometers per hour (km/h). (ch. 2, p. 41); fraction in which the numerator and denominator have different units. (ch. 6, p. 142)

reflection: occurs when a wave strikes an object or surface and bounces off. (ch. 5, p. 126)

reflex: automatic response, such as shivering, that does not involve the brain. (ch. 22, p. 611)

refraction: bending of a wave as it moves from one medium into another. (ch. 5, p. 127)

relative humidity: measure of the amount of water vapor that the air is holding compared to the amount it can hold at a specific temperature. (ch. 11, p. 298)

remote sensing: way of collecting information about Earth from a distance—for example, by satellites and sonar. (ch. 8, p. 220)

renewable: energy resources, such as wind and water, that can be recycled or replaced by natural processes in less than 100 years. (ch. 9, p. 238)

reptile: ectothermic vertebrate that has thick, dry, scaly skin, and does not depend on water for reproduction. (ch. 21, p. 585)

resistance force (Fr): force a machine must overcome. (ch. 7, p. 179)

respiration: series of chemical reactions by which all living cells break down food to release energy. (ch. 19, p. 528)

revolution (rev oh LEW shun): movement of Earth around the sun, which takes one year to do once. (ch. 23, p. 637)

rhizoids: threadlike roots that are only a few cells in length and that anchor liverworts and mosses in place. (ch. 18, p. 498)

ribosomes: small, two-part organelles on which cells make their own proteins. (ch. 14, p. 401)

Robinson projection: map projection that has accurate continent shapes and accurate land areas; has parallel latitude lines and curved longitude lines. (ch. 8, p. 215)

rotation (roh TAY shun): spinning of Earth on its axis, which occurs once every 24 hours and causes night and day. (ch. 23, p. 636)

S

saprophyte: any organism that uses dead material as a food and energy source; sprophytes decompose dead organisms and recycles nutrients so that they are available for use by other organisms; saprophytic bacteria keep dead material from building up over all of Earth. (ch. 16, p. 451)

science: process of trying to understand the world around us. (ch. 1, p. 7)

scientific methods: step-by-step procedures of scientific problem solving; can include recognizing the problem, forming a hypothesis, testing the hypothesis, analyzing the data, and drawing conclusions. (ch. 1, p. 14)

screw: inclined plane wrapped around a shaft. (ch. 7, p. 181)

sea breezes: daily movements of air created when cooler, denser air moving inland from the ocean forces warm air over the land to rise. (ch. 12, p. 288)

season: short-term period of climate change caused by regular differences in temperature, daylight, and weather patterns that are due to Earth's tilt on its axis as it revolves around the sun. (ch. 12, p. 338)

secondary succession: ecological succession that begins in a place that already has soil and was once the home of living organisms. (ch. 13, p. 356)

short-day plant: plant that needs twelve or more hours of darkness to begin the flowering process. (ch. 19, p. 535)

SI: International System of Units, which was designed to give a worldwide standard of physical measurement for science, industry, and commerce and uses units such as the meter, cubic meter, kilogram, and kelvin. (ch. 2, p. 37)

simple machine: machine that works with only one motion—an inclined plane, lever, wheel and axle, and pulley. (ch. 7, p. 178)

social behaviors: interactions among organisms of the same species, including courtship and mating, caring for the young, and getting food. (ch. 22, p. 620)

society: group of animals of the same species that live and work together in the same way and in which each member has a certain job. (ch. 22, p. 620)

solar energy: energy from the sun that is nonpolluting, renewable, and abundant but is available only when the sun is shining. (ch. 9, p. 239)

solar system: nine planets and other objects that orbit the sun. (ch. 23, p. 642)

species (SPEE sheez): smallest, most precise taxonomic classification. (ch. 15, p. 420)

spore: reproductive cell that forms new organisms without fertilization. (ch. 17, p. 477)

state of matter: physical property of a sample of matter—solid, liquid, gas, or plasma. (ch. 4, p. 89)

station model: shows the weather conditions at one specific location, using symbols on a map. (ch. 11, p. 314)

stomata: small pores in the leaf surfaces surrounded by guard cells; allow carbon dioxide, oxygen, and water to enter and leave a leaf. (ch. 18, p. 509) openings on leaf surfaces or leaflike structures through which gases like carbon dioxide and water vapor may enter and leave a plant. (ch. 19, p. 522)

substance: sample of matter that has the same composition and properties throughout. (ch. 3, p. 75)

symmetry: arrangement of the individual parts of an object; animals with bilateral symmetry have mirror image body parts; animals with radial symmetry have body parts arranged in a circle around a central point; asymmetrical animals have no definite shape. (ch. 20, p. 547)

T

table: tool used to display information in rows and columns so that it is easier to read and understand. (ch. 2, p. 45)

taiga (TI guh): cold region of cone-bearing evergreen trees that lies just below the tundra and is the world's largest terrestrial biome. (ch. 13, p. 364)

taxonomy (tak SAHN uh mee): the science of classification. (ch. 15, p. 418)

technology: use of knowledge gained through scientific thinking and problem solving to make products or tools people can use. (ch. 1, p. 9)

temperate deciduous forest: biome that lies at latitudes below about 50° in both the northern and southern hemispheres, usually has four distinct seasons, and supports a wide variety of plants and animals. (ch. 13, p. 365)

temperate zones: regions with moderate temperatures located between the tropics and the polar zones. (ch. 12, p. 328)

territory: area that an animal defends from other members of the same species and that contains food, shelter, and potential mates. (ch. 22, p. 618)

tissue: group of similar cells that work together to do one job. (ch. 14, p. 404)

topographic map: shows the changes in elevation of Earth's surface and shows natural features such as mountains and rivers and cultural features such as roads and cities. (ch. 8, p. 216)

tornado: violent, whirling wind that moves in a narrow path over land, forms a funnel, and can reach up to 500 km per hour and be highly destructive. (ch. 11, p. 308)

toxin: poison produced by a bacterial pathogen. (ch. 16, p. 453)

transpiration: loss of water vapor through the stomata of a leaf. (ch. 19, p. 523)

transverse wave: wave in which matter moves back and forth at right angles to the direction the wave travels. (ch. 5, p. 118)

tropical rain forest: hot, wet, equatorial biome that contains the largest number of species. (ch. 13, p. 367)

tropics: region between latitudes 23.5° north and 23.5° south that receives the most solar radiation and is always hot, except at high elevations. (ch. 12, p. 328)

tropism: response of a plant to an outside stimulus such as gravity or light. (ch. 19, p. 532)

troposphere: layer of the atmosphere closest to the ground; contains 75 percent of the atmospheric gases, dust, ice, and liquid water and is where weather, smog, and clouds occur. (ch. 10, p. 268)

tundra (TUN dra): cold, dry, treeless biome located at latitudes surrounding the north pole and that has winters six to nine months long. (ch. 13, p. 363)

U

ultraviolet radiation: type of energy that comes to Earth from the sun and is mostly absorbed by the ozone layer; can cause cancer and other health problems in many types of plants and animals. (ch. 10, p. 272)

upwarped mountains: mountains that are formed when crust is pushed up by forces inside Earth, and the material on top of the crust is eroded to form sharp peaks and ridges. (ch. 8, p. 207)

V

vaccine: preparation made from damaged virus particles that are no longer able to cause disease and that can prevent some viral disease such as polio and measles. (ch. 14, p. 410; ch. 16, p. 452)

vascular plant: plant with vascular tissue, a "pipeline" that moves water, food, and dissolved substances to cells throughout the plant. (ch. 18, p. 496)

vertebrates (VURT uh brayts): animals with a backbone; only about 3 percent of animals are vertebrates. (ch. 20, p. 547)

virus: nonliving structure that consists of a core of hereditary material surrounded by a protein coat. (ch. 14, p. 406)

volcanic mountains: mountains that form when molten material reaches Earth's surface through a weak area of crust, piles up in layers, and forms a cone-shaped structure. (ch. 8, p. 208)

W

water cycle: the continuous movement of water between Earth's surface and the atmosphere through evaporation, condensation, and percipitation. (ch. 10, p. 280)

wavelength: distance between a point on one wave and an identical point on the next wave, measured from crest to crest or trough to trough; in compressional waves, is measured from one compression or rarefaction to the next. (ch. 5, p. 122)

waves: in the ocean, waves move through seawater and occur as sea waves or long waves. (ch. 5, p. 116)

weather: present state of the atmosphere, including air pressure, wind, temperature, and the amount of moisture in the air. (ch. 11, p. 296)

wedge: moving inclined plane with one or two sloping sides. (ch. 7, p. 181)

weight: downward pull of gravity on an object. (ch. 6, p. 149)

wheel and axle: simple machine made from two rigidly attached wheels that rotate together. (ch. 7, p. 184)

work: occurs when a force produces movement parallel to the direction in which the force is applied; unit is the joule (J). (ch. 7, p. 172)

X

xylem (ZI lum): vascular plant tissue made up of tubular vessels that transport water and dissolved substances up from the roots throughout the plant. (ch. 18, p. 507)

Glossary/Glosario

Este glossario define cada término clave que aparece en **negrillas** en el texto. También muestra el número de página donde se usa dicho término.

A

acceleration/aceleración: Razón a la cual cambia la rapidez o la dirección. (Cap. 6, pág. 143)

acid rain/lluvia ácida: Lluvia, nieve, cellisca o granizo con un pH menor que 5.6 que se forma cuando el dióxido sulfuroso o los óxidos de hidrógeno se combinan con la humedad del aire; puede matar plantas y árboles. (Cap. 9, pág. 234)

adaptation/adaptación: Cualquier estructura o comportamiento que le ayuda a un organismo a sobrevivir en su ambiente. (Cap. 12, pág. 335)

aerobes/aerobios: Organismos que requieren oxígeno para sobrevivir; por ejemplo, los seres humanos y la mayoría de las bacterias. (Cap. 16, pág. 448)

aggression/agresión: Acto forzado que se usa con el propósito de dominar o controlar a otro animal. (Cap. 22, pág. 619)

air mass/masa de aire: Gran extensión de aire que posee las mismas propiedades que la superficie terrestre sobre la cual se desarrolla. (Cap. 11, pág. 304)

algae/alga: Protistas unicelulares o multicelulares que parecen plantas, contienen clorofila y pueden fabricar su propio alimento; organizadas en seis filos principales con base en sus estructuras, sus pigmentos y la manera en que fabrican alimento.(Cap. 17, pág. 465)

amphibian/anfibio: Vertebrado de sangre fría que pasa parte de su vida en agua y parte sobre tierra. (Cap. 21, pág. 582)

amplitude/amplitud: La mitad de la distancia entre una cresta y un valle de una onda transversal; una medida de la energía que transporta una onda. (Cap. 5, pág. 121)

anaerobes/anaerobios: Organismos con variaciones que les permiten vivir sin oxígeno. (Cap. 16, pág. 448)

angiosperms/angiospermas: Plantas vasculares que florecen y producen frutos con semillas. Son la forma de vida vegetal más común sobre la Tierra. (Cap. 18, pág. 511)

antibiotic/antibiótico: Sustancia producida por un organismo que inhibe o destruye otro organismo. La penicilina es un antibiótico muy conocido, el cual impide que las bacterias produzcan nuevas paredes celulares. (Cap. 16, pág. 452)

appendages/apéndices: Estructuras, tales como garras, patas o incluso antenas que crecen del cuerpo. (Cap. 20, pág. 564)

arthropod/artrópodo: Animal de patas articuladas, tal como un insecto o un crustáceo, que se clasifica de acuerdo con el número de segmentos corporales y apéndices y el cual tiene un exoesqueleto protector. (Cap. 20, pág. 564)

astronomical unit/unidad astronómica: Distancia promedio de la Tierra al sol (150 millones km), la cual se usa para medir las vastas distancias en el espacio. (Cap. 23, pág. 643)

atom/átomo: La partícula más pequeña que compone la mayoría de los tipos de materia. (Cap. 3, pág. 61)

atomic mass/masa atómica: Indica el peso de los átomos de un elemento en comparación con los átomos de otros elementos. (Cap. 3, pág. 70)

atomic number/número atómico: Indica el número de protones en el núcleo de cada átomo de un elemento. (Cap. 3, pág. 70)

auxin/auxina: Tipo de hormona vegetal. (Cap. 19, pág. 533)

average speed/rapidez promedio: La distancia

viajada entre el tiempo que llevó viajar dicha distancia. (Cap. 6, pág. 142)

B

balanced forces/fuerzas equilibradas: Ocurren cuando las fuerzas que actúan sobre un objeto se cancelan entre sí. (Cap. 6, pág. 150)

bar graph/gráfica de barras: Gráfica que utiliza barras para mostrar relaciones entre variables. (Cap. 2, pág. 46)

behavior/comportamiento: Manera en que actúa un organismo hacia su ambiente. (Cap. 22, pág. 610)

binomial nomenclature/nomenclatura binaria: Sistema de clasificación de Linneo que usa dos términos, o nombre científico, para nombrar cada organismo. (Cap. 15, pág. 420)

biomes/biomas: Áreas geográficas extensas que poseen climas y ecosistemas similares. (Cap. 13, pág. 363)

bird/ave: Vertebrado de sangre caliente con plumas, dos patas, dos alas y un pico, que pone huevos con cáscara dura. (Cap. 21, pág. 588)

budding/gemación: Es una forma de reproducción asexual en que un nuevo organismo crece de un lado del organismo progenitor. (Cap. 17, pág. 478)

C

cambium/cambium: Tejido que produce nuevas células de xilema y de floema. (Cap. 18, pág. 507)

carnivore/carnívoro: Animal que come la carne de otros animales. (Cap. 21, pág. 600)

cartilage/cartílago: Tejido flexible fuerte que se parece al hueso, pero que no es tan duro como el hueso. (Cap. 21, pág. 580)

cell membrane/membrana celular: Estructura que forma el límite exterior de la célula y la cual permite que solo ciertos materiales se muevan dentro y fuera de la célula. (Cap. 14, pág. 398)

cell theory/teoría celular: Una de las teorías principales de la ciencia basada en las observaciones y conclusiones de muchos científicos; enuncia que la célula es la unidad constitutiva de la vida, que los organismos están compuestos de una o más células y que todas las células provienen de otras células. (Cap. 14, pág. 392)

cell wall/pared celular: Estructura rígida que brinda apoyo y protección a la célula vegetal. Está formada por manojos de fibras celulosas fuertes. (Cap. 14, pág. 403)

cellulose/celulosa: Compuesto orgánico hecho de cadenas largas de moléculas de glucosa, del cual están formadas las paredes celulares de las plantas. (Cap. 18, pág. 494)

chemical change/cambio químico: Cambio de un material en otro material diferente. (Cap. 4, pág. 104)

chemical property/propiedad química: Característica de una sustancia que le permite convertirse en una nueva sustancia. (Cap. 4, pág. 93)

chlorofluorocarbons/clorofluorocarburos: Compuestos químicos que se usan en refrigeradores, atomizadores en aerosol y empaques de espuma; destruyen las moléculas de ozono. (Cap. 10, pág. 273)

chloroplast/cloroplasto: Organelo verde que se encuentra en el citoplasma y que contiene clorofila, el pigmento verde que atrapa la energía luminosa que las plantas usan para fabricar su propio alimento. (Cap. 14, pág. 403)

chordate/cordado: Animal con notocordio, cordón nervioso dorsal hueco en sus espaldas y hendiduras branquiales. (Cap. 21, pág. 578)

chromatin/cromatina: Tipo de material hereditario que se encuentra en el núcleo en forma de hebras largas, las cuales contienen las instrucciones genéticas para las operaciones de la célula. (Cap. 14, pág. 399)

cilia/cilios: Estructuras cortas que parecen unos hilos y que se extienden desde la membrana celular de los ciliados. (Cap. 17, pág. 471)

circle graph/gráfica circular: Gráfica que muestra las partes de un todo mediante un círculo. (Cap. 2, pág. 46)

class/clase: Grupo taxonómico que es más

grande que el orden, pero más pequeño que el filo o división. (Cap. 15, pág. 424)

classify/clasificar: Significa agrupar ideas, información u objetos basándose en sus semejanzas. (Cap. 15, pág. 418)

climate/clima: Patrón del tiempo que ocurre en un área a lo largo de muchos años. (Cap. 12, pág. 328)

climax community/comunidad clímax: Comunidad que ha alcanzado la etapa final de sucesión ecológica. (Cap. 13, pág. 357)

closed circulatory system/sistema circulatorio cerrado: Sistema circulatorio en que la sangre se transporta por el cuerpo a través de vasos sanguíneos. (Cap. 20, pág. 557)

cnidarians/cnidarios: Filo de animales acuáticos de cuerpo hueco que poseen células urticantes que usan para aturdir o atrapar presas de alimento; también poseen simetría radial. (Cap. 20, pág. 551)

compound/compuesto: Sustancia pura cuya unidad constitutiva está compuesta por átomos de más de un elemento. (Cap. 3, pág. 75)

compound light microscope/microscopio de luz compuesto: Tipo de microscopio en que la luz pasa a través de un objeto y luego pasa a través de dos o más lentes. (Cap. 14, pág. 389)

compound machine/máquina compuesta: Combinación de máquinas simples. (Cap. 7, pág. 178)

compressional wave/onda de compresión: Onda en la cual la materia en el medio se mueve de un lado a otro en la misma dirección en que viaja la onda. (Cap. 5, pág. 119)

conditioning/acondicionamiento: Modificación del comportamiento de modo que una respuesta antes asociada con un estímulo, se pueda asociar con otro estímulo. (Cap. 22, pág. 614)

conduction/conducción: Transferencia de energía que ocurre cuando las moléculas chocan unas con otras. (Cap. 10, pág. 279)

conic projection/proyección cónica: Se usa para producir mapas de áreas pequeñas proyectando puntos y líneas desde un globo a un cono. (Cap. 8, pág. 215)

conservation/conservación: Uso cuidadoso de los recursos, cuya meta es disminuir el daño al ambiente. (Cap. 9, pág. 253)

constant/constante: Factor que permanece igual en un experimento. (Cap. 1, pág. 19)

constellation/constelación: Grupo de estrellas que forman un patrón en el firmamento y el cual ha recibido su nombre de personajes reales o imaginarios como animales, personas u objetos. (Cap. 23, pág. 652)

contour feathers/plumas de contorno: Plumas fuertes y livianas que les dan a las aves sus bellos coloridos y sus perfiles aerodinámicos y las cuales usan para volar y para navegar. (Cap. 21, pág. 591)

contour interval/intervalo entre curvas de nivel: Diferencia en elevación entre dos curvas de nivel consecutivas. (Cap. 8, pág. 217)

contour line/curva de nivel: Línea en un mapa que conecta puntos de igual elevación. (Cap. 8, pág. 217)

control/control: Un estándar que se usa para comparar. (Cap. 1, pág. 19)

convection/convección: Transferencia de energía por medio de un flujo de material calentado. (Cap. 10, pág. 279)

Coriolis effect/efecto de Coriolis: Efecto que cambia la dirección de todos los objetos que se mueven libremente, tales como el aire y el agua, hacia la derecha en las regiones al norte del ecuador y hacia la izquierda en las regiones al sur del ecuador. (Cap. 10, pág. 285)

courtship behavior/comportamiento de cortejo: Mutuo reconocimiento entre las hembras y los machos, antes del apareo. (Cap. 22, pág. 619)

cuticle/cutícula: Capa cerosa protectora que cubre los tallos, hojas y flores de algunas plantas terrestres; es secretada por las paredes celulares de la planta y disminuye la evaporación de agua. (Cap. 18, pág. 495)

cyclic behaviors/comportamientos cíclicos: Comportamientos innatos que ocurren en un patrón repetitivo. (Cap. 22, pág. 622)

cytoplasm/citoplasma: Material que parece gelatina dentro de la membrana celular y fuera del núcleo. Contiene una gran cantidad de agua y otras sustancias químicas y estructuras que llevan a cabo las funciones vitales de la célula. (Cap. 14, pág. 400)

D

day-neutral plant/planta de día neutro: Planta que no requiere un fotoperíodo específico y en la cual el proceso de floración puede comenzar dentro de una gama de horas de oscuridad. (Cap. 19, pág. 536)

deforestation/deforestación: Tala y destrucción de árboles, la cual afecta la cantidad de dióxido de carbono en nuestra atmósfera. (Cap. 12, pág. 344)

density/densidad: Propiedad física importante que relaciona la masa de un objeto con la cantidad de espacio que el objeto ocupa. (Cap. 4, pág. 91)

dependent variable/variable dependiente: Es el factor que se mide en un experimento. (Cap. 1, pág. 19)

desert/desierto: El bioma terrestre más seco; recibe menos de 25 cm de lluvia al año y tiene poca vegetación. (Cap. 13, pág. 368)

dew point/punto de rocío: Temperatura a la cual el aire está saturado y se condensa. (Cap. 11, pág. 298)

dichotomous key/clave dicotómica: Lista detallada de características que se usan para identificar organismos y la cual incluye el nombre científico. (Cap. 15, pág. 431)

dicot/dicotiledónea: Tipo de angiosperma que contiene dos cotiledones dentro de sus semillas. (Cap. 18, pág. 512)

diffraction/difracción: Doblamiento de una onda alrededor de una barrera. (Cap. 5, pág. 128)

division/división: Reemplaza el filo en los reinos de las plantas; es el grupo taxonómico más pequeño que el reino, pero más grande que la clase. (Cap. 15, pág. 424)

Doppler radar/radar Doppler: Dispositivo que envía señales radiales repetitivas para inspeccionar las ondas reflejadas de las tormentas distantes y detectar la dirección en que se mueve una tormenta. (Cap. 11, pág. 309)

down feathers/plumón: Plumas suaves y esponjosas que proveen a las aves adultas una capa de aislamiento cerca de la piel y que cubren el cuerpo de las aves jóvenes. (Cap. 21, pág. 591)

E

eclipse/eclipse: Evento que sucede cuando la luna pasa entre el sol y la Tierra (eclipse solar) o la Tierra pasa entre el sol y la luna (eclipse lunar). (Cap. 23, pág. 639)

ecological succession/sucesión ecológica: Proceso de cambio gradual de una comunidad de organismos a otra. (Cap. 13, pág. 354)

ectotherm/de sangre fría: Animal vertebrado cuya temperatura corporal cambia con la del ambiente. (Cap. 21, pág. 578)

efficiency/eficiencia: La capacidad de una máquina para convertir el trabajo de entrada en trabajo de salida; siempre es menos de 100 por ciento en máquinas reales debido a la perdida por fricción o calor. (Cap. 7, pág. 186)

effort force (F_e)/fuerza de esfuerzo (F_e): La fuerza que se le aplica a una máquina. (Cap. 7, pág. 179)

electromagnetic wave/onda electromagnética: Tipo de onda como, por ejemplo, las ondas luminosas o radiales, que puede viajar en el vacío y también en otros materiales. (Cap. 5, pág. 118)

electron/electrón: Partícula invisible con carga negativa. (Cap. 3, pág. 64)

electron microscope/microscopio electrónico: Tipo de microscopio que usa un campo magnético para doblar los haces de electrones y que puede magnificar las imágenes hasta 1 000 000 de veces. (Cap. 14, pág. 390)

element/elemento: Material que no se puede descomponer en materiales más simples por medios comunes. (Cap. 3, pág. 68)

El Niño/El Niño: Evento climático que comienza en el Océano Pacífico tropical y que inicia cambios en la atmósfera. (Cap. 12, pág. 339)

endoplasmic reticulum (ER)/retículo endoplasmático (RE): Membrana con dobleces que mueve materiales de un lugar a otro de la célula y que se extiende desde el núcleo hasta la membrana celular. (Cap. 14, pág. 400)

endoskeleton/endoesqueleto: Sistema óseo interno de los vertebrados que apoya y protege los órganos internos del animal y al cual se adhieren los músculos. (Cap. 21, pág. 578)

endospores/endoesporas: Estructuras con paredes gruesas que rodean a muchas bacterias que producen toxinas, cuando las condiciones son desfavorables. (Cap. 16, pág. 453)

endotherm/de sangre caliente: Animal con temperatura corporal constante; es decir, la temperatura corporal de estos animales se mantiene constante sea cual sea la temperatura del ambiente. (Cap. 21, pág. 578)

equator/ecuador: Línea imaginaria que circunda la Tierra exactamente equidistante entre los polos norte y sur. Divide la Tierra en dos mitades iguales. (Cap. 8, pág. 210)

estimation/estimación: Valoración bruta de la medida de un objeto, haciendo una conjetura basada en la experiencia. (Cap. 2, pág. 31)

estivation/estivación: Período de inactividad durante los meses calurosos y secos del verano. (Cap. 21, pág. 583)

estuary/estuario: Área en donde un río desemboca en el océano y la cual contiene una mezcla de agua dulce y salada. Es un ambiente muy fértil y productivo que sirve de vivero para muchas especies de peces oceánicos. (Cap. 13, pág. 374)

exoskeleton/exoesqueleto: Cubierta corporal externa que protege y apoya el cuerpo de los artrópodos y que también impide que se seque el animal. (Cap. 20, pág. 564)

family/familia: Grupo taxonómico más pequeño que el orden, pero más grande que el género. (Cap. 15, pág. 424)

fault-block mountains/montañas de bloques de falla: Montañas formadas por inmensos bloques rocosos inclinados y separados de rocas circundantes por fallas. (Cap. 8, pág. 208)

fins/aletas: Estructuras en forma de abanico que usan los peces para cambiar de dirección, equilibrarse y moverse. (Cap. 21, pág. 579)

fish/pez: Animal de sangre fría que usa sus branquias para obtener oxígeno. (Cap. 21, pág. 579)

fission/fisión: La forma más simple de reproducción asexual, en la que se producen dos células con material genético idéntico al de la célula progenitora; es el método de reproducción más común de las bacterias. (Cap. 16, pág. 448)

flagella/flagelos: Estructuras en forma de látigo que poseen algunas bacterias para poder moverse en condiciones húmedas. (Cap. 16, pág. 445)

fog/neblina: Nube estrato que se forma cuando el aire se enfría a su punto de rocío y se condensa cerca del suelo. (Cap. 11, pág. 300)

folded mountains/montañas plegadas: Tipo de montañas que se forman cuando las capas rocosas son apretadas desde lados opuestos, haciendo que se doblen y plieguen. (Cap. 8, pág. 206)

force/fuerza: Cualquier empuje o atracción. (Cap. 6, pág. 149)

fossil fuel/combustible fósil: Recurso energético formado de los restos de plantas y animales antiguos, en proceso de descomposición. (Cap. 9, pág. 232)

free-living/de vida libre: Organismo que no depende de otro organismo en particular para su alimentación o morada. (Cap. 20, pág. 553)

frequency/frecuencia: Número de longitudes de onda que pasan por un punto en un segundo; se mide en ondas por segundo o hertz (Hz). (Cap. 5, pág. 123)

friction/fricción: Fuerza que resiste el movimiento entre dos objetos en contacto. (Cap. 6, pág. 155)

front/frente: Límite entre masas de aire caliente y frío, en donde ocurren las tormentas y la precipitación. (Cap. 11, pág. 305)

fulcrum/fulcro: El punto sobre el cual gira una palanca. (Cap. 7, pág. 182)

galaxy/galaxia: Grupo de estrellas, gas y polvo que se mantienen juntos debido a la gravedad. (Cap. 23, pág. 655)

genus/género: Grupo de diferentes organismos que poseen características parecidas. (Cap. 15, pág. 420)

geothermal energy/energía geotérmica: Energía térmica proveniente de las rocas calientes que rodean el magma y la cual se puede usar para generar electricidad. (Cap. 9, pág. 241)

gills/branquias: Órganos de los moluscos que intercambian oxígeno y dióxido de carbono con el agua. (Cap. 20, pág. 555)

global warming/calentamiento global: Aumento de las temperaturas globales. (Cap. 12, pág. 343)

Golgi bodies/cuerpos de Golgi: Pilas de sacos cubiertos por una membrana dentro de las células que empaquetan las proteínas que secreta la célula. (Cap. 14, pág. 401)

graph/gráfica: Representación gráfica que se usa para recoger, organizar y resumir datos de manera visual. (Cap. 2, pág. 45)

grasslands/praderas: Regiones tropicales y templadas que reciben de 25 a 75 cm de precipitación anual y en la cual dominan la comunidad clímax de hierbas. (Cap. 13, pág. 368)

gravity/gravedad: Atracción que existe entre toda la materia. (Cap. 6, pág. 149)

greenhouse effect/efecto de invernadero: Calentamiento natural que ocurre cuando los gases en la atmósfera atrapan el calor. (Cap. 12, pág. 342)

groundwater/agua subterránea: Agua que se filtra en el suelo y que se junta en los pequeños espacios entre pedacitos de roca y suelo. (Cap. 9, pág. 245)

guard cells/células guardianas: Células alrededor del estoma que lo abren y lo cierran. Junto con la cutícula y los estomas, son adaptaciones que ayudan a las plantas a sobrevivir sobre tierra. (Cap. 18, pág. 509)

gymnosperms/gimnospermas: Plantas vasculares que producen semillas en la superficie de las estructuras reproductoras femeninas. (Cap. 18, pág. 510)

herbivore/herbívoro: Animal de pastoreo que come plantas. (Cap. 21, pág. 600)

hibernation/hibernación: Respuesta cíclica a las temperaturas frías y al escaso suministro de alimentos en que la temperatura corporal de un animal baja, su ritmo respiratorio se reduce y el animal sobrevive de las grasas almacenadas hasta que el tiempo se hace más cálido. (Cap. 12, pág. 336; Cap. 21, pág. 583; Cap. 22, pág. 623)

host cell/célula huésped: Célula dentro de la cual se reproduce un virus. (Cap. 14, pág. 408)

humidity/humedad: Cantidad de vapor de agua que sostiene el aire. (Cap. 11, pág. 297)

hurricane/huracán: Sistema de baja presión, de gran alcance y turbulento. Se forma sobre los océanos tropicales. Es la tormenta más poderosa sobre la Tierra. (Cap. 11, pág. 310)

hydroelectric power/potencia hidroeléctrica: Producción de electricidad mediante la utilización del agua en movimiento. (Cap. 9, pág. 240)

hydrosphere/hidrosfera: Toda el agua que se encuentra en la superficie de la Tierra. (Cap. 10, pág. 280)

hyphae/hifas: Masas filamentosas multicelulares que, por lo general, componen el cuerpo de los hongos. (Cap. 17, pág. 476)

hypothesis/hipótesis: Enunciado que se puede probar y el cual está basado en observación, investigación y conocimiento previo del problema bajo estudio. (Cap. 1, pág. 18)

imprinting/impronta: Tipo de aprendizaje en el cual un animal forma un lazo social con otro organismo dentro un período específico de tiempo, después de haber nacido o empollado el animal. (Cap. 22, pág. 612)

inclined plane/plano inclinado: Superficie en declive, comúnmente llamada rampa, la cual permite levantar una carga pesada usando menos fuerza a lo largo de una mayor distancia. (Cap. 7, pág. 180)

independent variable/variable independiente: Es el factor que puedes cambiar en un experimento. (Cap. 1, pág. 19)

inertia/inercia: Medida de la capacidad de un objeto de permanecer en reposo o de continuar moviéndose. (Cap. 6, pág. 151)

inference/inferencia: Conclusión basada en la observación. (Cap. 1, pág. 18)

innate behavior/comportamiento innato: Comportamiento heredado con el cual nace un animal. (Cap. 22, pág. 610)

instinct/instinto: Patrón complejo de comportamiento innato. (Cap. 22, pág. 611)

interference/interferencia: La capacidad de dos o más ondas de combinarse y formar una nueva onda cuando se sobreponen una sobre la otra. (Cap. 5, pág. 130)

International Date Line/Línea Internacional de cambio de fecha: Es la línea de transición para los días del calendario. (Cap. 8, pág. 212)

intertidal zone/zona intermareal: Porción de la costa cubierta de agua durante la marea alta y expuesta al aire durante la marea baja. (Cap. 13, pág. 374)

invertebrates/invertebrados: Animal sin columna vertebral. (Cap. 20, pág. 547)

ionosphere/ionosfera: Capa importante de la termosfera, la cual es una capa de partículas cargadas eléctricamente. (Cap. 10, pág. 269)

isobar/isobara: Línea que se dibuja para conectar puntos de igual presión atmosférica. (Cap. 11, pág. 314)

isotherm/isoterma: Línea que conecta puntos de igual temperatura. (Cap. 11, pág. 314)

isotopes/isótopos: Átomos del mismo elemento que poseen diferentes números de neutrones. (Cap. 3, pág. 70)

J

jet stream/corriente de chorro: Banda estrecha de viento fuerte que sopla cerca de la parte superior de la troposfera. (Cap. 10, pág. 287)

K

Kelvin/Kelvin: Escala para medir la temperatura en el SI; comienza en cero Kelvin, la temperatura más fría posible en la naturaleza. (Cap. 2, pág. 41)

kilogram/kilogramo: Unidad de masa del SI. (Cap. 2, pág. 40)

kingdom/reino: La primera categoría taxonómica y la más grande. (Cap. 15, pág. 419)

L

land breezes/brisas terrestres: Movimientos del aire hacia el agua, producidos por corrientes de convección durante la noche, al enfriarse la tierra más rápidamente que el agua oceánica. (Cap. 10, pág. 288)

latitude/latitud: Distancia, en grados, ya sea al norte o al sur del ecuador. (Cap. 8, pág. 210)

law of conservation of matter/ley de conservación de la materia: Enuncia que la materia no puede ser creada ni destruida, sino que solo cambia de forma. (Cap. 3, pág. 62)

law of definite proportions/ley de proporciones definidas: Ley que enuncia que un compuesto dado siempre está formado por los mismos elementos en la misma proporción por masa. (Cap. 3, pág. 76)

lever/palanca: Máquina simple que consiste en una arra o tablón que gira alrededor de un punto. Una pala, un bate de béisbol y una escoba son ejemplos de palancas. (Cap. 7, pág. 182)

lichen/liquen: Organismo compuesto de un hongo y un alga verde o una cianobacteria. (Cap. 17, pág. 479)

light-year/año-luz: Distancia que la luz viaja en un año (aproximadamente 9.5 trillones de km), la cual se usa para medir las distancias entre las galaxias. (Cap. 23, pág. 657)

line graph/gráfica lineal: Representación gráfica que muestra la relación entre dos variables y en la cual ambas variables deben ser numéricas. (Cap. 2, pág. 45)

long-day plant/planta de día largo: Planta que necesita, generalmente, menos de diez a doce horas de oscuridad para comenzar el proceso de floración. (Cap. 19, pág. 535)

longitude/longitud: Se refiere a la distancia, en grados, al este o al oeste del primer meridiano. (Cap. 8, pág. 211)

lysosome/lisosoma: Organelo que contiene los químicos digestivos necesarios para descomponer las moléculas alimenticias, los residuos celulares y las células desgastadas. (Cap. 14, pág. 402)

M

mammal/mamífero: Vertebrado de sangre caliente que tiene pelo y produce leche para amamantar a las crías. (Cap. 21, pág. 594)

mantle/manto: Capa fina de tejido que cubre el cuerpo blando de los moluscos y secreta la concha protectora de los moluscos que poseen concha. (Cap. 20, pág. 555)

map legend/leyenda de un mapa: Explica el significado de los símbolos que se usan en un mapa. (Cap. 8, pág. 218)

map scale/escala de un mapa: Relación entre las distancias en el mapa y las distancias verdaderas en la superficie terrestre. (Cap. 8, pág. 218)

marsupial/marsupio: Mamífero con bolsa que tiene crías inmaduras, las cuales completan su desarrollo en dicha bolsa. (Cap. 21, pág. 596)

mass/masa: Unidad que mide la cantidad de materia. (Cap. 2, pág. 40; Cap. 6, pág. 151)

mass number/número de masa: Equivale a la suma de los protones y neutrones de un átomo. (Cap. 3, pág. 70)

matter/materia: Cualquier cosa que posee masa y que ocupa espacio. (Cap. 3, pág. 60)

measurement/medida: Una manera de describir el mundo haciendo uso de los números. (Cap. 2, pág. 30)

mechanical advantage (M.A.)/ventaja mecánica (V.M.): Compara la fuerza de esfuerzo que se le aplica a una máquina con la fuerza de resistencia que debe superar la máquina. (Cap. 7, pág. 180)

mechanical waves/ondas mecánicas: Ondas que solo pueden viajar a través de la materia; pueden ser transversales o de compresión. (Cap. 5, pág. 117)

medusa/medusa: Animal de vida libre, con cuerpo en forma de campana. (Cap. 20, pág. 551)

Mercator projection/proyección de Mercator: Tipo de mapa que muestra las formas correctas de los continentes, pero sus áreas están distorsionadas. (Cap. 8, pág. 215)

metalloids/metaloides: Elementos que poseen características tanto de los metales como de los no metales. Algunos son brillantes y muchos son conductores, pero no son tan buenos conductores de calor y electricidad como los metales. (Cap. 3, pág. 72)

metals/metales: Elementos que poseen características tanto de los metales como de los no metales y que son por lo general quebradizos y opacos; no son buenos conductores de calor y de electricidad como los metales. (Cap. 3, pág. 71)

metamorphosis/metamorfosis: Cambios por los que pasan muchos insectos y otros animales. Existen dos tipos de metamorfosis: completa e incompleta. (Cap. 20, pág. 566)

meteorologist/meteorólogo: Especialista que estudia el tiempo. (Cap. 11, pág. 313)

meter (m)/metro (m): Unidad de longitud del SI. (Cap. 2, pág. 38)

migration/migración: Movimiento instintivo de ciertos animales de mudarse a lugares nuevos cuando cambian las estaciones, en lugar de entrar en estado de hibernación. (Cap. 22, pág. 623)

mitochondria/mitocondria: Organelos en donde se descomponen las moléculas alimenticias y se libera energía, la cual se almacena en otras moléculas para propulsar fácilmente las reacciones celulares. (Cap. 14, pág. 402)

mixtures/mezclas: Combinaciones de dos o

más sustancias que no se han combinado para formar nuevas sustancias puras; pueden ser uniformes: en las que no se pueden ver las partes individuales, o no uniformes: en las que se pueden ver las partes individuales. (Cap. 3, pág. 77)

mollusk/molusco: Invertebrado de cuerpo blando, generalmente, con concha; posee un manto y una pata muscular grande. (Cap. 20, pág. 555)

monocot/monocotiledónea: Tipo de angiosperma que contiene un cotiledón dentro de sus semillas. (Cap. 18, pág. 512)

monotreme/monotrema: Mamífero que pone huevos con cáscara fuerte y correosa. (Cap. 21, pág. 596)

N

neutron/neutrón: Partícula que no posee ninguna carga eléctrica. (Cap. 3, pág. 66)

Newton's laws of motion/leyes de movimiento de Newton: Leyes descubiertas por Sir Isaac Newton para resolver cualquier problema de movimiento. (Cap. 6, pág. 154)

nitrogen-fixing bacteria/bacterias nitrificantes: Bacterias que convierten el nitrógeno del aire en una forma útil para ciertas clases de plantas y animales. (Cap. 16, pág. 452)

nonmetals/no metales: Elementos que por lo general son opacos y malos conductores de calor y electricidad. Muchos son gases a temperatura ambiente y los que son sólidos, generalmente, son quebradizos. (Cap. 3, pág. 72)

nonpoint source/emisión no puntual: Contaminación proveniente de muchas fuentes diferentes, tales como las industrias, los hogares y las fincas. (Cap. 9, pág. 247)

nonrenewable/no renovable: Recurso que no puede ser reemplazado mediante procesos naturales en menos de 100 años. (Cap. 9, pág. 236)

nonvascular plant/planta no vascular: Planta que carece de tejido vascular y que usa otros medios para mover agua y sustancias a través de la planta. (Cap. 18, pág. 496)

normal force/fuerza normal: La fuerza ascendente que ejerce la tierra sobre cualquier objeto, la cual es perpendicular a la superficie. (Cap. 6, pág. 150)

nuclear energy/energía nuclear: Energía que se produce del rompimiento de los núcleos de ciertos elementos. (Cap. 9, pág. 242)

nucleus/núcleo: Centro con carga positiva del átomo (Cap. 3, pág. 66); el organelo más grande en una célula eucariota y que dirige todas las actividades de la célula. (Cap. 14, pág. 399)

O

observations/observaciones: Información que recoges usando tus sentidos, principalmente tus sentidos de la visión y audición, pero también el tacto, el gusto y el olfato. (Cap. 1, pág. 18)

omnivore/omnívoro: Animal que come plantas y también come otros animales. (Cap. 21, pág. 600)

open circulatory system/sistema circulatorio abierto: Sistema circulatorio que no posee vasos sanguíneos y en el cual la sangre rodea los órganos. (Cap. 20, pág. 556)

order/orden: Grupo taxonómico más grande que la familia, pero más pequeño que la clase. (Cap. 15, pág. 424)

ore/mena: Mineral o roca que contiene sustancias útiles que pueden minarse lucrativamente. (Cap. 9, pág. 254)

organ/órgano: Estructura compuesta de diferentes tipos de tejidos que funcionan juntos para realizar una tarea específica; por ejemplo, tu corazón es un órgano compuesto de tejidos musculares, nerviosos y sanguíneos. (Cap. 14, pág. 404)

organelle/organelo: Estructura dentro del citoplasma de células eucariotas cuyas funciones incluyen la desintegración de moléculas alimenticias, la eliminación de residuos y el almacenamiento de materiales. (Cap. 14, pág. 400)

ozone layer/capa de ozono: Capa atmosférica con una alta concentración de ozono, ubicada en la estratosfera. (Cap. 10, pág. 272)

P

parasite/parásito: Organismo que depende de su huésped para obtener alimento y morada. (Cap. 20, pág. 553)

pathogen/patógeno: Cualquier organismo causante de enfermedades. (Cap. 16, pág. 452)

pheromone/feromona: Sustancia química producida por un animal, la cual influye en el comportamiento de otro animal de la misma especie. (Cap. 22, pág. 621)

phloem/floema: Tejido vegetal compuesto de células tubulares. Transporta alimentos desde el lugar en donde se fabrican hasta otras partes de la planta, en donde es usado o almacenado. (Cap. 18, pág. 507)

photoperiodism/fotoperiodismo: Respuesta de una planta al número de horas de luz y oscuridad que recibe diariamente. (Cap. 19, pág. 535)

photosynthesis/fotosíntesis: Proceso mediante el cual las plantas utilizan la energía luminosa para producir alimento. (Cap. 19, pág. 525)

phylogeny/filogenia: Historia de la evolución de un organismo. (Cap. 15, pág. 423)

phylum/filo: El grupo taxonómico más pequeño después del reino. (Cap. 15, pág. 424)

physical change/cambio físico: Cualquier cambio en tamaño, forma o estado de la materia. (Cap. 4, pág. 101)

physical properties/propiedades físicas: Cualquier característica que se puede observar en un material sin cambiar dicho material. Por ejemplo: color, forma y dureza. (Cap. 4, pág. 88)

pioneer community/comunidad pionera: Primera comunidad de organismos que se muda a un nuevo ambiente. (Cap. 13, pág. 355)

pioneer species/especie pionera: Organismos que son los primeros en crecer en áreas nuevas o que han sido alteradas. (Cap. 18, pág. 499)

placental mammal/mamífero placentario: Animal cuyos embriones se desarrollan dentro del útero de la hembra. (Cap. 21, pág. 597)

plain/llanura: Extensa superficie de terreno relativamente llano. (Cap. 8, pág. 202)

plankton/plancton: Algas, plantas y otros organismos microscópicos que flotan cerca de la superficie en las aguas cálidas y soleadas de lagos y lagunas de agua dulce. (Cap. 13, pág. 373)

plateau/meseta: Área llana situada en partes elevadas de terreno. (Cap. 8, pág. 204)

point source/punto de emisión: Fuente identificable y única que causa algún tipo de contaminación. (Cap. 9, pág. 247)

polar zones/zonas polares: Regiones que se extienden desde las latitudes 66.5° norte y sur, hasta los polos. (Cap. 12, pág. 328)

pollution/contaminación: Introducción de productos residuales, químicos y sustancias dañinas al ambiente. (Cap. 9, pág. 234)

polyp/pólipo: Animal que tiene forma de jarrón y que generalmente es sésil. (Cap. 20, pág. 551)

power/potencia: Describe la razón a la cual se realiza trabajo y mide cuánto trabajo se realiza en cierto período de tiempo: un segundo, por lo general. (Cap. 7, pág. 175)

precipitation/precipitación: Agua que cae de las nubes y que al caer, la temperatura del aire determina si cae en forma de lluvia, nieve, cellisca o granizo. (Cap. 11, pág. 301)

primary succession/sucesión primaria: Sucesión ecológica que comienza en un lugar que no tiene suelo. (Cap. 13, pág. 355)

prime meridian/primer meridiano: Punto de referencia para distancias de este a oeste, el cual representa longitud 0°. (Cap. 8, pág. 211)

protist/protista: Organismo unicelular o multicelular que vive en ambientes húmedos o lluviosos. (Cap. 17, pág. 464)

proton/protón: Partícula que posee una carga eléctrica positiva en el núcleo. (Cap. 3, pág. 66)

protozoans/protozoarios: Protistas unicelulares que parecen animales; son complejos y viven en agua, tierra y tanto en organismos vivos como muertos. (Cap. 17, pág. 469)

pseudopods/seudopodios: Extensiones temporales del citoplasma, o patas falsas, de los Rhizopoda, que usan para moverse y alimentarse. (Cap. 17, pág. 470)

pulley/polea: Superficie, como por ejemplo una rueda, que usa una cuerda para reaplicar la fuerza y que permite levantar un peso tirando de la cuerda, sin necesidad de alzarlo manualmente. (Cap. 7, pág. 185)

R

radiation/radiación: Transferencia de energía en forma de ondas electromagnéticas. (Cap. 10, pág. 277)

radula/rádula: Órgano de los moluscos que parece una lengua y que actúa como una lima con hileras de dientes para romper los alimentos en pedazos más pequeños. (Cap. 20, pág. 555)

rate/razón: Fracción en la cual el numerador y el denominador se expresan en diferentes unidades. (Cap. 6, pág. 142)

rate/tasa: Una razón de dos medidas que usan diferentes unidades. (Cap. 2, pág. 41)

reflection/reflexión: Ocurre cuando una onda choca contra un objeto o superficie y luego rebota. (Cap. 5, pág. 126)

reflex/reflejo: Respuesta automática que tienen todos los animales sin participación del cerebro. (Cap. 22, pág. 611)

refraction/refracción: Cambio en la dirección de propagación de una onda luminosa debido a un cambio en velocidad, al moverse la onda de un medio a otro. (Cap. 5, pág. 127)

relative humidity/humedad relativa: Medida de la cantidad de vapor de agua que contiene el aire, comparada con la cantidad que puede contener, a una temperatura específica. (Cap. 11, pág. 298)

remote sensing/teledetección remota: Es una manera de recopilar información, desde el espacio, acerca de la Tierra. Los satélites y el sonar son dispositivos usados para la detección remota. (Cap. 8, pág. 220)

renewable/renovable: Recurso energético que puede ser reciclado o reemplazado, mediante procesos naturales, en menos de 100 años. (Cap. 9, pág. 238)

reptile/reptil: Vertebrado de sangre fría con piel seca y escamosa y el cual no depende del agua para su reproducción. (Cap. 21, pág. 585)

resistance force (F_r) /fuerza de resistencia (F_r): La fuerza que debe superar una máquina. (Cap. 7, pág. 179)

respiration/respiración: Serie de reacciones químicas que llevan a cabo todos los organismos para descomponer el alimento y liberar energía. (Cap. 19, pág. 528)

revolution/revolución: Movimiento de la Tierra alrededor del sol, el cual dura un año. (Cap. 23, pág. 637)

rhizoids/rizoides: Raíces filamentosas con solo unas cuantas células de grosor que anclan las hepáticas y los musgos en su lugar. (Cap. 18, pág. 498)

ribosomes/ribosomas: Estructuras pequeñas de dos partes dentro del citoplasma que fabrican sus propias proteínas. Reciben instrucciones del material hereditario en el núcleo sobre cómo y cuándo fabricar ciertas proteínas. (Cap. 14, pág. 401)

Robinson projection/proyección de Robinson: Mapa que muestra las formas correctas de los continentes y extensiones territoriales precisas. (Cap. 8, pág. 215)

rotation/rotación: Movimiento de la Tierra sobre su eje, el cual ocurre cada 24 horas y ocasiona los días y las noches. (Cap. 23, pág. 636)

S

saprophyte/saprofito: Cualquier organismo que usa materia muerta como su fuente alimenticia y energética; las bacterias saprofitas evitan la acumulación de materias muertas, por todo el mundo. (Cap. 16, pág. 451)

science/ciencia: Es el proceso de tratar de entender el mundo. (Cap. 1, pág. 7)

scientific methods/métodos científicos: Pasos usados para resolver problemas en ciencia; involucran reconocer el problema, formular una hipótesis, probar la hipótesis, realizar el experimento, analizar los datos y sacar conclusiones. (Cap. 1, pág. 14)

screw/tornillo: Plano inclinado enrollado alrededor de un eje. (Cap. 7, pág. 181)

sea breezes/brisas marinas: Movimientos de aire producidos por corrientes de convección durante el día, porque la radiación solar calienta más la tierra que el agua. (Cap. 10, pág. 288)

season/estación: Período climático de corto plazo causado por una diferencia regular en la luz del día, la temperatura y los patrones climáticos. (Cap. 12, pág. 338)

secondary succession/sucesión secundaria: Sucesión que comienza en un lugar que ya tiene suelo y el cual fue la morada de organismos vivos. (Cap. 13, pág. 356)

short-day plant/planta de día corto: Planta que necesita doce o más horas de oscuridad para comenzar el proceso de floración. (Cap. 19, pág. 535)

SI/SI: Sistema Internacional de medidas establecido en 1960 y diseñado para proveer un estándar mundial de medidas físicas para la ciencia, la industria y el comercio. (Cap. 2, pág. 37)

simple machine/máquina simple: Máquina con un solo movimiento. (Cap. 7, pág. 178)

social behaviors/comportamientos sociales: Interacciones entre organismos de la misma especie. (Cap. 22, pág. 620)

society/sociedad: Grupo de animales de la misma especie que viven y trabajan juntos en forma organizada. (Cap. 22, pág. 620)

solar energy/energía solar: Energía renovable proveniente del sol, la cual no causa contaminación. (Cap. 9, pág. 239)

solar system/sistema solar: Los nueve planetas y otros objetos que giran alrededor del sol. (Cap. 23, pág. 642)

species/especie: La categoría de clasificación más pequeña y la más precisa. Los organismos pertenecientes a la misma especie pueden aparearse y producir progenie fértil. (Cap. 15, pág. 420)

spore/espora: Célula reproductora que forma nuevos organismos sin ayuda de la fecundación. (Cap. 17, pág. 477)

state of matter/estado de la materia: Propiedad física que indica si la muestra de un material es un sólido, un líquido o un gas. (Cap. 4, pág. 89)

station model/código meteorológico: Muestra las condiciones del tiempo en una localidad específica, usando símbolos en un mapa. (Cap. 11, pág. 314)

stomata/estomas: Pequeñas aberturas en la superficie de las hojas de las plantas, o en la superficie de estructuras que parecen hojas, las cuales permiten que el dióxido de carbono, el agua y el oxígeno entren y salgan de la hoja. (Cap. 18, pág. 509; Cap. 19, pág. 522)

substance/sustancia: Muestra de materia que tiene la misma composición y propiedades en toda su extensión. (Cap. 3, pág. 75)

symmetry/simetría: Se refiere al arreglo de las partes individuales de un objeto; los animales con simetría bilateral tienen partes corporales que son imágenes especulares una de la otra; los animales con simetría radiada poseen partes corporales arregladas en forma de círculo alrededor de un punto central y los animales asimétricos no tienen una forma corporal definitiva. (Cap. 20, pág. 547)

T

table/tabla: Representación gráfica de información en hileras y columnas para facilitar la lectura y entendimiento de los datos representados. (Cap. 2, pág. 45)

taiga/taiga: Región fría de árboles coníferos siempre verdes. (Cap. 13, pág. 364)

taxonomy/taxonomía: La ciencia que se encarga de clasificar. (Cap. 15, pág. 418)

technology/tecnología: Es la aplicación del conocimiento adquirido a través de la ciencia para elaborar productos o herramientas que la gente pueda usar. (Cap. 1, pág. 9)

temperate deciduous forest/bosque deciduo de zonas templadas: Comunidad clímax de árboles deciduos, los cuales pierden sus hojas en el otoño. (Cap. 13, pág. 365)

temperate zones/zonas templadas: Regiones ubicadas entre los trópicos y las zonas polares. (Cap. 12, pág. 328)

territory/territorio: Área que un animal defiende de otros miembros de la misma especie. (Cap. 22, pág. 618)

tissue/tejido: En organismos multicelulares, es un grupo de células similares que trabajan juntas para realizar una función. (Cap. 14, pág. 404)

topographic map/mapa topográfico: Mapa que muestra los cambios en elevación del relieve terrestre. (Cap. 8, pág. 216)

tornado/tornado: Viento violento y arremolinado que se mueve sobre una estrecha trayectoria sobre la tierra, por lo general, del suroeste al noreste. (Cap. 11, pág. 308)

toxin/toxina: Veneno que producen los patógenos bacteriales. (Cap. 16, pág. 453)

transpiration/transpiración: Pérdida de agua a través de los estomas de la hoja. (Cap. 19, pág. 523)

transverse wave/onda transversal: Tipo de onda mecánica en la cual la materia se mueve de un lado a otro formando ángulos rectos con la dirección en que viaja la onda. (Cap. 5, pág. 118)

tropical rain forest/bosque pluvial tropical: La comunidad clímax más importante en las regiones ecuatoriales del mundo y que posee una vegetación frondosa. (Cap. 13, pág. 367)

tropics/trópico: La región entre las latitudes 23.5° norte y 23.5° sur. (Cap. 12, pág. 328)

tropism/tropismo: Respuesta de una planta a un estímulo exterior. Puede ser positivo o negativo. (Cap. 19, pág. 532)

troposphere/troposfera: La capa de la atmósfera terrestre que se encuentra más cerca del suelo; contiene el 75 por ciento de los gases atmosféricos como también polvo, hielo y agua líquida. (Cap. 10, pág. 268)

tundra/tundra: Región fría, seca y sin árboles, que a veces se denomina desierto gélido porque tiene inviernos que duran de seis a nueve meses. (Cap. 13, pág. 363)

ultraviolet radiation/radiación ultravioleta: Es una de las muchas formas de energía que llega a la Tierra desde el sol. Una excesiva exposición a ella puede causar daños a la piel, cáncer y otros problemas de salud. (Cap. 10, pág. 272)

upwarped mountains/montañas plegadas anticlinales: Montañas que se forman cuando la corteza terrestre es empujada hacia arriba por fuerzas del interior de la Tierra. (Cap. 8, pág. 207)

vaccine/vacuna: Preparación hecha de partículas de virus dañados, los cuales ya no pueden causar enfermedades; se usa para prevenir algunas enfermedades causadas por virus, tales como la poliomielitis y la viruela. (Cap. 14, pág. 410; Cap. 16, pág. 452)

vascular plant/planta vascular: Planta con tejidos que forman un sistema que transporta agua, nutrientes y otras sustancias a lo largo de la planta. (Cap. 18, pág. 496)

vertebrates/vertebrados: Animal con columna vertebral. (Cap. 20, pág. 547)

virus/virus: Partícula no viva que consiste en un núcleo de material hereditario rodeado por una capa de proteínas. Es algo que no crece, no responde al ambiente ni come y sin embargo se reproduce dentro de las células. (Cap. 14, pág. 406)

volcanic mountains/montañas volcánicas: Montañas que comienzan a formarse cuando el material derretido llega hasta la superficie terrestre a través de un área debilitada de la corteza y forma una estructura en forma de cono. (Cap. 8, pág. 208)

water cycle/ciclo del agua: Viaje continuo del agua entre la atmósfera y la Tierra. (Cap. 10, pág. 280)

wavelength/longitud de onda: Distancia entre un punto de una onda y otro punto idéntico en la siguiente onda; como por ejemplo, de una cresta a la siguiente o de un valle al siguiente. (Cap. 5, pág. 122)

waves/ondas: Movimientos rítmicos que transportan energía a través de la materia o del espacio sin transportar materia; pueden tener diferentes amplitud, frecuencia, longitud de onda y velocidad. (Cap. 5, pág. 116)

weather/tiempo: Término que se refiere al estado actual de la atmósfera. (Cap. 11, pág. 296)

wedge/cuña: Plano inclinado en movimiento y que puede tener uno o dos lados inclinados. (Cap. 7, pág. 181)

weight/peso: La fuerza descendiente que ejerce la gravedad. (Cap. 6, pág. 149)

wheel and axle/rueda y eje: Máquina simple compuesta de dos ruedas unidas rígidamente y que giran juntas. (Cap. 7, pág. 184)

work/trabajo: En sentido científico, se realiza trabajo cuando una fuerza produce movimiento en dirección paralela a la dirección de la fuerza. (Cap. 7, pág. 172)

xylem/xilema: Tejido compuesto de vasos tubulares que transportan agua y sustancias disueltas desde las raíces a través de toda la planta. (Cap. 18, pág. 507)

Index

The index for *Science Voyages* will help you locate major topics in the book quickly and easily. Each entry in the index is followed by the numbers of the pages on which the entry is discussed. A page number given in **boldface type** indicates the page on which that entry is defined. A page number given in *italic type* indicates a page on which the entry is used in an illustration or photograph. The abbreviation *act.* indicates a page on which the entry is used in an activity.

Ecological succession, **354**–356, *354–355, 356,* 380

Ecosystems, *act.* 353, 354–383. *See also* Biomes; Environments

Ectotherms, **578,** 604

Efficiency, **186,** 195

Effort force, **179,** *179, 185,* 195

El Niño, **339,** *339,* 349

Electromagnetic waves, **118,** 122, *122–123,* 136

Electron, **64**–65, *65,* 82

Electron cloud, 67, *67*

Electron microscope, **390**–391, *390,* 412

Electronic calculators, 187, *187*

Elements, **68,** 83
  classification of, 71–72
  isotopes of, 70–71, *70,* 72, 83
  periodic table of, 69–74, *act.* 73, *74*

Elevation, and climate, 361, *361*

Endangered species, *act.* 358–359, 422

Endoplasmic reticulum (ER), *398,* **400**–401, *400, 403*

Endoskeleton, **578**

Endospore, **453,** *454*

Endotherms, **578,** 604

Energy
  amplitude and, 121–122, *121,* 136
  geothermal, **241**–242, *241,* 258
  heat, 241, *242*
  hydroelectric, **240**–241, *240,* 258
  nuclear, **242**–243, *242, 243*
  resources, *act.* 231, 232–237, *232–233, 234*
  solar, *act.* 237, 238–**239,** *238, 239,* 258, 277, 291
  transfer in atmosphere, 276–279, *276, 278, 279, act.* 282–283
  wind, 240, *240,* 345, *345*
  work and, 174

Environments
  land, 360–371, *363, act.* 370, 380
  water, 372–375, *372, 373, 374, 375,* 381, *381*

Equator, **210,** *210*

Estimation, **30**–31, *30,* 54

Estivation, 337, **583**

Estuaries, **374,** *374,* 381

Ethylene, 534, *534,* 541

Eubacteria, 425, 444, *444,* 446–448, *446, act.* 450, 458

Euglenoids, 465, *465,* 469, *469*

Eukaryotic cells, 397, *398,* 413, 424–425, 439, 492, 516, 528, *529,* 541

Evaporation, 281

Excavation, model of, *act.* 5

Exoskeleton, **564,** 573

Exosphere, *268,* 269

Extinction, *act.* 358, 422

F

Family, **424**

Fault-block mountains, **208,** *208*

Feathers, 591–592, *591, 592*

Ferns, **500,** 502, *502, act.* 504

Fertilizers, 247

Filter feeders, 550

Fins, **579,** 604

Fish, 30, *30,* 578–581, **579,** *579, 580, 581,* 604, *act.* 616–617

Fission, **448**
  by bacteria, 448, *448,* 458
  nuclear, 242, *242*

Flagella, **445,** *445*

Flagellates, 470, *470*

Flatworms, 553–554, *553, 554,* 572

Flight, 590, *590,* 593, *593,* 605

Flowering plants, 493

Fog, **300,** *301*

Folded mountains, **206,** *206*

Food
  bacteria and, *451,* 453, 454, *454, act.* 456–457, 459

breakdown of, 528–529, *529, 530*
  photosynthesis in making of, 525–526, *525,* 540

Foraminifera, 233

Force, **149**–151, 156, 166
  airplanes and, *act.* 164–165
  balanced, **150**
  effort, **179,** *179, 185,* 195
  measuring, 150–151
  net, 156–157, *157, 174*
  normal, **150,** *150,* 156, *157*
  resistance, **179,** *179, 185,* 195
  work and, 174

Forests
  coniferous, 363, 364, 365
  conservation of, 253–254
  deforestation and, 344–345, *344,* 366, *366*
  layers of vegetation in, 366, *366*
  redwood, 356–357, *357*
  as resource, 253, *253*
  temperate deciduous, *363,* **365**–366, *365, 366,* 378, *378*
  tropical rain, *363,* 366, *366,* 367–368, *367,* 379

Formulas, 76, *76,* 174–175

Fossil fuels, **232**–235, *232–233, 234, 236, 247,* 255, *255,* 258, 344

Fossil record, 493, *493*

Free-living organisms, **553,** *553,* 572

Freezing, 355

Frequency, **123,** 136

Freshwater biomes, 372–373, *372, 373,* 374, 381

Friction, **155**–156, *155*

Frogs, 583, *583,* 584, *584, act.* 587

Fronts, **305**–306, *305, 306, 315,* 323

Fruits, 90, 96, 534, *534*

Fuel, formation of, 502–503. *See also* Fossil fuels

Fuel rods, *243*

Fulcrum, **182,** *183*

Fungi, 425, *act.* 463, 476–480, *476,* 485

N

Art Credits

Photo Credits

567 Flip Nicklin/Minden Pictures; 568 Runk/Schoenberger from Grant Heilman; 569 NMSB/Custom Medical Stock Photo; 570 (l)Geri Murphy, (r)Geri Murphy; 571 The New Zealand Herald; 572 573 KS Studio; 574 (l)David M. Dennis, (r)Mark Moffett/Minden Pictures; 575 (t)Frans Lanting/Minden Pictures, (c)Jack Wilburn/Animals, Animals, (b)Sinclair Stammers/Animals, Animals; 576 Lynn Stone; 577 (t)G.I. Bernard/Animals, Animals, (c)E. R. Degginger/Animals, Animals, (b)Fred Bavendam/ Minden Pictures; 578 (tr)Ruth Dixon, (l)Fred Bavendam/Minden Pictures, (br)Fred Bavendam/Minden Pictures; 579 Fred Bavendam/Minden Pictures; 580 Dave Fleetham/Tom Stack & Associates; 581 KS Studio; 583 (tl)William J. Weber, (tr)Geri Murphy, (bl)Mark Moffett/Minden Pictures, (br)Frans Lanting/Minden Pictures.

Chapter 21 - 586-587 Roland Seitre/Peter Arnold, Inc.; 587 Dan Rest; 589 (t)Brian Parker/Tom Stack & Associates, (c)David R. Frazier, (b)Jesse Cancelmo; 591 (t)Breck P. Kent/Animals, Animals, (b)Kelvin Aitken/Peter Arnold, Inc.; 592 David M. Dennis; 595 (t)Mark Moffett/Minden Pictures, (lc)Michael Collier, (rc)Alvin R. Staffan, (b)Lynn Stone; 597 Hans Pfletschinger/Peter Arnold, Inc.; 598 (l)Roger K. Burnard, (r)Lynn Stone; 599 (left-1)Don C. Nieman, (left-2)Alan Carey, (left-3)Roy Morsch/The Stock Market, (left-4)Alvin E. Staffan, (right-1)David R. Frazier, (right-2)William J. Weber, (right-3)Alan Nelson, (right-4)William J. Weber; 601 Michael Quinton/Minden Pictures; 603 (l)Mary Evans Picture Library/Photo Researchers, (r)Culver Pictures; 604 Johnny Johnson; 605 Tom McHugh/Photo Researchers; 606 Roger K. Burnard; 607 (t)Sharon Remmen, (b)CNRI/Phototake; 608 (left-1)Tom McHugh/Photo Researchers, (left-2)William J. Weber, (left-3)Stephen Dalton/Animals, Animals, (left-4)Sharon M. Kurgis; (right-1)Sharon Remmen, (right-2)Alvin Staffan, (right-3)V. Berns; 609 (left-1)Tom Pantages, (left-2)Lynn Stone, (left-3)Alvin E. Staffan, (right-1)Alan Carey, (right-2)William J. Weber, (right-3)Frans Lanting/Minden Pictures; 610 (tr)Lynn M. Stone, (l)David R. Frazier, (br)Michael A. Keller/The Stock Market; 611 Gerard Lacz/Peter Arnold, Inc.; 612 Maslowski Photo; 614 (t)Kelvin Aitken/Peter Arnold, Inc., (c)Michael Collier, (b)David M. Dennis; 615 (t)Alan Nelson, (l)William J. Weber; (right-1)Don C. Nieman, (right-2)Stephen Dalton/Animals, Animals, (right-3)V. Berns.

Chapter 22 - 618-619 A. Boccaccio/Image Bank; 619 Aaron Haupt; 620 David L. Pearson/Visuals Unlimited; 621 (t)M. Reardon/Photo Researchers, (b)Joseph Van Os/Image Bank; 622 William J. Weber; 623 Nina Leen, Life Magazine, Time, Inc.; 626 Matt Meadows; 627 Aaron Haupt; 628 David W. Hamilton/Image Bank; 629 (t)Jim Brandenburg/Minden Pictures, (b)David Frazier; 630 Johnny Johnson/DRK Photo; 631 (t)A.L. Cooke/Oxford Scientific Films/Animals Animals, (b)Charles W. Melton; 632 Alan Carey; 633 (t)Brian Milne/Animals Animals, (b)SuperStock; 634 (l)Roger K. Bernard, (tr)Jeff Foott/DRK Photo, (br)Wayne Lankinen/DRK Photo; 635 Leonard Lee Rue III; 637 (l)Thomas Kitchin/Tom Stack & Associates, (r)Coco McCoy/Rainbow; 638 M. Reardon/Photo Researchers; 639 (t)Alan Carey, (b)courtesy Alfred Gonzales.

UNIT 7 Chapter 23 - 634-635 NASA/PhotoTake; 635 Morrison Photography; 639 NASA; 640 Jerry Lodriguss/Photo Researchers; 641 Morrison Photography; 642 (bl)NASA/JPL/TSADO/Tom Stack & Associates, (from left) NASA/Corbis, NASA/JPL/Tom Stack & Associates, Erich Karkoschka, University of Arizona Lunar & Planetary Lab, and NASA, NASA/Photo Researchers; 643 (from left)NASA, Calvin J. Hamilton, NASA; 650 Morrison Photography; 655 (t)Royal Observatory, Edinburgh/AATB/Science Photo Library/Photo Researchers, (bl) USNO/TSDAO/Tom Stack & Associates, (br)Luke Dodd/Science Photo Library/Photo Researchers; 657 Mike O'Brine/Tom Stack & Associates

End Matter: 647 (t)Runk/Schoenberger/Grant Heilman, (b)Dr. Richard Kessel; 648 (l)Matt Meadows, (r)GR Roberts; 649 (tl)Norbert Wu, (tr)Lynn M. Stone, (cl)Rich Brommer, (c)file photo, (cr)Sharon M. Kurgis, (bl)Aaron Haupt, (br)Sharon M. Kurgis; 650 (tl)Kevin Barry; 650 (tr)Nancy Sefton; 650 (c)Mike Hopiak for the Cornell Laboratory of Ornithology; 650 (bl)William J. Weber; 650 (br)Geri Murphy; 658 Timothy Fuller; 659 Thomas Veneklasen; 660 Franklin Over; 661 Dominic Oldershaw; 665 Jeff Smith/Fotosmith; 666 Dominic Oldershaw; 668 Phil Degginger/Color-Pic; 670 Timothy Fuller; 671 Dominic Oldershaw; 674 Thomas Veneklasen; 675 Dominic Oldershaw; 676 Jeff Smith/Fotosmith; 677 Dominic Oldershaw; 680 Oliver Benn/Tony Stone Images; 681 KS Studios; 682 Aaron Haupt; 683 Jeffery Muir Hamilton/Liaison Agency; 691 Aaron Haupt.

PERIODIC TABLE OF THE ELEMENTS

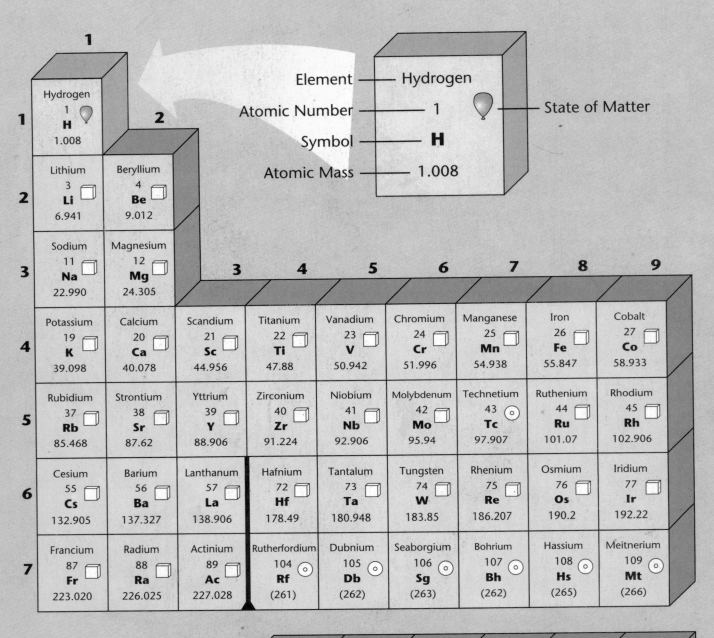

Element —— Hydrogen

Atomic Number —— 1 —— State of Matter

Symbol —— **H**

Atomic Mass —— 1.008

1								
Hydrogen 1 **H** 1.008	**2**							
Lithium 3 **Li** 6.941	Beryllium 4 **Be** 9.012							
Sodium 11 **Na** 22.990	Magnesium 12 **Mg** 24.305	**3**	**4**	**5**	**6**	**7**	**8**	**9**
Potassium 19 **K** 39.098	Calcium 20 **Ca** 40.078	Scandium 21 **Sc** 44.956	Titanium 22 **Ti** 47.88	Vanadium 23 **V** 50.942	Chromium 24 **Cr** 51.996	Manganese 25 **Mn** 54.938	Iron 26 **Fe** 55.847	Cobalt 27 **Co** 58.933
Rubidium 37 **Rb** 85.468	Strontium 38 **Sr** 87.62	Yttrium 39 **Y** 88.906	Zirconium 40 **Zr** 91.224	Niobium 41 **Nb** 92.906	Molybdenum 42 **Mo** 95.94	Technetium 43 **Tc** 97.907	Ruthenium 44 **Ru** 101.07	Rhodium 45 **Rh** 102.906
Cesium 55 **Cs** 132.905	Barium 56 **Ba** 137.327	Lanthanum 57 **La** 138.906	Hafnium 72 **Hf** 178.49	Tantalum 73 **Ta** 180.948	Tungsten 74 **W** 183.85	Rhenium 75 **Re** 186.207	Osmium 76 **Os** 190.2	Iridium 77 **Ir** 192.22
Francium 87 **Fr** 223.020	Radium 88 **Ra** 226.025	Actinium 89 **Ac** 227.028	Rutherfordium 104 **Rf** (261)	Dubnium 105 **Db** (262)	Seaborgium 106 **Sg** (263)	Bohrium 107 **Bh** (262)	Hassium 108 **Hs** (265)	Meitnerium 109 **Mt** (266)

Lanthanide Series

Cerium 58 **Ce** 140.115	Praseodymium 59 **Pr** 140.908	Neodymium 60 **Nd** 144.24	Promethium 61 **Pm** 144.913	Samarium 62 **Sm** 150.36	Europium 63 **Eu** 151.965

Actinide Series

Thorium 90 **Th** 232.038	Protactinium 91 **Pa** 231.036	Uranium 92 **U** 238.029	Neptunium 93 **Np** 237.048	Plutonium 94 **Pu** 244.064	Americium 95 **Am** 243.061